Advances in
PARASITOLOGY

VOLUME 4

Advances in

PARASITOLOGY

Edited by

BEN DAWES

Department of Zoology, Kings College,
University of London, England

VOLUME 4

1966

ACADEMIC PRESS

London and New York

ACADEMIC PRESS INC. (LONDON) LTD.
Berkeley Square House
Berkeley Square
London, W.1

U.S. Edition published by
ACADEMIC PRESS INC.
111 Fifth Avenue
New York, New York 10003

Copyright © 1966 by ACADEMIC PRESS INC. (LONDON) LTD.

Library of Congress Catalog Card Number: 62–22124

PRINTED IN GREAT BRITAIN
BY W. & J. MACKAY & CO. LTD, CHATHAM

CONTRIBUTORS TO VOLUME 4

D. S. BERTRAM, *Department of Entomology, London School of Hygiene and Tropical Medicine, London, England* (p. 255)

YOSHITAKI KOMIYA, *National Institute of Health, Shinagawa-ku, Tokyo, Japan* (p. 53)

D. L. LEE, *The Molteno Institute of Biology and Parasitology, University of Cambridge, Cambridge, England* (p. 187)

R. A. NEAL, *Wellcome Laboratories of Tropical Medicine, Beckenham, Kent, England* (p. 1)

D. POYNTER, *Research Division, Allen and Hanburys Ltd, Ware, Herts, England* (p. 321)

KRYSTYNA RYBICKA, *Department of Parasitology, Polish Academy of Sciences, Warsaw, Pasteura, Poland* (p. 107)

PREFACE

In the first three volumes of this series a promising start was made to survey the broad field of parasitological research by means of critical reviews by recognized specialists who are practised in the various disciplines which constitute modern biological science. Protozoological topics have included experimental research on avian malaria, coccidians and coccidiosis, *Leishmania* and leishmaniases, and the biological aspects of research on trypanosomiasis. The Platyhelminthes have been represented in reviews on larval Monogenea and their development, the relationships between species of *Fasciola* and their molluscan hosts, snail control in trematode diseases and the possible use of Sciomyzid larvae, the invasive stages of fascioliasis in mammalian hosts, *Paragonimus* and paragonimiasis, and the biology of the hydatid organisms. Nematodes have been considered in reviews on the infective stage and its significance, parasitic bronchitis in bovines, experimental trichiniasis, and the biology of the rat lungworm, *Angiostrongylus cantonensis*, in its relationship to neurological disorders which occur in man and animals. The parasitic helminths as a whole have been considered in reviews on host specificity and evolution, the anthelminthic treatment of domestic animals, and *in vitro* cultivation procedures. A contribution has also been made on the feeding habits of ectoparasitic Acari with special reference to ticks. The appearance of this fourth volume of the series extends the survey by means of contributions dealing with experimental studies on *Entamoeba* with reference to speciation, *Clonorchis* and clonorchiasis, embryogenesis in the Cestoda, some tissue reactions to the nematode parasites of animals, the dynamics of parasitic equilibrium in cotton rat filariasis, and the structure and composition of the helminth cuticle.

Dealing with the genus *Entamoeba*, R. A. Neal notes that the basis on which species are classified has not been assessed critically since Dobell published his monograph in 1919, although some new species have been described and much experimental research has been carried out. He has discussed debated points in the nomenclature of the genus, especially the usage of the names *Entamoeba* and *Endamoeba*, described the structural features of species and disclosed differences of subcellular organization between these amoebae and metazoan cells which electron microscopy has revealed. A list is then given of twenty-five species arranged in four groups of six, twelve, five and two species respectively in which the mature cyst contain eight nuclei, four nuclei, one nucleus, or else is unknown. Nuclear division is specially considered. The study of this process has been made more precise by the discovery of Feulgen staining for the locating of DNA. Chromatin granules in dividing nuclei of these amoebae are of two kinds,

vii

giving positive and negative results with this staining technique, although Heidenhain's haematoxylin will not differentiate between them. Feulgen-positive granules are called "chromosomes" because of their apparent mitotic division. In this review, possible cyclical change of DNA is considered, as is the specific variability of Feulgen-negative nuclear materials. Excystation and metacystic development are dealt with in some detail, as are host-restriction studies so far limited to nine species. The virulence of *E. histolytica* receives special consideration. This species is the one most often involved in physio-logical and biochemical studies, here considered in respect of metabolism, drug-sensitivity, growth and some other features. Serological differences between species and strains of *Entamoeba* are treated under various headings and the taxonomic significance of experimental data is fully discussed.

Yoshitaka Komiya has given a general account of the structure and development of all stages of *Clonorchis sinensis*, beginning with the egg and its mode of formation, varying rates of egg production and conditions which promote viability. The snail hosts of this trematode were once determined as *Bithynia striatula* var. *japonica*, later incorporated in the species *Parafossarulus manchouricus*, which is widely distributed in Japan, China, Korea, Taiwan and, probably, Indo-China. The other snails also serve as hosts, however; *Bulimus fuchsianus* in North China and *Alocima longicornis* in Central and South China. Snails ingest the eggs and miracidia promptly hatch in the alimentary canal, early sporocysts commencing their migration within a few hours of infection. Rediae are first produced and cercariae are later released, mainly to remain poised in water with downturned body and somewhat flexed tail, but responding to contact with solid bodies and even water move-ments by spasmodic bursts of swimming activity. Ultimately, after penetrating the skin of the fish host, usually near the caudal fin, they undergo some development in the subcutaneous tissues or muscles for 30–35 days. Fully developed metacercariae are about 0·4 mm long, which is about twice the length of the cercarial body. Various piscine hosts are known in different localities and these are named. The natural non-human final hosts include dogs, cats, pigs, rats and camels, and rabbits and guinea-pigs serve as experi-mental hosts. Flukes are known to live for at least eight years in man and more than three years in dogs. Komiya has been mainly concerned, however, with clonorchiasis, considering in some detail the pathology, clinical symp-toms, diagnosis, epidemiology, prevention and treatment. The source of infection with *Clonorchis sinensis* is the ingestion of encysted metacercariae in the raw of lightly cooked flesh of various freshwater fishes, which are named. The eating of raw fish is deeply rooted in Oriental people but abolition of the custom is desirable and likely to prevail in the future.

Krystyna Rybicka has given a very detailed account of gametogenesis and embryonic development in cestodes up to the formation of the oncosphere (hexacanth). Most of the available information concerns tapeworms of the orders Pseudophyllidea and Cyclophyllidea, the most important groups, which produce dissimilar eggs but similar larvae. In previous reviews the embryology of the two groups has not been unified but the analyses now made have revealed a common basic pattern of embryogenesis which may apply to all cestodes and, possibly, to digenetic trematodes. Spermatogenesis follows a typical platyhelminth plan and sixty-four spermatozoa arise in each cluster. Oogenesis commences in the ovary and oocytes mature in the uterus. Vitelline cells aggregate around each oocyte as it enters the uterus and liberate droplets of shell-forming materials after passing through the region bounded by Mehlis's gland. Three types of blastomeres are formed during cleavage: macromeres produce the outer envelope, micromeres degenerate at an early preoncospheral stage, and mesomeres multiply and differentiate in further development. In the preoncospheral stage differentiation yields cells which form the inner envelope, the hooklets and their muscles, glands, and both somatic and germinative cells. The oncospheral membrane is secreted by the embryo. The larva and the adult cestode seem to arise solely from the germinative cells of the oncosphere. It is stressed that despite structural and chemical differences which arise in the eggs of various cestodes, homologous structures are formed in accordance with the pattern described. Other patterns have been postulated and these are discussed. Some phylogenetic considerations are made but it is difficult at present to draw conclusions about the physiology of embryogenesis. More work is required on other orders of cestodes, more co-operation between embryologist and biochemist, and more use must be made of the techniques of cytology, histochemistry, electron microscopy and *in vitro* culture for further progress to be achieved.

Dealing with the structure and composition of the helminth cuticle, D. L. Lee shows that increased knowledge has resulted from the application of electron microscopy and other modern biological techniques. Available evidence indicates that the three main groups of helminths, the Platyhelminthes, Nematoda and Acanthocephala, have quite different external coverings. The cuticle of the digenetic trematodes and cestodes seems to be a syncytial cytoplasmic layer which is continuous with nucleated cytoplasm situated in the parenchyma underneath the musculature of the body wall. Lee claims, therefore, that in these instances the cuticle should be called "integument". This seems to me to be unnecessary because, according to my dictionary, an "integument" is "an external covering" and a "cuticle" is "an outermost or thin skin". However, the cuticle of Platyhelminthes has long been regarded as a secretionary layer and this impression must be corrected. The surface of tapeworms is formed into microvilli which increase an absorptive area and the most superficial layer contains mitochondria and enzymes which are believed to be concerned with active transport of substances which enter the body. Microvilli do not occur in the digenetic trematodes but vacuoles and vesicles, mitochondria and enzymes occur in the outermost layer of the body and these may serve the same purpose of transportation. In the Acanthocephala pores and canals in the cuticle and body wall are presumed to be conduits for nutrient materials passing into a body which, like that of cestodes, lacks an alimentary canal. On the other hand, the cuticle of nematodes has a very complex and also a varied structure, basically made up of three layers, but often subdivided layers. Cuticular structure varies from one nematode genus to another and generalizations concerning ultrastructure await further research, although Lee considers growth of the cuticle and changes which occur at moulting.

In his contribution on the dynamics of parasitic equilibrium D. S. Bertram has been concerned with infections of the cotton rat, *Sigmodon hispidus*, with the filarial worm *Litomodoides carinii*, which has a mite vector, *Ornithonyssus bacoti*. During the past twenty years this host–parasite–vector combination has proved valuable in research on filaricidal drugs and quantitative investigations on host–parasite relationships. The study of primary infections and superinfections has revealed several mechanisms which maintain in a cotton rat community microfilaraemias which are consistent with efficient transmission even when reinfections vary from slight to severe and transmissions from light and infrequent to heavy and continuous. Increasing worm numbers lead to inhibited growth and reduced microfilarial output by adult worms in the pleural cavity, but the microfilaraemia is augmented by secondary parasitization of the peritoneal cavity in which worms mature and reproduce more successfully. In reinfections an immune response tends to retard the establishment of new worm populations, but even when transmission is intermittent and infrequent successive populations of worms mature and produce microfilariae to sustain an existing microfilaraemia of some hundreds of larvae per mm³. Under such conditions, however, some suppression during reinfection and for about fifty days of development of a new worm population holds the microfilaraemia in check. This occurs at successive exposures to reinfection but as suppression is relaxed periodically the microfilaraemia increases again and a high and slowly increasing microfilarial density may persist. Older worms die and are encapsulated as the host ages, but the stock of adult worms is replenished periodically by the new worms of successive populations transmitted in reinfections and these maintain the microfilaraemia. Slowly there can be a gradual turnover from old to younger worms throughout the life-span of the cotton rat. This is less likely to happen if reinfections recur before the youngest worm population has been able to reproduce and contribute microfilariae to the blood-stream. Differences occur also with intensively continuous reinfections. However, sufficient has been said to indicate the finely detailed and interesting nature of Bertram's review, which ends with some comparisons with other experimental filarial models and also notes some wider implications of this remarkable synthesis of up-to-date knowledge on cotton rat filariasis.

D. Poynter notes that tissue reactions to nematode parasites have not been studied as intensively as reactions to other infective agents. His subject is still in the descriptive stage but lesions evoked in the host by parasites are becoming appreciated more and pathogenesis better understood. He has made a pioneering effort at my special request and he has dealt with nematodes according to the organs through which they pass or in which they live. Thus, he has been concerned with gastro-intestinal worms, pulmonary reactions, nematodes in blood vessels and the central nervous system, not to mention other sites, with visceral larval migrans and nematodes in relation to viral diseases and cancer. His efforts have been worthwhile because they concern a subject which is likely to gain in importance in the future, as well as one which merits greater effort and closer investigation. It is now no longer sufficient to collect parasites and name, classify and study them in isolation. Any parasitological investigation worthy of the name should in the future include such study of the host's tissues as is necessary to determine the host's reaction to its parasites, even when it is concerned primarily with the mode of life of the parasite. The conclusions reached in this review are that host-parasite association are of various kinds. In some instances the association is long-standing and the host then may show little reaction to its parasites, but in other instances reactions are intense and associated with disease. Foreign body and irritant responses are common, and eosinophilia is often an indication of parasitism when parasites are not readily found. In general, susceptible hosts do not react in the same way as immune animals, the responses of which may include lymphocyte and plasma cell proliferation. Hyperplastic reactions occur and metaplasia has been reported but true neoplasia seems to be rare. However, this indicates clearly the changing environment in which nematodes live.

Finally, I would like to proffer sincere thanks to these writers for their willing co-operation in the working out of my scheme, and to say also how grateful I am to the staff of the Academic Press for the great care which has been exercised in the production of this book.

BEN DAWES
Professor of Zoology
(Parasitology)
August 1966

KING'S COLLEGE
UNIVERSITY OF LONDON
STRAND, LONDON, W.C.2

CONTENTS

Experimental Studies on *Entamoeba* with Reference to Speciation

R. A. NEAL

Clonorchis and Clonorchiasis

YOSHITAKA KOMIYA

Embryogenesis in Cestodes

KRYSTYNA RYBICKA

The Structure and Composition of the Helminth Cuticle

D. L. LEE

Dynamics of Parasitic Equilibrium in Cotton Rat Filariasis

D. S. BERTRAM

Some Tissue Reactions to the Nematode
Parasites of Animals

D. POYNTER

Experimental Studies on *Entamoeba* with Reference to Speciation

R. A. NEAL

Wellcome Laboratories of Tropical Medicine
Beckenham, Kent, England

. . . if we examine and consider wherein their Differences consist, we shall find reason to doubt whether they be specifically distinct or no.

John Ray (1674–1682, published 1718)

1

I. Introduction

The basis of classification of species of *Entamoeba* has not been critically assessed in detail since Dobell's monograph was published in 1919. Since then a number of species have been described, on the tenuous basis of their discovery in a novel host. A considerable volume of results dealing with experimental host-specificity, physiology, biochemistry and serology has appeared subsequent to Dobell's monograph, and this article attempts to synthesize the morphological studies, with recent advances in research of a more experimental nature.

The present paper does not attempt to be a taxonomic monograph, and the taxonomic conclusions reached from the experimental work will have to be included in a strictly systematic monograph. But it is hoped that areas of doubt and uncertainty will be clearly defined to the reader and will facilitate further research. A complete bibliography is not given, but reference is made to recent papers, where available, which include a wide coverage of the earlier literature.

II. Nomenclature of Genus

It is not proposed to repeat in detail the discussions which have taken place over the usage of the names *Entamoeba* and *Endamoeba*. However, a brief outline is necessary to explain the otherwise puzzling situation in which both generic names have been used at different times and at the same time for the same amoeba of man.

In his classical monograph, Dobell (1919) referred three of the common amoebae of man to the genus *Entamoeba*: *E. coli*, *E. histolytica* and *E. gingivalis*. The genus *Endamoeba* he reserved for the large amoeba of the cockroach. This proposal was not accepted by some workers, and in an effort to resolve the resulting confusion, the problem was referred to the International Commission on Zoological Nomenclature. The Commission judged that *Entamoeba* ought to be suppressed, and retained *Endamoeba* (Opinion 99, 1928). This decision had taxonomic implications which were not accepted by some authors, who continued to use *Entamoeba* and *Endamoeba* for the human species of amoebae and the cockroach amoeba respectively. Dobell (1938) critically analysed Opinion 99 and concluded that protozoologists who write *Entamoeba coli* can do so "with a clear conscience. Truth, reason and even the International Code are on our side."

But the situation remained confused, with both generic names being used, until Kirby (1945) restated the problem and submitted it to the Commission. As a result of the new presentation of the case by Kirby (1951), Dougherty (1951) and Hemming (1951), Opinion 312 (1954) validated the proposal originally put forward by Dobell in 1919. Therefore, *Entamoeba* is the name for the amoebae of man, *Endamoeba* for the cockroach amoeba, while *Poneramoeba* is retained for use by those who consider *Entamoeba histolytica* is generically distinct from *E. coli*.

As a result of the previous nomenclatural chaos, some species have been described as *Endamoeba* which must be transferred to *Entamoeba*. This can only be done by a systematic taxonomic review, which is beyond the scope of the present article. It is clear that the amoeba from man, all amoebae morphologically indistinguishable from them and similar amoebae producing 1-nucleate cysts (these have been reported mainly from domestic animals) can be transferred to the genus *Entamoeba*. However, there will remain some areas of doubt, as, for instance, in the case of amoeba reported from termites and roaches. *E. philippinensis* from the roach *Panesthia javanica* (Kidder, 1937) is clearly an *Entamoeba*, while Kirby (1946) believes that the amoebae described by Henderson (1941) are a developmental stage of a polymastigote flagellate. Until further studies are available, the classification of other amoebae described by Kidder (1937) and Kirby (1927, 1932) is uncertain, though judging from their nuclear structure they are unlikely to be *Entamoeba* spp.

III. MORPHOLOGY

Species of *Entamoeba* can be divided into three groups based on the number of nuclei in the mature cyst, the number being eight, four or one. The best known species of the 8- and 4-nucleate cyst groups are the human parasites *E. coli* and *E. histolytica* respectively. The morphology of these species was described by Dobell (1919) and all other species in these groups are compared and contrasted with them. Excellent descriptions of the human amoebae are also given in a number of recent textbooks (see especially Hoare, 1949; Reichenow, 1952; Grassé, 1953; Kudo, 1966), and it is not intended to repeat these here. The structure of species in the 1-nucleate cyst group is less satisfactorily established. However, reference should be made to the papers by Simitch *et al.* (1959) and Noble and Noble (1952).

The number of morphological characteristics are small compared with most other organisms. Consequently great emphasis has been given to nuclear structure and other characteristics. When describing new species it is important to be aware of the existence of artifacts which may arise in the course of the preparation of material, especially during fixation and staining (Wenrich, 1941). The unhappy story of *"Councilmania"* contributes a salutary lesson in this respect (Stabler, 1932).

Although the morphology is not described in detail in this paper, the typical structure of species of the three groups of species is illustrated in Fig. 1. The species illustrated are: 8-nucleate cyst group, *E. coli* from man and *E. gallinarum* from fowl; 4-nucleate cyst group, *E. histolytica* and *E. hartmanni* from man; 1-nucleate cyst group, *E. chattoni* from monkey, *E. bovis* from cow and *E. debliecki* from goat.

There are also a number of inadequately known species for which cysts have not been described. Amongst this group are the amoebae found in the mouth. The amoeba of the human mouth, *E. gingivalis*, has been studied both from man and in culture, but no cysts have ever been discovered. In a short paper by Wantland *et al.* (1961), *E. gingivalis* has been studied and cysts containing eight nuclei observed. It will be interesting to learn of further details of this unique discovery when they are published in due course. Amoebae have been reported from the mouth of dogs, horses and donkeys (see Hoare, 1959) and pigs (Toomka, 1959).

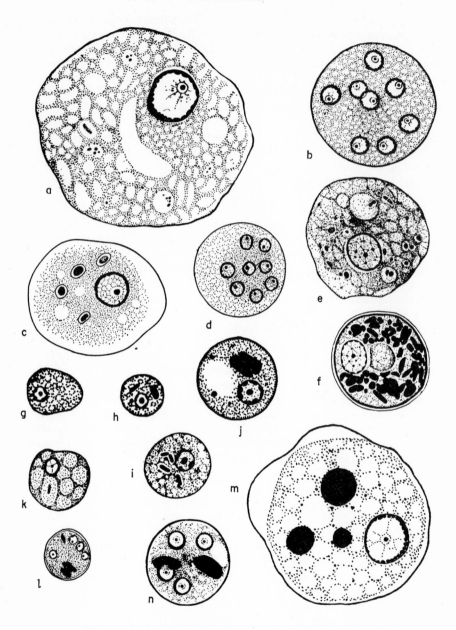

FIG. 1. Representative amoebae and cysts of species of the 8-nucleate, 4-nucleate and 1-nucleate cyst groups. a, b, *E. coli* (Hoare, 1949); c, d, *E. gallinarum* (Hegner, 1929a); e, f, *E. chattoni* (Salis, 1941); g, h, *E. bovis* (Nieschulz, 1924); i, j, *E. debliecki* (Hoare, 1940); k, l, *E. hartmanni* (Burrows, 1957); m, n, *E. histolytica* (Hoare, 1949). Figures from Hoare (1959). Approx. × 2 000.

Recent morphological studies have concentrated on three aspects: (1) the relationship of the large and small races of *E. histolytica* (known as *E. histolytica* and *E. hartmanni* respectively); (2) the occurrence in man of a different species of *Entamoeba* which forms 1-nucleate cysts, *E. polecki*; and (3) the electron microscopy of amoebae and cysts. In addition, a fourth section is added to this chapter, listing the species described throughout this article, thus establishing all these as *Entamoeba* not *Endamoeba* (see p. 8), and giving a reference to the best available morphological description of each species.

A. THE MORPHOLOGY OF *E. hartmanni*

1. *Size of Amoebae and Cysts*

Data relating to the presence of races of *histolytica*-like amoebae of different sizes, infecting man but otherwise morphologically similar, were first described by Wenyon and O'Connor (1917). Since the original descriptions many workers have published their observations (reviewed by Sapero *et al.*, 1942; see also Hoare, 1949; Sarkisian, 1957; Hussein, 1961; Barretto *et al.*, 1960; Barretto and Ferriolli, 1962; Gleason *et al.*, 1963). These workers showed by statistical analysis that only two sizes existed. A diameter of 10 μ served as the division between the two races of living cysts, and 9 μ for the diameter of fixed and stained cysts.

A number of observations have been made on the varying size of amoebae, and attempts have been made to distinguish between nutritive and genetic factors. Changes in cultural conditions relating to varying size of amoebae are well known to workers with cultures of *Entamoeba* (see McConnachie, 1954), for example the diameter of *E. hartmanni* amoebae increased from 9·1 to 14·7 μ on transference to enriched culture medium (Hajian and Ball, 1963). The amoebae returned to their previous size when cultured in the original medium. Goldman and Davis (1965) were able to select small and large amoebae from three standard strains of *E. histolytica* which bred true for a short time. However, with two strains, the substrains of large amoebae spontaneously became smaller, eventually reducing to a size below that of the selected small substrain.

The nutrition of amoebae in the host is known to affect the size of amoebae. *E. histolytica* amoebae obtained from intestinal ulcers are large, measuring about 20–40 μ, while those amoebae living in the gut lumen feed on bacteria and other particles and are smaller, measuring about 10–20 μ in diameter. A difference in size relating to feeding conditions has been also observed for *E. gingivalis* (Toomka, 1962).

This size difference was recognized for *E. histolytica* by early workers, and the older literature refers to the minuta form. This term has been confused in the past with the small race (or *E. hartmanni*), but in fact refers to the bacteria-feeding amoeba of *E. histolytica* (see Steenis, 1957; Lamy, 1961; Thiel, 1961).

It can be seen that great care must be taken in analysing biometric data obtained from amoebae, particularly from cultures. In addition to nutritive factors discussed above, there are technical difficulties associated with the plastic nature of the amoebic cell in obtaining a true measurement of the diameter. However, Freedman and Elsdon-Dew (1959) were able to show a true difference in size. They made a systematic analysis of the bacterial flora and culture media of strains of *E. histolytica* and showed that, although the size of a single strain could be varied by changing the bacterial associates, strains of *E. histolytica* and *E. hartmanni* (differing only in size) retained their relative diameters, giving a bimodal curve when mixed and cultured together.

Although the size of cysts is relatively stable, the diameter can vary by about 1·0 μ, and this was shown for *E. invadens* in culture (McConnachie, 1954) and *E. muris* in mice (Neal, 1950a). The difference between the average diameter of cysts of *E. histolytica* and *E. hartmanni* is about 4–5 μ (see Table I), which is greater than that which has so far been shown by experimental change of the environment *in vitro* or *in vivo*.

TABLE I

Summary of recent biometric studies of cysts of E. histolytica *and* E. hartmanni

E. histolytica		E. hartmanni		
Average diameter ($\mu \pm$ standard deviation*)	Size range (μ)	Average diameter ($\mu \pm$ standard deviation*)	Size range (μ)	Author
11·8	9·5–15·5†	6·8–7·7	4·5–10·5†	Faust, 1958
11·4	9·8–15·0	7·0	5·3–8·9	Sarkisian, 1957
12·74 $\pm$ 0·15	10·1–15·0	8·65 $\pm$ 0·09	7·6–9·4	Hussein, 1961
12·81	—	7·35	—	Barretto and Ferriolli, 1962
12·81 $\pm$ 1·26	10·5–15·5†	7·91 $\pm$ 1·05	4·0–10·0†	Barretto et al., 1960

*When given.   †Approximate figures.

2. Nuclear Structure and other Morphological Features

Burrows (1957, 1959, 1961, 1964) has described morphological differences between *E. hartmanni* and *E. histolytica*. The peripheral chromatin is arranged in *E. hartmanni* in a small number of larger granules (Fig. 2B and C), while in *E. histolytica* the peripheral chromatin is arranged evenly in small granules (Fig. 2A). A second difference is that the glycogen is stored in the form of several small vacuoles in *E. hartmanni*, while in *E. histolytica* it is stored in one large vacuole. Burrows (1957, 1961) also suggested using the nucleus diameter/cell diameter ratio as a taxonomic character, but difficulties involved in determining the diameter (see p. 5, also Gleason *et al.*, 1963) have led to this character being abandoned (Burrows, 1964).

The use of differences in distribution of peripheral chromatin seems a valid taxonomic criterion in the case of *E. hartmanni* and *E. histolytica*, but care must be taken in its future use. Artifacts may arise during preparation of material, and the small size of nuclei may lead to differences of interpretation. The earlier literature contains many "species" based solely on nuclear morphology.

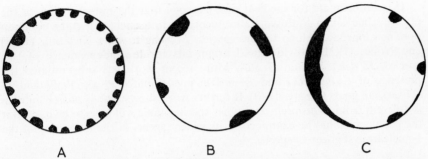

A   B   C

FIG. 2. Schematic drawings of the distribution of the nuclear peripheral chromatin showing the difference between *E. histolytica* (A) and *E. hartmanni* (B, C).

3. *Specific Status*

While the difference between *E. hartmanni* and *E. histolytica* was solely that of size, there was some doubt as to whether *E. hartmanni* should be a separate species. However, it is now known that the difference in size is not related to nutrition, but is genetically determined. Further, there are morphological differences and pathological differences in that the small race is avirulent (see p. 23). It is therefore appropriate to give this amoebae specific status as *E. hartmanni*. This conclusion was also reached by Barretto (1963) after an extensive survey of the literature.

B. STRUCTURE OF *E. polecki*

Occasionally large numbers of 1-nucleate cysts have been observed in faeces of patients. These were considered to be immature cysts of *E. histolytica* until Kessel and Johnstone (1949) suggested they represented a species previously found in pigs, *E. polecki*. Since Kessel and Johnstone's description, this species has been observed elsewhere (Lubinsky, 1952; Sumardjo and Joe, 1953; Lawless, 1954; Burrows and Klink, 1955; Ray and Mukherjee, 1958; Burrows, 1959). The main features distinguishing *E. polecki* cysts from those of *E. histolytica* are the presence of a single nucleus, an inclusion mass, cytoplasmic condensations and numerous small chromatoids. The karyosome of the cyst is usually large and often consists of a group of granules. This character, together with the inclusion mass and cytoplasmic condensation, have been observed in other species, and have been considered to be abnormal features. Lubinsky (1952) was unable to find amoebae with the corresponding nuclear structure to *E. polecki* cysts, but instead were indistinguishable from *E. histolytica* in the minuta form. These considerations led Lubinsky (1952) to suggest that the 1-nucleate cysts were immature cysts of *E. histolytica*.

It is known that species of *Entamoeba* which form 1-nucleate cysts are found in many domestic animals (Noble and Noble, 1952), and that there is no doubt that in these species the 1-nucleate cyst represents the mature stage. An alternative explanation to that of Lubinsky's regarding *E. polecki* in man, is that man is occasionally infected with one of these animal species, but that the environment is not suitable for the formation of normal 1-nucleate cysts (Neal, 1963).

It is unfortunate for medical protozoology that the nomenclature of the pig amoebae is in a confused state. According to Kessel (1928a) the common porcine amoebae, belong to one species, *E. polecki*, while Nieschulz (1924) and Nöller (1921) provide good arguments for the independence of two species, *E. debliecki* and *E. suis*. More recent work has substantiated the presence of *E. debliecki* and *E. suis* in pigs (Simitch *et al.*, 1959) and *E. debliecki* in goats (Hoare, 1940). If further work shows that *E. polecki* in man is different from *E. histolytica*, another specific name will have to be used. But the problem should be examined in its wider aspects of the taxonomy of the 1-nucleate cyst group of species.

C. ELECTRON MICROSCOPY

Electron microscopy has revealed some differences of subcellular organization between *Entamoeba* and metazoan cells. No mitochondria have been identified (Osada, 1959; Miller *et al.*, 1961; Fletcher *et al.*, 1962), though rod-like bodies were interpreted as representing mitochondria (Miller and Swartzwelder, 1960). The Golgi apparatus also was absent and the endoplasmic reticulum was rudimentary (Osada, 1959; Miller *et al.*, 1961). The nuclear membrane was two layered and perforated by a system of pores (Osada, 1959; Miller *et al.*, 1961). Food vacuoles were lined by a membrane similar to the plasma membrane of the cell (Fletcher *et al.*, 1962). Miller and Swartzwelder (1960) also described virus-like particles which were thought to be different from the ribonucleic acid (RNA) particles seen previously by Deutsch and Zaman (1959) in *E. invadens*.

All this work was carried out with *E. histolytica* amoebae derived from conventional bacteria-containing cultures. Studies with *E. invadens* have shown a similar structure whether grown with bacteria or in axenic culture (Zaman, 1962; Siddiqui, 1963b; Siddiqui and Rudzinska, 1963).

E. invadens differs from *E. histolytica* by the large numbers of crystalline particles in the cytoplasm of amoebae of the former species. Barker and his colleagues have made a special study of the chromatoids of *E. invadens* (see Barker, 1963a). This work shows that the cyst chromatoids consist mainly of RNA and protein, and arise by the accumulation of small particles present in amoebae, to form polycrystalline masses in immature cysts. In maturing cysts these fragment again into separate particles, though the total RNA content does not fall. The chromatoid is interpreted as a store of ribosomes which, when dispersed, enables the amoeba to undergo a period of rapid growth allowing the parasite to establish itself in a new host (Barker, 1963b; Barker and Svihla, 1964). Siddiqui and Rudzinska (1965) reported that the chromatoid showed a helical structure, but Barker (1964) considers the helical structure to be an optical image derived from viewing a three-dimensional crystalline structure.

D. LIST OF SPECIES DESCRIBED

This list represents the best-known species of *Entamoeba*. Reference is made to the most recent adequate description of their morphology. They are divided into four groups, according to the number of nuclei in the mature cyst, and those whose cysts are unknown. Within these four groups they are arranged in alphabetical order.

1. *Species with 8-Nucleate Cysts*

Entamoeba barretti (Taliaferro and Holmes, 1924); from the turtle, *Chelydra serpentina*.
Entamoeba cobayae (Nie, 1950); from laboratory guinea-pigs.
Entamoeba coli (Dobell, 1919); from man.
Entamoeba gallinarum (McDowell, 1953); from domestic fowls.
Entamoeba marmotae (Crouch, 1936); from *Marmota monax*.
Entamoeba muris (Neal, 1950a); from various rodents.

2. *Species with 4-Nucleate Cysts*

Entamoeba aulastomi (Bishop, 1932, 1937); from the leech.
Entamoeba dispar (Brumpt, 1925); from man, synonymous with *E. histolytica*.
Entamoeba hartmanni (Burrows, 1964); from man.
Entamoeba histolytica (Dobell, 1919); from man.
Entamoeba invadens (Geiman and Ratcliffe, 1936); from various reptiles, especially snakes.
Entamoeba knowlesi (Rodhain and Hoof, 1947); from tortoises.
Entamoeba moshkovskii (Neal, 1953); from sewage treatment plant.
Entamoeba nuttalli (see Wenyon, 1926); from monkeys, synonymous with *E. histolytica*.
Entamoeba philippinensis (Kidder, 1937); from roach, *Panesthia javanica*.
Entamoeba pyrrhogaster (Lobeck, 1940); from salamanders.
Entamoeba ranarum (Sanders, 1931); from various amphibians, especially frogs.
Entamoeba terrapinae (Sanders and Cleveland, 1930); from turtles.

3. *Species with 1-Nucleate Cysts*

Entamoeba bovis (Noble and Noble, 1952); from cattle.
Entamoeba chattoni (Salis, 1941); from various monkeys.
Entamoeba debliecki (Hoare, 1940); from goats and pigs.
Entamoeba polecki (Kessel and Johnstone, 1949); from man and pigs.
Entamoeba suis (Hoare, 1940); from pigs.

4. *Species in which Cysts are Unknown*

Entamoeba caudata (Carini and Reichenow, 1949); from dog, probably synonymous with *E. histolytica*.
Entamoeba gingivalis (Dobell, 1919); from man.

IV. NUCLEAR DIVISION

Nuclear division has been described in various species of *Entamoeba*, though *E. histolytica* has received most attention. Heidenhain's iron haematoxylin was mainly used by the earlier workers, and, although this stain gave a reliable picture of the resting nucleus, it was unreliable for dividing stages, since the technique involves differentiation. As it is almost impossible to standardize de-staining, some small granules were stained to a variable degree, and it is obvious from the illustrations of some publications that some granules were rendered invisible. The varying interpretations of the stages of division is also due to the small size of the chromatin granules which approaches the limit of resolution of the light microscope. For these reasons the earlier accounts were often oversimplified.

A great advance was the discovery of Feulgen's stain for location of deoxyribonucleic acid (DNA) and hence the identification of the chromosomes. The results of DNA distribution are discussed below, but the interpretation of morphological changes during nuclear division are dealt with first.

It is not proposed to discuss the earlier studies in detail (see Cleveland and Sanders, 1930, for references on *E. histolytica*, and Swezy, 1922; Kessel, 1924; Kofoid and Swezy, 1925; Child, 1926), but it is apparent that these accounts agree on two general points. First, the nuclear membrane is always intact, and second, there is one stage which is similar in all species. At this stage, when the nucleus has elongated but not started to constrict, there is at each pole of the nucleus a mass of granules of chromatin (in the papers cited above, termed polar masses, centrioles, polar caps, daughter centrosomes) and between them a number of fibres on which are arranged beads of chromatin, or discrete granules of chromatin which were generally regarded as the chromosomes.

There is one description of nuclear division to which the second generalization does not apply, that is *E. aulastomi* (Bishop, 1932). In this organism, large chromatin granules, composed of material from the karyosomes and the peripheral layer, appeared at the centre of the nucleus, these divide into two groups, the nucleus elongated and constricted, each daughter nucleus enclosing approximately equal numbers of granules. Thus in this organism apparently there are no chromatin masses at the poles of the dividing nucleus.

It is apparent that the earlier workers regarded the chromatin masses at the poles of the dividing nucleus as spindle organizers (centrioles) or as masses of chromatin of unknown function, whilst the chromatin granules which were observed migrating to each daughter nucleus were considered to be the true chromosomes. Recently, however, evidence derived from the use of Feulgen's stain has been published, which shows that the reverse is actually more correct.

In 1940, Stabler published an account of nuclear division in *E. gingivalis*. The first stage showed that the granules of the karyosome became more loosely arranged and granules surrounding the karyosome were more pronounced. The chromatin in the peripheral layer was reduced in amount, but never entirely lost. The next stage observed was that large definite granules of chromatin (in order to facilitate the description, these granules will be called chromosomes, though the use of this term will be qualified below) were arranged in two groups on either side of the nucleus, while the peripheral chromatin was found mainly in two groups on either side of the nucleus and between the groups of chromosomes. Fibres connected chromosomes of each group. All these changes in the organization of the nucleus occurred while the nucleus was still spherical. At this point the nucleus started to elongate and material derived from the peripheral chromatin appeared at the equatorial region of the elongate nucleus. Finally, the nucleus constricted with the karyosome re-forming from chromosomes. Stabler's description was, in the main, confirmed by Noble (1947). The latter author used Feulgen's staining technique, which showed that the chromosomes were Feulgen-positive. According to Noble, the chromosomes gradually became apparent from a central mass of granules derived from the karyosomes and small granules surrounding this structure. All these were Feulgen-positive. Noble was unable to determine whether or not the karyosome material was incorporated into the chromosomes.

In the same year as Stabler's account was published, Wenrich (1940) described nuclear division in *E. muris*. This description is similar to those of *E. gingivalis* in that chromosomes were observed to appear from the mass of granules originating from the karyosome and surrounding granules, all being Feulgen-positive. It differs in that Wenrich observed a second division of Feulgen-negative chromatin granules derived from the peripheral chromatin. As the divided chromosomes moved towards opposite poles of the nucleus, a second group of thread-like chromatin granules arranged in threads appeared at the equator. These, according to Wenrich, also divided mitotically and migrated towards the poles, following the chromosomes as the nucleus elongated. Neal (1950a) also observed the first division of the chromosomes, but was unable to observe a second mitotic division of Feulgen-negative chromatin, and concluded that this latter chromatin was distributed more or less at random between the daughter nuclei, in a similar manner to that observed by Stabler (1940) in *E. gingivalis*.

The use of Feulgen technique has thus shown that, although all chromatin granules in dividing nuclei stain a uniform black colour with Heidenhain's haematoxylin, they are of two kinds. The first series of granules are Feulgen-positive and divide mitotically, while the second series are Feulgen-negative. It is not possible to decide on present data whether or not the latter series divide mitotically.

The chromatin granules called chromosomes are so called by reason of their positive reaction to Feulgen's stain and their apparent mitotic division. However, their precise origin, their continuity with structures existing in the interphase nucleus, and exact manner of division and separation has not yet been determined. Owing to their small size, it is not known if they are structurally similar to the typical chromosomes of other protozoa (Cleveland, 1949) or metazoa. Their number was observed to be five for *E. gingivalis* (see Stabler, 1940; Noble, 1947), though Wantland *et al.* (1961) supported Child's (1926) estimate of six chromosomes. The number observed by Wenrich (1940) for *E. muris* was three to eight, and six by Neal (1950a). None of these latter authors could identify with certainty a centriole or its product, a centrodesmose.

The cyclical change of DNA was also observed by Pan and Geiman (1955) for *E. histolytica* and *E. coli*, and Ghosh (1963) for *E. invadens*. It was found in *E. histolytica* that DNA could only be identified during nuclear division, though it was not certain whether this was due to increased synthesis or to condensation for duplication of chromosomes. In contrast to *E. histolytica*, DNA was observed at all stages, including the interphase, in *E. coli*. In cysts of *E. histolytica*, DNA was present in nuclei of immature cysts with one or two nuclei. Since mature 4-nucleate cysts were Feulgen-negative, it is feasible to associate this change of DNA content again with nuclear division. Nuclei of *E. coli* cysts contained DNA at all stages, thus confirming the observation on *E. coli* amoebae.

The conclusion of Ray and Sen Gupta (1954, 1956), however, was different from that of the other workers. The Indian workers described a faint positive reaction with Feulgen's stain for DNA in amoebae of *E. histolytica* and in the similar amoebae from the rhesus monkey, *E. nuttalli*. However, since dividing nuclei were not observed, the significance of the faint staining cannot be established.

It can be seen that more work on the details of nuclear division in *Entamoeba* is required before the process is finally elucidated, though the present state of our knowledge can be summarized schematically as in Fig. 3. This figure shows the first division of the chromosomes (Feulgen-positive granules, Fig. 3A and B), while the other nuclear material (Feulgen-negative) divides next (Fig. 3C). It is uncertain whether or not the second division of nuclear material is mitotic. The amount of Feulgen-negative dividing material may vary in different species. *E. muris* and *E. coli*, for example, probably have a larger amount than *E. gingivalis*, while *E. aulastomi* has little or none of the chromatin comprising the second division (Bishop, 1932). Unfortunately there is no information on the reaction of *E. aulastomi* to Feulgen's stain. This difference between the species may, in turn, relate to the quantity of chromatin present in the peripheral layer of the nucleus, assuming that the karyosome material is used mainly in the formation of the chromosomes. Reorganization of the nucleus occurs by the Feulgen-negative chromatin being incorporated into the peripheral layer, while the Feulgen-positive chromosome appears to form the karyosome (Fig. 3D).

The nuclear division of *Entamoeba* has been discussed at some length, since the method of division has been used as a taxonomic criterion with other amoebae. It has been found that there are a number of different patterns of division used by small free-living amoebae and amoebo-flagellates (Singh, 1952). From the details available, it appears that *Entamoeba* differs from others so far described.

V. EXCYSTATION AND METACYSTIC DEVELOPMENT

The modern concept of excystation and the development of the newly hatched amoeba commenced with the work of Dobell (1928) on *E. histolytica*. The excystation of *E. histolytica* cysts, however, was first seen some eleven years earlier by Chatton, but he was unable to follow the subsequent development.

In the present account, the terminology of Dobell (1928) is followed. The amoeba which escapes from the cyst is termed the metacystic amoeba, and, because the nuclei in this amoeba are directly derived from the cyst, they are called cystic nuclei (or N). When a cystic nucleus divides, the daughter nuclei are given the symbol of n.

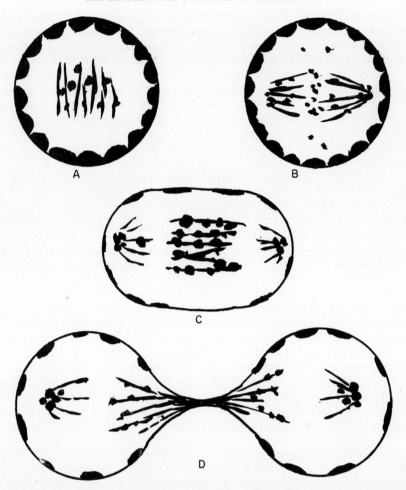

FIG. 3. Speculative schematic diagram of nuclear division of *Entamoeba*. A, Formation of Fculgen-positive granules, peripheral chromatin unchanged. B, Division of Feulgen-positive granules, beginning of Feulgen-negative series, peripheral chromatin reduced. C, Definite series of Feulgen-negative granules, peripheral chromatin almost disappeared, nucleus elongating. D, Karyosome beginning to be reconstituted from Feulgen-positive granules, Feulgen-negative granules disappearing, peripheral chromatin reappearing, daughter nuclei almost separated.

A. EXCYSTATION

Earlier attempts to stimulate excystation tried to imitate conditions that the cyst would encounter in the host, but it was soon established that the cyst would hatch without any enzymic or other kind of pre-treatment. Provided they have matured to the right stage for excysting, cysts of *E. histolytica* require little more than warmth (37°) and an anaerobic environment (see Rees *et al.*, 1950).

Cysts of species of the 4-nucleate cyst group of *Entamoeba* preparing to excyst were recognized by the absence of discrete vacuoles of glycogen and chromatoid bodies. In the living cysts, the amoeba moved inside the cyst until it perforated the wall. In *in vitro* studies, the perforation through the cyst wall was extremely small, so small that the nuclei were distorted as they passed through the opening. As the amoeba began to emerge, a partial vacuum developed inside the cyst, and this resulted in the cytoplasm flowing in and out of the cyst several times before the amoeba finally escaped. The empty shell appeared to be intact, no sign of the pore was found. This account of *E. histolytica*, described by Dobell (1928) from cultures, is different from that seen *in vivo* by other workers.

E. histolytica excysting in the small intestine and caecum of experimentally infected rats used another method in addition to the technique observed *in vitro* (Tanabe, 1934). In the second method, a larger perforation, more in the nature of a slit or rent, was produced, which enabled the amoeba to escape from the cyst more easily than through a pore. The larger slit in the cyst wall was also the method used by *E. histolytica* in experimentally infected dogs (Swartzwelder, 1939) and brown howler monkeys (Hegner *et al.*, 1932). It is not clear at the present time which of these methods of hatching is correct, or if both are used. There is no doubt that *in vitro* studies are technically simple to perform and give accurate results, and it could be argued that the large holes seen in cysts removed from experimentally infected animals are artifacts produced by smearing intestinal contents on a slide. On the other hand, it is equally feasible that the exterior of the cyst wall may be softened by the passage through the host's intestinal tract, which enables the amoeba to force a larger opening. Emergence of the amoeba through a small pore was also observed for *E. invadens*, *E. terrapinae*, *E. moshkovskii*, *E. aulastomi* and *E. ranarum*. Once the amoeba has emerged either *in vitro* or *in vivo*, the four nuclei were characteristically clumped into a single cluster.

The excystation of *E. coli* has been studied only *in vitro* (Dobell, 1938). This study showed that the amoeba emerged from the cyst by a small or large slit similar to that observed in *E. histolytica in vivo*. The minute pore, with the see-sawing movement of cytoplasm observed with *E. histolytica*, was not seen in *E. coli*. The wall was composed of two layers, which was studied most readily at the perforation. The inner wall was thick and rigid, while the outer layer was thin and elastic. The nuclei of *E. coli* did not clump into a single cluster.

The details of time taken to excyst and location of excystment in the host intestine of *Entamoeba* species are summarized in Table II.

B. METACYSTIC DEVELOPMENT

After the multinucleate amoeba has hatched, it undergoes a period of development before the final product—a series of uninucleate trophic amoebae—is formed. As the method of metacystic development varies between species, it is more convenient to deal with differences under individual species of *Entamoeba*.

TABLE II

Details of excystation and metacystic development of various species of Entamoeba

Species of Entamoeba	In vitro or host	Time to excyst (h)	Location of excystation in host	Time for completion of metacystic development (h)	Author
E. coli	In vitro	4–8	—	36	Dobell, 1938
E. histolytica	In vitro	3–5	—	11	Dobell, 1928
	In vitro	4–6	—	—	Cleveland and Sanders, 1930
	Rat	2–4*	Small intestine, caecum	12	Tanabe, 1934
	Dog	1·5–4·5*	Ileum, large intestine	—	Swartzwelder, 1939
	Monkey	2–3*	Small intestine, caecum	—	Hegner et al., 1932
E. invadens	Natrix spp.	5–7*	Jejenum	24	Geiman and Ratcliffe, 1936
E. terrapinae	In vitro	Within 7	—	—	Sanders and Cleveland, 1930
E. moshkovskii	In vitro	5–8	—	48	Neal, 1953
E. aulastomi	In vitro	1–4	—	—	Bishop, 1937

*Time after ingestion of cysts.

1. *E. histolytica*

After the 4-nucleate amoeba has hatched, it starts feeding and undergoes a complex series of nuclear and cytoplasmic divisions. Each cystic nucleus (*N*) divided once in rotation, followed by a cytoplasmic division. At the cytoplasmic division, the remaining cystic nuclei were parcelled at random between the daughter amoebae. There are a number of theoretically possible ways that the cystic and daughter nuclei can be distributed, and the number of possible combinations are increased as the remaining cystic nuclei divide and daughter amoebae are formed. All these possibilities are dealt with by Cleveland and Sanders (1930), but in actual fact mainly one method occurs. This development is shown in Fig. 4, and all stages shown here were observed by Dobell (1928). He found that the original 4-nucleate amoebae (*N N N N*) began to develop in five alternative ways. The four other methods, in addition to the first already described, are shown in Fig. 5. They are numbered in decreasing order of frequency of occurrence. The end result of any method of metacystic development was the same, eight uninucleate amoebae.

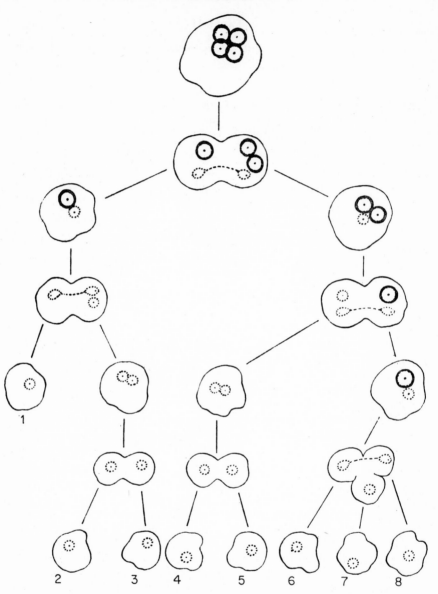

FIG. 4. The commonest method of metacystic development of *Entamoeba histolytica* (from Dobell, 1928), showing the formation of eight uninucleate amoebae.

Dobell's *in vitro* observations were confirmed by Cleveland and Sanders (1930), while Tanabe (1934) found an identical method of development using experimentally infected rats.

A unique observation on the metacystic development of *E. histolytica* was

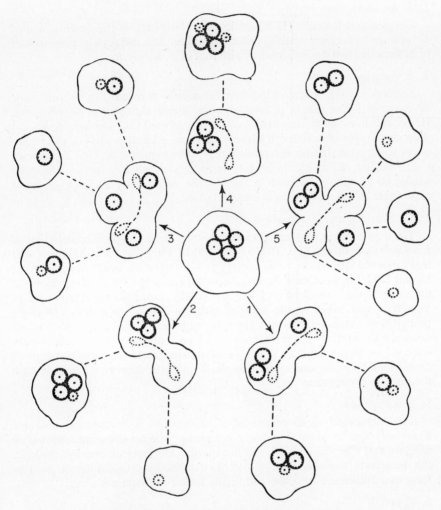

FIG. 5. The alternative methods of metacystic development of *Entamoeba histolytica*. Methods numbered in decreasing order of frequency (from Dobell, 1928).

that of Dutta (1961). He found amoebae in pathological human faeces, and after making permanent preparations identified them as metacystic amoebae. All developmental stages described by Dobell (1928) were seen. Reasons for the appearance of metacystic amoebae are obscure, though it is possible that the liquid consistency of the faeces acted as a culture medium in which cysts were able to develop.

The time for completion of metacystic development, that is until the population consisted only of 1-nucleate amoebae, was from 11 to 12 h (Dobell, 1928; Tanabe, 1934; see Table II).

2. *E. invadens*

Geiman and Ratcliffe (1936) made a detailed study of the development of *E. invadens* in experimentally infected snakes. The metacystic development of *E. invadens* is virtually identical with that of *E. histolytica*.

3. *E. ranarum*

Sanders's (1931) study of the frog *Entamoeba* showed that its metacystic development—like that of *E. invadens*—was identical to that of *E. histolytica*. Her conclusions have been criticized on the ground that the figures did not show any stages of actual cytoplasmic division. Although this is a valid comment, since other species morphologically indistinguishable from *E. ranarum* —*E. invadens*, *E. aulastomi* and *E. moshkovskii*—all develop in a manner similar to *E. histolytica*, and in the absence of contrary evidence, it seems reasonable to accept Sanders's interpretation.

4. *E. aulastomi and E. moshkovskii*

The development of these species was found to be closely similar to that of *E. histolytica* (see Bishop, 1937; Neal, 1953). However, one difference was that amoebae with three cystic nuclei (*N N N*) were frequently seen, whereas Dobell (1928) did not observe such metacystic amoebae in *E. histolytica*. On the other hand, Cleveland and Sanders (1930) illustrated their paper on *E. histolytica* with a metacystic amoeba with the nuclear constitution *N N N*, though they made no comment as to its frequency in their cultures. It is not known with certainty the manner by which such amoebae are formed, but in both *E. aulastomi* and *E. moshkovskii* it was found that the subsequent development was by one cystic nucleus dividing to form two amoebae with the nuclear constitution *Nn*.

5. *E. terrapinae*

The metacystic development of *E. terrapinae* is exceptional amongst *Entamoeba* species of the 4-nucleate cyst group. The development reported by Sanders and Cleveland (1930) did not involve any nuclear division. Instead, the 4-nucleate amoeba, after excysting, divided by cytoplasmic division to form two 2-nucleate amoebae and finally four 1-nucleate amoebae.

6. *E. coli*

E. coli is the only species of the 8-nucleate cyst group in which the metacystic development has been studied (Dobell, 1938). The method of development was similar to *E. terrapinae* in that the cystic nuclei did not divide. The multinucleate metacystic amoebae divided by cytoplasmic division with random distribution of cystic nuclei to daughter amoebae. The various ways that *E. coli* developed is shown in Fig. 6, which were all demonstrated by Dobell (1938). Further fission resulted finally in a series of 1-nucleate amoebae, which continued to grow and divide.

Ideally, the metacystic development of *E. coli* should result in the formation of eight 1-nucleate amoebae. However, it was usual for one to three cystic nuclei, and occasionally as many as four, to degenerate before the excystation commenced. The degenerating nuclei became smaller, their chromatin broke up, they stained less deeply and eventually became homogeneous granules which finally vanished completely. This process did not occur simultaneously in all nuclei which ultimately disappeared. An amoeba sometimes hatched

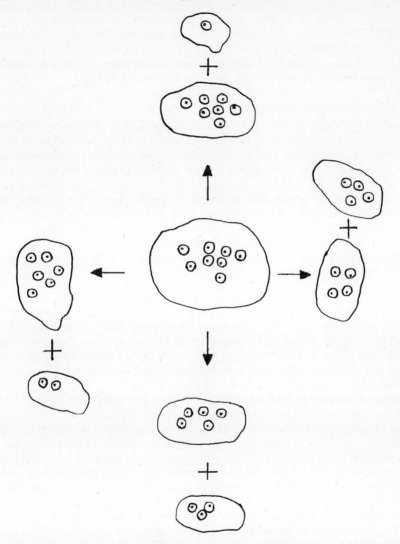

FIG. 6. Development of metacystic amoeba of *Entamoeba coli* by fission of amoebae with distribution of metacystic nuclei between daughter amoebae.

from the cyst with less than eight nuclei, but with some of the remaining nuclei obviously abnormal. In these circumstances, metacystic development commenced not with an 8-nucleate amoeba as in Fig. 6, but with amoebae containing seven, six, five or, more rarely, four cystic nuclei.

Mayfield (1944) in a short paper on establishing *E. coli* in culture, noted that amoebae hatching from the cyst contained degenerated nuclei and that the number of normal nuclei was five or more.

From this account of the metacystic development of *E. coli*, it is apparent that the number of trophic amoebae will usually be less than that of *E. histolytica* and other similar species which produce eight trophic amoebae from each 4-nucleate cyst.

E. coli has a longer time of development (36 h) than *E. histolytica* and *E. invadens*, though shorter than *E. moshkovskii* (see Table II).

7. *Multiple Fission of Amoebae*

Cleveland and Sanders (1930), in their study of *E. histolytica*, observed trophic amoebae containing two to four nuclei in their cultures. Since these multinucleate amoebae also contained black staining bodies, which appeared to be similar to the chromatoids known to occur in cysts, the authors considered that these amoebae might develop as metacystic amoebae without actually secreting a cyst wall. However, it is well known that multinucleate amoebae occur in all cultures prepared from various media (see Shaffer, 1965) and the liver infusion medium employed by Cleveland and Sanders is well known to promote vigorous growth of amoebae. It seems more likely that these amoebae represent abnormal development rather than another mode of multiplication *in vitro*.

VI. Host-restriction

As noted above, many species of *Entamoeba* have been described as morphologically indistinguishable from *E. coli* or *E. histolytica*, but, since they were found in a different host, were given specific status. Whether or not they are different, often can only be determined by cross-infection experiments. Such experiments are not difficult to perform, but require great attention to detail to give accurate results. The protozoan material, whether from animals or cultured *in vitro*, must be shown to contain only one species, and the experimental host must be free from any natural infection. It is the latter requirement which is the most difficult to satisfy. In past work it has been realized by two methods, either by rearing parasite-free animals (Hegner, 1929a; Cairns, 1953; Saxe, 1954) or by demonstrating the absence of amoebae by faecal examination. The difficulty of determining infection with intestinal amoebae by faecal examination has been discussed at length by Svensson (1935) and Svensson and Linders (1934), and has been stressed by Dobell (1931, 1936) in his experimental studies on simian protozoa. Having obtained the parasite-free animals, attention must be paid to their feeding and accommodation, so that they do not acquire infections during the course of the experiments.

These difficulties have deterred research workers from taking up the investigation of cross-infections of *Entamoeba*. However, carefully conducted experiments directly give information of taxonomic value, both positive and negative, although negative results are sometimes more difficult to interpret.

However, if the inoculum is shown to be viable (either by positive *in vitro* cultivation or preferably by successful infection of the natural host), if the inoculum contains a suitable number of mature cysts and if the experimental hosts are fed on a natural diet, it is highly probable that a negative result will reflect a true resistance to infection. The number of cysts inoculated will probably not materially affect the results if faecal examinations are carefully conducted, though with large inocula the infections will be heavier and therefore easier to detect with a shorter prepatent period. Infections have been reported with small inocula, one infection out of eight inoculations with one *E. coli* cyst in man and three infections out of ten inoculations with ten cysts (Rendtorff, 1954). The inoculum had to be increased to contain 10000 *E. coli* cysts to get 100% successful inoculations. Similarly for *E. gallinarum*, 6000 cysts had to be given to infect all animals inoculated (Richardson, 1934). These studies indicate that if sufficient cysts are available, it would be best to administer at least 10000 cysts to each experimental host.

Host-restriction studies have so far been limited to the following nine species, four belonging to the 8-nucleate cyst group, *E. coli, E. muris, E. gallinarum* and *E. barretti*, and five to the 4-nucleate cyst group, *E. histolytica, E. invadens, E. terrapinae, E. ranarum* and *E. moshkovskii*.

A. *E. muris*

E. muris is one of the species which have received considerable attention in regard to host-restriction. The results can be summarized as in Table III. In addition to this data, Miller and Saxe (1951) reported that *E. muris* cysts from *Peromyscus maniculatus bairdi* were not infective to *Citellus tridecimlineatus*. The results (Table III) show that the laboratory rodents, mice, rats and hamsters, are infected with a strain, or strains, of *E. muris* which are infective to

TABLE III

Summary of cross-infection of E. muris *strain to laboratory rodents*
(Compiled from Neal, 1950a; Miller and Saxe, 1951; Saxe, 1954.)

| Source of *E. muris* | Experimental hosts | | |
	Hamster*	Rat*	Mouse*
Mouse*	0	+	+
Rat*	+	+	+
Hamster*	+	+	0
Citellus tridecimlineatus	—	—	0
Tamias striatus griseus	—	—	0
Peromyscus maniculatus bairdi	—	0	0
Neotoma fuscipes	0	—	0
Microtus pennsylvaticus	0	—	0

* Mouse = laboratory *Mus musculus*; hamster = laboratory *Mesocricetus auratus*; rat = laboratory *Rattus norvegicus*.
+ = positive cross-infection; — = unsuccessful cross-infection; 0 = cross-infection not done.

all laboratory hosts. When the results with other rodents are considered, it seems that here there are strains which are not infective to laboratory rodents, and, in the case of amoebae from *Peromyscus* and *Citellus*, not infective to the alternative rodent species.

E. muris is morphologically indistinguishable from *E. coli* of man (Neal, 1950a), and it was important to determine their relationship. Previous attempts to infect rats and mice with *E. coli* were discussed by Neal (1950a), who, after further experimental work with human and simian strains, concluded that *E. coli* was not infective to laboratory rats and mice. Cross-infection experiments with *E. cobayae* from guinea-pigs (Holmes, 1923; Saxe, 1954) and *E. marmotae* from *Marmota monax* (Saxe, 1954) showed that they were not infective to laboratory rats. *E. marmotae* was also not infective to laboratory guinea-pigs (Saxe, 1954).

Since parasite-free chicks are readily available, Hegner (1929a, b) attempted to cross-infect with *E. muris* from rats and *E. cobayae* from guinea-pigs. The experiments with *E. muris* showed that the infections were short-lived, though in two cases the infections were still present after 6 days. Only short-term observations were made with *E. cobayae*, when the infections were present at 20 h.

B. *E. coli*

A detailed study of the host-restriction of *E. coli* was reported by Dobell (1936). He isolated *E. coli* from *Macacus rhesus*, and then transferred the cysts, formed in culture, to man. This infection was observed only for 6 weeks, when it apparently died out. *E. coli* was then isolated in culture from a marmoset *Hapale jacchus* and transferred in a similar manner to *Macacus sinicus* and then to *M. rhesus*. Finally *E. coli* from the experimentally infected *M. rhesus* was transferred to man. This infection was of a longer duration than the first experimental human infection, and had lasted over two years at the time the paper was written. In fact, the infection with *E. coli* was still present in 1950, or of 16 years' duration, since this strain was used in the experiments to infect rats (strain *MD*; Neal, 1950a). Thus this work showed that the 8-nucleate cyst species occurring in *M. rhesus*, *H. jacchus* and *M. sinicus* are identical to *E. coli* of man.

Earlier Kessel (1928b) reported that cysts of *E. coli* from man successfully infected *M. lasiotis* and *M. rhesus*. Since Kessel had made only twenty-eight negative examinations prior to inoculation, Dobell did not admit this as convincing evidence of freedom from natural infection, but regarded it as "fairly good evidence". Deschiens (1927) described the infection of a monkey, *M. sinicus*, by *E. coli* cysts from a chimpanzee, but, as Dobell points out, since the monkey was examined only eight times previous to inoculation the positive result may have been due to a latent natural infection.

Other animals, taxonomically less closely related to primates, have been used as experimental hosts. Cats and kittens were not susceptible to infection either by inoculation with cysts from man or with simian strains (see Dobell, 1936; Ristorcelli, 1939). Simić (1933) found one dog spontaneously infected with an *E. coli*-like amoeba, and subsequently infected four out of twenty-five dogs with cysts from man. The experimental infections proved transitory and disappeared by the 8th day. Finally, Hegner (1929b) failed to infect chicks with cysts of *E. coli* from man.

Since *E. coli*-like cysts were found in one out of 159 pigs examined, Kessel (1928a) attempted to infect amoebae-free pigs with cysts. After demonstrating by about twenty-eight negative faecal examinations the absence of *E. coli* in twelve pigs, human faeces containing cysts of *E. coli* were fed. Two of these twelve animals developed *E. coli* infections. No details of the duration or intensity of infection were recorded.

c. *E. gallinarum*

This species is an incompletely known amoeba of the 8-nucleate cyst group, first described by Tyzzer (1920). Because of the availability of parasite-free chicks, two studies on host-restriction have been carried out (Hegner, 1929a; Richardson, 1934). Chicks were inoculated by mouth with caecal contents from domestic fowls containing cysts of *E. gallinarum*, though these were not demonstrated before inoculation. Amoebae of *E. gallinarum* were first seen 2 days after inoculation, and were still present when the experiment was completed on the 14th day.

Amoebae apparently indistinguishable from *E. gallinarum* were found in chicks infected with material from other poultry. Table IV summarizes the successful cross-infection experiments so far carried out.

TABLE IV

Origin of E. gallinarum *successfully transmitted to young chicks*

Donor host	Author
Fowl	Tyzzer, 1920; Hegner, 1929a; Richardson, 1934
Duck	Hegner, 1929a; Richardson, 1934
Guinea fowl	Hegner, 1929a
Turkey	Richardson, 1934
Goose	Richardson, 1934

D. *E. histolytica* AND *E. hartmanni*

There are two aspects of the host–parasite relationship relating to these species which are of interest in the present context; one is the virulence of strains of *E. histolytica* and *E. hartmanni*, while the second is the host-specificity of amoebae indistinguishable from *E. histolytica* which have been described from various mammalian hosts. Virulence, as such, is outside the scope of the present paper, but a brief summary is necessary since Brumpt proposed to give avirulent strains specific status as *E. dispar*. For a recent summary of the literature see Hoare (1961).

1. *Virulence*

The differing reaction of individuals to infection with *E. histolytica* has puzzled observers and investigators for a number of years. The problem is that some members of a population become ill with intestinal symptoms, while others, although apparently infected just as heavily, have no symptoms. In addition to the distribution of the varying appearance of symptoms within a community, there is also the geographical location of symptomatic patients. Cases of dysentery occur in tropical or near tropical regions, but in temperate or colder zones symptoms due to *E. histolytica* are very rare. The distribution of cases of liver abscess is similar to that of amoebic dysentery.

The study of virulence in laboratory animals, kittens, rats, guinea-pigs, dogs and rabbits, has contributed a great deal of information, but has not conclusively solved this problem (see Anderson *et al.*, 1953; Neal, 1958; Faust, 1963). The fact remains that strains isolated from asymptomatic patients are usually less invasive or non-invasive to laboratory animals. This has been demonstrated especially with kittens and rats. Brumpt (1925) named such strains as *E. dispar*. Since it is likely that *E. histolytica* can change its virulent characteristics according to, as yet unknown, stimuli (see Neal, 1958), it seems unwise to give specific status to this unstable character.

Differences in structure between *E. histolytica* and the small race now known as *E. hartmanni* have been discussed above (p. 5), and it is generally agreed that *E. hartmanni* very rarely causes symptoms in man. Very few experimental studies have been recorded. Those which have been carried out confirm that *E. hartmanni* was less invasive than *E. histolytica* isolated from patients with amoebic dysentery. Immunological response has recently been implicated in relation to infection with *E. hartmanni*. It was found that splenectomized rats were more susceptible to infection than intact animals (Al-Dabagh, 1965).

2. *Host-restriction*

The earlier experimental studies on *E. histolytica* were carried out with the kitten (see Dobell, 1919, for earlier studies). It was soon established that when inoculated with *E. histolytica* isolated in culture from a patient suffering from amoebic dysentery, or with faeces containing amoebae, the kitten quickly contracted dysentery and usually died about 7 days after inoculation.

A number of studies have been made of *histolytica*-like amoebae by comparing the infections in kittens with those produced by *E. histolytica* of man. These are summarized in Table V. Dobell (1931) found that the infections produced by simian strains of *E. histolytica* were much more chronic in character than those obtained with human strains. However, Kessel (1928b, c) and Burova (1939) described the kitten infections as similar to those seen after inoculation with human strains.

Although the kitten infections show a similarity between various simian and human strains of *E. histolytica*, final proof of identity rests with direct cross-infection experiments. These have been studied by Kessel (1928b) and Dobell (1931). Their results showed that *E. histolytica* of man can be transferred to *Macacus rhesus* (Kessel, 1928a) and *M. sinicus* (Dobell, 1936). Although the infections were well established and lasted about 2 and 16 months respectively until autopsy, no symptoms of dysentery or diarrhoea were seen, nor intestinal ulceration at autopsy. Miller (1952) also observed the absence of tissue invasion in *M. mulatta* ($\equiv$ *rhesus*) after infection with human

TABLE V

Infectivity of animal strains of E. histolytica *to kittens*
(Unless otherwise stated, the inoculum was prepared from faeces containing cysts.)

Donor host	Proportion of kittens infected	Author
Cynocephalus anubis	10/23	Burova, 1939
Cynocephalus hamadrias	4/4	Burova, 1939
Macacus nemestrinus	3/7	Burova, 1939
Macacus rhesus	0/2	Dobell, 1931
Macacus rhesus culture cysts	0/6	Dobell, 1931
Macacus rhesus culture cysts	4/7	Kessel, 1928b
Macacus sancti-johannis	2/2	Kessel, 1928b
Macacus sinicus	0/5	Dobell, 1931
Macacus sinicus culture cysts	5/6	Dobell, 1931
Pig, culture amoebae	2/2	Kessel, 1928a

strains of *E. histolytica*. It cannot be automatically assumed that all monkeys are infective to human *E. histolytica*, since Ball (1935), after repeated attempts, was unable to infect the capuchin monkey (*Cebus capucinus*).

Dobell (1931) extended further the number of simian hosts for *E. histolytica*. After successfully infecting *M. sinicus* with a human strain, the *sinicus* infection was transferred to *M. rhesus*. Similarly, the natural infection in *M. rhesus* was transferred to *M. sinicus*, and the natural infection in *M. nemestrinus* to *M. rhesus* and then to *M. sinicus*. In all experimental infections, no symptoms were observed.

The experiments of these workers were well controlled, and the experimental animals shown to be free from natural infection by multiple negative microscopical faecal examinations, supplemented in the case of Dobell (1931) by cultural examinations. The cross-infection experiments of Hegner *et al.* (1932) do not give any reliable information, since their monkeys received only one examination before inoculation with *E. histolytica*.

The only study so far recorded of the reverse transfer of a simian strain of *E. histolytica* to man is that of Knowles and Das Gupta (1934). After a series of negative microscopical and cultural examinations, a man was administered *E. histolytica* cysts obtained from *M. rhesus*. On the 8th day after swallowing the cysts, faecal examination revealed the presence of *E. histolytica* cysts. The infection was still present after 2 months.

The observation of *E. histolytica*-like amoebae in Chinese pigs prompted Kessel (1928a) to attempt infection with human *E. histolytica*. With four different samples of human cysts he was able to infect a total of six pigs out of twelve inoculated. The experimental infections were recovered in culture and proved virulent to kittens. Kessel also infected one out of four pigs with cysts from *M. rhesus* and similarly showed the cultured amoebae to be virulent to kittens. However, Frye and Meleney (1934) failed completely to infect young pigs with *E. histolytica* cysts from man.

To summarize this section, the following monkeys are infected with an amoeba which cannot be distinguished in any way from *E. histolytica* of man: *Macacus rhesus*, *M. sinicus* and *M. nemestrinus*. Other simian hosts which, on the basis of the kitten infectivity experiments, are probably identical to *E. histolytica* of man: *Macacus sancti-johannis*, *Cynocephalus anubis* and *C. hamadrias*. In their natural environment, these animals will transfer *E. histolytica* from monkey to monkey. However, there are other animals which act as incidental hosts and acquire their infections from contact with man, such as pig, kitten, rat (Neal, 1948) and dog (Boyd, 1931).

E. *Entamoeba* OF REPTILES

It is convenient to deal with the entamoebae infecting reptiles under one heading, since there are three species which may be present in one host, two species of the 4-nucleate cyst group, *E. invadens* and *E. terrapinae*, and one species of the 8-nucleate cyst group, *E. barretti*.

1. *E. barretti*

This amoeba has not yet been studied morphologically to characterize it adequately. It was described by Taliaferro and Holmes (1924) from cultures and from the original turtle host, *Chelydra serpentina*. According to Geiman and Ratcliffe (1936) this amoeba produced 8-nucleate cysts in culture.

A study of cross-infection has shown that *E. barretti* will infect snakes (Geiman, 1937). Owing to the highly summarized method of the report, it is not possible to know which species of snake out of the four inoculated actually took the infection. It was not stated if lesions were produced in the snake by the amoeba.

2. *E. terrapinae*

This amoeba was isolated from a turtle (*Chrysemys elegans*) by Sanders and Cleveland (1930). It has been shown to be infective to snakes without producing any intestinal lesions. Geiman (1937) successfully infected *Natrix cyclopion*, while Miller (1951) found that the infection in *Thamnophis sirtalis* lasted 1 month. In a parallel experiment with *E. invadens*, three *T. sirtalis* snakes died within 2 weeks after inoculation (Miller, 1951).

3. *E. invadens*

The study of *E. invadens* started when an epizootic was observed in the reptiles at Antwerp Zoological Gardens (Rodhain and Hoof, 1934). Since then, similar epidemics have been reported from zoological gardens in the U.S.A. (Ratcliffe and Geiman, 1938), London (Hill and Neal, 1954) and Switzerland (Steck, 1961). The interest raised by the practical problem of keeping reptiles alive in captivity stimulated workers to test the infectivity of *E. invadens* for a number of potential hosts (see Tables VI and VII).

In general, when kept at a suitable temperature (see Barrow and Stockton, 1960), all snakes are very susceptible to infection (see Table VI), with ulceration of the intestine and subsequent extra-intestinal lesions. The snakes die

TABLE VI

Reptiles experimentally infected with E. invadens

Host	Authors
Lizards	
Anguis fragilis	Rodhain and Hoof, 1935; Hill and Neal, 1954
Lacerta muralis	Rodhain and Hoof, 1935
L. agilis	Stam, 1958
Agama atricollis	Stam, 1958
Snakes	
Natrix cyclopion	Ratcliffe and Geiman, 1938
N. natrix	Rodhain and Hoof, 1935
N. natrix helvetica	Hill and Neal, 1954
N. rhombifera	Ratcliffe and Geiman, 1938
N. sipedon	Meerovitch, 1958; Ratcliffe and Geiman, 1938; Barrow and Stockton, 1960
N. viperina	Rodhain and Hoof, 1934, 1935
Coluber constrictor	Geiman and Ratcliffe, 1936
Thamnophis sirtalis	Miller, 1951; Barrow and Stockton, 1960
T. sauritus	Barrow and Stockton, 1960
Lampropeltus doliata	Barrow and Stockton, 1960
Storeria occipitomaculata	Barrow and Stockton, 1960
S. dekayi	Barrow and Stockton, 1960
Opheodrys vernalis	Barrow and Stockton, 1960
Diadophis punctatus	Barrow and Stockton, 1960
Natrix maura	Steck, 1961
Turtles	
Chrysemys elegans	Geiman, 1937
C. picta	Geiman, 1937
Chelydra serpentina	Geiman, 1937
Tortoises	
Testudo tabulata	Rodhain and Hoof, 1935

TABLE VII

Animals which proved resistant to experimental infection with E. invadens

Animal inoculated	Author
Carassius auratus	Rodhain and Hoof, 1936
Rana pipiens, adults	Geiman, 1937
R. temporaria, adults (?)	Rodhain and Hoof, 1935
Anobis carolinensis	Ratcliffe and Geiman, 1938
Alligator mississippiensis	Ratcliffe and Geiman, 1938
Crocodiles	Rodhain and Hoof, 1936
Emys orbicularis	Rodhain and Hoof, 1936
Kittens	Ratcliffe and Geiman, 1938

in about 2 weeks. The two lizards and one species of tortoise which have been tested were also highly susceptible to infection, with intestinal ulceration. Turtles also proved susceptible to infection, but the infection did not kill the host and intestinal ulceration was not observed (Geiman, 1937).

Table VII lists animals which were not susceptible to infection with *E. invadens*. One frog out of fourteen inoculated with virulent amoebae proved to be infected in the absence of ulceration (Rodhain and Hoof, 1935). Three other frogs were inoculated with culture material from the one infected frog, but these latter frogs were not infected. The amoeba from the one frog was identified as being morphologically identical to *E. invadens*, and subsequent experiments proved it to be pathogenic for slow-worms (*Anguis fragilis*).

The infectivity studies with the European tortoise *Emys orbicularis* (Rodhain and Hoof, 1935) were not conclusive. Out of three tortoises inoculated, only one contracted a temporary infection. It is, therefore, included amongst the refractory hosts (Table VII) although, possibly with some justification, it could have been considered susceptible to *E. invadens*.

Reptilian hosts found spontaneously infected with *E. invadens* are listed by Hill and Neal (1954).

The observation that snakes die very quickly after infection with *E. invadens* suggests that they are not the natural host. Since turtles are easily infected and pass cysts in the faeces, it was thought that these animals could act as carriers (Rodhain and Hoof, 1936). This supposition has now been proved by the identification of *E. invadens* in the intestine of a turtle (*Chrysemys picta*) (Meerovitch, 1958).

4. *Summary of Host-restriction of Reptilian Amoebae*

On the basis of present evidence, it can be seen that turtles are infected by two amoebae, *E. terrapinae* and *E. invadens*, belonging to the 4-nucleate cyst group of species. Both of these are infective to snakes, one causing lesions and death, *E. invadens*, and the other living as a commensal in the gut, *E. terrapinae*. The question of whether these are virulent and avirulent strains of the same species has not been considered, but if they are merely strains differing only in virulence, the situation parallels that of *E. histolytica* in man. Turtles are also infected by an 8-nucleate cyst species, *E. barretti*, which is infective to snakes.

F. *E. ranarum*

The entamoeba of frogs and toads is called *E. ranarum*. The morphological resemblance of *E. ranarum* of the common frog *Rana temporaria* to *E. histolytica* prompted Dobell (1918) to attempt to infect tadpoles of *Rana temporaria* with *E. histolytica* cysts from man. The tadpoles were not infected.

Other studies of the amphibian parasite have been carried out by Cairns (1953) and Lobeck (1940). In addition to results summarized in Table VIII, Cairns found that amoebae from the salamander *Ambystoma tigrinum* would not infect *Triturus pyrrhogaster* or the turtle *Amyda spinifera*. In spite of the extensive work by Cairns, Table VIII shows that there are many gaps in the pattern of cross-infection experiments. If the negative results are accepted at the same value as the positive cross-infections (but see p. 20), it can be seen that no pattern emerges. However, it seems inconsistent that *E. ranarum* from *Rana clamitans* would not infect any experimental hosts, whereas the amoeba from the frog *R. catesbiana* was successfully transferred to two frogs and one toad. Lobeck (1940) described an amoeba from *Triturus pyrrhogaster* as *E. pyrrhogaster*, the morphology of which resembled *E. ranarum* very closely. Cross-infection experiments showed that *E. pyrrhogaster* would not infect *R. pipiens* tadpoles (Lobeck, 1940). This again is not consistent with Cairns's work, who showed that the amoeba from *Triturus torosus* was transferred to two species of frog and one toad.

TABLE VIII

Summary of cross-infection experiments with E. ranarum-*like amoebae to Amphibia*
(From Cairns, 1953; Lobeck, 1940.)

Source of E. ranarum	Experimental hosts				
	Rana pipiens	Rana sylvatica	Rana clamitans	Bufo terrestris	Ambystoma opacum
Rana clamitans	—	0	0	—	—
R. catesbiana	0	+	+	+	0
Hyla arenicola	0	0	0	0	—
Ambystoma tigrinum	+	0	0	0	0
A. maculatum	+	0	0	0	+
Triturus viridescens	+	0	0	0	0
T. torosus	+	0	+	+	0
T. pyrrhogaster	—	+	0	0	0

+ = positive cross-infection; — = unsuccessful cross-infection; 0 = cross-infection not done.

G. *E. moshkovskii*

This organism has been found in many parts of the world in sewage-treatment plants: Russia (Tshalaia, 1941, 1947; Gnezdilov, 1947), U.S.A. (Wright *et al.*, 1942), Brazil (Amaral and Leal, 1949), England (Neal, 1950b, 1953), Canada (Lachance, 1959), Poland (Hirschlerowa and Swiecicki, 1960), Costa Rica (Ruiz, 1960) and Singapore (Zaman, 1962). Because it is not associated with an animal host, it is sometimes considered to be a free-living *Entamoeba*. However, no morphological, physiological or biochemical characteristic has so far been found to distinguish *E. moshkovskii* from other *Entamoeba* species, and the habitat of *E. moshkovskii* in the sewage must resemble in many ways the environment of an animal's intestine. The free-living concept, on the other hand, is supported by the fact that all attempts to infect animals have so far proved negative (Table IX). Determined attempts have been made to infect mammals, especially by Carneri (1958c), so it seems unlikely to originate from this class of host. However, there are many lower chordate and invertebrate animals which could conceivably be the original host of *E. moshkovskii* and which have not yet been studied.

TABLE IX

List of animals not susceptible to infection with E. moshkovskii

Animal inoculated	Author
Rana temporaria, tadpoles	Neal, 1953; Hirschlerowa and Swiecicki, 1960
Salamandra maculosa, larvae	Neal, 1953
Kittens	Tshalaia, 1941
Guinea-pig	Leal and Amaral, 1950; Rogova, 1958; Hirschlerowa and Swiecicki, 1960
Rats	Neal, 1953; Carneri, 1958c
Hamster, *Mesocricetus auratus*	Carneri, 1958c
Man	Rogova, 1958

VII. BIOCHEMISTRY AND PHYSIOLOGY

The study of the physiology and biochemistry of *Entamoeba* has mainly been concerned with the human species *E. histolytica*, and little comparative work with other species has been attempted (see the review by Balamuth and Thompson, 1955, and the bibliography of Smith, 1965). However, a few points of taxonomic interest have emerged.

A. METABOLISM

Variations of metabolic characteristics between different strains of *E. histolytica* have been observed. Thus Shaffer and Iralu (1963) have shown differences in the ability of strains to lyse human and ox red blood cells, while Bragg and Reeves (1962) observed that glucose metabolism was different in the *Laredo* strain compared with other strains of *E. histolytica*.

The question of giving specific status to the avirulent strains of *E. histolytica* has been discussed in connexion with the host–parasite relationship (see p. 23), but it is appropriate here to mention enzyme studies. This aspect of virulence was studied by Neal (1960), who was unable to find any difference in proteolytic activity of cell-free extracts prepared from different strains of *E. histolytica*. However, Jarumilinta and Maegraith (1961) were able to show that a carboxypeptidase was detected in avirulent strains but not in virulent strains.

Comparative metabolic studies on parasitic amoebae would be interesting not only from the biochemical point of view, but would provide much valuable information of ecological and taxonomic importance. Such studies are now feasible, since the work of Diamond (1960) and Diamond and Bartgis (1965) on methods of axenic cultivation provides a source of material uncontaminated with bacteria or other associated living cells. The first investigations with the pure cultures would be to repeat the results so far obtained with bacterial cultures of *Entamoeba*.

B. DRUG SENSITIVITY

Differences between the sensitivity of *E. histolytica* and *E. coli* to emetine was noted by Bishop in 1929. Neal (1949) also found similar differences in rats experimentally infected with *E. histolytica* and *E. muris*. However, the more recent work deals with species of the 4-nucleate cyst group, *E. histolytica*, *E. invadens* and *E. moshkovskii*. It has been shown that *E. invadens* is less sensitive to amoebicidal drugs than *E. histolytica*, while *E. moshkovskii* occupies an intermediate position (Carneri, 1958a, 1959; Kaushiva, 1960). Using one particular drug clefamide (Mebinol), Carneri (1959) observed that it was inactive against *Hartmanella*, and suggested that this drug might have a specific action on members of the genus *Entamoeba*. In addition to differences between species, there were response differences according to the temperature at which the experiments are carried out. Thus the effect of drugs on *E. moshkovskii* incubated at 37°, 26° and 4°C showed that the speed of action was increased with a rise in temperature (Carneri, 1958b). In spite of this difficulty, this approach might yield valuable data for elucidating the relationship between the *Laredo*-type of *E. histolytica*, normal *E. histolytica* and *E. moshkovskii*. Some work with these anomalous strains of *E. histolytica* has already been done, and this shows that they are significantly more resistant to some amoebicidal drugs than normal strains of *E. histolytica* (Entner *et al.*, 1962; Entner and Most, 1965).

C. GROWTH AT DIFFERENT TEMPERATURES

When a species is successfully established in culture, it is general practice to maintain the culture at the body temperature of the host, for instance *E. histolytica* as isolated from man is incubated at 37°C with a tolerance of one or two degrees. The temperature limits of other species have been studied, and the results were summarized by McConnachie (1955). She concluded that the temperature requirements intergrade to form the series *E. aulastomi, E. ranarum, E. invadens, E. moshkovskii* and *E. histolytica*, which grow at increasingly higher temperatures. The situation has now been complicated by the discovery of a strain (*Laredo*), isolated from man and morphologically indistinguishable from *E. histolytica*, which will grow at a low temperature. The minimum previously accepted for *E. histolytica* was about 32°C (see Cabrera and Porter, 1958), but the *Laredo* strain will grow *in vitro* at any temperature between 20° and 37°C, and is therefore similar to *E. moshkovskii* (Entner and Most, 1965; Siddiqui, 1963a). Recently a further series of similar strains have been reported by Richards *et al.* (1965) and Entner and Most (1965). All strains were isolated from man, were morphologically similar to *E. histolytica*, but grew profusely at temperatures between 25° and 37°C.

Lachance (1963) determined the temperatures of growth of two reptilian species, *E. terrapinae* and *E. invadens*, and compared them with *E. moshkovskii*. He found that *E. terrapinae* was similar to *E. invadens*, and observed a difference in the lower critical temperature between *E. invadens* (12·5°) and *E. terrapinae* (5°). However, it is more convenient to study the growth at room temperatures and temperatures above, rather than below this. The temperature requirements of two other species, *E. knowlesi* and *E. ranarum*, was determined by a standard method by Neal using one step change of temperature to 37°, 30° and 25°C (unpublished data). This data is included in Table X, and shows that *E. knowlesi* was similar to *E. invadens* as described by

McConnachie (1955). The optimum temperature of *E. ranarum* was similar to that of *E. aulastomi* (Bishop, 1932).

If the temperatures of 37°, 30° and 25°C are selected, the growth limits of different species can be summarized as in Table X. The temperature of 37° was selected since *E. invadens* could not be grown above 35° (see Siddiqui, 1963a), and the choice of 30° was determined by the fact that Cabrera and Porter (1958) found the critical temperature of *E. histolytica* to be 32°. However, by gradual reduction of temperature, *E. histolytica* could be adapted to grow at 30° (Siddiqui, 1963a) and 29° (Cabrera, 1958). Although Cabrera (1958) was able to grow adapted strains at temperatures as low as 29°, he stated that strains of *E. histolytica* kept at 37° did not grow when the temperature was lowered in one step to 31·5°.

TABLE X

Summary of growth of in vitro cultures of species of Entamoeba at different temperatures

(Temperature changed in a single step. From McConnachie, 1955; Siddiqui, 1963a; Entner and Most, 1965; Neal, unpublished.)

Species	Growth of amoebae at various temperatures		
	37°C	30°C	25°C
E. histolytica	+	−	−
E. histolytica, Laredo-type strain	+	+	+
E. moshkovskii	+	+	+
E. invadens	−	+	+
E. terrapinae	−	+	+
E. knowlesi	−	+	+
E. ranarum	−	−	+
E. aulastomi	−	−	+*

*E. aulastomi grows well at 22°, but not at 30°.

All the work on critical temperatures deals with 4-nucleate cyst species. The only report on other species is that of Cabrera and Porter (1958), who studied *E. coli*. These authors found that the minimum temperature for *E. coli* was 33°C.

The work on temperature limits of *in vitro* cultures of *E. invadens* has been extended to the host–parasite system (Meerovitch, 1960, 1961; Barrow and Stockton, 1960). These experiments showed that experimentally infected snakes maintained at 34° or 13°C did not show pathological changes, although when kept at room temperature (20–25°) they developed gut and liver lesions. At the higher temperature of 34°, the amoebae did not become established in the gut of the snakes. Thus the temperature at which maximum virulence occurs coincides with the range of maximum growth *in vitro*.

These observations may shed some light on some anomalous reports published earlier. For instance, the report by Simitch and Petrovitch (1951) of the cultivation of *E. muris* at 22° and 23°C, shows that isolation of amoebae may be effected more easily if temperatures other than the host body temperature are also investigated.

At the present time the temperature growth data seem to provide stable characters, though the degree of growth at one particular temperature and the absolute limits of growth varies slightly from strain to strain of the same species, according to the culture associates and medium. Future work should employ a standard method, including medium and axenic condition or with defined associates. Using the temperature data, it is possible to divide the 4-nucleate cyst group of species, which have so far been investigated, into four sections:

(1) *E. histolytica.*
(2) *E. moshkovskii* and *Laredo*-type *E. histolytica.*
(3) *E. invadens, E. terrapinae* and *E. knowlesi.*
(4) *E. aulastomi* and *E. ranarum.*

D. LOCOMOTION AND POLARITY OF AMOEBAE

The classification of free-living amoebae is based on the type of pseudopodium structure and on the type of movement (see Schaeffer, 1926), and this criterion is adopted for identification of *E. histolytica* and *E. coli* amoebae as seen in faeces: *E. coli* amoebae are very sluggish, while *E. histolytica* amoebae are active. This criterion is a valid method of diagnosis for man. However, when culture methods first became available it was soon noticed that the differences in locomotion between *E. histolytica* and *E. coli in vitro* were less well marked (see Thomson and Robertson, 1925; Pavlova, 1938). It is now generally accepted that *E. coli* is much more sensitive to environmental changes than *E. histolytica*, and the amoebae quickly round up and cease moving when voided from the body.

Another morphological feature which has been used as a taxonomic character is the presence of a "uroid". This is not a new concept; it was used as long ago as 1879 by Leidy for free-living amoebae, and has been recently revived by Bovee (1949) as a possible generic character. This feature was used by Faust (1923), who described *Caudamoeba sinensis* from man, and by Carini and Reichenow (1949), who described *E. caudata* from a Brazilian dog. The new genus *Caudamoeba* was not generally accepted by protozoologists (see Wenyon, 1925), and recent advances in the study of amoeboid movement have thrown further light on the function of the "uroid" or "tail".

Considerable attention has been devoted to the study of polarity in amoebae—mainly dealing with free-living amoebae—and it is now generally accepted that a moving, monopodial amoeba has an anterior-posterior axis (see Allen and Kamiya, 1964; Jahn and Bovee, 1964). The exact mechanism and site of motive force is still disputed, but all theories take into consideration the existence of a tail region (or caudal region, uroid). The slug-like movement of *Entamoeba* has been observed by many investigators (see Thiel,

1956) and was re-examined by Bird (1956, 1958) in the light of the recent studies on amoeboid movement. He confirmed that the tail region was a constant feature in *E. histolytica* and other species of *Entamoeba* that he examined (*E. gingivalis, E. moshkovskii, E. muris, E. nuttalli, E. invadens, E. knowlesi* and *E. ranarum*). At the tail region, various particles of bacteria, cellular detritus, etc., adhere to the external surface and streamers of mucus-like material appear. Zaman (1961) examined the tail region of *E. invadens* by electron microscopy and described vacuoles being excreted at this region.

Since the existence of a tail region is part of the mechanism producing monopodial amoeboid movement and is present in amoebae of unrelated genera, this morphological feature cannot be considered by itself a valid taxonomic criterion.

E. CONTRACTILE VACUOLES

It has become axiomatic that parasitic protozoa, including amoebae, do not have contractile vacuoles when living in their natural environment. Further, because of the lack of a water-excretion mechanism, they cannot survive in a hypotonic medium. However, Tshalaia (1941) during her study of *E. moshkovskii*, observed that in hypotonic media an organelle developed in each amoebae which functioned as a contractile vacuole. The appearance of contractile vacuoles was confirmed by Neal (1953), though at the dilution of saline used (1:88 or more) the amoebae eventually died.

Recently Richards *et al.* (1965) have extended these observations to strains of *E. histolytica* which grow at 25°C. These strains multiplied and encysted, producing 4-nucleate cysts, in culture medium diluted in the proportion 1:64. In this medium the amoebae formed contractile vacuoles.

It is not yet certain if the contractile vacuoles produced by *Entamoeba* spp. in hypotonic media are identical to those of true free-living amoebae. It is clear, however, that if some species of *Entamoeba* can grow and encyst in such media and at room temperature, a reappraisal of the question of dispersal outside the host intestine becomes necessary.

VIII. SEROLOGICAL DIFFERENCES BETWEEN SPECIES AND STRAINS OF *Entamoeba*

As with the previous section on biochemistry and physiology, a great deal of research effort has been devoted to studying the immunology of the human species, *E. histolytica*. Various immunological methods have been adapted for use with *Entamoeba* antigens, for example precipitins (Maddison, 1965), indirect haemagglutination (Kessel *et al.*, 1961), complement fixation (Kessel *et al.*, 1965), inhibition of red blood cell phagocytosis by specific antisera (Shaffer and Ansfield, 1956), inhibition of amoebic growth (Nakamura, 1959) and fluorescent antibody (see Goldman and Gleason, 1962). The fluorescent antibody technique has not yet been employed for epidemiological studies, but has proved a useful research tool as discussed below. The other techniques have been investigated to determine their potential value as diagnostic methods and for epidemiological surveys (Maddison *et al.*, 1965; Kessel *et al.*, 1965; see also review by Blasi and Magaudda-Borzi, 1958).

Some of these methods have been further investigated and used to study differences between strains and species of *Entamoeba*. These results will be discussed in different sections according to the serological technique employed.

Amongst the earliest comparative studies were those of Menendez (1932) and Heathman (1932), who employed a variety of techniques. Menendez compared five strains of *E. histolytica* with *E. barretti*. The latter species was isolated from *Chelydra serpentina* and was believed by Menendez to be morphologically similar to *E. histolytica*. Serologically, however, it proved different to *E. histolytica* by a variety of tests, complement fixation, precipitin and lysis. However, this result could now be predicted, since *E. barretti* belongs to the group of species with 8-nucleate cysts (see p. 26) and, in fact, does not resemble *E. histolytica*. Two strains of *E. histolytica* were compared antigenically with a number of pond and marine amoebae, *Polychaos dubia*, *Chaos diffluens*, *Flabellula citata*, *F. myra*, *Mayorella conipa* and *M. bigemma* (Heathman, 1932). The antigenic relationships of these amoebae were studied with the complement fixation, hypersensitivity and lysis techniques. *E. histolytica* proved to be distinct from the other amoebae, though there was some cross-reaction with *F. citata*.

A. IMMOBILIZATION TEST

When amoebae are incubated in the presence of specific antiserum, they are affected to various degrees and in various ways according to the type of observation carried out. Thus they may be temporarily immobilized, their ability to ingest red blood cells may be changed and finally the growth rate may be affected. The inhibition of growth of *E. histolytica* in culture did not reveal any differences between strains (Nakamura, 1959; Swart and Warren, 1962), while red blood cell phagocytosis did show strain differences (Shaffer and Ansfield, 1956). The authors were unable to correlate the serological differences with the biological properties of the strains of *E. histolytica* used in their experiments.

The immobilization reaction has been studied by several workers (see Biagi and Buentello, 1961) as a method of serological diagnosis of amoebiasis in man. No differences between strains of *E. histolytica* was noticed during these investigations.

In contrast with the other studies utilizing the immobilizing reaction, Zaman (1960) carried out an extensive comparative study with several species of *Entamoeba*. He prepared antisera to several species and observed the degree of immobilization of the homologous and heterogeneous species. *E. coli* was found to be unsuitable for immobilization studies owing to its normal restricted activity. Some cross-reactions to *E. histolytica* were observed, since *E. histolytica* amoebae were partly immobilized by anti-*E. coli* serum.

If the results with *E. coli* are omitted, Zaman's results show that species of the 4-nucleate group can be divided into two groups. The first group consisted of *E. histolytica* and *E. invadens*, and the second group of *E. moshkovskii* and *E. ranarum*. There was no cross-reaction between these two groups, though cross-reactions did occur within each group. Zaman also studied a series of *E. histolytica* strains which differed by their virulent property. Immobilization tests showed that the virulent strains formed a group distinct from the avirulent strains. However, unlike results obtained with different species, there was a degree of cross-reaction. These results may be correlated with the invasive property, rather than innate specific differences.

The relationship between *E. histolytica* and *E. gingivalis* was studied by Sato and Kaneko (1957), who observed a complete absence of cross-reaction between these species.

The relationship of *Entamoeba* to the hartmannelid group of amoebae was described by Adam (1964). Using the immobilization test, she found the two groups were quite distinct without any degree of cross-reaction. Antisera to *E. histolytica*, *E. invadens* and *E. moshkovskii* were prepared and showed no immobilizing effect on four strains of *Hartmanella castellanii*. Similarly, antisera to four strains of *H. castellanii* did not immobilize *Entamoeba invadens*.

B. PRECIPITIN TEST

A precipitate often forms when an antigen and its antiserum are mixed. If a gel is the supporting medium and the reactants diffuse towards each other through the gel, the precipitate will be formed in one or more bands. This technique allows the analysis of antigenic structure of an organism. The investigations so far reported are of two kinds; one type of experiment uses antisera from patients, while in the second antisera was prepared experimentally.

The number of precipitation lines reported for *E. histolytica* vary from three to about ten (Nakamura and Baker, 1956; Maddison, 1965; Siddiqui, 1961; Sen *et al.*, 1961a, b; Atchley *et al.*, 1963). The results obtained seem to depend upon the potency of the antiserum and antigen. Nakamura (1961) observed that better results with human sera were found if antigen was prepared from newly isolated strains of *E. histolytica*. The presence of bacterial factors further complicates the analysis, and while these variables can be investigated in an experimental system, it is more difficult in the case of human serum. Maddison and Elsdon-Dew (1961) showed that one of the precipitin lines with human serum was not due to *E. histolytica*, but to accompanying *Clostridium welchii* antigen-antibody reaction.

While the antigenic structure of *E. histolytica* has not been fully elucidated, some observations on cross-reaction with other species have been made. Sen *et al.* (1961b) prepared anti-*E. histolytica* serum and found no reaction with *E. moshkovskii* antigen or antigen from the free-living amoebae *Naegleria gruberi* and *Schizopyrenus russelli*. Talis *et al.* (1962) showed that there were no common antigens between *E. histolytica* and *E. invadens*. Siddiqui and Balamuth (1963) reported that no reaction was found when heterologous antigens were tested against anti-*E. histolytica* and anti-*E. invadens* sera. The antigens were prepared from *E. histolytica*, *E. invadens*, *E. moshkovskii*, *Hartmanella rhysodes* and *Mayorella palestinensis*.

The results obtained by the precipitin test are summarized in Table XI.

TABLE XI

Summary of cross-reactions between Entamoeba *spp. and free-living amoebae from results of precipitin tests*

(Compiled from Sen *et al.*, 1961b; Talis *et al.*, 1962;
Siddiqui and Balamuth, 1963.)

Antigens	Antisera E. histolytica	E. invadens
E. histolytica	+	—
E. invadens	—	+
E. moshkovskii	—	—
Hartmanella rhysodes	—	—
Mayorella palestinensis	—	—
Naegleria gruberi	—	0
Schizopyrenus russelli	—	0

+ = positive cross-reaction; — = negative cross-reaction; 0 = not tested.

C. FLUORESCENT ANTIBODY TEST

The basis of the fluorescent antibody technique is that the antibody-antigen reaction is made visible by coupling a fluorescent dye to the antibody. It is then possible to observe fluorescence in the case of a positive reaction. Until recently the antigen used has been amoebae obtained from culture, but Zaman (1965) has shown that the fluorescent antibody test can also be applied to cysts. The disadvantage of this test is that, in general, cross-reactions are seen between zoologically related protozoa. However, differences in intensity are detectable, and a technique for measuring the intensity has been devised by Goldman (1960). Goldman and his colleagues have made a detailed study of relationships of *Entamoeba* spp. with this technique.

The relationship between *E. coli* and *E. histolytica* were first studied (Goldman, 1953, 1954). Antisera to both species were prepared and although some cross-reaction was observed the heterologous fluorescence was removed by absorption with the appropriate species of amoeba. The use of these antisera enabled Goldman (1954) to successfully identify unknown amoebae as either *E. histolytica* or *E. coli*. Other species and genera of parasitic amoebae were studied (Goldman, 1954) with this method. Amoebae of *Dientamoeba fragilis* and *Endolimax nana* showed virtually negligible fluorescence, while *Entamoeba invadens* reacted less than either *E. histolytica* or *E. coli*, but more than *Dientamoeba fragilis* or *Endolimax nana*. *Entamoeba moshkovskii* did not significantly stain with an anti-*E. histolytica* serum (Goldman *et al.*, 1960).

Further studies have been made on the relationships between strains of *E. histolytica* and *E. hartmanni* (Goldman *et al.*, 1960). Three strains of *E. histolytica* and two of *E. hartmanni* were stained with three anti-*E. histolytica* labelled sera and one anti-*E. hartmanni* serum. A labelled antiserum against the bacterial flora of one strain of *E. histolytica* was also tested. Three of the *E. histolytica* strains fluoresced strongly with the anti-*E. histolytica* sera, while *E. hartmanni* did not fluoresce significantly. Conversely, one anti-*E. hartmanni* serum stained the homologous species more brightly than *E. histolytica*. The third strain of *E. histolytica* (strain *Huff*) showed a reaction intermediate between *E. histolytica* and *E. hartmanni*. This difference was attributed to the lower virulence of strain *Huff* compared to the other strains of *E. histolytica*. This idea was supported by the observation that *E. histolytica* amoebae taken directly from a caecal ulcer of an experimentally infected guinea-pig, fluoresced brighter than amoebae after cultivation *in vitro* for 5 days or more. The anti-bacteria serum did not produce fluorescence of amoeba, though the bacteria fluoresced brightly. All the results obtained on interrelations between species of amoebae are summarized in Table XII.

TABLE XII

Summary of cross-reactions between Entamoeba *spp. and other parasitic amoebae from results of fluorescent antibody tests*

(Prepared from Goldman, 1954; Goldman *et al.*, 1960.)

| | Antisera | |
Antigens	E. Coli	E. histolytica
E. coli	+++ to ++++	+ to ++
E. histolytica	+ to ++	+++
E. hartmanni	± to +	+ to ++
E. invadens	++	+ to ++
E. moshkovskii	0	±
Dientamoeba fragilis	±	±
Endolimax nana	±	±

0 = not tested.

The experiments on serological differences between *E. histolytica* and *E. hartmanni* were then repeated using antisera to two strains of *E. histolytica* —one of these being strain *Huff*—and one of *E. hartmanni*, and adsorbing these with amoebae of the same strains (Goldman and Gleason, 1962). These results demonstrated that *E. histolytica* amoebae did not completely remove specific antibody from *E. hartmanni* antiserum, similarly the converse was true. Again, strain *Huff* proved different from the other strain of *E. histolytica*.

The reactions of the *Laredo* strain have also been studied by the fluorescent antibody technique (Goldman *et al.*, 1962). The critical temperatures of this anomalous strain of *E. histolytica* has been discussed above (p. 31), where it was shown that the *Laredo* strain grows at room temperature and at 37°C. The fluorescent staining of this strain of *E. histolytica* growing at 25° and 37° was compared with a normal strain of *E. histolytica* growing at 37° and *E. moshkovskii* also growing at 25° and 37°. Five anti-*E. histolytica* sera were used. It was found that *Laredo* amoebae grown at 37° fluoresced as brightly as *E. histolytica*, while *E. moshkovskii* also grown at 37° stained to a lesser degree. When grown at 25°, *Laredo* amoebae stained less than *E. histolytica* grown at 37°, and was similar to *E. moshkovskii* grown at 25°. From these data it seems that *Laredo* strain resembles *E. histolytica* more closely than *E. moshkovskii*, but it is not completely typical of *E. histolytica*. These data are summarized in Table XIII, with *E. hartmanni* included for comparison. The summary shows that the *E. histolytica Huff* strain resembles *Laredo* grown at 25° and *E. moshkovskii*, more than *E. histolytica*. This is an interesting conclusion, since it was subsequently reported that the *Huff* strain resembles *Laredo* in that it can grow at room temperature (Richards *et al.*, 1965). This strain therefore differs in two respects from *E. histolytica K9*, by its low virulence and ability to grow at room temperature.

TABLE XIII

Degrees of fluorescent staining of E. histolytica, E. moshkovskii *and* E. hartmanni
*by anti-*E. histolytica *serum*

(Summarized from Goldman *et al.*, 1960, 1962.)

Antigen species and strain	*E. histolytica* antisera		
	283	284	299
E. histolytica K9	+ to ++	++	++
Laredo 37°C	++++	+++	±
Laredo 25°C	+	+	+
Huff	± to +	+	+
E. moshkovskii 37°C	+	+	−
25°C	+	+	−
E. hartmanni 335	−	+	−

D. INDIRECT HAEMAGGLUTINATION TEST

This technique has been used by only one group of workers (Kessel *et al.*, 1961), who prepared antisera to, and antigens from, *E. histolytica* and *E. invadens*. The results showed a very slight cross-reaction between the two species.

E. COMPLEMENT FIXATION TEST

The serological differences between *E. histolytica* and *E. coli* were studied by Fulton *et al.* (1951) using the complement fixation technique. Their results show that the highest titres were found with the homologous antigen and antiserum. Some cross-reaction was found, but it was uncertain as to the extent to which bacterial factors contributed to the cross-reaction.

IX. TAXONOMIC SIGNIFICANCE
OF EXPERIMENTAL DATA AND CONCLUSIONS

It is clear that on morphological evidence the species of *Entamoeba* fall naturally into three groups, according to the number of nuclei present in the mature cyst. There is a fourth group, if it is accepted that amoebae similar to *E. gingivalis* do not form cysts. The morphological differences between two of these groups, those species with 4-nucleate and 8-nucleate cysts, are correlated with a difference in metacystic development. However, there is one exception —the development of *E. terrapinae*. The development of this species is so different to other species of this group that it stands in urgent need of re-examination. Although the metacystic development of the 4-nucleate cyst group has been shown to be very similar in five different species, that of the 8-nucleate cyst group has been elucidated only for one species, *E. coli*. The available knowledge of the 1-nucleate cyst group is very scanty. If some species of this group could be established in culture, it would yield information on morphology, metacystic development and physiological and biochemical data of taxonomic importance.

Host-restriction studies have not yet provided sufficient information on interrelationships between species of amoebae. However, in the case of the rodent amoebae, it seems there are a number of races of *E. muris* restricted to a particular rodent host or groups of rodents. Yet the relationship between *E. muris* and *E. coli* is also very close, differing only in the inability of *E. coli* to develop in rodents. The missing evidence here is that the metacystic development of *E. muris* is unknown.

If the metacystic development of *E. coli* and *E. muris* proves to be similar, their taxonomic relationship will need to be reassessed, but until this is done the independence of *E. muris* and *E. coli* can be maintained.

Considering a group of 4-nucleate cyst species, *E. ranarum*, *E. invadens* and *E. terrapinae*, all are morphologically indistinguishable with similar metacystic development (ignoring for the moment the peculiar development ascribed to *E. terrapinae*), *E. ranarum* shows a different host-restriction to the reptilian amoebae, *E. invadens* and *E. terrapinae*. The latter species have different degrees of pathogenicity and different critical temperatures to *E. ranarum*. Thus there are sufficient physiological differences to characterize these three species.

It seems that each species may consist of a series of strains or races adapted to a particular host or number of hosts. It would be useful to explore, with well-controlled experiments, the host-restriction of each species in a number of related potential hosts. This would require a plentiful supply of easily obtained amoebae-free experimental animals and wild strains of *Entamoeba* readily available from a variety of hosts. These conditions are not readily fulfilled, but probably most conveniently found with *E. gallinarum* in gallinaceous birds, *E. barretti* and *E. ranarum* in reptiles and amphibians, and some of the *Entamoeba* species in insects.

So far, biochemical and physiological studies have not resulted in a test which will distinguish species of *Entamoeba*. The most promising research in this respect is on drug sensitivity and growth at different temperatures. Drug sensitivity may be most useful to distinguish between closely related species, and it may be necessary to have a series of compounds for use with different groups of species. Further studies on critical temperatures are needed to define a suitable standard culture medium and technique. Provided that adaptation phenomena do not obscure the results, this method is most suitable, on grounds of speed and simplicity, for differentiating between morphologically indistinguishable species. It is important to use a standard medium, since the variations of growth at different temperatures has a biochemical basis.

Serological methods so far employed have not provided detailed quantitative data. When such tests become routinely available (for example, haemagglutination or complement fixation), identification may be possible with the appropriate antisera. Such analysis will require considerable laboratory facilities.

Owing to the unknown basis of many biochemical, physiological and serological characters, particularly in relation to environmental change, a great deal of care must be taken in allowing them specific status. At present there is no case for allowing them such status used alone in *Entamoeba*, though they are perfectly valid when combined with other characters. The fundamental basis of classification of *Entamoeba* must remain morphology, though with the structural simplicity of these organisms, it is expected that increasing emphasis will be placed on other characters.

When this paper was first envisaged, it was hoped to be able to recommend synonymy of various species. However, this survey shows the evidence is too fragmentary to assert with confidence that two species are identical in all but very few cases. There is, however, one taxonomic suggestion, and that is to give subgeneric names to the groups of species given above on p. 9. It is proposed to make a formal recommendation to this effect in a later publication.

ACKNOWLEDGEMENT

I would like to thank Miss Nicola Greening for her invaluable assistance in the preparation and typing of the manuscript.

REFERENCES

Adam, K. M. G. (1964). A comparative study of hartmannelid amoebae. *J. Protozool.* **11**, 423–430.

Al-Dabagh, M. A. (1965). The pathogenicity of the small race of *Entamoeba histolytica* to splenectomized rats. *Trans. R. Soc. trop. Med. Hyg.* **59**, 545–549.

Allen, R. D., and Kamiya, N. (Eds.) (1964). "Primitive Motile Systems in Cell Biology", Part II. Academic Press, New York and London.

Amaral, A. D. F., and Neal, R. A. (1949). Sôbre uma endamoeba semelhante à *Endamoeba histolytica* encontrado em materiál de esgôto. *Revta paul. Med.* **34**, 173–176.

Anderson, H. H., Bostick, W. L., and Johnstone, H. G. (1953). "Amoebiasis: Pathology, Diagnosis and Chemotherapy," p. 431. Thomas, Springfield.

Atchley, F. O., Auernheimer, A. H., and Wasley, M. A. (1963). Precipitate patterns in agar gel with sera from human amoebiasis and *Entamoeba histolytica* antigen. *J. Parasit.* **49**, 313–315.

Balamuth, W., and Thompson, P. E. (1955). Comparative studies on amebae and amebicides. *In* "Biochemistry and Physiology of Protozoa" (S. H. Hutner and A. Lwoff, eds.), Vol. 2, pp. 277–345. Academic Press, New York and London.

Ball, G. H. (1935). Is the capuchin monkey refractory to infection with *Endamoeba histolytica*? *J. Parasit.* **21**, 220.

Barker, D. C. (1963a). A ribonucleoprotein inclusion body in *Entamoeba invadens*. *Z. Zellforsch. mikrosk. Anat.* **58**, 641–659.

Barker, D. C. (1963b). Ribosome structures revealed by negative staining sub-cellular fractions from a crystalline ribonucleoprotein body. *Expl Cell Res.* **32**, 272–279.

Barker, D. C. (1964). A possible interpretation of helical images observed in ribo-nucleoprotein bodies of *Entamoeba invadens*. Proc. Third European Regional Conference on Electron Microscopy, Prague, 1964, Vol. B (Biology), p. 41.

Barker, D. C., and Svihla, G. (1964). Localization of cytoplasmic nucleic acid during growth and encystment of *Entamoeba invadens*. *J. Cell Biol.* **20**, 389–398.

Barretto, M. P. (1963). *Entamoeba histolytica*, Schaudinn 1903, and *Entamoeba hartmanni*, Prowazek, 1912. *Archos. Hig. Saúde publ.* **28**, 289–304.

Barretto, M. P., and Ferriolli, So., S. (1962). Correlaçâo entre o tamanho dos cistos e dos trofozoitas da *Entamoeba histolytica* Schaudinn 1903 e da *Entamoeba hartmanni* Prowazek 1912. *Revta bras. Biol.* **22**, 137–142.

Barretto, M. P., Zago, So., H. and Silva, G. A. (1960). Ocorrência de duos "raças" de *Entamoeba histolytica* distintas pelo tamanho dos cistos. *Revta bras. Biol.* **20**, 107–119.

Barrow, J. H., Jr., and Stockton, J. J. (1960). The influences of temperature on the host-parasite relationship of several species of snakes infected with *Entamoeba invadens*. *J. Protozool.* **7**, 377–383.

Biagi, F. F., and Buentello, L. (1961). Immobilization reaction for the diagnosis of amebiasis. *Expl Parasit.* **11**, 188–190.

Bird, R. G. (1956). A constant morphological feature in the trophozoite stage of *Entamoeba histolytica*. *Trans. R. Soc. trop. Med. Hyg.* **50**, 302.

Bird, R. G. (1958). The movement of some species of *Entamoeba* (film). *Trans. R. Soc. trop. Med. Hyg.* **52**, 10.

Bishop, A. (1929). Experiments on the action of emetine in cultures of *Entamoeba coli*. *Parasitology* **21**, 481–486.

Bishop, A. (1932). *Entamoeba aulastomi* Nöller. Cultivation, morphology and method of division; and cultivation of *Hexamita* sp. *Parasitology* **24**, 225–232.

Bishop, A. (1937). Further observations upon *Entamoeba aulastomi* Nöller. *Parasitology* **29**, 57–68.

Blasi, R. de, and Magaudda-Borzi, L. (1958). La sierologia dell'amebiasi. *Riv. Parassit.* **19**, 267–296.

Bovee, E. C. (1949). The use of the uroid as a taxonomic criterion for certain amebae. *Anat. Rec.* **105**, 630–631.

Boyd, J. S. (1931). Notes on an outbreak of amoebic dysentery occurring in the hounds of the Bangalore Hunt. *Jl R. Army med. Cps* **56**, 1–13.

Bragg, P. D., and Reeves, R. E. (1962). Pathways of glucose dissimilation in the Laredo strain of *Entamoeba histolytica*. *Expl Parasit.* **12**, 393–400.

Brumpt, E. (1925). Étude sommaire de l'*Entamoeba dispar* n.sp. amibe à kystes quadrinucléés parasite de l'homme. *Bull. Acad. Méd.* **94**, 943–952.

Burova, L. F. (1939). Experimental study of *histolytica*-like amoebae in lower monkeys. *Bull. Biol. Méd. exp. URSS* **7**, 249–253.

Burrows, R. B. (1957). *Endamoeba hartmanni*. *Am. J. Hyg.* **65**, 172–188.

Burrows, R. B. (1959). Morphological identification of *Entamoeba hartmanni* and *E. polecki* from *E. histolytica*. *Am. J. trop. Med. Hyg.* **8**, 583–589.

Burrows, R. B. (1961). Differentiation of *Entamoeba hartmanni* from the dwarf strain of *Entamoeba histolytica*. *Proc. VIth int. Congr. trop. Med. Malar.* **3**, 360.

Burrows, R. B. (1964). Identification of *Entamoeba hartmanni* trophozoites from nuclear structure. *Am. J. Hyg.* **79**, 29–36.

Burrows, R. B., and Klink, G. E. (1955). *Endamoeba polecki* infections in man. *Am. J. Hyg.* **62**, 156–167.

Cabrera, H. A. (1958). Temperature adaptation of *Entamoeba histolytica* and its effect on virulence. *Expl Parasit.* **7**, 276–284.

Cabrera, H. A., and Porter, R. J. (1958). Survival time and critical temperatures of various strains of *Entamoeba histolytica*. *Expl Parasit.* **7**, 285–291.

Cairns, J., Jr. (1953). Transfaunation studies on the host-specificity of the enteric protozoa of Amphibia and various other vertebrates. *Proc. Acad. nat. Sci. Philad.* **105**, 45–69.

Carini, A., and Reichenow, E. (1949). *Entamoeba caudata* n.sp. *Z. Tropenmed. Parasit.* **1**, 102–105.

Carneri, I. de (1958a). Spezifität und geschwindigkeit der Wirkung zweier verschiedener Reihen von Dichloracetamid-Derivaten auf 3 *Entamoeba* Arten. *Z. Tropenmed. Parasit.* **9**, 32–42.

Carneri, I. de (1958b). Studi su *Entamoeba moshkovskii*. I. Velocita' d'azione di 16 farmaci sui trofozoiti di *Entamoeba moshkovskii* Tshalaia 1941 a 3 diverse temperature. *Riv. Parassit.* **19**, 81–89.

Carneri, I. de (1958c). Studi du *Entamoeba moshkovskii*. II. *Entamoeba moshkovskii* Tshalaia 1941 come potenziale parassita: sua sporavvivenza nelle infezioni sperimentali intraepatiche dell'hamster e endociecali del ratto albino. *Riv. Parassit.* **19**, 161–168.

Carneri, I. de (1959). The use of specific anti-amoebic drugs for comparative taxonomic studies. *Trans. R. Soc. trop. Med. Hyg.* **53**, 120–121.

Child, H. J. (1926). Studies on the ingestion of leucocytes and on mitosis in *Endamoeba gingivalis*. *Univ. Calif. Publs Zool.* **28**, 251–284.

Cleveland, L. R. (1949). The whole life-cycle of chromosomes and their coiling systems. *Trans. Am. phil. Soc.* N.S. **39**, 1–100.

Cleveland, L. R., and Sanders, E. P. (1930). Encystation, multiple fission without encystment, excystation, metacystic development, and variation in a pure line and nine strains of *Entamoeba histolytica*. *Arch. Protistenk.* **70**, 223–266.

Crouch, H. B. (1936). The animal parasites of the woodchuck (*Marmota monax* L.) with special reference to protozoa. *Iowa St. Coll. J. Sci.* **11**, 48–50.

Deschiens, R. (1927). Sur les protozoaires intestinaux des singes. *Bull. Soc. Path. exot.* **20**, 19–23.

Deutsch, K., and Zaman, V. (1959). An electron microscopic study of *Entamoeba invadens* Rodhain 1934. *Expl Cell Res.* **17**, 310–319.

Diamond, L. S. (1960). The axenic cultivation of two reptilian parasites, *Entamoeba terrapinae* Sanders and Cleveland 1930 and *Entamoeba invadens* Rodhain 1934. *J. Parasit.* **46**, 484.

Diamond, L. S., and Bartgis, I. L. (1965). Axenic cultivation of *Entamoeba histolytica* in a clear medium. *In* "Progress in Protozoology", *Excerpta Med.*, Int. Congr. Ser. No. 91, p. 102.

Dobell, C. (1918). Are *Entamoeba histolytica* and *Entamoeba ranarum* the same species? *Parasitology* **10**, 294–310.

Dobell, C. (1919). "The Amoebae Living in Man." John Bale, Sons & Danielsson, London.

Dobell, C. (1928). Researches on the intestinal protozoa of monkeys and man. I. General introduction II. Description of the whole life-history of *Entamoeba histolytica* in cultures. *Parasitology* **20**, 357–412.

Dobell, C. (1931). Researches on the intestinal protozoa of monkeys and man. IV. An experimental study of the *histolytica*-like species of *Entamoeba* living naturally in macaques. *Parasitology* 23, 1–72.

Dobell, C. (1936). Researches on the intestinal protozoa of monkeys and man. VIII. An experimental study of some simian strains of *"Entamoeba coli"*. *Parasitology* 28, 541–593.

Dobell, C. (1938). Researches on the intestinal protozoa of monkeys and man. IX. The life-history of *Entamoeba coli*, with special reference to metacystic development. *Parasitology* 30, 195–238.

Dougherty, E. C. (1951). On the problems embraced in "Opinion" 99 (relating to the names *"Endamoeba"* Leidy 1879 and *"Entamoeba"* Casagrandi & Barbagallo 1895) rendered by the International Commission on Zoological Nomenclature. *Bull. zool. Nom.* 2, 253–276.

Dutta, G. P. (1961). Metacystic divisions in the life-cycle of *Entamoeba histolytica* Schaudinn 1903 in man. *Proc. natn. Inst. Sci. India* 27B, 108–115.

Entner, N., and Most, H. (1965). Genetics of *Entamoeba*. Characterization of two new parasitic strains which grow at room temperature (and at 37°). *J. Protozool.* 12, 10–13.

Entner, N., Evans, L. A., and Gonzalez, C. (1962). Genetics of *Entamoeba histolytica*: differences in drug sensitivity between Laredo and other strains of *Entamoeba histolytica*. *J. Protozool.* 9, 466–468.

Faust, E. C. (1923). A new type of amoeba parasitic in man observed in North China. *J. Parasit.* 9, 221–226.

Faust, E. C. (1958). Parasitologic surveys in Cali, Departamento de Valle Colombia. I. Incidence and morphologic characteristics of strains of *Entamoeba histolytica*. *Am. J. trop. Med. Hyg.* 7, 4–15.

Faust, E. C. (1963). The multiple facets of *Entamoeba histolytica* infection. *Int. Rev. trop. Med.* 1, 43–76.

Fletcher, K. A., Maegraith, B. G., and Jarumilinta, R. (1962). Electron microscope studies of trophozoites of *Entamoeba histolytica*. *Ann. trop. Med. Parasit.* 56, 496–499.

Freedman, L., and Elsdon-Dew, R. (1959). Size as a criterion of species in the human intestinal amebae. *Am. J. trop. Med. Hyg.* 8, 327–330.

Frye, W. W., and Meleney, H. E. (1934). Studies of *Endamoeba histolytica* and other intestinal protozoa in Tennessee. VIII. Observations on the intestinal protozoa of young pigs and attempts to produce infection with a human strain of *E. histolytica. Am. J. Hyg.* 20, 404–414.

Fulton, J. D., Joyner, L. P., and Price, I. N. O. (1951). Studies on protozoa. Part IV. A complement-fixation test for amoebiasis. *J. trop. Med. Hyg.* 54, 27–33.

Geiman, Q. M. (1937). Cross-infection experiments with three species of amoebae from reptiles. *J. Parasit.* 23, 557.

Geiman, Q. M., and Ratcliffe, H. L. (1936). Morphology and life-cycle of an amoeba producing amoebiasis in reptiles. *Parasitology* 28, 208–228.

Ghosh, T. (1963). Quantitative study of DNA (Feulgen) on *Entamoeba invadens. Proc. Ist int. Congr. Protozool.*, Prague 1961, p. 263.

Gleason, N. N., Goldman, M., and Carver, R. K. (1963). Size and nuclear morphology of *Entamoeba histolytica* and *Entamoeba hartmanni* trophozoites in cultures and in man. *Am. J. Hyg.* 77, 1–14.

Gnezdilov, V. G. (1947). Materials on the geographical distribution, epidemiology and prophylaxis of amoebiasis. *Medskaya Parazit.* 16, 13–32.

Goldman, M. (1953). Cytochemical differentiation of *Endamoeba histolytica* and *Endamoeba coli* by means of fluorescent antibody. *Am. J. Hyg.* 58, 319–328.

Goldman, M. (1954). Use of fluorescein-tagged antibody to identify cultures of *Endamoeba histolytica* and *Endamoeba coli*. *Am. J. Hyg.* **59**, 318–325.

Goldman, M. (1960). Antigenic analysis of *Entamoeba histolytica* by means of fluorescent antibody. I. Instrumentation for microfluorimetry of stained amoebae. *Expl Parasit.* **9**, 25–36.

Goldman, M., and Davis, V. (1965). Isolation of different-sized substrains from three stock cultures of *Entamoeba histolytica* with observations on spontaneous size changes affecting whole populations. *J. Protozool.* **12**, 509–523.

Goldman, M., and Gleason, N. N. (1962). Antigenic analysis of *Entamoeba histolytica* by means of fluorescent antibody. IV. Relationships of two strains of *E. histolytica* and one of *E. hartmanni* demonstrated by cross-absorption techniques. *J. Parasit.* **48**, 778–783.

Goldman, M., Carver, R. K., and Gleason, N. N. (1960). Antigenic analysis of *Entamoeba histolytica* by means of fluorescent antibody. II. *E. histolytica* and *E. hartmanni*. *Expl Parasit.* **10**, 366–388.

Goldman, M., Gleason, N. N., and Carver, R. K. (1962). Antigenic analysis of *Entamoeba histolytica* by means of fluorescent antibody. III. Reactions of the *Laredo* strain with five anti-*histolytica* sera. *Am. J. trop. Med. Hyg.* **11**, 341–346.

Grassé, P. P. (Ed.) (1953). "Traité de Zoologie," Vol. I, part II. Masson, Paris.

Hajian, A., and Ball, G. H. (1963). Increase in size of *Entamoeba hartmanni* trophozoites cultured on enriched medium. *Am. J. trop. Med. Hyg.* **12**, 709–718.

Heathman, L. (1932). Studies of the antigenic properties of some free-living and pathogenic amoebae. *Am. J. Hyg.* **16**, 97–123.

Hegner, R. (1929a). The infection of parasite-free chicks with intestinal protozoa from birds and other animals. *Am. J. Hyg.* **10**, 33–62.

Hegner, R. (1929b). Transmission of intestinal protozoa from man and other animals to parasite-free fowls. *Am. J. Hyg.* **9**, 529–543.

Hegner, R., Johnson, C. M., and Stabler, R. M. (1932). Host-parasite relations in experimental amoebiasis in monkeys in Panama. *Am. J. Hyg.* **15**, 394–443.

Hemming, F. (1951). Report on the investigation of the nomenclatural problems associated with the generic names "*Endamoeba*" Leidy 1879 and "*Entamoeba*" Casagrandi & Barbagallo 1895 (Class Rhizopoda). *Bull. zool. Nom.* **2**, 277–281.

Henderson, J. C. (1941). Studies of some amoebae of a termite of the genus *Cubitermes*. *Univ. Calif. Publs Zool.* **43**, 357–378.

Hill, W. C. O., and Neal, R. A. (1954). An epizootic due to *Entamoeba invadens* at the gardens of the Zoological Society of London. *Proc. zool. Soc. Lond.* **123**, 731–737.

Hirschlerowa, Z., and Swiecicki, A. (1960). Two strains of *Entamoeba moshkovskii* (Calaja 1941) in the coastal area. *Biul. Inst. Med. morsk. Gdańsku* **11**, 147–155. Abstract in *Biol. Abstr.* (1961) **36**, 3482.

Hoare, C. A. (1940). On an *Entamoeba* occurring in English goats. *Parasitology* **32**, 226–237.

Hoare, C. A. (1949). "Handbook of Medical Protozoology." Baillière, Tindall and Cox, London.

Hoare, C. A. (1959). Amoebic infections in animals. *Vet. Revs Annot.* **5**, 91–102.

Hoare, C. A. (1961). Considérations sur l'etiologie de l'amibiase d'après le rapport hôte-parasite. *Bull. Soc. Path. exot.* **54**, 429–441.

Holmes, F. O. (1923). Observations on the cysts of *Endamoeba cobayae*. *J. Parasit.* **10**, 47–50.

Hussein, Z. H. (1961). The pathogenicity of *Entamoeba histolytica*. I. The mean cyst diameter in large and small race infections. *Trans. R. Soc. trop. Med. Hyg.* **55**, 265–271.

Jahn, T. L., and Bovee, E. C. (1964). Protoplasmic movement and locomotion of protozoa. *In* "Biochemistry and Physiology of Protozoa" (S. H. Hutner, ed.), Vol. 3, pp. 62–129. Academic Press, New York and London.

Jarumilinta, R., and Maegraith, B. G. (1961). The patterns of some proteolytic enzymes of *Entamoeba histolytica* and *Acanthamoeba* sp. II. The action of *E. histolytica* and *Acanthamoeba* sp. on various synthetic substrates. *Ann. trop. Med. Parasit.* **55**, 518–528.

Kaushiva, B. S. (1960). Comparative action of some standard and newer amoebicides. *J. scient. ind. Res.* **19C**, 204–205.

Kessel, J. F. (1924). The distinguishing characteristics of the parasitic amoebae of culture rats and mice. *Univ. Calif. Publs Zool.* **20**, 489–533.

Kessel, J. F. (1928a). Intestinal protozoa of the domestic pig. *Am. J. trop. Med.* **8**, 481–501.

Kessel, J. F. (1928b). Intestinal protozoa of monkeys. *Univ. Calif. Publs Zool.* **31**, 275–306.

Kessel, J. F. (1928c). Amoebiasis in kittens infected with amoebae from acute and "carrier" human cases and with tetranucleate amoebae of the monkey and the pig. *Am. J. Hyg.* **8**, 311–355.

Kessel, J. F., and Johnstone, H. G. (1949). The occurrence of *Endamoeba polecki*, Prowazek 1912, in *Macaca mulatta* and in man. *Am. J. trop. Med.* **29**, 311–316.

Kessel, J. F., Lewis, W. P., Ma, S., and Kim, H. (1961). Preliminary report on a hemagglutination test for entamoebae. *Proc. Soc. exp. Biol. Med.* **106**, 409–413.

Kessel, J. F., Lewis, W. P., Pasquel, C. M., and Turner, J. A. (1965). Indirect hemagglutination and complement fixation tests in amebiasis. *Am. J. trop. Med. Hyg.* **14**, 540–550.

Kidder, G. W. (1937). The intestinal protozoa of the wood-feeding roach *Panesthia*. *Parasitology* **29**, 163–205.

Kirby, H., Jr. (1927). Studies on some amoebae from the termite *Microtermes* with notes on some other protozoa from the Termitidae. *Q. Jl microsc. Sci.* **71**, 189–222.

Kirby, H., Jr. (1932). Protozoa in termites of the genus *Amitermes*. *Parasitology* **24**, 289–304.

Kirby, H. (1945). *Entamoeba* versus *Endamoeba*. *J. Parasit.* **31**, 177–184.

Kirby, H. (1946). *Gigantomonas herculea* Dogiel, a polymastigote flagellate with flagellated and amoeboid phases of development. *Univ. Calif. Publs Zool.* **53**, 163–226.

Kirby, H. (1951). "*Entamoeba coli*" versus "*Endamoeba coli*". *Bull. zool. Nom.* **2**, 243–252.

Knowles, R., and Das Gupta, B. M. (1934). Some observations on *Balantidium coli* and *Entamoeba histolytica* of macaques. *Indian med. Gaz.* **69**, 390–392.

Kofoid, C. A., and Swezy, O. (1925). On the number of chromosomes and type of mitosis in *Entamoeba dysenteriae*. *Univ. Calif. Publs Zool.* **26**, 331–352.

Kudo, R. R. (1966). "Protozoology." Thomas, Springfield.

Lachance, P. J. (1959). A Canadian strain of *Entamoeba moshkovskii* Chalaia 1941. *Can. J. Zool.* **37**, 415–417.

Lachance, P. J. (1963). Experimental studies on *Entamoeba*. I. Temperature: a microclimatic factor in the cultivation of three species of *Entamoeba*. *Can. J. Zool.* **41**, 1079–1093.

Lamy, L. (1961). Le facteur taille dans ses rapports avec la spécificité des amibes du genre *Entamoeba* et avec leur comportement biologique chez l'hôte. *Bull. Soc. Path. exot.* **54**, 48–55.

Lawless, D. K. (1954). Report on a human case of *Endamoeba polecki* Prowazek, 1912. *J. Parasit.* **40**, 221–228.

Leal, R. A., and Amaral, A. D. (1950). New studies on the amoebae found in sewage, with special reference to an *Endamoeba* (*E. moshkovskii*) which is similar to *E. histolytica*. *Archos Fac. Hig. Saúde públ. Univ. S Paulo* **4**, 125–133.

Lobeck, E. A. (1940). *Entamoeba pyrrhogaster* n.sp. with notes on other intestinal amoebae from salamanders. *J. Parasit.* **26**, 243–272.

Lubinsky, G. (1952). The occurrence in Pakistan of a human *Entamoeba* of the *polecki*-type. *Parasitology* **42**, 48–51.

McConnachie, E. W. (1954). The influence of environmental factors on the size of the cysts of *Entamoeba invadens* Rodhain 1934. *Parasitology* **44**, 342–348.

McConnachie, E.W.(1955). Studies on *Entamoeba invadens* Rodhain 1934 *in vitro* and its relationship to some other species of *Entamoeba*. *Parasitology* **45**, 452–481.

McDowell, S. (1953). A morphological and taxonomic study of the caecal protozoa of the common fowl. *J. Morph.* **92**, 337–399.

Maddison, S. E. (1965). Characterization of *Entamoeba histolytica* antigen-antibody reaction by gel diffusion. *Expl Parasit.* **16**, 224–235.

Maddison, S. E., and Elsdon-Dew, R. (1961). Non-specific antibodies in amebiasis. *Expl Parasit.* **11**, 90–92.

Maddison, S. E., Powell, S. J., and Elsdon-Dew, R. (1965). Application of serology to the epidemiology of amebiasis. *Am. J. trop. Med. Hyg.* **14**, 554–557.

Mayfield, M. F. (1944). The excystation, cultivation and encystation of *Endamoeba coli. Proc. Soc. exp. Biol. Med.* **55**, 20–22.

Meerovitch, E. (1958). A new host of *Entamoeba invadens* Rodhain 1934. *Can. J. Zool.* **36**, 423–427.

Meerovitch, E. (1960). Thermal barrier to the infectivity of *Entamoeba invadens* in snakes. *Nature, Lond.* **185**, 631.

Meerovitch, E. (1961). Infectivity and pathogenicity of polyxenic and monoxenic *Entamoeba invadens* to snakes kept at normal and high temperatures and the natural history of reptile amoebiasis. *J. Parasit.* **47**, 791–794.

Menendez, P. E. (1932). Serological relationships of *Entamoeba histolytica*. *Am. J. Hyg.* **15**, 785–808.

Miller, C. D., and Saxe, L. H. (1951). Studies on the host specificity of the enteric protozoa of rodents. *J. Parasit.* **37**, suppl. p. 10.

Miller, J. H., and Swartzwelder, J. C. (1960). Virus-like particles in an *Entamoeba histolytica* trophozoite. *J. Parasit.* **46**, 523–524.

Miller, J. H., Swartzwelder, J. C., and Deas, J. E. (1961). An electron microscopic study of *Entamoeba histolytica*. *J. Parasit.* **47**, 577–587.

Miller, M. J. (1951). *Entamoeba terrapinae* infections in snakes. *J. Parasit.* **37**, suppl. p. 30.

Miller, M. J. (1952). The experimental infection of *Macaca mulatta* with human strains of *Entamoeba histolytica*. *Am. J. trop. Med. Hyg.* **1**, 417–428.

Nakamura, M. (1959). Inhibition of *Entamoeba histolytica in vitro* by specific antibody. *Parasitology* **49**, 104–107.

Nakamura, M. (1961). A serological study of amebiasis using the agar gel technique. *J. Protozool.* **8**, suppl. pp. 18–19.

Nakamura, M., and Baker, E. E. (1956). Inhibition of *Entamoeba histolytica* cultures by specific antibody. *J. Protozool.* **3**, suppl. p. 2.

Neal, R. A. (1948). *Entamoeba histolytica* in wild rats caught in London. *J. Hyg., Camb.* **46**, 90–93.

Neal, R. A. (1949). *Entamoeba muris*: a complicating factor in the experimental infection of rats with *E. histolytica*. *Nature, Lond.* **163**, 99.

Neal, R. A. (1950a). An experimental study of *Entamoeba muris* (Grassi, 1879); its morphology, affinities and host-parasite relationship. *Parasitology* **40**, 343–365.

Neal, R. A. (1950b). A species of *Entamoeba* from sewage. *Trans. R. Soc. trop. Med. Hyg.* **44**, 9.

Neal, R. A. (1953). Studies on the morphology and biology of *Entamoeba moshkovskii* Tshalaia 1941. *Parasitology* **43**, 253–268.

Neal, R. A. (1958). The pathogenicity of *Entamoeba histolytica. Proc. VIth int. Congr. trop. Med. Malar.* **3**, 350–359.

Neal, R. A. (1960). Enzymic proteolysis by *Entamoeba histolytica*: biochemical characteristics and relationship with invasiveness. *Parasitology* **50**, 531–550.

Neal, R. A. (1963). Morphological identification of the etiological agent. *Proc. VIIth int. Congr. trop. Med. Malar.*, Rio de Janeiro, **2**, 275.

Nie, D. (1950). Morphology and taxonomy of the intestinal protozoa of the guinea-pig, *Cavia porcella. J. Morph.* **86**, 381–494.

Nieschulz, O. (1924). Ueber *Entamoeba debliecki* mihi, eine Darmamöbe des Schweines. *Arch. Protistenk.* **48**, 365–370.

Noble, E. R. (1947). Cell division in *Entamoeba gingivalis. Univ. Calif. Publs Zool.* **53**, 263–280.

Noble, G. A., and Noble, E. R. (1952). Entamoebae in farm animals. *J. Parasit.* **38**, 571–595.

Nöller, W. (1921). Ueber einiger wenig bekannte Darmprotozoen des Menschen und ihre nächsten Verwandten. *Arch. Schiffs-u. Tropenhyg.* **25**, 35–46.

Opinion 99 (1928). *Smithson. misc. Collns* **73**, 4–8.

Opinion 312 (1954). F. Hemming, ed. *Opin. Decl. int. Commn zool. Nom.* **9**, 1–16.

Osada, M. (1959). Electron-microscopic studies on protozoa. I. Fine structure of *Entamoeba histolytica. Keio J. Med.* **8**, 99–103.

Pan, C.-T., and Geiman, Q. M. (1955). Comparative studies of intestinal amoebae. I. Distributions and cyclic changes of the nucleic acids in *Endamoeba histolytica* and *Endamoeba coli. Am. J. Hyg.* **62**, 66–79.

Pavlova, E. A. (1938.) Étude comparée de la mobilité de l'*Entamoeba histolytica* et de l'*Entamoeba coli. Medskaya Parazit.* **7**, 110–118.

Ratcliffe, H. L., and Geiman, Q. M. (1938). Spontaneous and experimental amebic infection in reptiles. *Archs Path.* **25**, 160–184.

Ray, H. N., and Mukherjee, A. K. (1958). *Entamoeba polecki* infection in man. *Bull. Calcutta Sch. trop. Med. Hyg.* **6**, 156–157.

Ray, H. N., and Sen Gupta, P. C. (1954). A cytochemical study of *Entamoeba histolytica. J. Indian med. Ass.* **23**, 529–533.

Ray, H. N., and Sen Gupta, P. C. (1956). A cytochemical study of *Entamoeba nuttalli. Bull. Calcutta Sch. trop. Med. Hyg.* **4**, 76.

Rees, C. W., Reardon, L. V., and Bartgis, I. L. (1950). The excystation of *Entamoeba histolytica* without bacteria in microcultures. *Parasitology* **40**, 338–342.

Reichenow, E. (1952). "Lehrbuch der Protozoenkunde," Vol. 2, Fischer, Jena.

Rendtorff, R. C. (1954). The experimental transmission of human intestinal parasites. I. *Endamoeba coli* cysts given in capsules. *Am. J. Hyg.* **59**, 196–208.

Richards, C. S., Goldman, M., and Cannon, L. T. (1965). Cultivation at 25°C. and behavior in hypotonic media of strains of *Entamoeba histolytica. J. Parasit.* **51**, suppl. p. 45.

Richardson, F. L. (1934). Studies on experimental epidemiology of intestinal protozoan infections in birds. *Am. J. Hyg.* **20**, 373–403.

Ristorcelli, M. (1939). Essais d'infestation expérimentale du chat par *Entamoeba coli*, par la voie intestinale haute, après laparotomie. *Bull. Soc. Path. exot.* **32**, 597–599.

Rodhain, J., and Hoof, M.-T. van (1934). *Entamoeba invadens* n.sp. parasite de serpents. *C.r. Séanc. Soc. Biol.* **117**, 1195–1199.

Rodhain, J., and Hoof, M.-T. van (1935). Sur le rôle pathogène d'*Entamoeba invadens*. *C.r. Séanc. Soc. Biol.* **118**, 1646–1650.

Rodhain, J., and Hoof, M.-T. van (1936). Les chéloniens porteurs d'*Entamoeba invadens*. *C.r. Séanc. Soc. Biol.* **121**, 156–158.

Rodhain, J., and Hoof, M.-T. van (1947). *Entamoeba knowlesi* n.sp. parasite de deux tortues: *Terrapina cinosternoides* et *Platysternum megacephalum*. *Annls Parasit. hum. comp.* **22**, 129–137.

Rogova, L. I. (1958). On *Entamoeba moshkovskii*. *Medskaya Parazit.* **27**, 330–334. Abstract in *Trop. Dis. Bull.* (1958) **55**, 1227.

Ruiz, A. (1960). *Entamoeba moshkovskii* Tshalaia 1941 en Costa Rica. *Revta Biol. trop.* **8**, 253–261.

Salis, H. (1941). Studies of the morphology of the *E. histolytica*-like amoebae found in monkeys. *J. Parasit.* **27**, 327–341.

Sanders, E. P. (1931). The life-cycle of *Entamoeba ranarum* Grassi (1879). *Arch. Protistenk.* **74**, 365–371.

Sanders, E. P., and Cleveland, L. R. (1930). The morphology and life cycle of *Entamoeba terrapinae* spec. nov., from the terrapin, *Chrysemys elegans*. *Arch. Protistenk.* **70**, 267–272.

Sapero, J. J., Hakansson, E. G., and Louttit, C. M. (1942). The occurrence of two significantly distinct races of *Endamoeba histolytica*. *Am. J. trop. Med.* **22**, 191–208.

Sarkisian, M. A. (1957). Observations on *Entamoeba hartmanni* (Prowazek, 1912). *Medskaya Parazit.* **26**, 618–623.

Sato, R., and Kaneko, M. (1957). A cross immunity test between *Entamoeba histolytica* and *Entamoeba gingivalis*. *Jap. J. Parasit.* **6**, 5–7.

Saxe, L. H. (1954). Transfaunation studies on the host specificity of the enteric protozoa of rodents. *J. Protozool.* **1**, 220–230.

Schaeffer, A. A. (1926). Taxonomy of the amebas with descriptions of thirty-nine new marine and fresh water species. *Pap. Dep. mar., Biol. Carnegie Instn Wash.* **24**, no. 345, p. 116.

Sen, A., Ghosh, S. N., Mukerjee, S., and Ray, J. C. (1961a). Antigenic structure of *Entamoeba histolytica*. *Nature, Lond.* **192**, 893.

Sen, A., Mukerjee, S., and Ray, J. C. (1961b). Observations on the antigenic makeup of amoebae. *Ann. Biochem. exp. Med.* **21**, 323–326.

Shaffer, J. G. (1965). A study of the occurrence of multi-nucleate trophozoites of three strains of *Entamoeba histolytica* in the Shaffer-Frye and C.L.G. media. *Am. J. trop. Med. Hyg.* **14**, 207–210.

Shaffer, J. G., and Ansfield, J. (1956). The effect of rabbit antisera on the ability of *Entamoeba histolytica* to phagocytose red blood cells. *Am. J. trop. Med. Hyg.* **5**, 53–61.

Shaffer, J. G., and Iralu, V. (1963). The selective ability of strains of *Entamoeba histolytica* to hemolyse red blood cells. *Am. J. trop. Med. Hyg.* **12**, 315–317.

Siddiqui, W. A. (1961). Demonstration of antigen-antibody reaction with a mono-bacterial culture of *Entamoeba histolytica* in agar gel and on cellulose acetate membrane. *J. Parasit.* **47**, 371–372.

Siddiqui, W. A. (1963a). Comparative studies of effect of temperature on three species of *Entamoeba*. *J. Protozool.* **10**, 480.

Siddiqui, W. A. (1963b). An electron microscope study of axenically grown trophozoites of *Entamoeba invadens* Rodhain. *J. Protozool.* **10**, suppl. p. 14.

Siddiqui, W. A., and Balamuth, W. (1963). Serological comparison of selected parasitic and free living amoebae *in vitro* using diffusion-precipitation and fluorescent antibody techniques. *Proc. Ist int. Congr. Protozool.*, Prague 1961, pp. 162–163.

Siddiqui, W. A., and Rudzinska, M. A. (1963). Electron microscope studies of chromatoid bodies of axenically grown trophozoites of *Entamoeba invadens*. *Biol. Bull. mar. biol. Lab.*, *Woods Hole* **125**, 357–358.

Siddiqui, W. A., and Rudzinska, M. A. (1965). The fine structure of axenically grown trophozoites of *Entamoeba invadens* with special reference to the nucleus and helical ribonucleoprotein bodies. *J. Protozool.* **12**, 448–459.

Simić, T. (1933). L'infection spontanée et expérimentale du chien par l'*Entamoeba coli*. *Annls Parasit. hum. comp.* **11**, 329–338.

Simitch, T., Chibalitch, D., Pétrovitch, Z., and Heneberg, N. (1959). Contribution à la connaissance de la faune des protozoaires intestinaux du porc de Yougoslavie; leur identification expérimentale. *Archs Inst. Pasteur Algér.* **37**, 401–408.

Simitch, T., and Petrovitch, Z. (1951). Culture d'*Entamoeba muris* de la souris à la temperature de 22–23°C. *Annls Parasit. hum. comp.* **26**, 389–393.

Singh, B. N. (1952). Nuclear division in nine species of small, free-living amoebae and its bearing on the classification of the order *Amoebida*. *Phil. Trans. R. Soc.* **236**, 405–461.

Smith, J. C. (1965). Bibliography on the metabolism of endo-parasites exclusive of anthropods, 1951–1962. *Expl Parasit.* **16**, 236–290.

Stabler, R. M. (1932). An extended study of variations in a single race of a *coli*-like amoeba and its bearing on the specificity of *Councilmania lafleuri*. *Am. J. Hyg.* **16**, 1–31.

Stabler, R. M. (1940). Binary fission in *Entamoeba gingivalis* (Protozoa). *J. Morph.* **66**, 357–367.

Stam, A. B. (1958). The relationship between *Entamoeba invadens* Rodhain and its host. Thesis, Leyden University.

Steck, F. (1961). Amoebendysenterie bei Reptilien. *Zentbl. Bakt. ParasitKde* Orig. **181**, 551–553.

Steenis, P. B. van (1957). The problem of the minuta forms in amoebic dysentery and amoebiasis. *Documenta Med. geogr. trop.* **9**, 325–330.

Sumardjo, B., and Joe, L. K. (1953). Uni- and binuclear cysts morphologically resembling *Entamoeba polecki* Prowazek 1912 found in an Indonesian boy. *Documenta Med. geogr. trop.* **5**, 1–4.

Svensson, R. (1935). Studies on human intestinal protozoa especially with regard to their demonstrability and the connection between their distribution and hygienic conditions. *Acta med. scand.* suppl. 70, p. 115.

Svensson, R., and Linders, F. J. (1934). The chances of detecting infections with intestinal protozoa. *Acta med. scand.* **81**, 267–324.

Swart, D. L., and Warren, L. G. (1962). The origin of antigenic substances in *Entamoeba histolytica* Schaudinn 1903 and serologic manifestations of their antibody-inducing properties. *J. Parasit.* **48**, 124–130.

Swartzwelder, J. C. (1939). Experimental studies on *Endamoeba histolytica* in the dog. *Am. J. Hyg.* **29**C, 89–109.

Swezy, O. (1922). Mitosis in the encysted stages of *Endamoeba coli* (Loesch). *Univ. Calif. Publs Zool.* **20**, 313–332.

Taliaferro, W. H., and Holmes, F. O. (1924). *Endamoeba barretti* n.sp. from the turtle *Chelydra serpentina*; a description of the amoeba from the vertebrate host and from Smith and Barretto's cultures. *Am. J. Hyg.* **4**, 155–168.

Talis, B., Lahav, M., and Ben-Efraim, S. (1962). Differentiation of *E. invadens* from *E. histolytica* by gel diffusion and immuno-electrophoresis. *Bull. Res. Coun. Israel* **10E**, 110.

Tanabe, M. (1934). The excystation and metacystic development of *Entamoeba histolytica* in the intestine of white rats. *Keijo J. Med.* **5**, 238–253.

Thiel, P. H. van (1956). Constant morphological feature in the trophozoite stage of *Entamoeba histolytica*. *Trans. R. Soc. trop. Med. Hyg.* **50**, 615.

Thiel, P. H. van (1961). Réconciliation entre les conceptions concernant la biologie de l'*Entamoeba histolytica* en rapport avec la perturbation de l'equilibre entre l'homme et le parasite par le traitement médical. *Bull. Soc. Path. exot.* **54**, 824–829.

Thomson, J. G., and Robertson, A. (1925). Notes on the cultivation of certain amoebae and flagellates of man using the technique of Boeck and Drbohlav. *J. trop. Med.* **28** (19), 345–349.

Toomka, A. F. (1959). A new species of parasitic amoeba of the mouth cavity—*Entamoeba suigingivalis* sp.n. *Zool. Zh.* **38**, 481–483.

Toomka, A. F. (1962). Results of biometric study of *Entamoeba gingivalis* (Gros 1849) in relation to their feeding intensity and conditions of existence in the host organism. *Zool. Zh.* **39**, 509–513.

Tshalaia, L. E. (1941). On a species of *Entamoeba* detected in sewage effluents. *Medskaya Parazit.* **10**, 244–252.

Tshalaia, L. E. (1947). Contributions to the study of *Entamoeba moshkovskii*. *Medskaya Parazit.* **16**, 66–69.

Tyzzer, E. E. (1920). Amoebae of the caeca of the common fowl and of the turkey—*Entamoeba gallinarum* sp.n. and *Pygolimax gregariniformis* gen. et spec. nov. *J. Parasit.* **6**, 124–130.

Wantland, W. W., Wantland, E. M., and Remo, J. W. (1961). Cytology and morphogenesis of *Entamoeba gingivalis*. *J. dent. Res.* **40**, 624.

Wenrich, D. H. (1940). Nuclear structure and nuclear division in the trophic stages of *Entamoeba muris* (Protozoa Sarcodina). *J. Morph.* **66**, 215–239.

Wenrich, D. H. (1941). The morphology of some protozoan parasites in relation to microtechnique. *J. Parasit.* **27**, 1–29.

Wenyon, C. M. (1925). The genera *Councilmania*, *Karyamoeba* and *Caudamoeba*. *Trop. Dis. Bull.* **22**, 333–338.

Wenyon, C. M. (1926). "Protozoology," p. 1563. Baillière, Tindall and Cox, London.

Wenyon, C. M., and O'Connor, F. W. (1917). "Human Intestinal Protozoa in the Near East." John Bale, Sons & Danielsson, London.

Wright, W. H., Cram, E. B., and Nolan, M. O. (1942). Preliminary observations on the effect of sewage treatment processes on the ova and cysts of intestinal parasites. *Sewage Wks J.* **14**, 1274–1280.

Zaman, V. (1960). Studies with the immobilization reaction in the genus *Entamoeba*. *Ann. trop. Med. Parasit.* **54**, 381–391.

Zaman, V. (1961). An electron-microscopic observation of the "tail" end of *Entamoeba invadens*. *Trans. R. Soc. trop. Med. Hyg.* **55**, 263–264.

Zaman, V. (1962). Isolation of *Entamoeba moshkovskii* from Singapore sewage. *Trans. R. Soc. trop. Med. Hyg.* **56**, 344.

Zaman, V. (1965). The application of fluorescent-antibody test to cysts of *Entamoeba invadens*. *Experientia* **21**, 357–358.

Clonorchis and Clonorchiasis

YOSHITAKA KOMIYA

National Institute of Health, Shinagawa-ku, Tokyo, Japan

I. INTRODUCTION

Clonorchiasis commonly occurs in several countries of the Orient, including China, Japan, Korea, Taiwan and North Vietnam. The responsible trematode, *Clonorchis sinensis*, was discovered by McConnel (1875) in Calcutta at the autopsy of a Chinese carpenter. The liver was tense and enlarged, the bile-ducts distended, and sections revealed an involved pathological condition that McConnel attributed to the presence of the flukes, which were identified and named by Cobbold (1875). McConnel (1878) recorded an infection in a Chinese cook from Hong Kong, and Ishizaka (1878) one in a farmer in Okayama Prefecture in Japan. In the meantime, Leuckart (1876) inadvertently named the trematode *Distomum spathulatum*, now recognized as a synonym of *C. sinensis*. Baelz (1883) obtained specimens at the autopsy of a patient in Tokyo University Hospital and recognized two forms; the smaller was regarded as pathogenic and named *Distoma hepatis endemicum sive perniciosum*, the larger as non-pathogenic and named *D.h.e.s. innocuum*, but Iijima (1886) regarded them as identical and named the fluke *D. endemicum*.

The genus *Opisthorchis* was erected by Blanchard (1895) for elongate distomes with small suckers, unbranched caeca, lateral vitellaria and posterior testes situated one behind the other in the hind-body, and *D. sinense* Cobbold was placed in this genus. However, Looss (1907) erected the genus *Clonorchis* for this oriental liver fluke with branched instead of lobed testes, and he recognized two species, a larger form, *C. sinensis*, commonly distributed throughout China and less commonly found in Japan, and a smaller form, *C. endemicus*, found mainly in Japan and French Indo-China. However, Kobayashi (1912) concluded that size depended on the nature and size of the host and the intensity of infection, and that even the shape of the eggs is not distinctive in the two forms, recognizing only *C. sinensis*, which was first recorded in French Indo-China by Grall (1887) and in Chinese subjects in various parts of the world by Heanley (1908).

II. STRUCTURE AND BIOLOGY

A. THE EGG AND ITS MODE OF FORMATION

1. *Copulation and Fertilization*

Copulation has never been observed in *C. sinensis* and may occur only rarely, because the fluke has an ejaculatory duct, but not a true cirrus or cirrus pouch. Cross-fertilization by the use of Laurer's canal may occur periodically (Faust and Khaw, 1927) but self-fertilization is probably typical. Spermatozoa usually traverse the entire length of the uterus to the ootype, there to meet and fertilize the mature oocytes (ova), although Nakayama (1912) asserted that fertilization sometimes occurs in the oviduct before the shell is formed and Ujiie (1936) believed that the ovum encounters sperms from the time of entry into the oviduct to the time when the operculum has been formed because active spermatozoa abound in the oviduct.

2. *Formation of the Egg-shell* (Fig. 1)

Shell formation was studied by Ujiie (1936), who observed that the genital products are propelled by rhythmical movements of the oviduct and vitelline reservoir (median vitelloduct), the latter pushing vitelline cells one by one into the ootype. When five to seven vitelline cells have been arranged around the ovum these movements cease momentarily and the opening into the ootype is closed, but the ootype itself enlarges and in the space surrounding the group of cells, including the ovum, droplets of shell-forming materials are liberated from vitelline cells and form the egg-shell, which has a small terminal process due to a small space at the end of the constricted oviduct. The operculum is formed of materials from the same source at the open end of the capsule. Ujiie considered also that the secretion of the glands of Mehlis around the ootype might play a part in shell formation.

3. *Embryonic Development*

This phase of the life cycle was studied by Nakayama (1910), Kobayashi (1922) and Faust and Khaw (1927). The fertilized ovum, which is situated near the opercular end of the egg, divides and at a morula stage one cell detaches itself, wanders to the posterior pole, flattens out and gradually forms an investing membrane around the embryo. According to Komiya and Suzuki (1964) two other cells become detached, assume a foamy appearance and

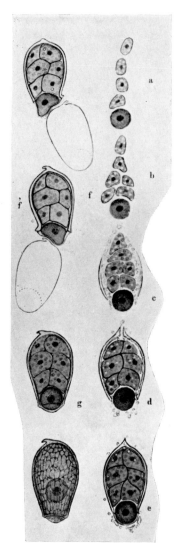

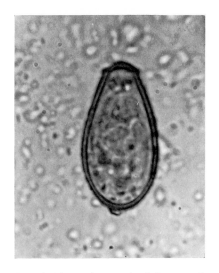

FIG. 2. Photomicrograph of the normal egg of *Clonorchis sinensis*.

FIG. 1. The formation of the egg-shell of *Clonorchis sinensis*. (Ujiie, 1936.)

adhere to this membrane. The cells of the embryo then grow and differentiate, the superficial cells becoming flattened and transformed into a ciliated epithelium. Supporting mesodermal tissue is derived from clefts arising at the posterior end of the embryo and the organs of the miracidium—a primitive gut, elongate secretory gland, nervous system, excretory system with one pair of flame cells and germinal cells—are formed (Fig. 3). The various stages of embryonic development can be traced out in eggs found in successive uterine loops, the middle coils containing embryos, and as development proceeds the vitelline cells disintegrate and derived products are utilized.

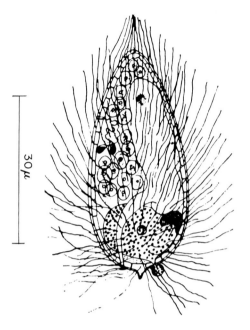

FIG. 3. The miracidium of *Clonorchis sinensis*. (Faust and Khaw, 1927.)

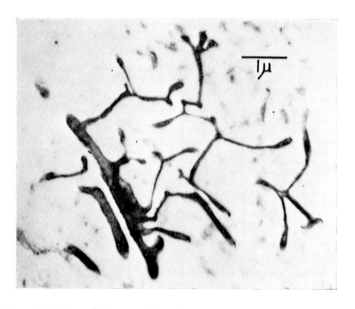

FIG. 4. Etchings of the egg surface of *Clonorchis sinensis*. (Inatomi, 1962.)

4. *The Structure of the Egg-shell* (Fig. 2)

The mature egg is ovoid, yellowish brown in colour, 26–30 μ long and 15–17 μ broad. The operculum is shaped like a watch-glass, fitting into a shoulder-like rim at the open end of the capsule, and it is inconspicuous in newly formed eggs, becoming more prominent as the eggs pass along the uterus. The shape of the mature egg, with its well-marked shoulder annulus, is distinctive and the shell is 5–8 μ thick. According to Faust and Khaw (1927), Ishii (1929a) and Hasegawa (1929), the surface of the egg is etched by markings (Fig. 4) which appear to arise from the opercular ring and zigzag towards the opposite pole, ramifying and crossing one another to form a polygonal pattern. Hasegawa believed that these markings are projected to the surface of the egg, which according to Yumoto (1936) is composed of two layers.

It is sometimes necessary to distinguish the eggs of *C. sinensis* from those of *Opisthorchis, Metorchis, Heterophyes, Metagonimus* and *Dicrocoelium* species, because these also commonly occur in human or animal faeces. Diagnosis is not difficult if colour, size, shape and special characters such as the shoulder annulus are noted, but the nature of the miracidium is crucial in diagnosis. Abnormal eggs (Fig. 5) sometimes appear, and these have been studied by Kitamura (1916) and Faust and Khaw (1927). Yumoto (1936) recognized two types of malformed eggs and Ishii (1929a) four types. Such eggs may appear throughout the life of the fluke, although generally produced by young flukes at maturity or by senile flukes, and sometimes as a result of drug treatment.

5. *Egg Production*

The numbers of eggs produced by *C. sinensis* varies in different kinds of hosts, the daily rate of production being 1 125 in dogs, 1 600 in guinea-pigs and 2 400 in cats (Faust and Khaw, 1927). In such hosts numbers may remain constant for 6 months after infection (Kawai, 1937), although the daily rate in experimental dogs has been put as high as 2 000 (Yumoto, 1934). In rabbits, Wykoff (1959) found that up to the 17th week of infection eggs appear in increasing numbers steadily and thereafter cyclical variations occur at intervals of 10 weeks. The mean number of eggs per day per worm (E.P.D./fluke) was about 4 000 and the mean number per g of faeces per fluke (E.P.G./fluke) about 100. According to Saito and Hori (1961) the mean E.P.G./fluke remains fairly constant in different degrees of infection, the figures being 260, 216 and 231 in instances when recovered flukes numbered 19, 77 and 444 respectively.

6. *Viability of Eggs*

According to Faust and Khaw (1927), eggs are soon killed by drying, live for 6 months in an ice chest (4–8°C) and 1 month at room temperature, but only 1 h at 50°C. In old night soil at 26°C they die within 2 days, but will live therein for 5 days at a lower temperature (4–8°C). In fresh urine they remain viable for 2 days at 37°C and 4 days in an ice chest, but in stale urine they die in 9 h at 26°C. Viability was also considered in other media.

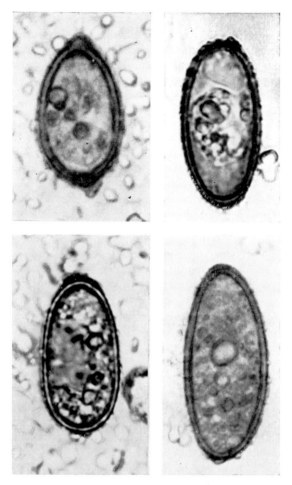

FIG. 5. Abnormal eggs of *Clonorchis sinensis*. (Saito and Hori, 1964.)

B. ADULT STRUCTURE (Figs. 6, 7 and 8)

The structure of the adult *C. sinensis* was elucidated by Kobayashi (1912, 1915) but his account was supplemented by Ujiie (1936) and Ozaki (1960). However, this trematode is familiar to students and only the most outstanding characters are given here.

The elongate body tapers in front to a rounded anterior extremity and the hind-body is somewhat truncated. The size of the adult varies with the duration of infection, type of host, worm burden and manner of preservation, but the dimensions of well-developed specimens are 8–15 × 1·5–4 mm. The living fluke is colourless and translucent, but eggs *in utero* have a brownish colour and the body may have a pinkish tinge. Yellow pigment occurs in the parenchyma of encysted metacercariae, but this becomes scattered during juvenile life and tends to disappear in the adult. Minute blackish granules appear which may be derived from blood which is included in the diet of the fluke.

The oral sucker is usually slightly larger than the ventral sucker (ratios of diameters about 6:5) and the former is turned somewhat ventrally while the latter is only slightly raised from the body surface. The cuticle is thin (about 1 μ) and spines are not present. Muscle fibrils are arranged in three layers, transverse, diagonal and longitudinal, and the transverse muscles form a thinner layer dorsally.

FIG. 6. The living *Clonorchis sinensis*.

The alimentary system comprises a muscular pharynx 0·2–0·3 mm diam., a short oesophagus and simple intestinal crura which extend almost to the posterior extremity. A prepharynx is not present. Longitudinal and transverse muscles occur in post-pharyngeal regions and are somewhat thickened in the oesophagus. The excretory system has a terminal excretory pore with a sphincter in its wall. The excretory vesicle has been described as I-shaped, but at the level of the receptaculum seminis it divides, usually at different levels and the left fork slightly in advance of the right. At the level of the intestinal bifurcation these branches join the main anterior and posterior excretory canals on either side of the body. Further divisions are noted below (p. 80) in connexion with the development of the flame-cell pattern.

Ozaki (1960) described the nervous system as comprising a supra-oesophageal commissure and a pair of stout ventral nerves, together with more slender dorsal and lateral nerves (see Komiya and Suzuki, 1964). Nerve cells are distributed along both sides of the body.

The common genital pore is situated just in front of the ventral sucker. The most unusual character of the male system is the occurrence of an ejaculatory duct and absence of cirrus and cirrus pouch. The two testes are posterior in position, one behind the other, but much more branched than in *Opisthorchis*, occupying nearly one-third of the body (Fig. 8). They lie one on either side of the excretory bladder, the anterior one having four main lobes, the posterior

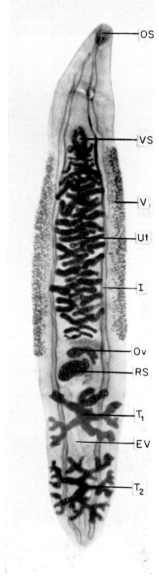

FIG. 7. Adult *Clonorchis sinensis* (stained specimen). *OS*, oral sucker; *VS*, ventral sucker; *V*, vitellaria; *Ut*, uterus; *I*, intestine; *Ov*, ovary; *RS*, seminal receptacle; *T*, testes; *EV*, excretory vesicle.

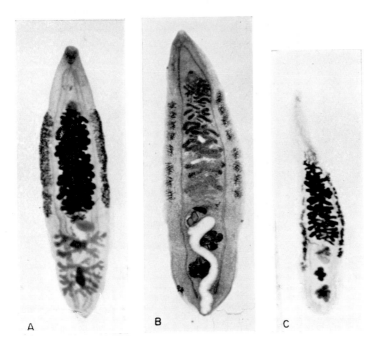

Fɪɢ. 8. Species of *Clonorchis* and *Opisthorchis* (stained specimens). A, *Clonorchis sinensis*; B, *Opisthorchis felineus*; C, *Opisthorchis viverrini*.

five. The main characters of the female system and especially the arrangement of the ducts concerned in egg production can be seen in Fig. 9. The ovary has three lobes and according to Ujiie (1936) ripe oocytes occur in the dorsal part of the central lobe, from which the oviduct arises. Kobayashi (1915) described a mechanism whereby oocytes are transported into the oviduct. The vitellaria extend lateral to the caeca on each side of the body between the ventral sucker and the ovary, and the main ducts unite in a median reservoir, which opens into the oviduct near its opening into the ootype. The receptaculum seminis occurs at the termination of Laurer's canal, forming a prominent chamber, which is linked with the oviduct by a fine canal. The ootype is a spindle-like chamber within which the eggs are moulded and is surrounded by the glands of Mehlis which open into it (see Ujiie, 1936). Formed eggs pass from the ootype into a uterus with many transverse folds between the caeca, the ovary and the genital pore.

C. FOOD OF THE ADULT

According to Faust and Khaw (1927), the secretions from the mucosa of the bile-ducts serve as food for the adult fluke. They noted marked proliferation of the mucosa in heavy infections and the secretion of large amounts of a mucin-like substance. Hsü (1939a, b) noted that materials in the caeca of the fluke include epithelial cells, leucocytes and other cells in a state of disintegration and regarded these as ingesta, but he supported also the contention of Faust and Khaw.

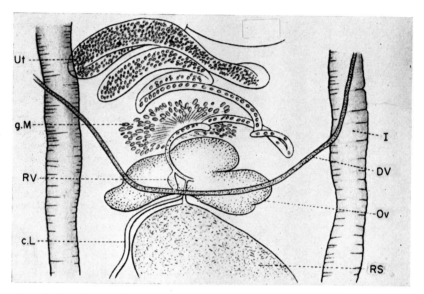

FIG. 9. Female genitalia of *Clonorchis sinensis*. *Ut*, uterus; *g.M.*, Mehlis's gland; *RV*, yolk sac; *c.L.*, Laurer's canal; *I*, intestine; *DV*, yolk duct; *Ov*, ovary; *RS*, receptaculum seminis. (Kobayashi, 1915.)

D. FIRST INTERMEDIATE HOST AND DEVELOPMENT THEREIN

1. *The First Intermediate Host* (Figs. 10 and 11)

The snail host of *C. sinensis* was first determined as *Bithynia striatula* var. *japonicus* as a result of the work of Muto (1918) (see Komiya and Suzuki, 1964, for details). Abbott (1948) proposed that *B. striatula* of Japan and China

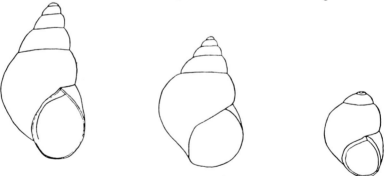

FIG. 10. The snail hosts of *Clonorchis sinensis*. Left, *Parafossarulus manchouricus*; centre, *Bulimus fuchsianus*; right, *Alocima longicornis*. (Abbott, 1948.)

should be incorporated in the species *Parafossarulus manchouricus*. This species of snail is widely distributed in Japan and China and also in Korea and Taiwan and probably Indo-China. Two other snails serve as experimental hosts; they are *Bulimus fuchsianus* (= *Bithynia fuchsiana*) and *Alocima longicornis* (= *B. longicornis*) (Hsü, 1939a; Hsü and Li, 1940a, b), and the former occurs in northern China, the latter in central and southern China.

FIG. 11. A living specimen of *Parafossarulus manchouricus*.

2. *Entry of* C. sinensis *into the Snail Host*

The eggs of the fluke do not hatch spontaneously in isotonic or slightly hypertonic media even when left therein for 3 months or more, although they then remain viable. The eggs are ingested by the snail and miracidia hatch in the alimentary canal (intestine or rectum) within 1 h.

3. *The Miracidium* (Fig. 3)

The miracidium is somewhat ovate and measures about $32 \times 17 \mu$. At the surface there is a layer of ciliated cells about 16μ long, or somewhat longer at the anterior end. The anterior papilla has a blunt process about 2μ long at its tip, and beneath it there is a rudimentary gut and a sausage-like ventral gland which opens at the base of the papilla. Within the body eight to twenty-five germinal cells can be seen and also a pair of flame cells and a rudimentary brain. Eyespots do not exist, however, and other sense organs have not been detected (Faust and Khaw, 1927). The newly hatched miracidia penetrate into the wall of the snail's intestine or rectum to become sporocysts within 4 h of infection and some penetrating forms have been observed in the gills of the snails, and sporocysts in lymph spaces around the stomach and oesophagus.

4. *The Sporocyst* (Fig. 12)

Early sporocysts measuring about $90 \times 65 \mu$ contain a nearly solid mass of germinal cells, which become separated as the sporocysts enlarge. At one pole of the sporocyst an indentation appears and this becomes a distinct groove in the elongate mature sporocyst, which remains quiescent throughout its development, while the germinal cells become germinal balls which differentiate to form the redial stage of development. Young rediae occur in all snails 17 days after infection and they appear to be liberated from sporocysts by the 16th day, then occurring in various locations such as the lymph spaces around the oesophagus, pharynx, buccal capsule and even the mantle and the foot.

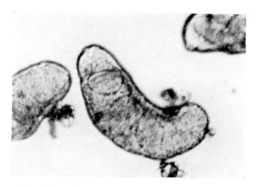

FIG. 12. The sporocyst of *Clonorchis sinensis.*

5. *The Redia*

Small rediae measure about 0·35 × 0·09 mm, mature forms about 1·7 × 0·13 mm (see Komiya and Suzuki, 1964). The pharynx is about 22 μ diam. and is followed by a sac-like intestine which often contains ingesta of brownish colour (Komiya and Tajimi, 1940). Around the mouth there are eight supposedly sensory hairs. Germinal cells within the redia ultimately form five to fifty developing cercariae, the older forms of which are more anterior. At no stage during development do cercariae contain eyespots or scattered pigment masses, and this indicates that they are liberated prematurely from the rediae into the digestive gland of the snail, as is usual in pleurolophocercous cercariae. In fact, many free cercariae with newly formed tails occur in this location.

6. *The Cercaria* (Figs. 13, 14 and 15)

The cercariae of *C. sinensis* mature in the digestive gland of the snail and when mature the body measures 0·22–0·24 × 0·06–0·09 mm, is beset with spinelets and bears six long and seven short sensory hairs on the lateral margins. Masses of brown pigment granules are scattered within the body, which also has one pair of eyes. The oral sucker (anterior penetration organ) measures 40–45 × 22–31 μ and has four rows of small tooth-like structures on the dorsal margin of the mouth. It is about three times as large as the ventral sucker, which is just in the posterior half of the body, and it is pierced by the main ducts of the penetration glands, of which there are seven pairs. The more internal duct drains four glands, the external duct three. Just behind the ventral sucker there is a genital rudiment and behind this a large transversely oval excretory bladder with a wall composed of tall cells. The main excretory canals extend from the antero-lateral angles of the bladder and continue to mid-body level, there meeting anterior and posterior canals which divide into two and three branches respectively, each branch being provided with three flame cells, thus giving a flame-cell formula 2[(3 + 3) + (3 + 3 + 3)]. Within the cercarial body also there are fourteen pairs of cystogenous gland cells arranged in lateral rows.

The tail of the cercaria is covered by transversely striated cuticle and does not contain excretory canals (see Inatomi *et al.*, 1964, for electron photomicrographs). The cuticle forms a fin-like terminal membrane.

Usually, cercariae hang in water with the body downturned and the tail somewhat flexed (Fig. 13). They gradually sink in the water, but when some part of the body touches the bottom or some solid object the larva is stimulated to rapid reaction, rising in the water with vigorous movements to take up the resting posture as before. Even small water movements may evoke such a response in the cercaria (Yamaguti, 1935; Komiya and Tajimi, 1940).

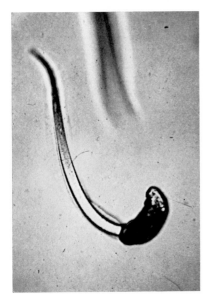 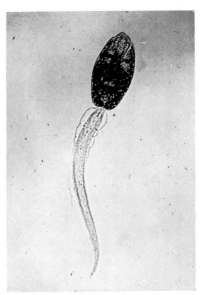

FIG. 13. The cercaria of *Clonorchis sinensis*; posture in water.

FIG. 14. The cercaria of *Clonorchis sinensis* (stained specimen).

E. PISCINE HOST AND DEVELOPMENT THEREIN

1. *Invasion of the Piscine Host*

The cercariae of *C. sinensis* never actively seek a fish host. However, the slightest disturbance of water caused by a fish is sufficient to evoke the spasmodic movements of the cercaria which make contact with the fish possible and, if contact is made, cercariae cling to the host by means of the suckers.

During attachment, the tail of the cercaria may be raised at right-angles to the body of the fish or remain parallel with it and adhesion is by the entire ventral surface of the larva. What might be called the predilection site is in the caudal region of the fish, near the fin, possibly because it is an actively moving part

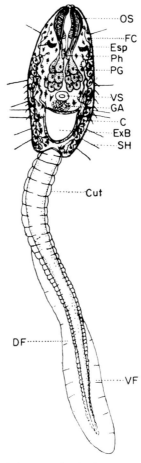

FIG. 15. The morphology of the cercaria of *Clonorchis sinensis*. *OS*, oral sucker (penetration organ); *FC*, flame cell; *Esp*, eyespots; *Ph*, pharynx; *PG*, penetration gland; *VS*, ventral sucker; *GA*, genital rudiment; *C*, cystogenous glands; *ExB*, excretory bladder; *SH*, sensory hair; *Cut*, cuticle; *DF*, dorsal fin; *VF*, ventral fin. (Komiya and Tajimi, 1940.)

which stimulates the larva and induces it to swim, then attach and penetrate. Invading cercariae creep on the surface of the fish and penetration is a rapid process taking 6–15 min for completion (Hsü, 1939a, b; Komiya and Tajimi, 1940). A few minutes after attachment the tail of the cercaria breaks away from the larval body.

2. *Development in the Piscine Host* (Fig. 17)

Invading cercariae enter the subcutaneous tissues or muscles of the fish and may creep about therein, but within several hours of penetration they usually encyst. At 18–23 h after penetration many large transparent vacuoles appear in the body, and Komiya (1965) termed this the "vacuolation process" (Fig. 16). The vacuoles soon disappear, however, and when a true ovoid cyst measuring 83–110 μ in length and about 2 μ thick has been formed by the larva a second, outer cyst develops as a result of the local tissue reaction of the host.

FIG. 16. The vacuolation process of *Clonorchis* metacercaria. *V*, vacuole.

Within the cyst the metacercaria has freedom to contract and elongate its body, which now contains scattered pigment granules, although the eyes as yet show no signs of the disintegration which ultimately ensues. The oral sucker has become modified from the condition in the cercaria to a sucker-like form, but the ventral sucker is unchanged. The excretory vesicle is now a thick-walled ovoid chamber containing a few (twenty to thirty) excretory granules and particles of lipid materials appear in the parenchyma. The metacercaria is now at a stage of growth and further development. During 3 days of infection the cyst has apparently enlarged, now measuring 84–114 ×

108–130 μ and eyes are still present. At 7 days after infection the cyst is slightly larger (92–119 × 100–140 μ) and the eyes are beginning to disintegrate. The excretory vesicle is now filled with granules and numerous discoidal bodies are seen in the caeca. The oral sucker is still larger than the ventral sucker. At 10–15 days after infection the cyst is slightly larger and has apparently reached a maximum size of 97–132 × 110–140 μ. Movements of the metacercaria are now lively and this form has now attained its characteristic structure. The eyes have disappeared, the suckers are of approximately equal size and excretory granules up to 7 μ diam. completely fill the excretory vesicle. When such encysted metacercariae are placed in gastric juice for 20 min and then in artificial intestinal juice at 37°C they may excyst, although these forms are considered to have attained full development 30–35 days after infection (Komiya and Tajimi, 1940), but they can be used to infect guinea-pigs and rabbits about 23 days after infection (Muto, 1920a).

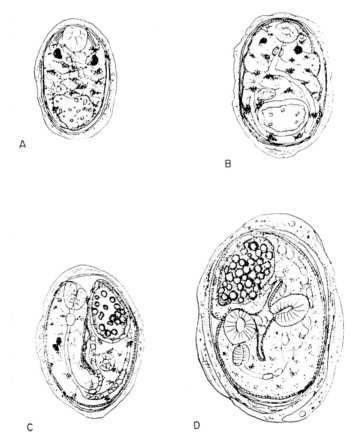

FIG. 17. The development of *Clonorchis* metacercaria in the fish host. A, 24 h; B, 3 days; C, 7 days; D, 15 days. (Komiya and Tajimi, 1940.)

3. *The Piscine Hosts*

Kobayashi (1912) first identified the second intermediate hosts of *C. sinensis* in Japan, finding metacercariae in the muscles of freshwater fishes such as *Leucogobio güntheri* and *Pseudorasbora parva*. He fed cats with cysts from the former species and recovered adult specimens of *C. sinensis* from the bile-ducts 1 month later. Subsequently, he demonstrated that twelve species of freshwater fishes could serve as hosts of this trematode in Japan (Kobayashi, 1912) and that five species of freshwater fishes in central China, including *P. parva*, harboured encysted forms (Kobayashi, 1923, 1924). He also showed that eight species of freshwater fishes were implicated as hosts of the trematode in Korea.

Many writers later reported piscine hosts in various countries (Tables I–IV).

TABLE I

The second intermediate hosts of Clonorchis sinensis *in Japan*

Name of fish	Author	Year of discovery
Abbotina rivularis (Basilewsky)	Kobayashi	1912
Acheilognathus cyanostigma (Jordan and Fowler)	Kobayashi	1912
Acheilog. lanceolata lanceolata (T. and S.)	Kobayashi	1910
Acheilog. l. moriokae (Jordan and Thompson)	Horiuchi	1956
Acheilog. l. limbata (T. and S.)	Kobayashi	1910
Acheilog. rhombea (T. and S.)	Kobayashi	1910
Biwia zezera (Ishikawa)	Kobayashi	1910
Carassius carassius (L.)	Kobayashi	1912
Cyprinus carpio L.	Muto	1919
Gnathopogon elongatus caerulesens (Sauvage)	Ando *et al.*	1924
Gnathop. elong. elongatus (T. and S.)	Kobayashi	1910
Gnathop. elong. gracilis (T. and S.)	Okabe	1938
Gnathop. elong. japonicus (Sauvage)	Kobayashi	1912
Hemibarbus barbus (T. and S.)	Ide	1935
Hemigrammocypris rasborella (Fowler)	Izumi	1935
Hypomesus olidus (Pallas)	Ide	1935
Mogurunda obscura (T. and S.)	Koga	1922
Opsariichthys uncirostris (T. and S.)	Satomi	1931
Pseudogobio esocinus (T. and S.)	Kobori	1927
Pseudoperilampus typus (Bleeker)	Kobayashi	1910
Pseudorasbora parva (T. and S.)	Kobayashi	1910
Rhodeus ocellatus (Kner)	Okabe	1938
Sarcocheilichthys variegatus (T. and S.)	Kobayashi	1910
Sinogobio biwae (Jordan and Snyder)	Sakai	1953
Tribolodon hakonensis (Günther)	Ichioka	1930
Zacco platypus (T. and S.)	Muto	1917
Zacco temmincki (T. and S.)	Izumi	1935

TABLE II

The second intermediate hosts of Clonorchis sinensis *in China*

Name of fish	Author	Locality	Year of discovery
Abbotina rivularis (Basilewsky)	Kobayashi	Soochow	1923
Acanthobrama simoni (Bleeker)	Komiya	Hankow	1944
Acanthorhodeus asmussi (Dybowski)	Asada	Mutan-Kiang	1940
Acanthorhodeus atranalis (Günther)	Kobayashi	Soochow	1923
Acanthorhodeus taenianalis (Günther)	Chung *et al.*	Peiping Tientsin	1960
Acheilognathus sp.	Komiya and Kawana	Shanghai	1936
Aphyocypris chinensis (Günther)	Asaka	Tiehling	1940
Carassius carassius (L.)	Ishii	Canton	1929
Ctenopharyngodon idellus (C. and V.)	Ishii	Canton	1929
Culter alburnus (Basilewsky)	Faust *et al.*	Canton	1927
(*Culter brevicauda* syn, Cult. al.)	Chung *et al.*	Peiping	1960
Culter mongolicus (Basilewsky)	Asada	Tiehling	1940
Cyprinus carpio (L.)	Ishii	Canton	1929
Eleotris swinhonis (Günther)	Chung *et al.*	Peiping	1960
Elopichtys bambusa (Richardson)	Komiya *et al.*	Shanghai	1936
Gnathopogon herzensteini (Günther)	Hsü *et al.*	Peiping	1936
Gnathopogon polytaenia (Nicols)	Komiya *et al.*	Shanghai	1942
Gnathopogon strigatus (Regan)	Asada	Tiehling	1940
Gobio gobio (L.)	Asada	Mutan-Kiang	1940
Hemibarbus maclatus (Bleeker)	Hsü *et al.*	Peiping	1936
Hemiculter clupeoides (Nicols)	Hsü *et al.*	Peiping	1936
Hemiculter leucisculus (Basilewsky)	Hsü *et al.*	Peiping	1936
Hypophthalmichthys molitrix (C. and V.)	Ishii	Canton	1929
Hypophthalmichthys nobilis (Richardson)	Ishii	Canton	1929
Labeo collaris (Nicols and Pope)	Hsü *et al.*	Canton	1936
Labeo contius (Jordon)	Ishii	Canton	1929
Leucogobio herzensteini	Hsü *et al.*	Peiping	1936
Mylopharyngodon aethiops (Basilewsky)	Hsü *et al.*	Canton	1937
Ophicephalus argus (Cantor)	Asada	Harbin	1937
Orizias latips (T. and S.)	T'ang *et al.*	Fukien	1963
Parapelecus tingchowwensis (Tchang)	Chung *et al.*	Peiping	1960
Parapelecus argenteus (Günther)	Komiya *et al.*	Shanghai	1936
Parabramis bramula (C. and V.)	Hsü *et al.*	Canton	1937
Pseudorasbora parva (T. and S.)	Kobayashi	Shanghai, Soochow, Hangchow	1923
Rhodeus atremis	Hsü *et al.*	Peiping	1936
Rhodeus notatus (Nicols)	Miyanaga	Mukden	1939

TABLE II *contd.*

Name of fish	Author	Locality	Year of discovery
Rhodeus ocellatus (Kner)	Hsü *et al.*	Peiping	1936
Rhodeus sericeus (Pellas)	Asada	Mutan-Kiang	1940
Rhinogobius giurinus (Rutter)	T'ang *et al.*	Fukien	1963
Sarcocheilichthys lacustris (Dybowski)	Asada	Harbin Mutan-Kiang	1937
Sarcocheilichthys nigripinnis (Günther)	Komiya *et al.*	Shanghai	1936
Sarcocheilichthys sinensis (Bleeker)	Kobayashi	Shanghai Soochow	1924
Sarcocheilichthys soldatovi (Berg)	Asada	Harbin	1937
Sarcocheilichthys variegatus (T. and S.)	Kobayashi	Shanghai	1923
Saurogobio dabri (Bleeker)	Kubo *et al.*	Chahar	1941
Squaliobarbus curriculus (Richardson)	Hsü *et al.*	Soochow	1936
Caridinia nilotica gracilipes (de Man)	T'ang *et al.*	Fukien	1963
Macrobrachium superbum (Heller)	T'ang *et al.*	Fukien	1963
Palemonetes sinensis (Sollaud)	T'ang *et al.*	Fukien	1963

TABLE III

The second intermediate hosts of Clonorchis sinensis *in Taiwan*

Name of fish	Author	Year of discovery
Acheilognathus himantegus	Kim *et al.*	1964
Aphyocypris kikuchii	Kim *et al.*	1964
Carassius carassius (L.)	Kim *et al.*	1964
Ctenopharyngodon idellus (C. and V.)	Ohoi	1919
Cultericulus kneri (Warpachowski)	Muto	1938
Erythroculter oxycephalus	Kim *et al.*	1964
Hemiculter akoensis	Kim *et al.*	1964
Hemiculter kneri	Kim *et al.*	1964
Hemiculter macrolepis	Kim *et al.*	1964
Ophicephalus maculatus	Kim *et al.*	1964
Pseudorasbora parva (T. and S.)	Kim *et al.*	1964
Rhodeus ocellatus (Kner)	Kim *et al.*	1964
Tilapia mosambica (Peters)	Chow	1960
Zacco platypus (T. and S.)	Kim *et al.*	1963
Zacco temmincki (T. and S.)	Kim *et al.*	1963

TABLE IV

The second intermediate hosts of Clonorchis sinensis *in Korea*

Name of fish	Author	Year of discovery
Abbotina rivularis (Basilewsky)	Kobayashi	1923
Achanthorhodeus asmussi (Dybowski)	Kim	1961
Acheilognathus gracilis (Regan)	Kobayashi	1924
Acheilognathus yamatstsute (Mori)	Kim	1961
Acheilognathus signifer (Berg)	Kim	1961
Coreobargus brevicorpus (C. and V.)	Kim	1961
Culter alburnus (Basilewsky)	Nishimura	1938
Culter brevicauda (Günther)	Kim	1961
Gnathopogon koreanus (Berg)	Kobayashi	1924
Gnathopogon strigatus (Regan)	Kobayashi	1924
Gnathopogon maejimae	Chung	1962
Hemibarbus longirostris (Regan)	Nishimura	1938
Hemibarbus labeo (Pallas)	Kim	1961
Ilisha elongata (Bennet)	Lee *et al.*	1958
Microphysogobil koreensis (Mori)	Kim	1961
Parapelecus eigenmanni (Jordan and Metz)	Kobayashi	1928
Pseudogobio esocinus (T. and S.)	Chung	1962
Paracheilognathus rhombea (T. and S.)	Kobayashi	1928
Pseudopreilampus notatus (Bleeker)	Lee *et al.*	1958
Pseudorasbora parva (T. and S.)	Lee *et al.*	1958
Puntungia herzi (Herzenstein)	Nishimura	1938
Sarcocheilichthys kobayashii (Mori)	Kobayashi	1928
Sarcocheilichthys mori (Jordan and Hubbs)	Kobayashi	1924
Sarcocheilichthys variegatus (T. and S.)	Kobayashi	1924
Sarcocheilichthys wakiyae (Mori)	Kim	1961
Zacco platypus (T. and S.)	Chun	1962
Zacco temmincki (T. and S.)	Chun	1962

Several dubious records have been excluded from the lists: one which is included is noteworthy because recorded by some writers in various countries as a host of *C. sinensis*, but in Japan many investigators have failed to find encysted metacercariae in it. However, the experimental infection of this fish, *Zacco platypus*, has been effected, but encysted forms have degenerated so that after about 10 weeks they could not be identified (Fig. 18). Two species of *Ophicephalus* Channa have also been recorded as hosts, *O. argus* in China and *O. maculatus* in Taiwan. However, Kubo and Makino (1941) concluded that *O. argus* does not serve as a host in Manchuria, and the present writer examined some hundreds of specimens of this species and found only one infected with a score of poorly developed specimens.

Chinese investigators have stated that certain crayfish (*Caridinia nilotica*, *Macrobrachium superbum* and *Palaemonetes sinensis*) transmit *C. sinensis* in Fukien Province (China). T'ang *et al.* (1963) fed guinea-pigs with cysts and obtained adult specimens, although hitherto only fishes have been recorded as hosts.

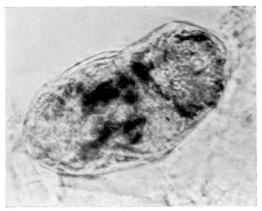

FIG. 18. Degenerated metacercaria of *Clonorchis sinensis* in the fish host, *Zacco platypus*.

4. *Intensity of Infection with Metacercariae*

The numbers of cysts which occur in fishes varies with species, even in the same water areas. *Pseudorasbora parva* is usually the most heavily infected fish and the mean number of metacercariae per fish in streams and ponds of Chiai Hsien (Taiwan) was 176·7; comparable figures for other species being *Zacco platypus* 18·9, *Hemiculter kneri* (*H. leucisculus*) 0·8, *Acheilognathus himantegus* 0·3, *Erythroculter oxycephalus* and *Rhodeus ocellatus* 0·1, *Carassius auratus* 0·4 and *Tilapia mossambica* 0·03 (Kim and Kuntz, 1964).

In general, excluding *P. parva*, the moderately heavily infected fishes in Japan are *Sarcocheilichthys variegatus*, *Tribolodon hakonensis*, *Gnathopogon* spp. and *Acheilognathus* spp. The larger (cyprinid) fishes of Japan, namely *Cyprinus carpio* and *Carassius carassius*, are lightly infected, containing only a few cysts when *P. parva* from the same waters contains more than 1000. These larger fishes are preferred by the Japanese and are eaten raw, whereas the larger fishes of China which are eaten raw by the Chinese are *Ctenopharyngodon idellus*, *Mylopharyngodon aethiops* and *Hypothalmichthys* sp., which are far more heavily infected. Perhaps cercariae have difficulty in penetrating the skin of fishes such as *Cyprinus carpio* and *Carassius carassius*; when experimentally exposed to cercariae of *C. sinensis* under the same conditions, *P. parva* is heavily infected, whereas *C. carassius* is lightly infected (Muto, 1919).

F. THE METACERCARIA

1. *The Structure of the Mature Metacercaria* (Figs. 19, 20 and 21)

From a cyst measuring about 0·13–0·15 × 0·09–0·10 mm a spatulate metacercaria is liberated which measures about 0·41 × 0·12 mm. This form

makes lively creeping movements over a substratum when placed in physiological saline and is able to extend the fore-body to about twice the length of
the hind-body. The cuticle contains spinelets, except anterodorsally, and
fourteen to sixteen small sensory papillae occur in the lateral regions. A double
circlet of twelve papillae in all occur around the mouth and nine similar
papillae around the margin of the ventral sucker. The suckers are slightly

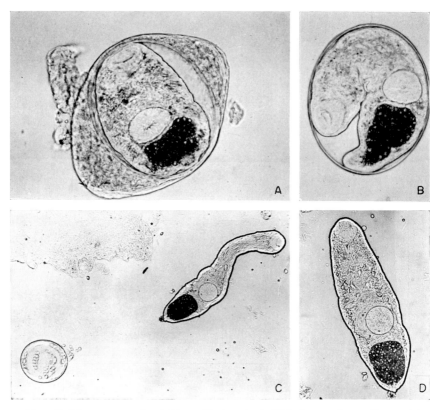

FIG. 19. The metacercaria of *Clonorchis sinensis*. A, With the outer layer of host origin;
B, without the layer of host origin; C, and D, excystment (note granules in excretory bladder).

unequal in size, the oral 0·5 mm diam. and the ventral 0·6 mm. Two kinds of
glands which open externally have been described; a lateral series of twelve
pairs (skin glands) extend between the suckers and open ventrally and a group
of twelve (cephalic glands) just in front of the ventral sucker have long ducts
which open on the dorsal margin of the mouth. [Possibly, these are the
remains of cystogenous gland cells and penetration gland cells respectively.
Ed.]

    The alimentary canal comprises a small pharynx, long oesophagus and long
caeca. Relative attenuation of the fore-body is indicated by the position of the

ventral sucker behind the mid-body and the bifurcation of the intestine mid-way between the two suckers. The genital rudiment occurs above and to some extent behind the ventral sucker. The excretory vesicle occupies the greater part of the hind-body and is filled with spherical granules which, according to Watanabe (1942), consist of carbonate and phosphate of calcium. The main canals, the anterior and posterior canals and their respective double and triple endings provided with flame cells are little changed, so that the flame-cell formula is the same as that of the cercaria (Komiya and Tajima, 1940).

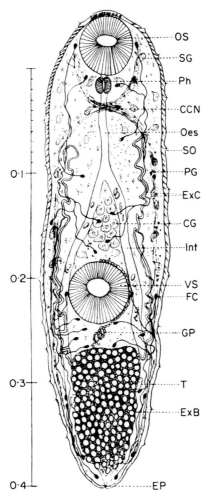

FIG. 20. The structure of the metacercaria of *Clonorchis sinensis. OS*, oral sucker; *SG*, skin gland; *Ph*, pharynx; *CCN*, central nerve commissure; *Oes*, oesophagus; *SO*, sensory organ; *PG*, pigment granules; *ExC*, excretory canal; *CG*, cephalic glands; *Int*, intestine; *VS*, ventral sucker; *FC*, flame cell; *GP*, genital primordia; *T*, testis; *ExB*, excretory bladder; *Ep*, excretory pore.

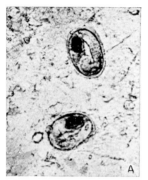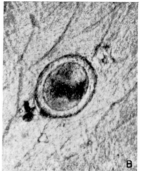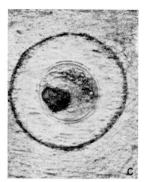

FIG. 21. Comparison of the metacercaria of *Clonorchis* (A) with those of (B) *Metorchis orientalis* and (C) *Metorchis taiwanensis*.

2. The Identification of Encysted Metacercariae

As many as ten different kinds of encysted metacercariae can be found in the subcutaneous tissues and muscles of freshwater fishes which serve as hosts of *C. sinensis*, and although identification is preferably based on living materials it is possible with formalin-fixed materials. Living specimens of *C. sinensis* can be distinguished by the size and shape of the cyst, the thickness of the cyst wall, the brownish-yellow pigment granules dispersed in the body, the size ratio of the suckers, the shape of the excretory vesicle and the size and shape of excretory granules within the vesicle. The most distinctive characteristic of *C. sinensis* at this stage, however, is the large excretory vesicle compactly filled with large, spherical granules, but it is to be noted that in formalin-fixed cysts these granules may disappear within about 3 weeks of fixation (Komiya and Shimizu, 1965).

3. The Distribution and Isolation of Cysts

Cysts usually occur in the subcutaneous connective tissues and muscles and they are fewer in the deeper tissues remote from the skin. Iwata (1937) found 71 % in subcutaneous tissue when only 15 % occurred in superficial muscles. The distribution of cysts of *C. sinensis* is mainly in the vicinity of the caudal fin (Table V), but 7–21 % may occur in the soft tissues of the head, which suggests that cercariae may be drawn into the buccal cavity and penetrate the mucosa of this region and near-by parts (Komiya and Murase, 1944). Cysts are rarely found in the scales of the hosts, although this is a common location in the hosts of *Metagonimus yokogawai* (Fig. 22).

Cysts may be collected with the aid of a dissecting microscope and dissecting needles, but in isolating cysts from muscles it is usual to cut the flesh from appropriate regions into small pieces and treat these with artificial gastric juice in a homogenizer. Cysts are then isolated from the sediment which falls to the bottom of a container. This method can be used also with formalin-preserved materials.

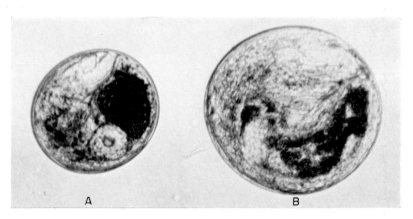

Fig. 22. Comparison of the metacercaria of *Clonorchis sinensis* (A) with that of *Metagonimus yokogawai* (B).

TABLE V

The distribution of metacercariae of Clonorchis *in the fish host*

Name of fish: (No. examined): Location	Pseudr. parva (40) No. of metac. found	Pseudr. parva (15) No. of metac. found	Sarchoc. sin. (15) No. of metac. found
Scales	5 (0·2%)	1 (0·3%)	169 (1·6%)
Gills	16 (3·6%)	13 (3·6%)	125 (1·2%)
Tail fin	185 (10·8%)	3 (0·8%)	651 (6·2%)
Dorsal fin	12 (0·7%)	0	300 (2·9%)
Breast fins	11 (0·6%)		
Ventral fins	3 (0·2%)	1 (0·3%)	324 (3·1%)
Other fins	0		
Muscles	1328 (77·4%)	320 (87·9%)	6616 (63·4%)
Head	155 (9·0%)	26 (7·1%)	2550 (21·6%)
Inner organ	0	0	0
Total	1715	364	10735

4. *The Effect of Digestive Juices on Encysted Forms*

Young encysted metacercariae apparently cannot tolerate the effects of the intestinal juices and 10-day-old forms die within 20 min when placed in artificial intestinal juice at 37°C (Komiya and Tajimi, 1940). When mature cysts are placed in artificial gastric juice (dilute HCl 1 ml; pepsin 0·3–0·5 g; water 100 ml) for 3–4 h at 37–39°C, the encysted forms remain alive, but do not excyst (Nagano, 1927; Komiya and Murase, 1944). The same result accrues usually when cysts are placed directly in artificial intestinal juice (NaHCO₃ 0·2 g; trypsin 0·5 g; physiological saline 50 ml) or bile. Early excystment occurs, however, when gastric juice treatment for 30–40 min is followed by the addition of intestinal juice at 37–39°C (Komiya and Tajimi, 1941).

TABLE VI

The resistance of metacercariae of Clonorchis *to various chemicals*
(Shimazono and Hasui, 1916)

Chemical		Survival time of metacercaria
Tap water	54 h	
Saline solution (5%)	3 h	
	5 h	
Lugol's solution	5 min	Cyst wall intact
Methyl blue (1% solution)	4 h	
Eosin (0% solution)	1 h	
Methanol	10 min	
Sodium hydroxide 1%	20 min	Larvae died after 20 min
(n/10)	2 h	Larvae liberated alive after 19 h
(n/15)	2 h	Larvae alive when liberated but died soon after
Sodium carbonate (10% solution)	19 h	
(1% solution)	21 h	
(0·5% solution)	48 h	
Diluted hydrochloric acid		Cyst wall intact
(20% solution)	2·5 h	
(n/5)	24 h	
(n/10)	48 h	
Diluted acetic acid (3% solution)	6 h	

G. FINAL HOSTS AND DEVELOPMENT THEREIN

The natural non-human final hosts of *C. sinensis* include dogs, cats, pigs, rats and camels (see Komiya and Suzuki, 1964, for references). Cats, dogs, rabbits and guinea-pigs have been experimentally infected, and cats appear to be highly susceptible (Kawai and Yumoto, 1935). Wykoff (1958a) regarded rabbits and guinea-pigs as equally susceptible to infection, about one-third of orally administered cysts yielding adult flukes, whereas rats are less susceptible, only 6% yields of adults being obtained. It is likely that nearly all fish-eating mammals can be infected with *C. sinensis* and cats and dogs form important reservoir hosts. In central and northern China human clonorchiasis is rare, even where heavily infected fish hosts occur, but cats and dogs are commonly infected.

Asada (1920) showed that birds may be infected with *C. sinensis*; he examined six night herons (*Nycticorax nycticorax*) and found in the gall-bladder of one of them thirteen adult specimens. He administered cysts to this bird and also the domestic duck and obtained small adults from them. Komiya and Kondo (1951) recovered seventeen ill-developed specimens in the gall-bladder of the domestic duck, but failed to infect this bird experimentally, suggesting that it is not a satisfactory final host.

1. *The Route of Migration and the Final Location in the Final Host*

When Kobayashi (1912) infected cats with cysts of *C. sinensis* young flukes appeared in the gall-bladder 15–24 h later. In infected rabbits the bile-duct contained some young flukes after 6 h and many of them 10–40 h after infection, and similar results were obtained with dogs and guinea-pigs (Mukoyama, 1921). Infections of rabbits with a ligatured bile-duct were negative after 9 days in respect of liver, bile-duct and abdominal cavity, although many young forms were recovered from the duodenum. When young forms were placed directly in the abdominal cavity of rabbits flukes were absent from the liver and bile-duct after 24 days, and Mukoyama concluded that young flukes are unable to penetrate the intestinal wall. However, Wykoff and Lepes (1957) carried out experiments which involved both ligaturing and draining the bile-duct in rabbits and arrived at the opposite conclusion.

The usual location of *C. sinensis* is the intrahepatic bile-ducts and occasionally the gall-bladder and main bile-duct. In fairly heavy infections most flukes are found in the hepatic ducts and only a few in the gall-bladder. In heavy infections flukes have been reported in the pancreas and duodenum (Iwata, 1937). In rabbits most flukes are found in the right lobe of the liver, especially in the anterior part (Ito and Muto, 1925). Many flukes occur in the peripheral regions, although they are said to migrate into the deeper parts when the host has died, and a temperature effect was postulated in an attempted explanation. Yoshida (1931) believed that adult flukes may develop in the pancreas and that young flukes display positive chemotaxis to pancreatic juice, although less markedly than to bile.

2. *Development in the Final Host*

Kobayashi (1912) studied the growth of young forms of *C. sinensis* in guinea-pigs during the 1st month of infection and provided the following figures [which yield a smooth curve. Ed.]:

Days	mm
2	0·27–0·36 × 0·07–0·08
3	0·3–0·4 × 0·07–0·10
4	0·5–0·6 × 0·10–0·12
5	0·6–0·7 × 0·14–0·16
7	1·1–1·2 × 0·20–0·26
10	1·5–2·0 × 0·3–0·4
16	3·2–4·0 × 0·56–0·60
19	4·5–5·0 × 1·0–1·2
26	6·5–7·5 × 1·5–2·0

According to this writer, the suckers show differential growth, the ventral sucker being the larger up to the 4th day of infection, the diameters being the same after 5–7 days and the oral sucker becoming the larger from the 10th day onwards. The testes rudiments become lobulated on the 5th day of infection and by the 7th day are lobed as in the adult. The ovary rudiment also becomes lobed on the 5th day and lateral loops of the uterus appear on the 7th day.

Egg production begins on days 12–15, although the vitellaria are ill defined until the 16th day. The uterus becomes filled with eggs after 20–23 days and on the 26th day they can be recovered from the faeces.

Important developments take place in the excretory system (Komiya and Kawana-Tajimi, 1953). In mice, the arrangement of flame cells is the same as that in the cercaria up to 5 days after infection, but after 10 days flame cells are added to the anterior collecting canal and the flame-cell formula becomes $2[(4+4)+(3+3+3)]$. By the 12th day (when the flukes measure 2.9×0.45 mm) each of the original five groups of flame cells on each side of the body has increased considerably, bringing the flame-cell formula to $[(4+4+5)+(6+5+9)] + [(3+6+3)+(3+3+5)+(3+6+5)]$ on each side (R and L) (Fig. 23). After 24 days, when the flukes measure 5.5×1.7 mm, a further increase of flame cells has made evaluation of this formula extremely difficult.

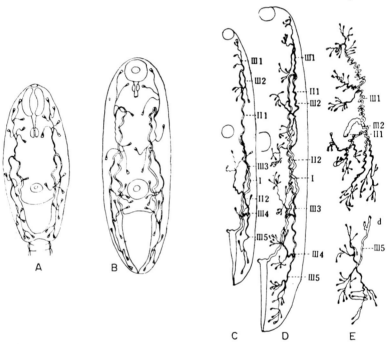

FIG. 23. Development of flame cell formula in *Clonorchis sinensis*. Flame cell pattern of cercaria (A) and metacercaria (B). Flame cell pattern in the final host after 10 days (C), 12 days (D) and 24 days.
I, main excretory canal; II, secondary collecting tube; III, tertiary collecting tube. Arabic numerals to the right of the roman numerals show the rank of each collecting tube. (Komiya and Kawana-Tajimi, 1953.)

In respect of the longevity of *C. sinensis* in the final host, it is noteworthy that Kobayashi (1922) described his own infection during 1910 and the observation that eggs appeared in samples of faeces 1 month later. By 1919 the egg-count was markedly reduced and he had established the fact that *C. sinensis* has a life-span of at least 8 years in the human body. In dogs experimental infection persisted for 3½ years, although at the end of this period the recovered flukes showed some degeneracy.

III. CLONORCHIASIS

A. PATHOLOGY

By the time young flukes reach the bile-ducts and become mature some proliferative and inflammatory reactions have been initiated in the biliary epithelium and soon encapsulating fibrosis of the ducts ensues. Such changes have been explained as due to the action of hypothetical toxic substances, but Katsurada (1922) regarded them as attributable to mechanical stimulation by flukes. Hsü (1938) considered that this pathogenicity is the result of the destructive mechanical action of flukes, claiming that the flukes break down biliary epithelial cells. The degree of pathological change would therefore seem to depend on the intensity as well as the duration of infections.

Katsurada believed that more than 1000 flukes are required to produce a lethal effect, and he recorded a case which at autopsy yielded more than 9400 flukes. Heavy infections are not infrequent and they account for rapidly developing liver damage with acute symptoms. Samback and Baujean (1913) recovered 21000 flukes at a single autopsy in Indo-China. However, the mean intensity of infection in most endemic areas is 20–200 flukes.

The main pathological changes occur in the bile-ducts and liver, and they may be slight in light infections, whereas the main bile-duct and gall-bladder are involved in moderate or heavy infections, with proliferation and desquamation of the biliary epithelium, crypt formation and the appearance of new biliary ductules, peri-epithelial fibrosis, periportal connective tissue hyperplasia and fibrous formations around eggs which infiltrate into the hepatic parenchyma (Faust and Khaw, 1927; Hoeppli, 1933). At about 9% of autopsies Laennec's cirrhosis is revealed (Hou, 1955; Germer *et al.*, 1955), but there is lesser tendency to multilobular cirrhosis than to circumscribed fibrosis of the bile-ducts. The pathological findings in infested organs have been described in some detail by Yamagata and Yaegashi (1964) in respect of organs such as the gall-bladder, pancreas, spleen, kidneys and adrenals and in the development of ascites.

The gall-bladder is often dilated and contains thin bile, and thickening of the walls is due to connective tissue proliferation when gall-stones are present. Changes in the pancreas occur only when flukes are present therein, but may then include atrophy of Langerhans' islet cells in severe cases. Splenomegaly may occur in 22–40% of autopsies (Katsurada, 1922), and is considered to be the result of congestion of the portal vein. It has been noted in rabbits 2 weeks after infection, when the spleen may be twice its normal size, and Young (1930) has noted at the end of this period various effects, indicating also that after 2 months the spleen returns to normal size, showing splenic atrophy and a tendency to a cirrhotic condition.

The development of ascites is also believed to be due to portal stagnation and ascites can nearly always be found in fatal cases, although it is infrequently found clinically. Ariyoshi (1929a, b) affirmed that dilatation of the bile-duct follows the development of ascites and that some cause other than portal stagnation might be responsible for both splenomegaly and the development of ascites. The aetiology of jaundice is also not clear, and Iwata (1937) considered that its infrequent occurrence in clonorchiasis is due to bile retention and functional disturbance of the liver.

Gall-stones may form eventually around the eggs and dead worms in the gall-bladder. Katsurada (1898) recorded two cases in seventy human autopsies, and both Miyake (1929) and Fujii (1957) have reported cases due to eggs. Maki (1952) suggested that the eggs of *Clonorchis* may mechanically stimulate Oddi's muscle less than do those of *Ascaris*, also found in pigmented calculi, thus accounting for the rarer appearance of gall-stones in clonorchiasis than in ascariasis.

Yamagata and Yaegashi (1964) gave a number of references to reports of tumours and cancer associated with clonorchiasis and suggested that not only the immediate parasitism but also associated cirrhosis should be kept in mind in aetiological inquiries. Yamagata and colleagues considered that the association of liver cancer and cirrhosis of the liver is more frequent in Japan than elsewhere and has tended to increase and that this correlation cannot be ignored.

B. CLINICAL SYMPTOMS

The symptoms evoked in clonorchiasis fall into three categories, mild, moderate and severe, and manifestations are progressive, depending on the period of infection, condition of the host and possibility of hyperinfection in long-standing parasitism. Subjective difficulties as well as objective findings appear or are aggravated by large numbers of flukes or long periods of infection. Heavy infections produce sudden effects, with chills and fever up to 40°C. In the acute stage the liver is enlarged and tender, with splenomegaly in some cases and 10–40% eosinophilia (Koenigstein, 1949). The chronic stage with classical symptoms of cholecystitis and hepatitis follows a few weeks later. In light infections an acute stage cannot usually be observed. In Japan, about 60–80% of cases in endemic areas are mild and due to no more than 100 flukes. In the survey of Yamagata (1962) in the endemic area of Miyagi Prefecture, Japan, a questionnaire revealed that 80% of mild infections were associated with vague gastrointestinal disturbances indicating hepatic dysfunction. However, Strauss (1962) considered the cases of fifty-seven Orientals and forty-eight Caucasians and uninfected controls of both groups in San Francisco and expressed the belief that many of the symptoms might be due to other causes.

Moderate or progressive cases, estimated as due to 100–1000 flukes, show irregularities of appetite, sensations of fullness in the abdomen, diarrhoea, oedema and some hepatomegaly. Yamagata (1962) surveyed the clinical symptoms of patients with complaints simulating clonorchiasis, most cases (93%) giving at initial examination indications of discomfort in the upper abdomen, which were mainly in the right upper quadrant and often periumbilical. In severe cases the symptoms include marked gastrointestinal disturbances, with a syndrome associated with portal cirrhosis, splenomegaly, ascites and oedema. Yamagata and Yaegashi (1964) have considered much more fully all the clinical aspects of clonorchiasis in respect of objective findings as well as subjective symptoms.

These writers also discuss the results of haematological investigations, and consider the effects of gastrointestinal disturbances on gastric-juice excretion, abnormalities of intestinal secretions, urinary disturbances and hepatic dysfunction in relation to clonorchiasis.

C. DIAGNOSIS

When symptoms such as have been mentioned are encountered in an endemic area the possibility of clonorchiasis is borne in mind. The disease has to be distinguished from others such as schistosomiasis, syphilis of the liver, Laennec's and Hanot's cirrhosis of the liver and pseudocirrhosis which are associated with splenomegaly and ascites (Yamagata and Yaegashi, 1964). Diagnosis ultimately depends, however, on the recovery of eggs of *C. sinensis* in the faeces or in duodenal aspirates.

1. *The Recovery and Detection of Eggs*

The direct-smear method of recovering eggs from the faeces is possible in cases of heavy infection, because eggs are then numerous. In mild infections, however, eggs may not be recoverable by this method from 3–5 mg of faeces, the standard quantity used. The mean E.P.G./fluke of *C. sinensis* in human faeces according to Saito and Hori (1963, 1964) is about 30, when the E.P.D./fluke is 3000–6000. If the infection were with ten flukes, the mean number of eggs in 5 mg of faeces is only 1·5, and in this case 22% of observed samples would not contain any eggs because eggs in faecal samples are considered to be distributed according to Poisson's law. The direct-smear method may thus be unreliable in light infections of less than ten flukes.

The method of ether sedimentation is more reliable for determining the numbers of eggs in samples of faeces, because more than 1 g of faeces can be used for one determination. According to Oshima *et al.* (1965), however, methods such as AMS III (Hunter *et al.*, 1948), MCL (Ritchie, 1948), MIFC (Blagg *et al.*, 1955), "Saitama Eiken" (1961) and dilute HCl (Miyagawa, 1913) fail to recover more than 5% of the eggs of *Metagonimus yokogawai* from faeces, although these eggs are similar in size, shape and specific gravity to those of *C. sinensis*. Of the methods mentioned, AMS III and "Saitama Eiken" methods have been the most reliable. On the other hand, Oshima *et al.* (1965) regard pH and the concentration of the mixed solution of detergent as most important factors. The highest recovery values for eggs of *Metagonimus* and *Clonorchis* is pH 2·2–4·0 when Tween 80 is the detergent used. An enhanced effect of Tween 80 on the recovery rate for eggs of both species is observed in concentrations greater than 0·1%, and as a buffer at pH 4·0 McIlvane's was preferred. Accordingly, these writers recommended the following solution for use in the recovery of eggs of *C. sinensis*: McIlvane buffer pH 4·0; 0·5% Tween 80; with 0·01% Merthiolate as a preservative. With this solution and an ether-sedimentation procedure the recovery values for eggs of *C. sinensis* were increased to 90–100% in small amounts of the sediment. Only in exceptional cases of fibrous stool were the results unsatisfactory.

It is sometimes desirable to obtain eggs from samples of bile, for instance for evaluating therapeutic effects after treatment of a patient, and in this connexion the Meltzer-Lyon method gives excellent results (Nishigishi, 1924). A strong solution of $MgSO_4$ is injected into the duodenum in order to paralyse the sphincter of Oddi and produce reflex contraction of the gall-bladder, thus facilitating the collection of separate bile fractions from which eggs can easily be recovered.

2. *Immunodiagnosis*

A number of attempts have been made to utilize immune reactions for the diagnosis of infection with *C. sinensis*. Immunological tests applied in this way include the intradermal, complement fixation, the precipitation and agglutination tests, which appear to be the most promising.

Various antigen preparations have been used, emersions of worms (Tominaga, 1942), saline extracts (Chung *et al.*, 1956; Morishita *et al.*, 1956), a crude antigen (Hunter *et al.*, 1958) and an ether extraction (Wykoff, 1958b). The antibody response appears to have been evaluated on a relative basis. Sudun *et al.* (1959) prepared four different antigens from adult worms: relatively crude fat-free antigen (CC), a lipid-free, borate buffer extraction (CTP), an acid-soluble protein fraction (CM) and an acid-insoluble, alkali-soluble protein fraction (CM-ins). These were used in connexion with intradermal and complement fixation tests on patients with clonorchiasis, the antigen in the intradermal test and CM-ins and CTP in the complement fixation test produced the most consistent and reliable results. With the intradermal test 129 out of 132 patients gave positive reactions, whereas only two out of 120 trematode-free individuals yielded positive results.

Good correlation was shown in results of the intradermal test and faeces examinations of 356 young asymptomatic individuals, although many infections may have been light and recently acquired. Apparently, by use of this purified antigen, it is possible to eliminate most of the false results reported by Hunter *et al.* (1958). Moderate cross-reactions were observed in individuals with paragonimiasis and schistosomiasis. However, as the reaction to the homologous antigen is usually much greater when surveys are conducted in areas where two or more of these trematodes are endemic, it should be possible to differentiate infections by introducing the respective antigens at the same time and by comparing the areas ensuring wheals.

Ryoji (1922) and Wykoff (1958a, b) performed the complement fixation test on patients with clonorchiasis, the former using the alcohol extract of the worm and the latter its ether extraction, but gained the antibody response only on a relative basis. Sudun *et al.* (1959) obtained a sensitive and specific complement fixation test using as antigens an acid-soluble, alkali-insoluble protein fraction or a lipid-free borate buffer extraction of the adult worms. Two of twenty-five sera from patients with clonorchiasis reacted negatively and only one out of twenty sera from trematode-free persons gave a positive reaction. Some cross-reactions with individuals infected with paragonimiasis, schistosomiasis, tuberculosis and leptospirosis were observed. All the sera from patients with tuberculosis and leptospirosis which gave false positive results were old. CM-ins reacted, however, at low titres with pre-infection rabbit sera and the antibody response following infection had to be evaluated on a relative basis. No positives with pre-infection sera were observed with CTP antigens. However, the complement fixation test of clonorchiasis requires further investigation before it can be applied on a large scale. Morishita *et al.* (1956) used a saline extract of the adult worms, and recognized the positive precipitation reaction in 100% of patients discharging *Clonorchis* eggs, only 2% of patients positive for eggs showing a negative reaction, although Mori (1957) suggested that this reaction is positive only in massive infections.

D. EPIDEMIOLOGY

1. Geographical Distribution

Clonorchis sinensis is largely confined to the Orient, namely Japan, China, Taiwan, Korea and North Vietnam. Komiya and Suzuki (1964) gave much epidemiological information concerning Japan.

a. Japan. Kojima Bay and its environs in Okayama Prefecture and the basin of the River Kitakami in Miyagi Prefecture have long been known as areas of heavy infection. In the former the endemic area a few miles south of Okayama City consists of small farms supplied with water from irrigation canals. It was here 80 years ago that Ishizaka obtained many flukes at the autopsy of a 42-year-old farmer, providing the first record for Japan. About that time the records of the Prefecture (1886, 1898) showed the incidence of infection among the residents of various villages to be 30–67%. The examination of faecal samples in the village of Mitsumasa-mura revealed 44·4% infection in 1917, 69·6% in 1931, 31·3% in 1942 and 26·0% in 1948 (Suzuki *et al.*, 1950).

In reservoir hosts Muto (1920b) found eggs in fifteen out of twenty domestic cats and in four dogs, and after World War II Inatomi and Kimura (1955) showed that 20·6% of dogs and 45·5% of cats were infected. According to Nagano (1927), the snail host is confined to a rectangular area, 60 × 15 km, in the southern part of the Prefecture, but Inatomi (1953) and Inatomi and Kimura (1955) noted that the distribution of snail hosts had diminished, and in conformity with the data Inagaki (1954) demonstrated a low incidence of cysts in piscine hosts about that time. During this period the incidence of human clonorchiasis has also diminished; in Mitsumasa-mura from about 31% in 1942 to about 26% in 1947, and in Tsuda-mura from 50·7% in 1931 to 8·6% in 1948 (Suzuki *et al.*, 1950).

The records of infection in the basin of the River Kitakami go back to 1886 and the autopsy of a resident with a cryptic disease known locally as Kiushi-disease, which proved to be clonorchiasis and which has prevailed in the plain area north of Sendai City along the Kitakami River. Originally, the incidence of infection was 55·6% amongst residents in the Kiushi area, and 52·5% amongst those in the Ishigai area (Inoue, 1900).

Suzuki (1955) and Yuda (1955–61) made extensive surveys of infection with *C. sinensis* in Miyagi Prefecture and showed that it was widespread throughout the Prefecture in cats, 54–87% of which were infected, while human infection reached the relatively high value of 34% in the northern part.

In addition to the two areas mentioned, light infections were reported in other endemic areas such as the basin of the River Tone, Lake Kasumigaura and its environs, Nobi Plain in Aichi and Gify Prefecture, the area around Lake Biwa in Shiga Prefecture and the basin of the River Onga and Chikugo. The incidence of infection has been determined in recent years in places such as Noshira in Akita Prefecture, the downstream area of the River Yoshino in Tokushima Prefecture and the area around Lake Suwa in Nagano Prefecture (see Fig. 24). It seems that heavy human infection has diminished up to the present time in Japan. Formerly infection caused many deaths in the endemic areas in Miyagi and Okayama Prefectures, but Yamagata et al. (1952) indicated that only 19% of infected persons showed slight enlargement of the liver, 3% oedema and 1% ascites. In many endemic areas of Japan most infected persons scarcely display clinical symptoms.

b. China. The most serious human infections in China occur in Kwantung Province, with heavy infections in Canton and Chaochowfu. Near Canton the area of heavy infections is in the southern part of the "mulberry district", with Siulam in the centre (Faust and Khaw, 1927). Here about 10% of the land once consisted of ridges of mulberry bushes situated between rectangular fish-ponds and about 60% of the ground was under water, perhaps because fish culture is more profitable than mulberry farming. Fishes such as *Ctenopharyngodon idellus* and *Hypothalamichthys molitrix* are bred in these ponds and, apart from rice, they constitute the principal food of the country population and are not only sold in near-by towns, but shipped alive in large numbers to the markets of Canton and Hong Kong. In this district also latrines were once commonly placed over the ponds so that faecal matter could conveniently fall therein. Culture procedures continue throughout the year, but in early spring and sometimes in autumn water was pumped out of the ponds and the fish were harvested. Mud from the ponds was placed on intervening ridges of ground to serve as fertilizer for mulberry plants, and this favoured infection, because numerous snail hosts (*Parafossarulus manchouricus* and *Alocima* (= *Bithynia*) *longicornis*) occurred in the ponds, which also contain abundant *Clonorchis* eggs in faecal materials. The mean infection amongst inhabitants of the mulberry district was more than 40% and in certain villages there may have been almost 100% infection.

In Pang K'oi district near Chaochowfu fishes are raised for raw consumption in ponds contaminated by human faeces and infection has been 50%. Heavy infection had been noted in Canton and Hong Kong, which import some fish from endemic centres, and Faust and Khaw (1927) estimated 30% infection in the Canton area. It has been suggested that about 4% of the population was infected, using egg determinations, but Hou (1955) reported 40·6% positives when studying anatomical changes due to flukes in the bile-duct. According to Hou and Pang (1964) infections of varying severity and duration occur in 65·6% of the population in Hong Kong (infants under 1 year excluded) and there is a steady rise in individuals aged between 2 and 21 years.

Occasional cases of human infection have been found along the Yangtse

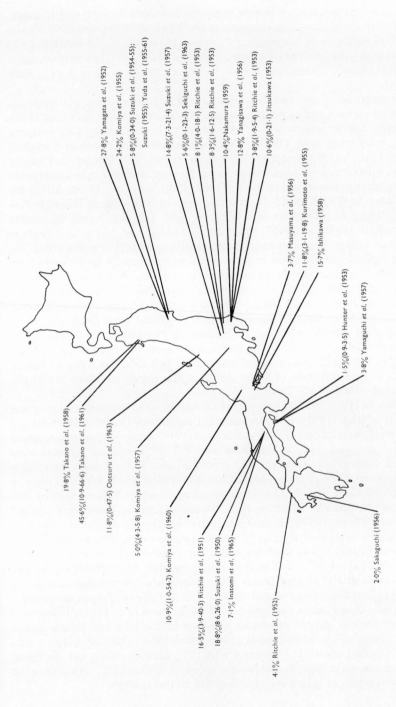

19·8% Takano et al. (1958)

45·6%(10·9-66·6) Takano et al. (1961)

11·8%(0-47·5) Ootsuru et al. (1963)

5·0%(4·3-5·8) Komiya et al. (1957)

10·9%(1·0-54·2) Komiya et al. (1960)

16·5%(3·9-40·3) Ritchie et al. (1951)

18·8%(8·6,26·0) Suzuki et al. (1950)

7·1% Inatomi et al. (1965)

4·1% Ritchie et al. (1952)

27·8% Yamagata et al. (1952)

24·2% Komiya et al. (1955)

5·8%(0-34·0) Suzuki et al. (1954-55);
Suzuki (1955); Yuda et al. (1955-61)

14·8%(7·3-21·4) Suzuki et al. (1957)

5·6%(0·1-23·3) Sekiguchi et al. (1963)

8·1%(4·0-18·1) Ritchie et al. (1953)

8·3%(1·6-12·5) Ritchie et al. (1953)

10·4% Nakamura (1959)

12·8% Yanagisawa et al. (1956)

3·8%(1·9-5·4) Ritchie et al. (1953)

10·6%(0·21·1) Jitsukawa (1953)

3·7% Masuyama et al. (1956)

11·8%(3·1-19·8) Kurimoto et al. (1955)

15·7% Ishikawa (1958)

1·5%(0·9-3·5) Hunter et al. (1953)

3·8% Yamaguchi et al. (1957)

2·0% Sakaguchi (1956)

FIG. 24. Prevalence of clonorchiasis in Japan. (See Komiya and Suzuki, 1964, for the references.)

Valley, in the Provinces of Hupeh, Anhwei, Northern Kiangsi and Kiangsu, but cases of clonorchiasis in hospitals in the Yangtse Valley usually showed a history of residence in Kwangtung Province. However, 8% of inhabitants in Whuan area were infected (Andrews, 1932) and 2–7% of Chinese residents in Shanghai, mostly Cantonese, but of Japanese emigrants there 3–21% were infected.

The infection of cats and dogs was light in southern China, but moderate in northern China and heavy in central China (Chen, 1934a; Kawana, 1936). Formerly, human infection was considered to be non-existent in northern China, but Chung et al. (1959, 1960a, b) discovered infections in Yungfeng hsiang, Liulit'un of Ch'angping district in Peking and Palit'ai in Tientsin. Human infections were found also among Korean residents in two villages in Tehling hsiang, Liaoning Province (Asada, 1940; Li et al., 1958). About the same time, Li (1958) found the endemic area in Yütu hsieng (Kiangsi Province), Wang et al. (1958) in Chienyang and Tzeyang hsiang (Szechuan Province), T'ang et al. (1963) in southern Fukien and Ma et al. (1964) in T'uanwan village near Tsingtao (Shantung Province). It is noteworthy that raw or roasted fish are eaten in these endemic areas except southern Fukien, where raw crayfish take the place of fish in the diet. When three species of crayfish (*Caridina nilotica gracilipes* de Man, *Macrobrachium superbum* (Heller) and *Palaemonetes sinensis* Sollaud) were examined cysts were found in them, and when fed to a guinea-pig they produced adult flukes.

Regarding human infections in Kwantung Province, recent innovations have improved the situation; the disposal of faeces has been controlled, the fouling of fish-ponds discontinued and regular fish food has replaced human excreta so that infection of water snails in the ponds has been practically eliminated (Weng et al., 1960).

c. *Taiwan* (Fig. 25). The first report on infections of indigenous Taiwanese was that of Ohoi (1915), who examined 221 patients in Taichung Hospital and found eight cases of clonorchiasis. Furuichi (1919) examined faecal samples of patients here and 29% of Japanese and 9% of Taiwanese patients were infected. Ohoi (1919) made the first report of cysts in local freshwater fishes of the species *Ctenopharyngodon idellus*, and Muto (1938) reported cysts in *Cultericulus kneri*. Recent faecal examinations in south Taiwan showed that 22·4% of residents of Meinung in north-east Kaosiung hsien were infected (Hsieh and Chow, 1959). This town is surrounded by mountains except to the south and is inhabited mainly by Hakka people originating in Kwangtung Province, China, whose customs and dietary habits deviate from those of immigrants from Fukien and include eating raw fish. The "Chung-chen lake" and more than 100 smaller ponds greatly facilitate fish-farming, and at the request of customers fish are sold, dressed and served raw. *Tilapia mossambica* is a popular choice, and cysts have been demonstrated in it. The snail host here is *Parafossarulus manchouricus* and it occurs in the lake and ponds and in small streams. Chow (1960) made skin tests on local inhabitants of this area and recognized about 25% positive and 16% dubious cases, but his faecal examinations gave high figures with a mean of about 52%, although more positive reactors in skin tests were involved in the analysis.

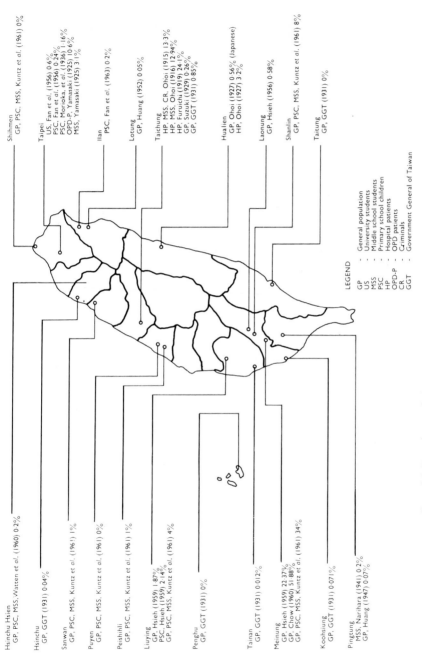

Shihmen
GP, PSC, MSS, Kuntz et al. (1961) 0%

Taipei
US, Fan et al. (1956) 0.6%
PSC, Fan et al. (1956) 0.24%
PSC, Morioka, et al. (1936) 1.16%
OPD-P, Yamasaki (1925) 10.6%
MSS, Yamasaki (1925) 3.1%

Ilan
PSC, Fan et al. (1963) 0.2%

Lotung
GP, Huang (1952) 0.05%

Taichung
HP, MSS, CR, Ohoi (1915) 13.3%
HP, MSS, Ohoi (1916) 12.94%
HP, Furuichi (1919) 24.1%
GP, Suzuki (1929) 0.26%
GP, GGT (1931) 0.85%

Hualien
GP, Ohoi (1927) 0.56% (Japanese)
HP, Ohoi (1927) 3.2%

Laonung
GP, Hsieh (1956) 0.58%

Shanlin
GP, PSC, MSS, Kuntz et al. (1961) 8%

Taitung
GP, GGT (1931) 0%

LEGEND

GP	-	General population
US	-	University students
MSS	-	Middle school students
PSC	-	Primary school children
HP	-	Hospital patients
OPD-P	-	OPD patients
CR	-	Criminals
GGT	-	Government General of Taiwan

Hsinchu Hsien
GP, PSC, MSS, Watten et al. (1960) 0.2%

Hsinchu
GP, GGT (1931) 0.04%

Sanwan
GP, PSC, MSS, Kuntz et al. (1961) 1%

Puyen
GP, PSC, MSS, Kuntz et al. (1961) 0%

Peishihli
GP, PSC, MSS, Kuntz et al. (1961) 1%

Luying
GP, Hsieh (1959) 1.87%
PSC, Hsieh (1959) 2.14%
GP, PSC, MSS, Kuntz et al. (1961) 4%

Penghu
GP, GGT (1931) 0%

Tainan
GP, GGT (1931) 0.012%

Meinung
GP, Hsieh (1959) 22.37%
GP, Chow (1960) 51.88%
GP, PSC, MSS, Kuntz et al. (1961) 34%

Koohsiung
GP, GGT (1931) 0.071%

Pingtung
MSS, Narihara (1941) 0.2%
GP, Huang (1947) 0.07%

FIG. 25. Prevalence of clonorchiasis in Taiwan (Kim and Kuntz, 1964).

Kim and Kuntz (1964) have observed that at least fourteen species of fresh-water fishes can serve as hosts of *C. sinensis* in Taiwan; they also prepared a detailed map showing the distribution of human infection in the island (Fig. 25).

d. Korea. Since Kobayashi first reported on human infections in South Korea, clonorchiasis has become recognized as highly endemic in the Naktong, Kum, Nam, Sumgin and Hun river valleys, and the principal cause of many known cases of liver cirrhosis in Korea. Kim (1959) noted that infection is not restricted to the Naktong and Hyongsan Rivers, but is widespread throughout the province, the incidence in the general population being about 22 %. Using intradermal tests with purified antigens, Shin (1961) showed that there is 30–63 % infection along the Hyung-San Kan area, and Lee (1960) revealed 24 % infection in Kyonsang-Puk to, but only about 4 % in Kang-Wha island.

Walton and Chyu (1959) surveyed infection in South Korea (Fig. 26) by similar methods and the results of intradermal tests indicated that in Kyong-

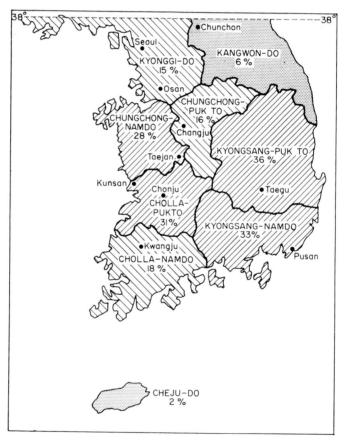

FIG. 26. Prevalence of clonorchiasis in the Republic of Korea (Walton and Chyu, 1959).

sang-Puk to 53% of males and 14% of females were infected, whereas in Cheju-Do the corresponding figures were 3% and 1% only. The higher rate of infection in males was consistent and, in general, increase is correlated with age up to 41–50 years. These results are probably related to social customs such as gatherings for drinking the rice wine sul, with raw fish eating as a traditional accompaniment, women rarely participating in the ceremony.

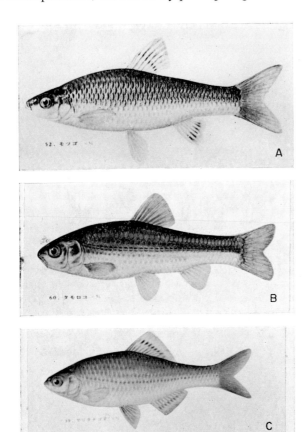

Fig. 27. Small fish hosts of *Clonorchis*. A, *Pseudorasbora parva*; B, *Gnathopogon elongatus*; C, *Acheilognathus lanceolata*.

The snail host in Korea is *Parafossarulus manchouricus*. Kobayashi (1924) showed that nine species of freshwater fishes serve as second intermediate hosts, and Chun (1962) found cysts in nine species of fishes, considering *Pseudorasbora parva* most important because of 100% natural infection (Fig. 27).

    e. North Vietnam (former French Indo-China). Human infection with *C. sinensis* in French Indo-China was discovered by Grall (1887) and its distribution was summarized by French workers (Léger, 1910; Mathis and

Léger, 1911). The heaviest infections (73%) occurred on the delta of the Red River in and around Haiphong and Hanoi and for the entire region infection averaged more than 40% in adults and 8% in children. To the west and north of this region infections were low although such areas bordered on the southernmost endemic area of China, namely Kwangtung and Kwangsi. *Parafossarulus manchouricus* was common in the Tonkin delta and the most usual fishes there were various cyprinids, including forms well known to serve as hosts elsewhere. The rice farmers and boatmen commonly infected, like the country population in Kwantung Province, were notable fish-eaters, suggesting that degrees of infection may be much the same in the two areas. No information on clonorchiasis has emanated from this region in recent years.

2. Infection

It is well known that most Japanese like to eat raw fish prepared in various ways (Komiya, 1935). Slices of raw flesh are dipped in vinegar for 10–20 min (Sunomono), eaten with soybean sauce, or Shoyu (Sashimi), coated with salted soybean paste, or Miso (Miso-ae), or coated with Shoyu or Miso, common Japanese flavourings. Large fishes such as *Cyprinis carpio* and *Carassius carassius* (Fig. 28) are preferred, but in one area *Tribolodon hakoensis* is eaten raw. Sakai (1953) made a survey among the local inhabitants of cooking procedures for fishes from Lake Biwa and these are noted also for hosts of *C. sinensis* (Table VII). Masuyama *et al.* (1956) showed that crucian carp and common carp were favoured and eaten raw in the endemic area of Aich Prefecture, small fishes being preserved by boiling with soybean sauce, and Kato and Takeda (1958) gave similar indications for the endemic area of Mie Prefecture, so that these fishes should be considered as the main source of infection in Japan although they contain only a few cysts. Heavily infected small fishes are not generally eaten raw by the Japanese, but they may be eaten after imperfect roasting and may transmit infection.

TABLE VII

Methods of cooking the fish hosts of Clonorchis (*Sakai*, 1953)

Fish	Eaten raw	Roasted	Boiled	Not eaten
Pseudorasbora parva	1	9	90	20
Acheilognathus lanceolata	1	5	18	91
Tribolodon hakonensis	5	15	56	53
Sarcocheilichthys variegatus	1	44	58	29
Gnathopogon elongatus	3	129	111	63
Sinogobio biwae	1	65	54	21
Pseudogobio esocinus	4	12	74	40
Carassius carassius	81	20	164	34
Cyprinus carpio	89	6	103	2

The survey was made on 112 families in the vicinity of Lake Biwa.

In China, Cantonese people with a marked preference for raw fish in their diet are notably infected with *C. sinensis* and the fishes concerned are *Ctenopharyngodon idellus* and *Hypothalamichthys nobilis*. In central and northern

FIG. 28. Large fish hosts of *Clonorchis sinensis* in Japan and in China. A, *Cyprinus carpio*; B, *Carrasius carassius*; C, *Ctenopharyngodon idellus*; D, *Mylopharyngodon aethiops*.

China, however, fish is not eaten raw and there is little or no infection except in certain endemic areas, although fishes and reservoir hosts may be heavily infected. The Hakka people in Upper Kwangtung eat raw fish and are heavily infected, as are Hakka emigrants in Meining (Taiwan) (Hsieh and Chow, 1959; Chow, 1960). Korean people also habitually eat raw fish and Korean emigrants in Tehling (Liaoning Province, China) retain the habit and are heavily infected (Asada, 1940; Li et al., 1958). The residents of endemic areas recently disclosed in central and northern China eat either raw or imperfectly cooked fish, but in the endemic area of South Fukien Province the residents eat raw crayfish, which is considered to be the only source of infection (T'ang et al., 1963).

In Japan, some writers consider that infection with *C. sinensis* may be contracted by the agency of water. Muto (1919) claimed that rabbits can be infected by taking water in which *Pseudorasbora parva* has been reared, and a similar claim was made by Ishii and Matsuoka (1935) in respect of water in which dead infected fishes had been kept. However, other writers (Hasui, 1917; Maekawa and Fukase, 1922) obtained negative results from similar experiments. Nagano (1951) gave rabbits water which had flowed over a basket of dead and living fishes in a stream, but also obtained negative results, and Jitsukawa (1953) studied water utilization by persons found to be infected and denied the possibility of waterborne infection. The present writer believes that, although theoretically possible, such a mode of infection is unlikely because of the remote possibility of obtaining cysts liberated from the bodies of fishes. [It would be interesting to know, however, if encystment may occur in the open, because forms such as *Fasciola hepatica* which encyst on herbage may form cysts on a water surface. Ed.]

The age distribution of human infections with *C. sinensis* in various endemic areas of Japan has been well studied (Inoue, 1892; Ide, 1936; Tominaga, 1942; Yamagata et al., 1952; Jitsukawa, 1953; Komiya and Sato, 1955; Yanagisawa et al., 1956; Suzuki et al., 1957; Komiya et al., 1957). To summarize, the incidence of infection is greater in the higher age groups and greatest in persons 30–50 years old. In the endemic area of Kwangtung Province in China, in Hong Kong and in Taiwan human adults are also infected more highly than younger persons. However, in recently discovered endemic areas of Szechuan (Wang et al., 1958), South Fukien (T'ang et al., 1963), East Shantung (Ma et al., 1964) and other localities, clonorchiasis occurs in children less than 15 years old, and this may be due to a greater tendency for children to eat fishes imperfectly roasted and crayfishes raw.

In Japan there is no apparent difference in the incidence of infection in male and females, although males have been shown to be more highly infected than females in Canton, Meinung (Taiwan) and T'uanwan (China) (Faust and Khaw, 1927; Chow, 1960; Ma et al., 1964).

The survey of Kamiyama (1910) showed that farmers and government officers were more highly infected than other persons in the endemic area of Okayama Prefecture (Japan). Komiya et al. (1957) found that the incidence of infection was high among farm workers around Lake Suwa (Japan), and this was also the case in an endemic area along the River Tone. Conversely,

TABLE VIII

Familial accumulation of Clonorchis infection (Komiya and Sato, 1955)

	No. of family (n)												Total
	1	2	3	4	5	6	7	8	9	10	11	12	
0	3 (3·1)	5 (3·0)	3 (3·3)	7 (6·2)	6 (3·9)	2 (2·9)	4 (2·4)	2 (1·1)	2 (0·7)	1 (0·3)	1 (0·3)	1 (0·1)	37 (27·3)
1	1 (0·9)	0 (1·7)	3 (2·8)	5 (7·6)	6 (5·7)	5 (4·9)	2 (4·8)	3 (2·8)	0 (1·9)	0 (0·9)	1 (1·0)	0 (0·3)	26 (35·3)
2		0 (0·3)	1 (1·6)	2 (3·2)	2 (3·3)	2 (3·5)	4 (4·1)	3 (2·7)	1 (2·3)	0 (1·2)	1 (1·4)	0 (0·5)	16 (24·1)
3			0 (0)	3 (0·6)	0 (0·9)	3 (1·3)	1 (1·9)	1 (1·6)	1 (1·2)	2 (0·9)	2 (1·2)	0 (0·5)	13 (10·1)
4				1 (0)	0 (0·1)	1 (0·2)	3 (0·5)	0 (0·5)	2 (0·5)	1 (0·4)	0 (0·6)	0 (0·3)	8 (3·1)
5					0 (0)	0 (0)	0 (0·1)	0 (0·1)	0 (0·1)	0 (0·1)	0 (0·2)	1 (0·1)	1(0·7)
6						0 (0)	0 (0)	0 (0)	0 (0)	0 (0)	0 (0)	0 (0)	0 (0)
7							0 (0)	0 (0)	1 (0)	0 (0)	0 (0)	0 (0)	1 (0)
Total	4	5	7	18	14	13	14	9	7	4	5	2	102

No. of positive (x)

The figures in parentheses represent the expected number of households theoretically calculated ($P = 0.24$, $q = 0.76$). $n = 2$ $p_r(x^2 = 17.31) < 0.001$.

infection was greater amongst merchants and students in Kwangtung Province (China) and amongst merchants and office workers in Mainung (Taiwan).

Komiya and Sato (1955) classified families in the endemic area of Miyagi Prefecture according to the number of members and of infections, and found statistically sound evidence for the belief that infections accumulate in families. Ma *et al.* (1964) indicated that such familial cases of infection were common in T'uanwan, East Shantung Province, at least two members of each family being infected.

E. PREVENTION OF INFECTION

Infection with *C. sinensis* may be prevented by the application of various methods aimed at the interruption of transmission, the destruction of eggs in the faeces, control of the snail hosts, elimination of infection from piscine hosts or modification of human feeding habits as a result of public health education. Nagano (1964) has outlined preventative measures.

The eggs of *C. sinensis*, which occur in "night soil", die within 48 h at 26°C or 5 days at 4–8°C in this medium or within 1 week at normal temperatures. Methods of disposal of human faeces have been improved in China within recent years and the possibility of snails becoming infected has been practically eliminated in Kwangtung Province (Weng *et al.*, 1960). In Japan, however, suitable methods of "night soil" disposal have not been utilized fully for the purpose of eliminating clonorchiasis.

1. Control of the Snail Host

The snail host of *C. sinensis*, *Parafossarulus manchouricus*, also serves as the host of *Notocotylus attenuatus*, an intestinal trematode of the duck, which destroys the gonads and thus brings about the parasitic castration of the snail host. Nagano (1929) suggested that this fact could be utilized in controlling snails and Shimizu and Kawata (1937) applied this method in an endemic area of Okayama Prefecture, namely Kojo village in Gojima-Gun and succeeded in diminishing the numbers of snails, although this method has not been put into practice.

The crayfish *Cambarus clarkii*, recently imported from U.S.A., is a natural enemy of *P. manchouricus*, and Nagano (1951, 1960) and Inagaki (1954) noted that by eating young snails the crayfish multiplied at the expense of the snail population. However, contradictory results were obtained by Nishimoto (1958) and Ikuyama (1960a, b) and this ecological relationship requires further study. Young snails are also a prey of small fishes, but they avoid these predators by aggregating in the foliage of water plants. Nagano (1928) showed that the fortnightly removal of weeds from the habitat of snails in an endemic area (Okayama Prefecture) resulted in marked reduction of the snail population.

Water pollution may also reduce snail densities. In recent years the use of pesticides on rice plantations has been extended, particularly the use of dilute Parathion ($C_{10}H_{14}NO_5PS$) against *Chilo simplex* during June and July. This compound is highly toxic to fishes and molluscs, a solution of 0·05 p.p.m. of

Parathion killing the snail hosts of *C. sinensis* in a week. Inatomi and Kimura (1955) also considered that in Okayama Prefecture marked diminution of snail habitats can be attributed to the use of parathion in rice fields, while Nishimoto (1958) showed that the population density of such snails is much less in feeder streams and ditches near the River Oike than in the river itself, and for the same reason.

Effluents from factories which have arisen along river banks in endemic areas have also lowered the density of snail populations (Inatomi and Kimura, 1955; Nishimoto, 1958) and this has been operative also on the Onga River in Kyushu district (Nagamoto, 1958). Other recent developments include land reclamation, which has also reduced the extent of snail habitats. In the Prefecture of Gifu the upper basin was long known to be an endemic area, but during the past ten years practically no infections have been reported, although in the lower basin of the river sporadic cases of clonorchiasis could be found. A survey revealed that the swampy area of the upper basin has been completely reclaimed, so that snail habitats do not now exist there.

As has been stated already, the direct source of infection with *C. sinensis* is by the ingestion of cysts derived from the raw or imperfectly cooked flesh of various freshwater fishes, notably species of *Pseudorasbora*, *Gnathopogon*, *Acheilognathus* and *Sarcocheilichthys*, which are small fishes and usually the more heavily infected, or larger fishes which are species of *Ctenopharyngodon*, *Mylopharyngodon* (in China), *Cyprinus* and *Carassius* (in Japan).

The custom of eating the raw or imperfectly cooked flesh of freshwater fishes is deeply rooted in oriental peoples and difficult to modify even when education in public health is attempted. However, the abolition of this custom is desirable and likely to prevail in the future. In the Kiushi area of Miyagi Prefecture, Japan, the incidence of clonorchiasis reached 56% of the population in 1883, but in 1955 was practically zero, and this could be attributed largely to public health education.

F. TREATMENT

Several kinds of chemical compounds have been recommended for the treatment of clonorchiasis, but it appears that no definitive therapeutic effects have been harvested yet by the application of any of them.

1. *Gentian Violet*

Faust and Khaw (1927) tested the anthelmintic effect of gentian violet for *C. sinensis* using cats as experimental animals, and showed that gentian violet is clonorchicidal. While results can be obtained rapidly with the administrations of 50 mg per kg body weight, 35 mg is almost equally effective and lies within the limit of tolerance. In heavy infections the drug may be administered in smaller doses, using not more than 20 mg per kg body weight per day. It seems likely that clonorchicidal amounts of the drug gradually accumulate in the bile-duct. Clonorchicidal action can, therefore, be obtained by administering per os 7–35 mg of gentian violet per kg body weight per day.

Kawai and Yumoto (1936) reported that the oral administration of gentian

violet (hexa- and penta-methyl-rosaniline) to experimental dogs harbouring
Clonorchis in total amounts of 1·2–5·4 g for 5–15 days resulted in the reduction
of eggs in faeces 2 months later. However, oral administration of gentian
violet produced side effects and was less effective than antimony preparations.

2. *Antimony Preparations*

Since antimony preparations proved to be effective for the treatment of
schistosomiasis, they have been applied for treatment of other trematode
diseases. Brug (1921) realized the value of tartar emetic for schistosomiasis;
he administered the drug for the first time in a severe *Clonorchis* infection and
reported improvement in the patient. Shattuck (1923, 1924) used antimony
and arsenic compounds on six infected Chinese patients and believed that he
had effected cures in four of them. Faust and Khaw (1927) reported that a
patient improved after treatment with tartar emetic. Eggs were absent from
the faeces for a period of 3 months, but reappeared some months later.

Miyagawa (1923), aware that the side effect of tartar emetics (stibiokalium
tartaricum) is often prominent, replaced potassium of this compound by
sodium and named it "Stibnal". Katada (1924) and Ryoji (1927a, b) experimented with Stibnal using rabbits, and the results proved its effectiveness for
the treatment of clonorchiasis. In general, Stibnal has been regarded as less
toxic than, but as effective as, tartar emetic.

Stibnal is usually administered intravenously in a single dose of 0·03 g, the
dose being increased by 0·01 g each day until it becomes 0·06 g and is given
every other day or once in every 4 days. After few days interval this course is
repeated.

Shirai (1926) found that sodium antimony tartrate becomes alkaline by
adding a certain amount of sodium tartaricum to it, and then named it
"Neostibnal", which proved to be less toxic to hosts but retaining its clonorchicidal action. The intravenous administration of Neostibnal in a dose of
9–11 mg per kg every other day repeated 25 times for experimentally infected
dogs resulted in 40–75% clonorchicidal effects. No remarkable toxic side
effects could be observed at that time, but Ariyoshi (1929a, b) reported several
in the host after administering the drug.

Similar antimony preparations such as Antimosan (Heyden), Stibosan
(Heyden), Fuadin (Neoantimosan; Bayer), Neostibosan (Bayer) and Stibenyl
(Uhlenhut *et al.*) have been introduced by several commercial enterprises, all
of them showing similar clonorchicidal effects.

Miyagawa and Shimizu (1942) reported that combined use of Stibnal and
sulphonamide preparations was more effective than Stibnal alone. They also
stated that intravenous injection of 1% powdered antimony colloid produced
beneficial effects in clonorchiasis. By the administration of antimony colloid
to patients with clonorchiasis, Yamagata *et al.* (1952a) observed the disappearance of eggs in 42·8% of treated cases.

3. *Dithiazanine Iodide*

Dithiazanine was introduced as an effective broad-spectrum anthelmintic
by Swartzwelder *et al.* (1957). Yamaguchi and Mineda (1960) exposed adult

C. sinensis in test tubes to about sixty different products and dithiazanine iodide had the best clonorchicidal effect. Yamaguchi *et al.* (1962) carried out a series of investigations on the effect of dithiazanine iodide on clonorchiasis in rabbits, results of which were summarized as follows. The administration of 5–20 daily doses of 30–80 mg per kg of dithiazanine iodide is eminently efficacious. Toxic effects were not apparent when 10–20 daily doses of 20–100 mg per kg were administered 10–20 times. A total of 344 patients were given dithiazanine iodide in daily doses of about 30 mg per kg (1·5 g) as a mass-treatment experiment. About 70% of cases gave negative results for *Clonorchis* eggs after 10 doses of the drug. Side effects noted (diarrhoea, nausea, abdominal pain, etc.) were generally mild and transient.

4. 4, 7-*Phenanthroline*-5, 6-*quinone* ("*Entobex*"; *Ciba*)

This compound was developed as amoebicide, but later proved effective for the treatment of clonorchiasis (Coudert and Garin, 1959). Ikuyama (1960a) administered daily 300 mg of Entobex to patients for 1 week or more and in over half of them *Clonorchis* eggs disappeared from the faeces, but Katsuta *et al.* (1960) reported that after such treatment for 1 week the egg numbers in the faeces diminished directly, but increased after cessation of the administration. Yamaguchi *et al.* (1961a) also administered this compound to patients with clonorchiasis in doses of 600 mg per day for 7–10 days, but afterwards in all cases the faeces contained eggs of *Clonorchis*. They also carried out animal experiments using this compound and after the administration they invariably found living *Clonorchis* at autopsy, concluding that this compound shows little promise in clonorchiasis.

5. *Phosphorchloroquine*

Phosphorchloroquine, 7-chloro-4-(4'-diethylamino-14-methyl-4-butyl-amino) quinone, was introduced in 1934 as an antimalarial agent. Basnuevo (1949) first administered this compound to two patients with clonorchiasis and proved it to be effective. Later Chung *et al.* (1955) and Crane *et al.* (1955) applied the drug to the treatment of clonorchiasis with similar results.

Sugimura *et al.* (1957b) administered chloroquine diphosphate (Resochin; Bayer) to thirty-four patients with clonorchiasis in daily doses of 500 mg for 12–100 days and noted the disappearance of eggs in the duodenal juice in about 40% of treated cases. In some instances the side effects included dizziness, headache, nausea, lack of appetite, general fatigue and diarrhoea. Nagamoto (1958) also to a certain extent recognized the effectiveness of this compound in clonorchiasis, and Okabe *et al.* (1959) treated fifteen patients by administering 500 mg of Resochin daily and within 6 weeks noted the disappearance of eggs in faeces in thirteen of them. In almost all cases there were decreased clinical symptoms, such as eosinophilia and hepatoma, but side effects, such as dizziness, headache, nausea and numbness of hands and feet, were observed in some cases.

Miyagawa *et al.* (1957) reported, however, that the treatment of clonorchiasis with the antimony compound Fuadin alone or combined with chloroquine produced a better effect than treatment with chloroquine alone. Wada *et al.* (1958) administered 500 mg of phosphorchloroquine (Resochin) daily on 41 successive days (total dose 20·5 mg) combined with Melzer-Lyon's method (twelve duodenal tubings with $MgSO_4$) and noted that the disappearance of eggs in the faeces of all the treated patients was maintained for 40 weeks even one year after treatment. Tsuda (1958) reported that combined therapy with Resochin and Fuadin for 56 days brought about the disappearance of eggs in the faeces. Yamaguchi *et al.* (1961a, b), from the results of both animal experiments and mass treatment of patients, concluded that the complete cure of clonorchiasis could not be expected by administering chloroquine (Resochin) in daily doses of 500 mg for 8–10 weeks.

6. *Hexachloroparaxylol* ($Cl_3CPhCCl_3$)

Hexachloroparaxylol has recently been used in the treatment of clonorchiasis. Plotnikov and Sinovich (1964) successfully treated nine infected cats by administering this compound on 2 successive days in total doses of 0·1 g per kg (2 cats), 0·2 g per kg (3 cats) and 0·3 g per kg (4 cats). John *et al.* (1965) exposed adult *C. sinensis in vitro* to emetine, chloroquine, hexachlorophene and hexachloroparaxylol, and reported that the degree of clonorchicidal effect of these compounds was as follows: hexachlorophene $>$ hexachloroparaxylol $>$ emetine $\doteqdot$ chloroquine. They proceeded to use hexachloroparaxylol in human clonorchiasis and found that 0·5 g per kg per day for 10 successive days gave 100% apparent cure in all heavily infected cases 3 months after initial dosage, and that in lightly infected cases 0·25 g per kg per day for 10 successive days effected a complete cure. Clinically, gastro-intestinal irritation was not marked, and although a few patients had visual and auditory hallucinations during the course of treatment, no damage to the liver, heart or kidney was observed. More recently, Chung *et al.* (1965) cured six cases of clonorchiasis with only 0·05–0·125 g per kg and the course of treatment was shortened to less than 12 days for the mild cases. This was achieved by increasing the solubility and the absorption rate of the drug, which was given with 200 ml milk, or by dispensing the drug as a 20% solution in peanut oil.

7. 1, 4-*Bis-trichloromethylbenzol* (*Hetol; Hoechst Co.*)

Hetol was used for the treatment of *Fasciola hepatica* in cattle, but Yokogawa *et al.* (1965) applied this compound for the treatment of clonorchiasis, in experimentally infected dogs, rabbits and rats. They administered orally 100 mg per kg every other day in 5 doses without noting any side effects. E.P.G. gradually decreased to zero about 21 days after the first dose, and no living flukes were found at autopsy of the animals. They (personal communication) are now proceeding with a mass treatment experiment on human clonorchiasis using this compound, and the results appear to be promising.

REFERENCES

Abbott, R. H. (1948). *Bull. Mus. comp. Zool. Harv.* **100** (3), 246–328.

Andrews, M. N. (1932). *Chin. med. J.* **17**, 390–397.

Ariyoshi, C. (1929a). *Nippon byori gakkai kaishi* **19**, 562–563; *Byorigaki Kiyo.* **6** (2), 277–362.*

Ariyoshi, C. (1929b). *Iji Shimbun* (1251), 976–992. (In Japanese with Esperanto summary.)

Asada, J. (1920). *Nippon byori gakkai kaishi* **10**, 347–350.*

Asada, J. (1940). *Tairiku Kagaku In Iho*, **4** (6), 932–956.*

Baelz, E. (1883). *Berl. klin. Wschr.*, 1883, 234–238.

Basnuevo, J. G. (1949). *Revta Kuba Med. trop. Parasit.* **5**, 105.

Blagg, W., Schlaeget, E. L., Mansoun, N. H., and Khalal, G. I. (1955). *Am. J. trop. Med. Hyg.* **4**, 23–29.

Blanchard, R. (1895). "Traité de zoologie médicale et agricole," 2nd ed. Paris.

Brug, S. L. (1921). *Bull. Soc. Path. exot.* **14**, 161–162.

Chen, H. T. (1934a). *Lingnan Sci. J.* **13** (1), 57–87; (2), 261–273.

Chow, L. P. (1960). *Formosan Sci.* **14** (3), 134–166.

Chun, S. K. (1962). *Bull. Fish. Coll.* **4** (1/2), 21–38. (In Korean with English summary.)

Chung, H. L., Weng, H. C., and Hou, T. C. (1955). *Chin. med. J.* **73** (1), 1–14.

Chung, H. L., Hou, T. C., and Weng, H. C. (1956). *Chin. med. J.* **74** (2), 207–221.

Chung, H. L., Huang, S. J., Li, T. H., Hsü, H. C., Hu, Y. M., and Hsü, F. N. (1959). *Sci. Rec. Acad. sin.* N.S. **3** (10), 499–503.

Chung, H. L., Hou, T. C., Huang, S. J., Mo, P. S., Ho, L. Y., and Kuang, C. H. (1960a). *Sci. Rec. Acad. sin.* N.S. **4** (1), 19–25.

Chung, H. L., Ho, L. Y., Hsü, H. C., Mo, P. S., and Weng, H. C. (1960b). *Sci. Rec. Acad. sin.* N.S. **4** (1), 26–32.

Chung, H. L., Hsü, C. P., Tsáo, W. C., K'o, H. Y., Kuo, C. H., Li, P. H., Cheng, S., Chang, H. Y., Yuan, C. T., and Chang, Y. C. (1965). *Chin. med. J.* **84** (4), 232–247.

Cobbold, T. S. (1875). *Veterinarian, Lond.* **48**, 780–781.

Coudert, J., and Garin, J. P. (1959). *Pamphlet. Ciba Co.*, pp. 1–16.

Crane, P. S., Bush, O. B., Jr., and Won, P. C. (1955). *Tr. Roy. Soc. Trop. Med. Hyg.* **49**, 68–70.

Faust, E. C., and Khaw, O. K. (1927). *Am. J. Hyg.* Monograph Series (8) 1–284.

Fujii, J. (1957). *Tokyo-iji-shinski* **74** (5), 273.*

Furuichi, T. (1919). *Taiwan igakkai zasshi* (195/196), 117–131.*

Germer, W. D., Young, M. H., Schalze, W., Jeltch, R., and Ortahood, M. D. (1955). *Z. Hyg.* **141**, 132–145.

Grall, (1887). *Arch. Méd. nav.* **48** (12), 459–470. Cited from Faust and Khaw (1927).

Hasegawa, T. (1929). *Okayama igakkai zasshi* **41** (10), 2424.*

Hasui, N. (1917). *Okayama igakkai zasshi* (325), 33–40.*

Heanley, C. N. (1908). *J. trop. Med.* **2**, 38–39.

Hoeppli, R. (1933). *Chin. med. J.* **47**, 1125–1141.

Hou, P. C. (1955). *J. Path. Bact.* **70**, 53–64.

Hou, P. C., and Pang, S. C. (1964). *J. Path. Bact.* **87**, 245–250.

Hsieh, H. C., and Chow, L. P. (1959). *Formosan Sci.* **12** (2), 23–33.

*In Japanese.

Hsü, H. F. (1938). *Trans. Xth Congr. F.E.A.T.M. Hanoi*, 637–641.
Hsü, H. F. (1939a). *Chin. med. J.* **55**, 542–545.
Hsü, H. F. (1939b). *Chin. med. J.* **56**, 122–130.
Hsü., H. F., and Li, S. Y. (1940a). *Chin. med. J.* Suppl. 3, pp. 241–243, 244–254.
Hunter, G. W. III., Hodges, E. P., Jalnes, W. G., Diamond, L. S., and Ingalls, J. W. Jr. (1948). *Bull. U.S. Army med. Dep.* **8** (2), 128–131.
Hunter, G. W., Ritchie, L. S., Pan, C., Lin, S., Sugiura, S., Nagano, K., and Yokogawa, M. (1958). *Milit. Med.* **122**, 85–96.
Ide, K. (1936). *Saikingaku zasshi* (470), 253–256.*
Iijima, I. (1886). *J. Coll. Sci. Imp. Univ. Tokyo* **1**, 47–59.
Ikuyama, T. (1960a). *Kiseichugaku zasshi* **9** (4), 423–424.*
Ikuyama, T. (1960b). *Kurume igakkai zasshi* **23** (7), 2730–2753, 2754–2776. (In Japanese with English summary.)
Inagaki, M. (1954). *Kiseichugaku zasshi* **2** (3, 4), 209–215.*
Inatomi, S. (1953). *Okayama igakkai zasshi* **65** (1), 45–49.*
Inatomi, S. (1962). *Okayama igakkai zasshi* **74** (1, 2, 3), 31–81. (In Japanese with English summary.)
Inatomi, S., and Kimura, M. (1955). *Okayama igakkai zasshi* **67** (3/4), 651–653.*
Inatomi, S., Sakumoto, D., Itano, K., and Tsubota, T. (1964). *Kiseichugaku zasshi* **13** (4), 339–340.
Inoue, Z. (1892). *Tokyo igakkai zasshi* **6** (12), 556–562.*
Inoue, Z. (1900). *Tokyo igakkai zasshi* **14** (13), 503–562.*
Ishii, N. (1929). *Jikken igaku zasshi* **12** (2), 39–59; **13** (2), 171–183.*
Ishii, N., and Matsuoka, F. (1935). *Tokyo iji shinshi* (2912), 80–83.*
Ishizaka, K. (1878). *Igaku zasshi* (40), 20–26.*
Ito, K., and Muto, M. (1925). *Byorigaku Kiyo* **15**, 565–571; *Aichi igakkai zasshi* **32** (6), 1073–1087.*
Iwata, S. (1937). *Jikken Shokakibyo gakkai zasshi* **12** (1), 1872–1886; (2) 1887–1898.*
Jitsukawa, W. (1953). *Chiba igakkai zasshi* **29** (1), 25–31. (In Japanese with English summary.)
John, L., Wang, C. N., Tseng, F. J., Fan, K. C., Tu, C. C., Chang, T. F., Sun, K. J., Chin, C. M., Cheng, S., and Tu, S. F. (1965). *Chin. med. J.* **84** (1), 8–16.
Kamiyama, Y. (1910). *Okayama igakkai zasshi* (247), 523–531.*
Katada, T. (1924). *Aichi igakkai zasshi* **31** (5), 1059–1079.*
Kato, K., and Takeda, M. (1958). *Kiseichugaku zasshi* **7** (3), 281–282.*
Katsurada, F. (1898). *Tokyo igakkai zasshi* **12** (14), 621–632.*
Katsurada, F. (1922). *Nisshin Igaku*; Suppl. for 1922, pp. 1–26.*
Katsuta, K., Sasakawa, T., Hasegawa, K., Watanabe, G., Fukuchi, K., Chosogabe, K., Suzuki, S., and Otsuru, M. (1960). *Kiseichu gaku zasshi* **9** (4), 410–411.*
Kawai, T. (1937). *Taiwan igakkai zasshi* **36** (5), 927–934. (In Japanese with English summary.)
Kawai, T., and Yumoto, Y. (1935). *Taiwan igakkai zasshi* **35** (4), 880–887. (In Japanese with English summary.)
Kawai, T., and Yumoto, Y. (1936). *Taiwan igakkai zasshi* **36** (5), 923–934.*
Kawana, H. (1936). *J. Shanghai Sci. Inst.* Sect. IV, Vol. II. Sep. P. No. 2, 75–83.
Kim, D. C., and Kuntz, R. E. (1964). *Chin. med. J.* Republic of China, 11–47; Report of N.I.H. **1** (1), 167–180.
Kim, T. C. (1959). *J. Korean Parasit. Soc.*, 67–68.
Kitamura, K. (1916). *Jikken iho* **2** (16). Cited from Yumoto (1936a).

*In Japanese.

Kobayashi, H. (1912). *Saikingaku zasshi* (202), 1–66.*
Kobayashi, H. (1915). *Zentbl. Bakt. Parasitkde.* Orig. **75** (4), 299–318.
Kobayashi, H. (1922). *Nisshin igaku*, Suppl. 1–56.*
Kobayashi, H. (1923). *Chosen igakkai zasshi* **42**, 80–87.*
Kobayashi, H. (1924). *Keijo Isen Kiyo. Seoul*, 10 pp.
Kobayashi, H. (1928). *Acta medicin. Keijo* **11** (2), 109–124.
Koenigstein, R. P. (1949). *Trans. R. Soc. Trop. Med. Hyg.* **42**, 503–506.
Komiya, Y. (1935). *J. Shanghai. Sci. Inst.* Sect. 4, **2**, 61–73.
Komiya, Y. (1965). *In* "Progress of Medical Parasitology in Japan" (K. Morishita, Y. Komiya and H. Matsubayashi, eds.), Vol. 2. Megro Kiseichu Kan, Tokyo. (In press.)
Komiya, Y., and Kawana-Tajimi, T. (1953). *Jap. J. Med. Sci. Biol.* **6** (6), 571–575.
Komiya, Y., and Kondo, S. (1951). *Jap. med. J.* **4** (3), 157–161.
Komiya, Y., and Murase, K. (1944). *Shanghai shizen kagaku kenkyujo iho* **14** (6), 419–434.*
Komiya, Y., and Tajimi, T. (1940). *J. Shanghai Sci. Inst.* Sect. 4, **5**, 91–106.
Komiya, Y., and Tajimi, T. (1941). *J. Shanghai Sci. Inst.* N.S. **1**, 69–106.
Komiya, Y., and Sato, K. (1955). *Koshu eisei* **17** (1), 50–53.*
Komiya, Y., and Shimizu, S. (1965). *Kiseichugaku zasshi* **14** (4). (In press.)
Komiya, Y., and Suzuki, N. (1964). *In* "Progress of Medical Parasitology in Japan" (K. Morishita, Y. Komiya and H. Matsubayashi, eds.), Vol. 1, pp. 551–645. Meguro Parasitological Museum, Tokyo.
Komiya, Y., Suzuki, N., Kumada, M., Shiga, M., and Obi, E. (1957). *Nippon koshu-eisei zasshi* **4** (4), 200–202.*
Kubo, M., and Makino, M. (1941). *Nippon kiseichu gakkai kiji* **13**, 56–58.*
Lee, S. H. (1960). *J. Korean Parasit. Soc.* **1** (1), 68. (In Korean with English summary.)
Léger, A. (1910). Thèse, Bordeaux, 74 pp.
Leuckart, R. (1876). "Die Parasiten des Menschen", Bd. II, 822 pp. 1901. Leipzig.
Li, L. F. (1958). *Zhonghua yixue zazhi* **44** (10), 988–989. (In Chinese.)
Li, P. C., Li, D. H., and Wan, W. L. (1958). *Zhonghua chisangzonping chuasienping zasshi* **1** (3), 139–144.
Looss, A. (1907). *Ann. trop. Med. Parasit.* **1**, 123–152.
Ma, H. C., Yeh, Y. C., Feng, Y. S., Ts'ao, C. C., and Li, C. C. (1964). *Chin. med. J.* **83**, 812–818.
McConnel, J. F. P. (1875). *Lancet* **2**, 271–274.
McConnel, J. F. P. (1878). *Lancet* **1**, 406.
Maekawa, K., and Fukase, T. (1922). *Okayama igakkai zasshi* (385), 96–98.*
Maki, T. (1952). *Nippon rynsho geka zasshi* **13** (2), 33–45.*
Masuyama, T., Goto, J., Sato, K., Uchida, K., Kushida, A., and Hiramatsu, S. (1956). *Aichiken eisei kenkyujo hokoku* **7**, 45–46.*
Mathis, C., and Léger, M. (1911). "Recherches de parasitologie et pathologie humaines et animals au Tonkin", pp. 172–187. Paris. Cited from Faust and Khaw (1927).
Miyagawa, Y. (1913). *Zentbl. Bakt.* Orig. **69**, 132–142.
Miyagawa, Y. (1923). *Jikken iho* **9** (104), 1201–1207.*
Miyagawa, Y., and Shimizu, S. (1941). *Chiryo oyobi shoho* **22** (6), 735–736.*
Miyagawa, Y., and Shimizu, S. (1942). *Chiryo oyobi shinryo* **23** (1), 12–17.*
Miyagawa, M., Tsuda, H., and Nakase, M. (1957). *Kiseichugaku zasshi* **6** (3, 4), 284–285.*

*In Japanese.

Miyake, H. (1929). *Igaku chuo zasshi* **34**, 459–460.*
Mori, H. (1957). *Gifu daigaku kiyo* **5** (6), 601–603.*
Morishita, T., Hori, H., and Kani, S. (1956). *Nippon koshu eisei zasshi* **3** (11), 475.*
Mukoyama, T. (1921). *Nippon byori gakkai shi* **11**, 443–445.*
Muto, M. (1918). *Nippon byori gakkai shi* **8**, 228–230.*
Muto, M. (1919). *Iji shimbun* (1025), 769–788.*
Muto, M. (1920a). *Nippon byori gakkai shi* **10**, 351–365.*
Muto, M. (1920b). *Tokyo ijishinshi* (2188), 1–10.*
Muto, S. (1938). *Taiwan igakkai zasshi* **37** (10), 1537–1539.*
Nagamoto, T. (1958). *Kurume igakkai zasshi* **21** (5), 1167–1172. (In Japanese with English summary.)
Nagano, K. (1927a). *Okayama igakkai zasshi* (444), 124–132; (452), 1313–1314. (In Japanese with English summary.)
Nagano, K. (1928). *Tokyo iji shinshi* (2563), 547–558.*
Nagano, K. (1929). *Nippon kiseichu gakkai kiji* **1**, 20–21.*
Nagano, K. (1951). *Saishin kiseichu byo gaku*, No. 4, 1–43. Igaku Shoin, Tokyo.*
Nagano, K. (1960). *Nippon kiseichu gakkai higashi nippon shibu taikai kiji* **20**, 20.*
Nagano, K. (1964). *In* "Progress of Medical Parasitology in Japan" (K. Morishita, Y. Komiya and H. Matsubayashi, eds.), Vol. 1, pp. 725–753. Meguro Parasitological Museum, Tokyo.
Nakamoto, T. (1958). *Kurume igakkai zasshi* **21** (5), 1167–1171.*
Nakayama, H. (1910). *Tokyo igakkai zasshi* **24** (12), 1–51.*
Nakayama, H. (1912). *Tokyo igakkai zasshi* **26** (2), 1–13; (3), 18–65; (4), 10–48.*
Nishigishi, S. (1924). *Chugai iji shimpo* (1061), 771–781; (1962) 870–878.*
Nishimoto, M. (1958). *Shikoku igakkai zasshi* **12** (4), 580–595. (In Japanese with English summary.)
Ohoi, T. (1915). *Taiwan igakkai zasshi* (154), 816–825.*
Ohoi, T. (1919). *Taiwan igakkai zasshi* (195/196), 107–117.*
Okabe, K., Nagamoto, T., Oba, N., Ikuyama, T., and Shigematsu, N. (1959). *Kurume igakkai zasshi* **22** (4), 1425–1429. (In Japanese with English summary.)
Oshima, T., Kagei, N., Kihata, M., Fujino, N., Noguchi, H., and Fujioka, K. (1965). *Kiseichugaku zasshi* **14** (2), 195–203. (In Japanese with English summary.)
Ozaki, H. (1960). *Hirochima daigaku kaibogaku kyoshitsu daiichi koza gyoseki shu.* (7), 27–36.*
Plotnikov, N. N., and Sinovich, L. I. (1964). *Med. Parasit. Parasit. Dis.* (3), 301–302. (In Russian with English summary.)
Ritchie, L. S. (1948). *Bull. U.S. Army med. Dep.* **8**, 326.
Ryoji, S. (1922). *Okayama igakkai zasshi* (384), 1–12.*
Ryoji, S. (1927a). *Okayama igakkai zasshi* **39** (453), 1657–1698. (In Japanese with German summary.)
Ryoji, S. (1927b). *Okayama igakkai zasshi* **39** (454), 1809–1825. (In Japanese with German summary.)
Saito, S., and Hori, M. (1961). *Kiseichu gaku zasshi* **10** (4), 503.*
Saito, S., and Hori, M. (1962). *Kiseichugaku zasshi* **11** (4), 272–273.*
Saito, S., and Hori, M. (1963). *Kiseichugaku zasshi* **12** (4), 104.*
Saito, S., and Hori, M. (1964). *Kiseichugaku zasshi* **13** (4), 297–298.*
Sakai, K. (1953). *Kyoto furitsu ikadaigaku zasshi* **56** (3), 409–418. (In Japanese with English summary.)
Samback, E., and Baujean, R. (1913). *Bull. Soc. Med.-Chir. Indo-Chine* **4**, 425–429.

*In Japanese.

Shattuck, G. C. (1923). *Am. J. trop. Med.* **3**, 475–494.
Shattuck, G. C. (1924). *Am. J. trop. Med.* **4**, 507–518.
Shimazono, I., and Hasui, N. (1916). *Okayana igakki zasshi* (314), 202–2410.*
Shimizu, M., and Kawata, T. (1937). *Nippon koshu hoken kyokai zasshi* (385), 1–12.*
Shin, D. S. (1961). *J. Korean Parasit. Soc.* **1**, 80–81. (In Korean.)
Shin, D. S. (1964). *Korean J. Parasit.* **2** (1), 1–13. (In Korean with English summary.)
Shirai, M. (1926). *Jikken igaku zasshi* **10**, 37–87.*
Strauss, W. G. (1962). *Am. J. trop. Med. Hyg.* **11**, 625–630.
Sudun, E. H., Walton, B. C., Buck, A. A., and Lel, B. K. (1959). *J. Parasit.* **45** (2), 129–134.
Sugimura, S., Nakada, H., Obata, Y., and Machii, A. (1957a). *Konnichi no rynsho* **2** (2), 34–36.*
Sugimura, S., Nakada, H., Machii, A., and Obata, U. (1957b). *Kiseichugaku zasshi* **7** (3), 266–268.*
Suzuki, M., Kinoshita, T., Inatomi, S., and Tawara, J. (1950). *Okayama igakkai zasshi* **62** (3), 125–128.*
Suzuki, N. (1955). *Kiseichugaku zasshi* **4** (4), 355–358. (In Japanese with English summary.)
Suzuki, N., Komiya, Y., Kumaka, M., Arai, K., and Kawashima, K. (1957). *Kiseichugaku zasshi* **6** (2), 203–207. (In Japanese with English summary.)
Swartzwelder, J. C., Frye, M. W., Muhleisen, J. P., Miller, J. H., Lambert, R., Chavarrina, A. P., Abadie, S. H., Antony, O., and Sappenfield, R. W. (1957). *J. Am. med. Ass.* **165**, 2063–2067.
T'ang, C. C., Lin, Y. K., Wang, P. C., Ch'en, P. H., T'ang, C. T., Ch'en, T. S., Lin, C. H., Huang, C. K., Ch'en, C. C., and Ch'en, S. H. (1963). *Chin. med. J.* **82** (9), 545–652.
Tominaga, K. (1942b). *Osaka koto igaku semmon gakko zasshi* **9** (4), 467–476.*
Tsuda, H. (1958). *Nippon Naika gakkai zasshi* **46**, 1477.*
Ujiie, N. (1936). *Taiwan igakkai zasshi* **35** (8), 1862–1896.*
Wada, K., Omura, M., and Kono, Y. (1958). *Sogo rinsho* **7**, 843.*
Walton, B. C., and Chyu, I. (1959). *Bull. Wld Hlth Org.* **21**, 721–726.
Wang, K., Sun, C. O., and Pan, K. (1958). *Chonghua chisangzonping chuasienping zashi* **1** (3), 145–146.*
Watanabe, H. (1942). *Shanghai shizen kagaku kenkyujo iho* **12** (4), 289–294. (In Japanese with English summary.)
Weng, H. C., Chung, H. L., Ho, L. Y., and Tsung, T. C. (1960). *Chin. med. J.* **80**, 441–445.
Wykoff, D. E. (1958a). *Expl. Parasit.* **8** (1), 51–57.
Wykoff, D. E. (1958b). *J. Parasit.* **44** (5), 461–466.
Wykoff, D. E. (1959). *J. Parasit.* **45** (1), 91–94.
Wykoff, D. E., and Lepes, T. J. (1957). *Am. J. trop. Med. Hyg.* **6** (6), 1061–1065.
Yamagata, S. (1962). *Nakayama shoten. Tokyo* **1**, 134–137; 146–147.*
Yamagata, S., and Yaegashi, A. (1964). *In* "Progress of Medical Parasitology in Japan" (K. Morishita, Y. Komiya and H. Matsubayashi, eds.), Vol. 1, pp. 663–721. Meguro Parasitological Museum, Tokyo.
Yamagata, S., Maekawa, K., Ono, T., Sakamoto, T., and Takeuchi, M. (1952). *Nippon shokaki byo gakkai zasshi* **49** (12), 1068–1072; *Rinsho* **5** (112), 1068–1072.*
Yamaguchi, T., and Mineda, H. (1960). *Jap. J. Parasit.* **9**, 409–410.*

*In Japanese.

Yamaguchi, T., Uehara, K., Shinoto, M., and Mineta, H. (1961a). *Naika no ryoiki* **9** (6), 503–506.*

Yamaguchi, T., Uehara, K., Shinoto, M., and Mineta, H. (1961b). *Naika no ryoiki* **9** (7), 534–539.*

Yamaguchi, T., Uehara, K., Shinoto, M., Takachi, K., Horie, N., Mineda, H., Fukunaga, M., Kunishige, Al, and Yanagawa, H. (1962). *Tokushima J. exp. Med.* **8** (4), 307–334.*

Yamaguti, S. (1935). *Z. Parasit.* **8** (2), 183–187.

Yanagisawa, R., Nishi, S., and Nakano, B. (1956). *Kiseichu gaku zasshi* **5** (2), 167.*

Yoshida, T. (1931). *Okayama igakkai zasshi* **43** (4), 920–934. (In Japanese with German summary.)

Young, T. (1930). *Jikken igaku zasshi* **14** (5), 505–537.*

Yuda, K. (1955–61). *Miyagi eisei kenkyujo hokoku* **30**, 57–60, 61–64; **31**, 47–51, 52–55; **32**, 57–60, 61–64, 65–68; **33**, 6–10; **34**, 11–16; **35**, 23–28; **36**, 17–20, 21–24; **37**, 137–142; **39**, 26–32.*

Yumoto, Y. (1934). *Taiwan igakkai zasshi* **33** (12), 1851–1852.*

Yumoto, Y. (1936a). *Taiwan igakkai zasshi* **35** (8), 1836–1846. (In Japanese with English summary.)

Yumoto, Y. (1936b). *Taiwan igakkai zasshi* **35** (8), 1908.*

*In Japanese.

Embryogenesis in Cestodes

Department of Parasitology, Polish Academy of Sciences,
Warsaw, Pasteura, Poland

I. INTRODUCTION

Perhaps because of its great technical difficulties, the embryology of Cestoda has been somewhat neglected. This review intends to cover the available data on cestode gametogenesis and embryonic development up to the formation of the oncosphere. As most of the data deal with cyclophyllidean and pseudophyllidean cestodes, the embryogenesis of the groups is chiefly discussed. In previous reviews, the embryology of these groups has been regarded separately. Thus, it is somewhat surprising to find that an analysis of the available data has revealed a common basic pattern of embryogenesis in pseudophyllideans and cyclophyllideans, which represent the main groups in Cestoda. Although the embryology of other cestode groups has not been studied, as yet, it can be speculated that the outline of development presented in this paper may prove to be common for all cestodes, and probably also for trematodes.

II. GAMETOGENESIS

A. SPERMATOGENESIS

1. *General Account*

Spermatogenesis in cestodes has been studied in only a few species. The first detailed studies were those of Child (1907) and Young (1913). These authors were mainly interested in whether mitosis or amitosis took place during spermatogenesis, but found it difficult to solve because at this time haematoxylin was used chiefly for staining chromosomes. The introduction of modern histochemical methods (and the Feulgen technique in particular) permitted detailed investigations to be made. Such investigations were carried out on one pseudophyllidean *Triaenophorus lucii* by Rybicka (1962a) and on four cyclophyllideans, *Baerietta diana* and *Distoichometra kozloffi*, by Douglas (1957, 1963), *Dipylidium caninum* by Rybicka (1962b, 1964a) and *Taeniarhynchus saginatus* by Pashchenko (1961). The general pattern of spermatogenesis (Fig. 1) is similar in all cestodes studied, resembles that of Trematoda,

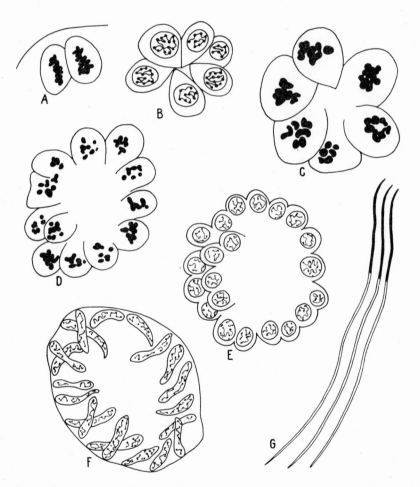

FIG. 1. Spermatogenesis in *Triaenophorus lucii*. A, Mitosis of spermatogonia; B, quaternary spermatogonia; C, primary spermatocytes in metaphase of meiosis; D, secondary spermatocytes in mitosis; E, spermatids; F, elongation of spermatid nuclei; G, sperm. (After Rybicka, 1962a.)

and can be summarized as follows. Primary spermatogonia arising in a young testis divide, each producing two secondary spermatogonia. Further divisions occur simultaneously, resulting in a cluster of four tertiary spermatogonia, then eight quaternary spermatogonia, subsequently sixteen primary spermatocytes are formed. These enlarge, their nuclei move to the periphery and the cluster of cells takes on the form of a rosette. After the first meiotic division, a cluster of thirty-two secondary spermatocytes is formed. The nuclei of these are smaller and the cell membranes near the centre of the rosette become indistinct as the displacement of the nuclei toward the periphery continues. The second maturation division results in sixty-four spermatids whose nuclei subsequently elongate and differentiate into spermatozoa. These are released, leaving behind a residual cytoplasmic mass in the testis as a large, deeply stained body. In the mature testis all the different phases of spermatogenesis can be seen.

The presence of mitotic division in spermatogonia is still confused. Rybicka (1962a, b) and Douglas (1963) have pointed out how difficult it is to find mitotic phases, an effect which may be due to periodicity of mitotic activity. This may explain why, in the original studies, spermatogonial division was interpreted as amitosis (Child, 1907) or "chromidial extrusions" (Young, 1913). Recently Pashchenko (1961) returned to Child's interpretation, claiming that in *Taeniarhynchus saginatus* spermatogonia divide both by mitosis and amitosis. However, even from a theoretical point of view, the simultaneous occurrence of mitosis and amitosis in the same type of cell seems rather improbable, particularly in cestode spermatogenesis where the developmental pattern as well as number of cells formed is so precise.

The meiosis of the first maturation division and the formation of large bivalents were described in all the species studied. This is followed by the second maturation division without the interphase condition (Douglas, 1963).

As mentioned above, the general pattern of spermatogenesis in cestodes resembles that of trematodes. However, in the former sixty-four spermatozoa are formed in one cluster, whereas thirty-two are typical for the latter. This indicates that in Cestoda one more division of spermatogonia takes place. This comparison is of some interest where the pseudophyllideans are concerned, as this group resembles in structure of the genitalia and in the system of early embryonic development the Trematoda rather than the Cyclophyllidea. The results obtained by Rybicka (1962a) in *Triaenophorus lucii* suggest, however, the uniformity of pattern of spermatogenesis in all Cestoda.

2. *Spermatozoon Structure*

Spermatogenesis has been studied in detail in two cestode species only (*Distoichometra kozloffi* and *Baerietta diana*; see Douglas, 1963) (Fig. 2). In the former, after the second maturation division, a centriole is formed which elongates and divides. A third centriole appears at the centrifugal pole of the spermatid cytoplasm. Then a bifurcated fibril connecting the centrioles develops and this divides into two along its entire length. One fibril becomes a straight axoneme (Fig. 2A). By this time the nucleus has elongated considerably (Fig. 2B). The sperm structure of *B. diana* (Fig. 2K) differs slightly

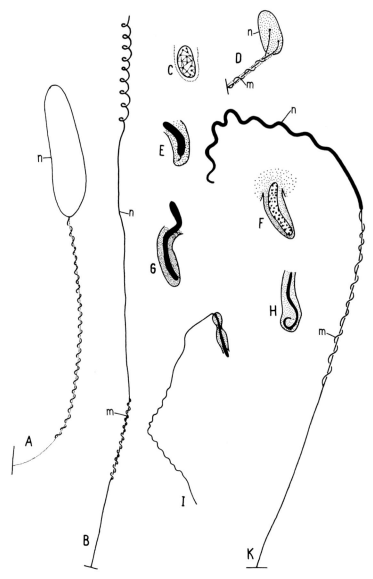

FIG. 2. Spermiogenesis in *Distoichometra kozloffi* (A, B) and in *Baerietta diana* (C–K). A, An advanced spermatid illustrating the elongating nucleus, middle piece and a portion of the tail piece. × 33000. B, Spermatozoon. × 33000. C, A spermatid nucleus which has begun to elongate. × 2800. D, A slightly later stage of nuclear elongation, the centrioles and middle piece are illustrated. × 3750. E–H, Further stages of nuclear elongation. × 2800. I, The nucleus has ruptured from its cytoplasmic pedicle and extends beyond it. × 2800. K, A mature spermatozoon; the nucleus is loosely coiled and the middle piece is much better defined than in *D. kozloffi* (compare B). × 3750. *m*, Middle piece; *n*, nucleus. (After Douglas, 1963.)

from that of *D. kozloffi*, although both resemble the modified sperm type described by Franzen (1956) in his classification of invertebrate sperm types. This type is characterized by the presence of an elongated middle piece in contrast to the short one with distinct mitochondrial spheres occurring in the primitive sperm; the head of a modified type of sperm is elongated and its spiralization can be regarded as a further step in modification. The occurrence of this modified type of sperm in parasites seems to confirm Franzen's conclusions that it occurs in animals with an aberrant biology and fertilization.

The first study on the ultrastructure of cestode sperm flagellum has been carried out by Gresson (1962) in *Proteocephalus pollanicola*. The flagellum consists of an axial filament with two central fibrils and nine double peripheral fibrils. A cross-section of a flagellum of late spermatids frequently may show two, three or four axial filaments. As the tails of the ripe spermatozoa possess a single filament, it was concluded by Gresson that at a certain stage of spermatogenesis the axial filament becomes coiled or twisted within the external sheath of the tail.

More details of ultrastructure in spermatogenesis were recently described by Rosario (1964) in *Hymenolepis nana* and *H. diminuta*. Unfortunately, the electron microscope pictures produced by this writer have not been compared with recent studies on cestodes and his interpretation of the early phases of spermatogenesis needs some revision. For example, in Fig. 3, which represents various phases of spermatogenesis, the cells with relatively large nuclei (n_1) visible at the upper left side are similar to spermatogonia. A cluster of very large cells (upper right side), interpreted as spermatogonia by Rosario, resembles typical primary spermatocytes in the first maturation division. The cell group in the centre with relatively small nuclei (n_2) placed peripherally in a cytoplasmic cluster is clearly the spermatids. Mitochondria (m) and a thread-like structure interpreted by Rosario as endoplasmic reticulum (er) can be seen readily. At the bottom left early spermatogenesis is visible. Here Rosario (1964) observed the "arching membrane-bound clefts" (1–4) in the cytoplasm which were found in close relation to nuclei and also stages of cleft elongation leading to the formation of a membraneous arch; these arching structures finally enclose the nuclei.

The spermatozoon structure is illustrated in Fig. 4A, B. It is characterized by three main features: (a) a cylindrical body, the plasma membrane of which is covered by striations; (b) an elongate nucleus, variable in position inside the body of the sperm; and (c) a flagellum, parallel to the longitudinal axis of the body and nucleus. The cross-section of the flagellum reveals the typical array of nine peripheral and two central filaments (Fig. 4B). However, the two central filaments do not conform to the arrangement observed in most other cells with cilia and flagella. One of the central filaments is enclosed by the other and in longitudinal section the outer filament seems to be wound in a helix around the central one (Fig. 4A).

Quite different results have been recently obtained by Bonsdorff and Telkkä (1965) in their studies on the ultrastructure of the sperm of *Diphyllobothrium latum*. The sperm nucleus in this species is surrounded by two complexes of axial filaments which line symmetrically the part of the sheath between these

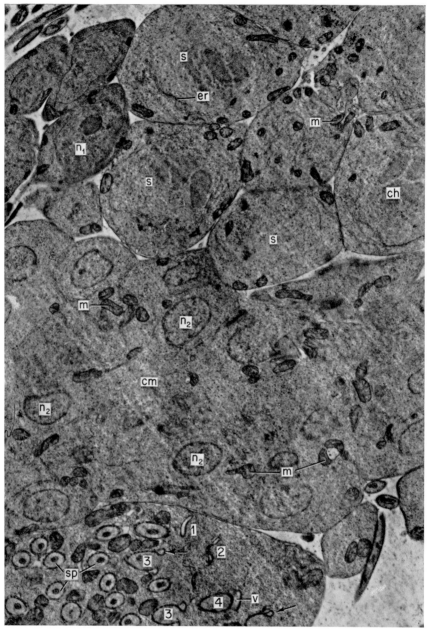

FIG. 3. An electron micrograph through part of the testis of *Hymenolepis nana*. *ch*, Bivalent chromosomes; *cm*, cytoplasmic mass of a cluster of spermatids; *er*, endoplasmic reticulum; *m*, mitochondria; n_1, nuclei of spermatogonia; n_2, nuclei of spermatids; *s*, primary spermatocytes in meiosis; *sp*, sperm formation; *v*, vacuole. 1–4, Process of spermiogenesis; arrows indicate the bulbous swellings and the vacuole (*v*) remaining in the cytoplasm when the spermatozoon is formed. × 8000. (After Rosario, 1964; explanation according to present author.)

complexes (Fig. 5). The sperm tail (Fig. 6) contains the same double axial filaments, but at its tip only one has been found. The axial filament complex in
D. latum corresponds to the nine-plus-one pattern.

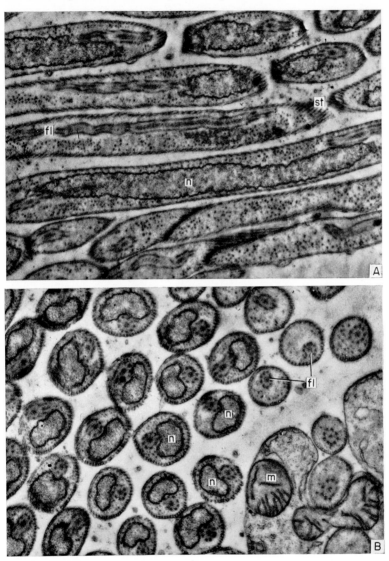

F_IG. 4. Spermatozoa in longitudinal (A) and cross sections (B). *fl,* Flagellum; *m,* mitochondria; *n,* nucleus; *st,* striations in the plasma membrane. A, × 20000; B, × 25000.
(After Rosario, 1964.)

The observations on sperm ultrastructure in Cestoda are of particular
interest when compared with some results in Trematoda. Hendelberg (1962)

described some interesting aspects of spermatogenesis in *Fasciola* and *Dicrocoelium*. According to him, in the spermatid, two flagellum-like structures and a "middle snook" are formed. These three elements together form the common

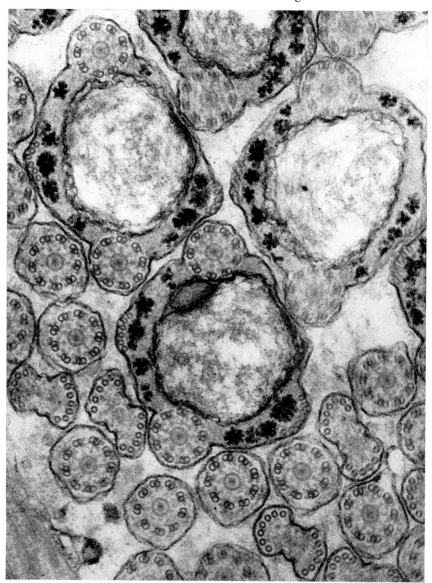

FIG. 5. Cross-section at the nucleus end of the spermatozoon of *Diphyllobothrium latum*. A group of sperm tails have been sectioned transversely at the level where the nucleus is largest. Beside the nuclei star-shaped glycogen aggregates. The sheath without the axial filament complex represents the "middle snook". × 87000. (After Bonsdorff and Telkkä, 1965.)

sheath of spermatid along which the nucleus migrates to the distal end. Bonsdorff and Telkkä (1965) suppose that the mode of sperm formation in *D. latum* is the same as described by Hendelberg. The single filaments lining the sheath represent the "middle snook", their role possibly being to conduct the migrating nucleus. The variable position of sperm nucleus observed by Rosario (1964) also suggests that it moves inside the sperm of *Hymenolepis*.

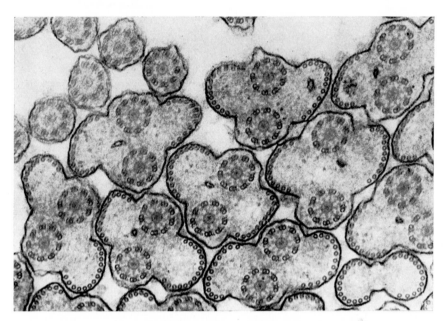

FIG. 6. Cross-section of the flagellum at different levels. Both paired and unpaired axial filament complexes are seen. The tops of the nuclei can be seen in most of the tails. × 70000. (After Bonsdorff and Telkkä, 1965.)

The presence of a double axial filament complex is interesting phylogenetically. Hendelberg (1962) pointed out that, in some Trematoda, biflagellate spermatozoa have been observed (Retzius, 1909; Dhingra, 1954; Nez and Short, 1957). His own observation on the uniting of paired filaments is confirmed by electron microscope studies (Gresson and Perry, 1961; Shapiro *et al.*, 1961) revealing double axial filament in the trematode sperm tail. Thus Hendelberg (1962) concluded that "the occurrence of biflagellate spermatozoa within different systematic groups of Digenea suggests that we are concerned with an original feature of Digenea. This assumption is extended by a comparison among Turbellaria."

The presence of one axial filament in *Hymenolepis* (see Rosario, 1964) and a double in *Diphyllobothrium* (see Bonsdorff and Telkkä, 1965) seems to be the most striking difference in sperm structure between these species. Although two observations are too few for any generalization, it is worth noting that in this aspect a pseudophyllidean species resembles trematodes rather than cyclophyllideans.

Gresson (1965) interpreted the sperm ultrastructure differently. According to him the micrograph showing two sections of an axial filament within a common sheath may be due to the coiling of a single axial filament like that described in *Proteocephalus* by Gresson (1962). However, until further studies clarify the matter it is useful to keep in mind all possible interpretations.

3. Cytochemical Observations

Cytochemical observations on spermatogenesis are too fragmentary to be generalized.

The presence of ribonucleic acid (RNA) in cells dividing during spermatogenesis has been mentioned by a few writers (Rybicka, 1962b; Cheng and Jacknick, 1964). Perhaps the presence of this material is so obvious in the cytoplasm of developing cells that some workers do not even mention it. The residual cytoplasm remaining in the testis after sperm release also stains with pyronin (Rybicka, 1962a, b, 1964a). Brachet (1959) affirmed that RNA is not always metabolically active. The testes of mammals often contain numerous extracellular basophilic bodies, corresponding to the extrusion of cytoplasmic RNA during spermatogenesis. These "residual bodies" show little or no activity in amino-acid incorporation. No RNA was detected in the sperm of *Triaenophorus lucii* and *Dipylidium caninum* by Rybicka (1964a, b), although this substance was found by Cheng and Jacknick (1964) in the sperm of *Hymenolepis diminuta* (not confirmed by Rybicka, unpublished).

A conspicuous amount of deoxyribonucleic acid (DNA) has often been detected in cestode sperm. As the cytoplasmic region is difficult to see by means of the light microscope, many workers have maintained that cestode and trematode sperms consist of nuclear material only. The elongated nucleus, as described by Douglas (1963), partly explains such an interpretation. In contrast, the pictures presented by Rosario (1964) and those of Hendelberg (1962) for trematodes show a relatively short nucleus in comparison with the length of the sperm. As different species studied by various methods are being considered here, it is difficult to say which differences are due to specific features and which to the methods of study.

The glycogen content differs in sperm of various species. Glycogen has not been found in early spermatogenesis, but was detected in sperms of *H. diminuta* by Hedrick and Daugherty (1957) and Cheng and Dyckman (1964), in *Raillietina cesticillus* by Hedrick and Daugherty (1957) as well as in *Penetrocephalus ganapatii* by Hanumantha-Rao (1960a) and in *Callibothrium coronatum* by Ortner-Schönbach (1913). In the last-named species, glycogen granules were observed among the sperms passing down the sperm ducts. In the sperm of *Diphyllobothrium latum* (Fig. 5) the star-shaped aggregates of glycogen granules beside the nucleus have been revealed by Bonsdorff and Telkkä (1965) in lead-stained sections studied by electron microscopy. The sperms of *Anoplocephala perfoliata* studied by Ortner-Schönback (1913), and of *Triaenophorus lucii*, *D. caninum* and *Moniezia expansa* examined by Rybicka (respectively 1962a, b, 1964b) had no glycogen. In *Moniezia* sperms observed in the vas deferens stained red with toluidine blue and this colour changed to green in the recepta-culum seminis.

Hedrick (1958) found a conspicuous deposit of phospholipids in testes of *H. diminuta*.

B. OOGENESIS AND FERTILIZATION

1. *General Account*

Only the onset of oogenesis takes place in the ovary; the oogonia appear early in the primordium of the ovary and multiply by mitotic divisions. After some divisions, primary oocytes are formed which grow rapidly and leave the ovary before the first division of maturation.

The detailed cytological study on oogenesis in cestodes was carried out by Douglas (1963) on *Baerietta diana*. This author concluded that the prophase precedes the pachytene stage in the ovary at which time the nuclei appear to be in the interphase.

The oocyte leaves the ovary and enters the oviduct, where it is surrounded by sperms. In a pseudophyllidean species *Archigetes appendiculatus* Moto-mura (1929) actually observed sperms penetrating the oocyte while it was in the oviduct. After passing through the ootype, the oocyte arrives in the uterine ducts, where thread-like or spirally coiled sperms have been observed on its surface surrounded by vitelline cells and the capsule. In *Triaenophorus lucii* (Rybicka, unpublished observations) a spirally coiled spermatozoon was found in the cytoplasm of an oocyte while it was in the uterine duct. In both observations the sperm had contracted after entering the uterus, forming an oval mass of chromatin.

In Cyclophyllidea the first contact between the oocyte and the sperm also takes place in oviduct as observed by Rybicka (1964a) in *Dipylidium caninum*. Although sperm penetration was not observed in this species it seems possible that this occurs immediately after first contact. However, Douglas (1963) observed fertilization in *Baerietta diana* in the uterus: the penetrating sperma-tozoon nucleus was usually seen to encircle a cytoplasmic knob on the ovum. The exact method by which the sperm penetrated the oocyte could not be determined, but Douglas suggested that the sperm nucleus constricts itself beneath the plasma membrane rather than following the anterior end through a single point of entry. Immediately after entering the oocyte, the sperm nucleus contracts until it eventually becomes an irregular mass of chromatin which remains in the cytoplasm while the egg matures. The sperm middle piece and tail remained outside the oocyte and were often seen adhering to the surface of it (Douglas, 1963).

In other observations, the maturation division of the oocyte appears to occur immediately after it enters the uterus (Richards, 1909; Motomura, 1929; Rybicka, 1964a, b). There are two subsequent maturation divisions in which two polar bodies are formed. The oocyte containing the sperm and the metaphase of maturation division are shown in Fig. 7A, B.

During oocyte maturation the sperm nucleus enlarges and then the ovum containing two pronuclei is formed. According to Douglas (1962, 1963), both pronuclei begin the first division of cleavage.

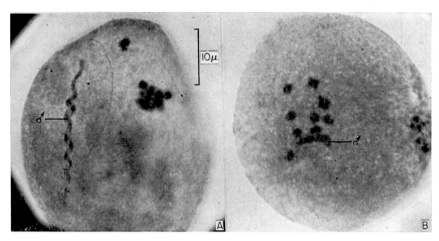

FIG. 7. The oocytes of *Raillietina* sp. A, Primary oocytes with sperm; B, metaphase. (Courtesy of Dr I. M. Sandeman.)

2. *Cytochemical Observations*

Cytochemical work shows that RNA is present in the cytoplasm and nucleolus of the oogonia and oocytes (Ogren, 1956a; Rybicka, 1964a, b). In *Dipylidium caninum* the most mature oocytes lost a part of their cytoplasmic RNA, which was observed in the ovary as irregular droplets (Rybicka, 1964a).

Numerous observations have confirmed the lack of glycogen in tapeworm oocytes (Ortner-Schönbach, 1913; Hedrick and Daugherty, 1957; Hanu-mantha-Rao, 1960a; Pavlova, 1963; Rybicka, 1964a, b; Cheng and Dyckman, 1964). A weak periodic acid–Schiff (PAS)-positive reaction was noticed in oocytes of *Diorchis ransomi* (Rybicka, 1960) which disappeared after they entered the uterus. Tests for fats (Hedrick, 1958; Pavlova, 1963) in the ovary have also given negative results. No accumulation of new materials has been observed in the oocytes after they have entered the uterus.

Many writers have remarked upon the characteristic "granular" structure of the oocyte and the ovum. This granular material is commonly regarded as a "yolky" substance accumulated in the oocyte. In species such as *Oochoristica symmetrica* and *Dipylidium caninum*. Ogren (1957a, b) and Rybicka (1964a), respectively, found this material to be dispersed in very small irregular granules. In other species—*Anoplocephala mamillana* (see St Remy, 1900), *Paricterotaenia porosa* (see Bona, 1957), *Hymenolepis nana* (see Ogren, 1955a), *Mesocestoides corti* (see Ogren, 1956a) and *Moniezia expansa* (see Rybicka, 1964b)—large discrete granules were clearly visible. In *Taenia serrata* (see Janicki, 1907), *Multiceps smythi* (see Johri, 1957) and *Dilepis undula* (see Ogren, 1962b) the granules accumulated in a single large yolk mass after the oocyte entered the uterus.

Unfortunately, very little is known about the chemical composition of this vitelline substance in tapeworms. Johri (1957) found acidophil proteins in the vitelline material in oocytes of *Multiceps smythi*. Pavlova (1963) noticed that the yolk granules of *Taeniarhynchus saginatus* resemble cytochemically the yolk lipids found in oocytes of other animals.

It is remarkable that no description has been given of yolk material in pseudophyllidean oocytes, and Pavlova (1963) stated that the oocytes of *Diphyllobothrium latum* are alecithal. In Pseudophyllidea most of the yolk reserve may be accumulated in the many vitelline cells attached to one oocyte. In Cyclophyllidea the nutritive role of the vitelline cells is greatly reduced and the nutritive function is probably carried out by the oocyte. Ogren (1953, 1957b) distinguished two types of oocytes by their yolk reserves, namely "conglomerate oocytes" containing vitelline particles in the cytoplasm, typical for Cyclophyllidea, and "granular oocytes" which appear to have fine granular material in the cytoplasm, typical for Pseudophyllidea and Proteocephalidae.

The vitelline material within the oocyte remains unchanged in the ovum when in the uterus, but is later divided between the macromeres formed during cleavage. This has been observed in species in which yolk reserves were clearly distinguishable (St Remy, 1900; Janicki, 1907; Spätlich, 1925; Bona, 1957; Rybicka, 1964b). However, Ogren (1956a) records the complete absence of a vitelline mass from the fertilized oocyte.

The subsequent fate of vitelline mass in the embryo will be discussed later.

III. Vitelline Cells and Capsule Formation

A. PSEUDOPHYLLIDEA

The vitelline cells of various pseudophyllidean species have uniform structure, being relatively large spherical cells containing numerous globules in their cytoplasm. In this group of tapeworms some vitelline cells associate with the fertilized oocyte, and after passing through the ootype the whole mass becomes enclosed by a thick capsule. For an account of the mechanism and chemistry of the formation of the operculate egg of the pseudophyllidean *Schistocephalus solidus*, see Smyth (1956). The mechanism is represented in Fig. 8. Globules of shell-forming materials are released from vitelline cells in the ootype and they coalesce to form the capsule which encloses the ovum and the vitelline cells which produced the secretion.

An earlier study of the operculate egg capsules of Trematoda indicates that they consist of a sclerotin or quinone-tanned protein formed from materials secreted by the vitellaria. The resemblance between the genitalia of trematodes and pseudophyllidean cestodes, and also the structure and behaviour of the eggs, suggests that the modes of shell formation in these groups are closely related.

The basic principle of sclerotization is the conversion of an o-diphenol into o-quinone by phenolase ($=$ polyphenol oxidase) which then reacts with free NH_2 groups on adjacent protein chains to give a highly cross-linked and stable brown protein called sclerotin (Reaction I):

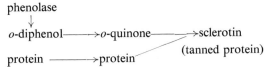

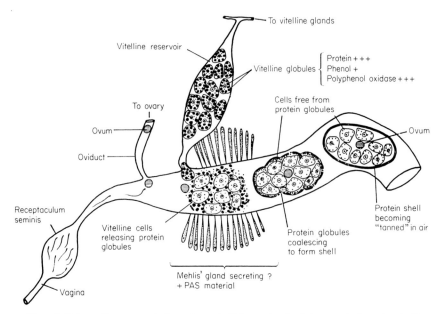

FIG. 8. Schematic representation of egg-shell formation in *Schistocephalus*. The vitelline cells pass from the vitelline glands into the reservoir and so to the uterus. Here, their contained globules (= shell globules = protein globules) are released and these become moulded together to form an egg-shell which surrounds an ovum and the vitelline cell remnants (serving now as nutriment). (After Smyth, 1956.)

Smyth (1956) has indicated the presence of sclerotin precursors (polyphenol oxidase, basic proteins and phenols) in the globules present in vitelline cells of *Schistocephalus solidus*. Whole worms cultured *in vitro* were tested by the catechol method (Smyth, 1954) for polyphenol oxidase. The distribution of this enzyme varied in a remarkable manner; in nearly mature proglottids it was concentrated in the ripening vitelline cells, but in gravid proglottids in the egg capsules within the uterus (Fig. 9).

A convenient test for proteins is the Mazia bromophenol blue method (Smyth, 1956). This has revealed the presence of basic proteins in the vitelline cells, as well as in the capsule. The protein within the vitelline globules is localized in granules and microscopic evidence suggests that this "granular" protein is embedded in a labile matrix. On release from the vitelline cells the labile phase appeared to be moulded into the shape of an egg, supported by the granular basic protein. As an egg passes up the uterus and so to the outside, the phenolic material becomes converted to a quinone, the protein becomes "tanned" and the hardening egg loses its affinity for protein stains.

In addition to the "shell" globules, small basic protein globules were found in vitelline cells which were stained by nuclear stains. These remained in vitelline cells after egg formation and were interpreted by Smyth (1956) as true yolk for the nourishment of the developing embryo.

Tests for phenols gave only weakly positive results in vitelline cells, as well as in the capsule.

The formation of the egg capsules in *Diphyllobothrium latum* was studied by Bogomolova and Pavlova (1961), who confirmed the results obtained by Smyth (1956) although some differences were found. As in *S. solidus* the globules observed in vitelline cells of *D. latum* were composed of granular basic proteins embedded in the labile matrix, but in the latter species the protein granules were released from the vitelline cells in the vitelline duct, before the cells passed into the ootype. The release of whole globules was not observed in *D. latum*. The labile matrix remained in the vitelline cell after the release of shell granules. RNA appeared in the matrix after a vitelline cell entered the uterus. Its synthesis was followed by a synthesis of basic proteins. These components were regarded as a nutritive store for the developing embryo. Bogomolova and Pavlova (1961) found glycogen also in vitelline cells in the vitellaria, as well as in the uterus, but tests for fats gave negative results.

The same was noticed by Ortner-Schönbach (1913) in *Callibothrium coronatum* and *Caryophyllaeus mutabilis*. In the former species, an increase of glycogen was noted after a vitelline cell entered the uterus. In both species glycogen was intracellularly dispersed within the cytoplasm in the form of granules, but in *C. mutabilis* it also accumulated in the nucleus.

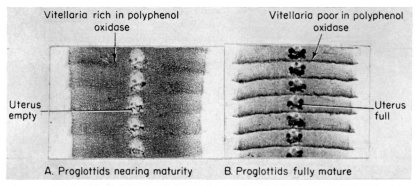

FIG. 9. Proglottids of *Schistocephalus solidus* showing distribution of polyphenol oxidase. A, After 34 h cultivation *in vitro*; proglottids are nearing maturity and the enzyme is concentrated in ripening vitelline cells. B, After 72 h cultivation *in vitro*; proglottids are mature and the enzyme is now concentrated in egg-shells in the uterus. (After Smyth, 1956.)

As in *S. solidus* the phenolic properties observed in vitelline cells of *D. latum* were relatively weak by comparison with those known in Trematoda. Bogomolova and Pavlova (1961) observed that the use of 33 % HNO_3 reduced the stain intensity in *Fasciola hepatica*, whereas in *D. latum* this remained unaltered. These writers concluded that the results indicate the presence of tyrosine in a phenolic compound in *F. hepatica*, and of histidine in *D. latum* and *S. solidus*.

Hanumantha-Rao (1960a) observed in *Penetrocephalus ganapatii* that the extrusion of globules from the vitelline cells occurs on entering the uterus after passage through the ootype, which matches the results of Smyth (1956) for *S. solidus*. The vitelline cells of *P. ganapatii* observed in the vitellarium and in the ootype were PAS-negative. After release of capsule-forming material, they turn PAS-positive—fast to saliva and α-amylase digestion. Hanumantha-Rao (1960a) suggested that vitelline cells are first of all vehicles for transport of capsule precursors and then, after release of capsule globules, are sites of synthesis of food reserves. These conclusions on the double role of vitelline cells agree generally with results obtained in *S. solidus* and *D. latum*, but specific differences should be pointed out. In *D. latum*, *C. coronatum* and *C. mutabilis*, glycogen is present in vitelline cells in the vitellarium and the uterus; the vitelline cells of *P. ganapatii*, on the other hand, lack glycogen while in the vitellarium, but synthesize non-glycogenous polysaccharides within the uterus.

The mode of formation and nature of the non-operculate capsule of some pseudophyllideans (e.g. Amphicotylidae) is not known, but in this group fewer vitelline cells are associated with one oocyte. In *Eubothrium*, the embryo develops and the capsule enlarges with the uterus (Schauinsland, 1886; Vik, 1963) (Fig. 10), which may indicate that the egg-shell is not formed of a stable quinone-tanned protein.

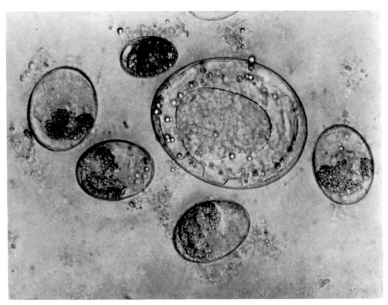

FIG. 10. Eggs of *Eubothrium salvelini* showing different stages of development within one worm. × 640. (After Vik, 1963.)

B. CYCLOPHYLLIDEA

The vitelline cells of Cyclophyllidea are very small by comparison with those of Pseudophyllidea. In most species a peculiarity of these cells is that the small nucleus, surrounded by a thin layer of compact cytoplasm, is placed peripherally on the large vesicle (Fig. 11A). Such type of vitelline cell has been observed in some Anoplocephalidae by Bischoff (1913) and Rybicka (1964b), some Taeniidae by Janicki (1907) and Johri (1957), *Dipylidium caninum* by Venard (1938) and Rybicka (1964a), *Mesocestoides corti* by Ogren (1956a), and *Oochoristica symmetrica* by Ogren (1957a). In the vesicle, accumulations of so-called "vitelline" material have been disclosed. In some cases there is one large mass, in others small irregular granules. Presumably these differences depended on the methods of fixation used by different workers. In other cyclophyllideans, e.g. *Dilepis undula* (see Ogren, 1959b), *Diorchis ransomi* (see Rybicka, 1960, 1961a) or *Drepanidotaenia lanceolata*, the vesicle was not observed in the vitelline cell. Its cytoplasm formed a relatively thick layer, containing the "vitelline" granules (Fig. 11B). In these instances the appearance of the vitelline cell changes after entering the uterus. The vesicle observed in the first group, as well as the cytoplasmic granules described in the second, are then lost and a nucleus surrounded by thin layer of compact cytoplasm remains in the uterus as the residue of a vitelline cell.

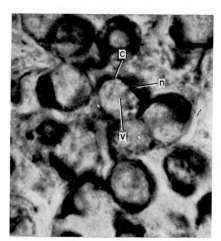 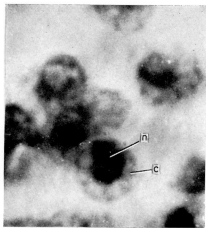

FIG. 11. Vitelline cells in Cyclophyllidea. A, *Dipylidium caninum*; B, *Drepanidotaenia lanceolata*. c, Cytoplasm; n, nucleus; v, vesicle. Toluidine blue. (A, After Rybicka, 1964a.)

Histochemical research shows that materials accumulated in the vitelline cells are used for the formation of a thin capsule surrounding the oocyte together with the remains of vitelline cell. In *Moniezia expansa* (see Rybicka, 1964b), the content of the vitelline vesicle showed strongly red metachromasia when stained with toluidine blue and observed in water. The metachromasia disappeared after passage through alcohol and in mounted slides the vesicles of vitelline cells remained green. Although such methods are not very specific, this type of metachromasia may indicate the presence of acid mucopolysaccharides (Pearse, 1953). The green stain of vitelline cells after toluidine blue was observed by Ogren (1956a) in *Mesocestoides corti*, by Ogren (1957a) in *Oochoristica symmetrica*, by Ogren (1959b) in *Dilepis undula* and by

Rybicka (unpublished observation) in *Echinococcus granulosus*. These results suggest that in all species mentioned above, as in *M. expansa*, according to Rybicka (1964b), acid mucopolysaccharides are present in vitelline cells. Ogren (1956a, 1957a) observed a red staining after PAS which also indicates the possible presence of mucopolysaccharides. Metachromasia in vitelline cells was also noticed by Bona (1957).

Some glycogen was found in vitelline cells of *P. porosa* by Bona (1957), *H. diminuta* by Hedrick and Daugherty (1957) and Cheng and Jacknick (1964), *Raillietina cesticillus* by Hedrick and Daugherty (1957), *Diorchis ransomi* by Rybicka (1960), *Taeniarhynchus saginatus* by Pavlova (1963) and *Dipylidium caninum* by Rybicka (1964a), but this compound was not found in *Taenia* sp. by Brault and Loeper (1904), *Multiceps smythi* by Johri (1957), *Anoplocephala perfoliata* by Ortner-Schönbach (1913) and *Moniezia expansa* by von Brand (1933), Wardle (1937), Yamao (1952) and Rybicka (1964b).

The vitelline cells of *Multiceps smythi* contain acidophil proteins indicated by the use of the full PAS technique (Johri, 1957). The presence of basic proteins in vitelline cells of *Dilepis undula* was also observed by Ogren (1959b) using bromophenol blue. Tests for fat gave negative results in vitelline cells of *M. smythi* (see Johri, 1957) and *T. saginatus* (see Pavlova, 1963). The lack of phospholipids was noticed in the vitellaria of *R. cesticillus* (see Hedrick, 1958). A comparison of these results indicates specific differences in the chemical content of vitelline cells, polysaccharide being the most common constituent.

Attempts to find sclerotin precursors in the vitelline cell similar to those found in pseudophyllideans have been unsuccessful (Johri, 1957).

As mentioned above, after entering the uterus the vitelline cell loses its vesicle and so discharges its reserve material, which can then be found in the thin membraneous capsule formed simultaneously around the embryo (Ogren, 1955a, 1956a, 1957a; Bona, 1957; Rybicka, 1964a, b).

The accumulation of glycogen in vitelline cells after the passage through the ootype was observed by Rybicka (1960) in *Diorchis ransomi*. In this species the cells of the vitellarium also contained a small amount of dispersed glycogen. In the uterus an apparently large agglomeration of glycogen granules was observed near the vitelline cell.

These results indicate that vitelline cells of Cyclophyllidea can play the same double role for the embryo as those of Pseudophyllidea; namely transport of materials for capsule formation and in some cases accumulation of nutritive reserves. However, a comparison of both groups indicates that the role of vitelline cells in embryogenesis is greatly reduced in Cyclophyllidea as compared with Pseudophyllidea, and this is due to the different method of development. The protective function of the capsule in pseudophyllideans is largely taken over by the mother organism in cyclophyllideans where only a thin membraneous capsule is formed. The same is true of the nutrition of the embryo. In Pseudophyllidea, a store of nutritive material must be retained in the egg, and this is accumulated as granules in numerous vitelline cells. In Cyclophyllidea, the nutritive function is transferred to the mother organism, and the nutritive role of the vitelline cells is reduced.

A recent study of *Moniezia expansa* by J. Hoy and J. A. Clegg (unpublished) suggests that the cyclophyllidean capsule is possibly a lipoprotein derived from Mehlis's gland (see Section IV, p. 126).

IV. MEHLIS'S GLAND

The function of Mehlis's gland has long been in question. It was originally believed to secrete the "egg-shell" and was sometimes called the "shell gland", but Leuckart (1886) concluded that the shell is formed from globules of material contained in the vitelline cells and this has been proved (see above).

Recent histochemical researches throw some light on the role of this gland. The well-known morphological uniformity of the gland in all cestodes and its resemblance to that of trematodes is confirmed by histochemical studies showing that the gland gives a strongly PAS-positive reaction in all the species studied (Trematoda: Smyth and Clegg, 1959; Hanumantha-Rao, 1959; Pseudophyllidea: Smyth, 1956; Pavlova, 1963; Hanumantha-Rao, 1960a, b; Cyclophyllidea: Johri, 1957; Hedrick and Daugherty, 1957; Rybicka, 1960, 1964a, b; Pavlova, 1963). It was shown (Smyth, 1956; Johri, 1957; Hedrick and Daugherty, 1957; Hanumantha-Rao, 1960a, b) that the secretion of Mehlis's gland is fast to amylase and hyaluronidase, and did not fall into any of the known PAS-positive groups (Smyth, 1956). With regard to the histochemical similarity of Mehlis's gland in Cestoda and Trematoda, Smyth and Clegg (1959) concluded that presumably the same kind of material is secreted in both groups. It is unlikely that the secretion is directly involved in capsule formation, because the capsules of cyclophyllideans are chemically different from those of pseudophyllideans and trematodes.

Hanumantha-Rao (1960a) showed that the PAS-positive reaction in Mehlis's gland in *Penetrocephalus ganapatii* disappears after extraction with pyridine. The gland also gave a positive reaction to the Methasol fast blue and neutral red procedure for phospholipids. These results led this writer to conclude that Mehlis's gland in this cestode elaborates and secretes phosphatides or, more specifically, a phospholipid-like substance. Hanumantha-Rao (1960a) observed minute droplets of the glandular secretion infiltrating into the lumen of the ootype through a narrow region at its origin. Beyond this region no trace of glandular secretion could be detected, but the ova and vitelline cells passing through are bathed in the secretion of Mehlis's gland. In the initial coils of the uterus the vitelline cells around the ovum extruded the shell material. The vitelline cells were PAS-negative, but when denuded of all shell material they became PAS-positive, fast to saliva and amylase digestion. These observations suggest that the secretion of Mehlis's gland stimulates the release of globules of shell material, as well as the active synthesis of food reserves in the vitelline cells.

Hanumantha-Rao (1960b) supposed that the phospholipid secreted by Mehlis's gland may be lecithin, because unsaturated fatty acids are known to be PAS-positive. The lack of a PAS-positive reaction in vitelline cells absorbing the secretion, and the appearance of this reaction in the vitelline cells after the capsule has been formed, is explained as follows. The lecithin can be enzymatically converted into lysolecithin by loss of the unsaturated fatty acid radical, thus making the secretion PAS-negative. After the capsule is constructed the re-esterification of lysolecithin converts it back to lecithin which forms the food yolk and thus the vitelline cells become strongly PAS-positive.

This conclusion is of particular interest when compared with our present knowledge on other species. The release of the material transported by vitelline cells for capsule formation, as well as some accumulation of food reserves in these cells after their passage through the ootype, has been observed in all groups of cestodes so far studied, as well as in trematodes (see above). The only exception reported has been in a study on *D. latum* by Bogomolova and Pavlova (1961), who claimed that the vitelline cells released capsule globules in the vitelline duct before they entered the uterus. On the other hand, the mechanism and chemistry of capsule formation, similar in Trematoda and Pseudophyllidea, is very different in Cyclophyllidea. The same is true of the accumulation of nutritive materials in the vitelline cells in these groups, which differs even in various species of the same group. Therefore, even if it is useful to suggest that in general Mehlis's gland has two functions, it can be expected that the specific differences in its secretion will occur, despite the apparent uniformity revealed by the PAS reaction.

A new light has been thrown recently on the function of Mehlis's gland by Clegg (1966) in his study on *Fasciola hepatica* and by Hoy and Clegg (unpublished) in their study on *Moniezia expansa*. Clegg (1966) extracted water-soluble lipoproteins from Mehlis's gland in *Fasciola* and showed by histochemical studies that the lipoprotein was found in the form of thin membrane on both sides of the capsule. Dawes (1940) originally suggested that the gland may secrete this membrane which forms the basal layer on the inside of which a shell could form, and the present study by Clegg (1966) seems to support this conclusion.

Hoy and Clegg (unpublished) state that the secretion of Mehlis's gland in *M. expansa* gives much the same reaction as that in *Fasciola*, and then concluded that a lipoprotein membrane occurs around the ovum and the vitelline cells of this species. Bearing in mind the findings of Rybicka (1964b) on the role of vitelline cells in capsule formation in *M. expansa*, it seems that in this species, as in *Fasciola* and other trematodes, Mehlis's gland is responsible for secretion of a basal layer inside which a vitelline cell secretion is laid down.

V. Embryonic Development

Embryonic development in Cestoda shows some specificity in comparison with other animals. Three phases of embryonic development can be distinguished: cleavage, the preoncospheral phase and the oncospheral phase. In spite of their peculiarities, these phases are comparable to the phases of embryonic development recognized in other animals. Cleavage, the period of early segmentation of the ovum, does not need any explanation. The preoncospheral phase is the one following cleavage and leading to the formation of the oncosphere. It can be regarded as a phase of morphogenesis. The introduction of a specific term "preoncosphere" (Rybicka, 1961a) seems to be justified in this particular pattern of embryonic development where the oncosphere is the final form. Some authors use the term "early" or "young" oncosphere, but it is difficult to define precisely the boundary between "early" and "late" or "old" oncospheres. Morphologically, the late preoncosphere resembles the oncosphere. The above proposed division into preoncosphere and oncosphere is based on physiological rather than morphological differences. The preoncospheral phase is one of intense cell multiplication and differentiation and therefore it is a phase of great metabolic activity in the embryo. The term "oncosphere" is reserved for the more stable phase in which no visible changes occur. The oncosphere is potentially ready for further development, but this cannot occur until it reaches the intermediate host. The metabolism of this "waiting" phase seems to be greatly reduced. Recognition of these two phases has some value in respect of physiological differences, and it is useful in comparative studies of embryos.

A. CLEAVAGE

Although numerous studies of cestode embryology exist, few of them contain detailed descriptions of the cleavage process. A comparison of these results with some other more or less fragmentary descriptions indicates that the same basic pattern of cleavage prevails in the various groups of Cestoda (see Rybicka, 1964c). There is total, unequal cleavage resulting in three types of blastomeres, macromeres, mesomeres and micromeres.

The macromeres are the largest cells found in the developing embryo, and resemble the ovum in size and structure, especially in the presence of yolk material supplied by the oocyte. The macromeres undergo some unequal divisions leading to the formation of both the other types of blastomeres (meso- and micromeres). One or two equal divisions also take place in the macromere, but this will be discussed in detail later.

The mesomeres are of smaller size, but they can be easily seen in all developing embryos. Their nucleus usually contains a nucleolus rich in RNA. According to most authors (Janicki, 1907; Spätlich, 1925; Motomura, 1929; Douglas, 1963; Rybicka, 1964a, b), the mesomeres arise during cleavage as a result of further unequal divisions of macromeres and begin to divide only late during the preoncosphere phase. However, Bona (1957) observed at a very early stage the division of mesomeres during cleavage.

The micromeres are also formed by unequal division of macromeres, appearing as small nuclei whose cell boundaries are often not clearly visible. They are not easily found, but in spite of difficulties the micromeres have been distinguished by many authors (St Remy, 1900; Spätlich, 1925; Motomura, 1929; Bona, 1957; Douglas, 1963; Rybicka, 1964a, b).

There exists some confusion in the terminology employed since some authors (e.g. Janicki, 1907; Motomura, 1929) have used the term micromeres for mesomeres. To avoid this confusion, the term "mesomere" will be used throughout, where relevant, even when the writers cited have used "micromeres".

1. Pseudophyllidea

The only detailed study on cleavage in pseudophyllideans known to the author, is that of Motomura (1929) dealing with the caryophylleid cestode,

Archigetes appendiculatus (Fig. 12). The first cleavage division in this species is nearly equal, resulting in two macromeres (Fig. 12A) which divide further but not simultaneously. The divisions are unequal, leading to the formation of some mesomeres. In the seven- or eight-cell stage very small micromeres,

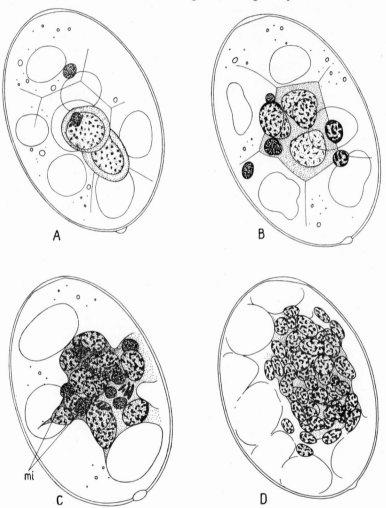

FIG. 12. Early embryonic development in *Archigetes appendiculatus.* A, Two blastomeres; B, eight blastomeres; C, 22- or 24-cell stage, pycnotic nuclei of micromeres (*mi*) are seen; D, multiplying cells in the preoncosphere, the pycnotic nuclei have disintegrated. (After Motomura, 1929.)

resembling polar bodies, appear (Fig. 12B). Motomura (1929) interpreted these as transformed mesomere nuclei. However, a comparison with later cyclophyllidean studies (see below) suggests that the smallest nuclei observed in *A. appendiculatus* were really micromeres arising from further unequal division of macromeres. Such divisions were probably repeated many times because, according to Motomura's illustrations, the number of micromeres has increased by the end of cleavage (Fig. 12C).

2. *Cyclophyllidea*

An analysis of the relatively numerous studies on cleavage in cyclophyllideans allows us to distinguish two cleavage patterns in this group (Rybicka, 1964c). The difference is determined mainly by the time at which the equal division of macromeres occurs.

a. *First cleavage pattern* (Fig. 13A, B)

The first division of the cleaving embryo is equal, resulting in the formation of two almost identical macromeres, which undergo several unequal divisions to form two to three micromeres and three mesomeres. By the end of cleavage, one of the macromeres divides once more equally and, therefore, the embryo entering the preoncosphere phase contains three macromeres; these seem to contain the whole yolk material supplied by the ovum.

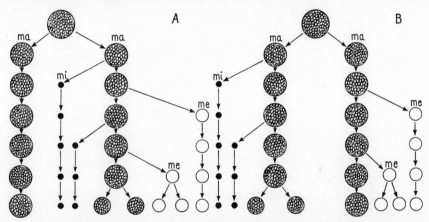

FIG. 13. Schematic diagram of first cleavage pattern in Cyclophyllidea. A and B, Two possible versions of the cleavage pattern in *Baerietta diana* (according to the description given by Douglas, 1963). *ma*, Macromere; *me*, mesomere; *mi*, micromere. (After Rybicka, 1964c.)

Figure 13A, B presents a schematic diagram of the first cleavage pattern, constructed by the author from the detailed description of cleavage in *Baerietta diana* given by Douglas (1963). As no simultaneous division of both macromeres was observed, it was impossible to judge whether one of them divided unequally (Fig. 12A) or both divided alternatively (Fig. 13B). Therefore two possible versions (A and B) are presented. The details of first cleavage pattern are shown on Fig. 14. The first cleavage pattern has been observed in *Taenia* spp. by St Remy (1901a, b) and Janicki (1906, 1907), in *Dipylidium caninum* by Moniez (1881), Venard (1938) and Rybicka (1964a), in *Mesocestoides corti* by Ogren (1956a), in *Oochoristica symmetrica* by Ogren (1957a, b), and in *Baerietta diana* and *Distoichometra kozloffi* by Douglas (1963).

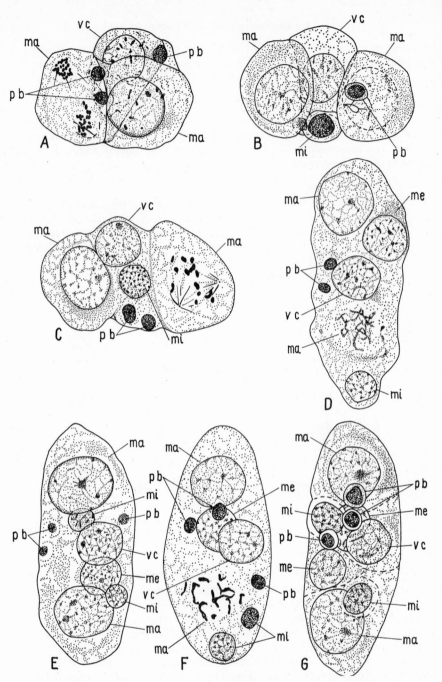

FIG. 14. The cleavage in *Baerietta diana*. A, The second cleavage; B, the three-cell stage; C, the third cleavage; D, cleavage in the four-cell stage; E, a five-cell stage; F, a five-cell stage in which one macromere is beginning to divide; G, the six-cell stage. *ma*, Macromere; *me*, mesomere; *mi*, micromere; *pb*, polar body; *vc*, vitelline cell. (After Douglas, 1963.)

b. Second cleavage pattern (Fig. 15A–C)

The first cleavage division is unequal, resulting in a macromere and a micro- or mesomere. The macromere divides several times, forming some mesomeres and micromeres, and near the end of cleavage the macromere undergoes one equal division. A nearly equal division of one daughter macromere is a typical event for this pattern in which a specific type of cell is produced. This cell resembles the macromere in dimensions, but it lacks the vitelline material usually found in macromeres. It has been called a third macromere. Some differences in the sequence of cell division observed in various species undergoing the second cleavage pattern are presented respectively in Fig. 14 as A, B and C. In spite of these differences, the obvious similarity in the cellular composition of each embryo can be seen by the end of cleavage. It is composed of two granular macromeres containing the vitelline material, one specific third macromere, three mesomeres and two to three micromeres (Fig.15 A–C). The details of the second cleavage pattern are shown on Fig. 16.

The second pattern of cleavage has been observed in *Moniezia expansa* by Moniez (1881) and Rybicka (1964b), in *Anoplocephala mamillana* by St Remy (1900), in *Diorchis inflata* by Spätlich (1925) and in *Paricterotaenia porosa* by Bona (1957). *Dilepis undula* seems to belong also to this group (see Ogren, 1962b).

In both cleavage patterns, the macromeres have separated from other embryonic cells by the end of cleavage, forming the rudiment of the outer envelope of the embryo. At the same time intense cell multiplication begins in other embryonic cells, and this moment is regarded as the end of the cleavage and the transition to the preoncosphere phase.

A comparison of the cleavage observed in a cyclophyllidean with that known in a pseudophyllidean indicates that the latter resembles the first cleavage pattern of the former. This could lead to the supposition that perhaps the first cleavage pattern of cyclophyllideans is the more primitive. However, present knowledge in this matter is too meagre to permit an equivocal conclusion to be drawn.

The cleavage patterns distinguished by Ogren (1953, 1957b) will be discussed in Section VI.

B. PREONCOSPHERAL PHASE

The preoncospheral phase can be briefly defined as one of cell multiplication and differentiation, resembling organogenesis in higher animals. In contrast to cleavage, where simultaneous division of cells has never been observed, embryonic cells divide intensively in the preoncospheral phase, so that in almost every section of the embryo some mitoses can be found. As a result of such rapid increase in the number of embryonic cells, no writer has been able to follow the fate of a particular cell as is possible during cleavage. The new cells arising also differentiate in a different way, forming the organs of the future oncosphere. The precise definition of this phase may be useful for future comparisons of development in different species. As the term is a relatively new one, the preoncospheral phase has been clearly defined in three

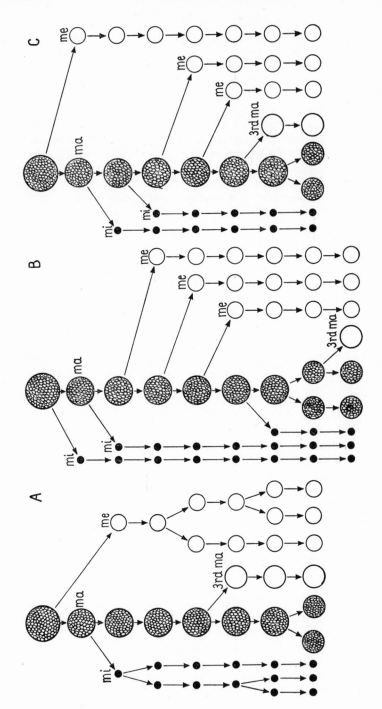

FIG. 15. Schematic diagram of second cleavage pattern in Cyclophyllidea. A, Cleavage in *Paricterotaenia porosa* (after Bona, 1957); B, cleavage in *Moniezia expansa* (after Rybicka, 1964b); C, cleavage in *Diorchis inflata* (according to description given by Spätlich, 1925). *ma*, Macromere; *me*, mesomere; *mi*, micromere. (After Rybicka, 1964c.)

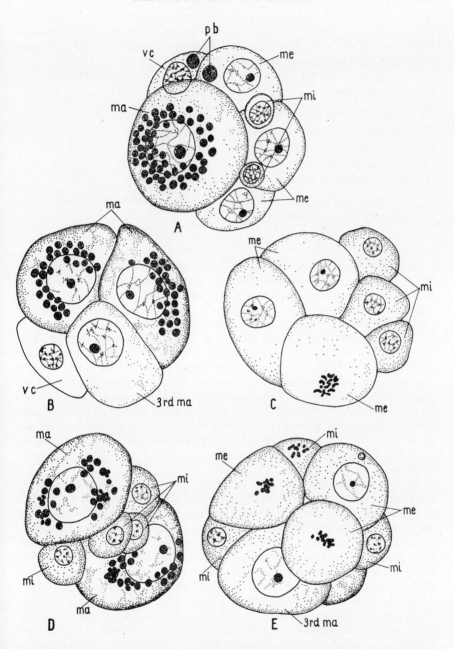

FIG. 16. The cleavage in *Moniezia expansa*. A, Six-cell stage; B and C, nine-cell stage (subsequent sections of one embryo); D and E, thirteen-cell stage (subsequent sections of one embryo). *ma*, Macromere; *me*, mesomere; *mi*, micromere; *pb*, polar body; *vc*, vitelline cell. (After Rybicka, 1964b.)

species only: *Diorchis ransomi*, *Dipylidium caninum* and *Moniezia expansa* by Rybicka (1961a, 1964a, b, respectively). Analysis of other studies, however, indicates that the same phase can be easily distinguished in the embryonic development of all Cestoda studied so far.

The following morphogenetical process can be distinguished in the pre-oncospheral phase:

(1) Degeneration of micromeres
(2) Formation of embryonic envelopes
(3) Development of hooks and their musculature
(4) Development of glands
(5) Differentiation of somatic and germinative cells.

These processes can now be discussed comparatively for pseudophyllidean and cyclophyllidean cestodes.

1. *Degeneration of Micromeres*

Micromeres arising during cleavage have particularly small nuclei and their resemblance to polar bodies has been noticed by many authors. This resemblance is due to pycnosis (shrinking of the nucleus into a single spherical mass) which occurs in micromeres. This event has not been described in pseudophyllideans, but some conclusions can be drawn from the detailed drawings of Motomura (1929) (Fig. 12). He showed in *Archigetes appendiculatus* a phase consisting of about twenty-two cells in which at least eight pycnotic nuclei are seen (Fig. 12C). The total number of embryonic cells present indicate that it was an early preoncosphere. The pycnosis of nuclei suggest that they do degenerate and, in fact, the later phases drawn by Motomura (1929) (Fig. 12D) do not contain these elements. Twenty to twenty-five pycnotic nuclei were also found by the present author (unpublished work) in early embryos of *Triaenophorus lucii*. Eggs developing in water were squashed each day. Degenerating micromere nuclei were seen in 4-day-old embryos and these were observed to disintegrate later.

In cyclophyllideans the early degeneration of micromeres has been described in detail for *Baerietta diana* by Douglas (1963) and for *Dipylidium caninum* by Rybicka (1964a), where it was clearly demonstrated by the use of the Feulgen technique. In both these species no division of micromeres was observed. Their nuclei became progressively smaller, showing pycnosis in very early preoncospheres; somewhat later they disintegrated. The micromeres in *Paricterotaenia porosa* (see Bona, 1957) and in *Moniezia expansa* (see Rybicka, 1964b), however, continued to divide before pycnosis appeared (Fig. 17B).

Janicki (1907) described in *Taenia serrata* some "chromidial extrusions" which could represent pycnosis as well as karyorrhexis (breakdown of the dying nucleus into a number of spherical bodies inside the nuclear membrane). According to Brachet (1960), pycnosis and karyorrhexis are so prevalent in developing eggs as to suggest that these are normal processes in morphogenesis. The breakdown of certain cells may release substances necessary for the development of the others.

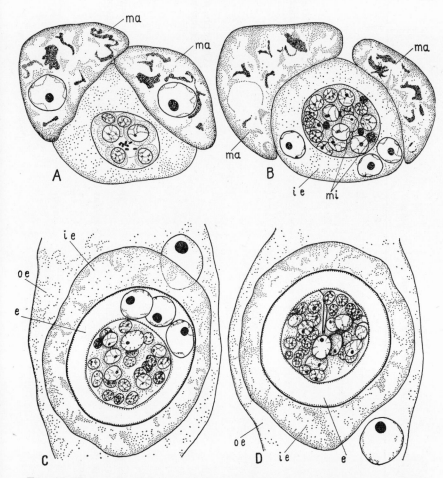

FIG. 17. The preoncosphere in *Moniezia expansa*. A and B, Subsequent sections of early preoncosphere; C and D, subsequent sections of late preoncosphere. *e*, Embryophore; *ie*, inner envelope; *ma*, macromere forming the outer envelope; *mi*, micromere nuclei; *oe*, outer envelope. (After Rybicka, 1964b.)

2. Formation of Embryonic Envelopes

The formation of embryonic envelopes is one of most confused topics in the embryology of cestodes. The envelopes in various species undergo some specific modification during embryonic development leading to different final structures, which are often arbitrarily interpreted by various writers. A comparative study is made more difficult by the lack of a uniform terminology which makes it sometimes almost impossible to compare the structures described in one species with those in another. Some examples of the terminology used are presented in Table I. The best way to determine the homologous structures in various cestodes seems to be to review ontogenetically

TABLE I

Terminology Used by Various Authors to Describe the Embryonic Envelopes in Cyclophyllidea

Author	Species	1	2	3	4
			General considerations		
Rybicka, terminology proposed	Cyclophyllidea	Capsule	Outer envelope ↘ Coat / Outer envelope	Inner envelope ↘ Inner envelope / Embryophore	Oncospheral membrane
Smyth and Clegg, 1959	Cyclophyllidea	Capsule	Gelatinous granular layer	Embryophore	
Smyth, 1963	Cyclophyllidea	Capsule	Vitelline layer / Subcapsular membrane	Embryophore	Oncospheral membrane
			Recent embryological studies		
Bona, 1957	*Paricterotaenia porosa*	Membrana vitellina (yolk membrane)	External envelope	Internal envelope ↘ Granular layer / Embryophore	Oncospheral membrane
Douglas, 1963	*Baerietta diana*		I. Extra-embryonic layer	II. Extra-embryonic layer = embryophore	Oncospheral membrane

Douglas, 1963	*Distoichometra kozloffi*			Outer embryo-derived membrane	Embryophore	
Ogren, 1955b	*Hymenolepis nana*	Outer capsule			Pseudoembryophore	
Ogren, 1956a	*Mesocestoides corti*	Capsule = vitelline shell	Collagenic rigid membrane	Irregular accretions	Embryophore	
Ogren, 1957a, b	*Oochoristica symmetrica*	Vitelline shell	Outer shell		Pseudoembryophore	
Ogren, 1958, 1959	*Dilepis undula*	Shell capsule		Colloidal sub-shell region	Inner capsule	Delicate membrane
Rybicka, 1961a	*Diorchis ransomi*	Membrana vitellina		Outer membrane	Inner membrane = embryophore	Oncospheral membrane
Rybicka, 1964a	*Dipylidium caninum*	Capsule		Gelatinous envelope	Embryophore	Embryonic membrane
Rybicka, 1964b	*Moniezia expansa*	Capsule	Coat → Outer envelope	Outer envelope → Inner envelope	Inner envelope → Embryophore	Oncospheral membrane
Silverman, 1954	*Taenia pisiformis T. saginata*		Chorionic membrane		Embryophore with basement membrane	
Venard, 1938	*Dipylidium caninum*	Shell	Yolk shell	Albuminous material	Inner envelope = embryophore	

TABLE I (*contd*)

Author	Species	1	2	3	4
			Descriptions of oncospheres		
Freeman, 1949	*Monoecocestus americanus*		Outer coat (with spines)	Middle coat	Inner coat (pyriform)
Jarecka, 1961	*Diorchis* (6 sp.) *Anomotaenia ciliata Aploparaxis furcigera*		Transparent film		External egg membrane	Internal egg membrane	Membrane of the onco-sphere
Jarecka, 1961	*Paricterotaenia porosa Hymenolepis* (7 sp.) *Drepanidotaenia lanceolata Diploposthe laevis*		External egg membrane	Transparent film	Internal egg membrane	Space filled with a structureless substance	Membrane of the onco-sphere
Moriyama, 1961a	*Hymenolepis diminuta*		1. Outer shell 2. Inner shell		1. Shell mem-brane 2. Clear medium	1. Embryophore 2. Embryophoral membrane
Moriyama, 1961b	*Hymenolepis nana*		1. Outer shell 2. Inner shell		1. Shell mem-brane 2. Granules 3. Transparent layer	1. Embryo-phore 2. Embryophoral membrane

Reference	Species					
Moriyama, 1961c	*Taenia saginata*	Shell			1. Embryophore	2. Embryophoral membrane
Ogren, 1961	*Hymenolepis diminuta*	Outer capsule	Colloidal envelope		Inner capsule	
Voge and Berntzen, 1961	*Hymenolepis diminuta*	Thin membrane egg-shell		Vitelline membrane	Coat	Delicate membrane
			Classical studies			
Van Beneden, 1881	*Taenia serrata* *Paricterotaenia porosa*	Coque d'oeuf	Couche albumino-gène		Couche chitinogène *enveloppe chitin.* Capsule ovoide	Membrane secrete par embryo
Janicki, 1906, 1907	*Taenia serrata*	Membrane	Äussere Hülle		Innere Hülle = Chitin-schale	Cuticula
Moniez, 1881	*Cyclophyllidea varia*	Membrane vitelline	I. Couche delamine		II. Couche delamine	
St Remy, 1900, 1901	*Anoplocephala mammillana* *Taenia serrata*		Enveloppe externe		Enveloppe interne	
Spätlich, 1925	*Diorchis inflata*	Eischale	1. Embryonal-hülle		2. Embryonal-hülle	3. Embryonal-hülle

the envelope development. Such a review has revealed that, in general, a similar pattern of development can be found in species so far studied.

Four embryonic envelopes can be distinguished in development; namely, capsule, outer envelope, inner envelope and oncospheral membrane. Two of them, the capsule and oncospheral membrane, are simply thin membranes, while the outer and inner envelopes are thick cytoplasmic layers formed by certain cells. These undergo the greatest modification during development. The formation of embryonic envelopes is diagrammatically presented in Figs. 18 and 19.

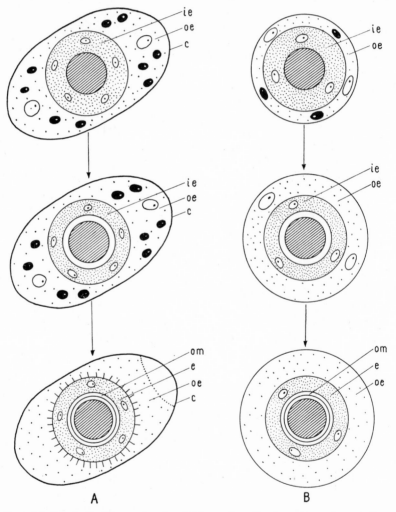

A   B

FIG. 18. Schematic diagram showing the formation of embryonic envelopes in Pseudo-phyllidea (A) and Proteocephalidae (B). *c*, Capsule; *e*, embryophore; *ie*, inner envelope; *oe*, outer envelope; *om*, oncospheral membrane.

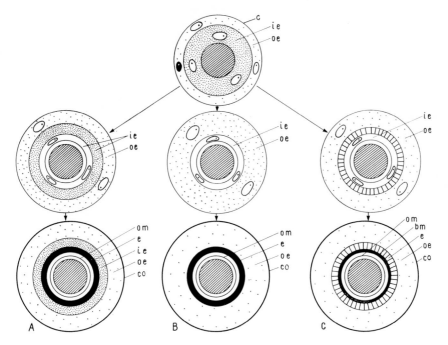

FIG. 19. Schematic diagram showing the formation of embryonic envelopes in Cyclophyllidea. A–C, Three patterns described in the text. *bm*, Basement membrane; *c*, capsule; *co*, coat; *e*, embryophore; *ie*, inner envelope; *oe*, outer envelope; *om*, oncospheral membrane.

a. Capsule

The capsule, formed before the oocyte enters the uterus, has already been discussed above. Its fate, however, is not completely clear in Cyclophyllidea, as it has never been followed throughout the entire embryonic development. The commonest view is that the coat, formed by the end of development as a superficial layer, is a thickened capsule. Bona (1957) and Rybicka (1964a) even identified the coat and the capsule by the presence of glycogen in both elements. However, it seems quite possible that glycogen can accumulate in the outer envelope after the disintegration of the capsule. In other studies (Venard, 1938; Rybicka, 1964b) the disintegration of the capsule has been pointed out. Thus, the capsule in Cyclophyllidea can only be regarded as a protective membrane for the cleaving embryo, disintegrating later after the true embryonic envelopes are formed. This question clearly needs further study.

b. Outer envelope

(i) *Pseudophyllidea.* The most detailed study on the formation of the outer envelope in Pseudophyllidea is that of Schauinsland (1886) (Fig. 20). The age of this paper could cause some reservation as to his results. However, a comparison with recent studies on other tapeworms reveals such good accord, that

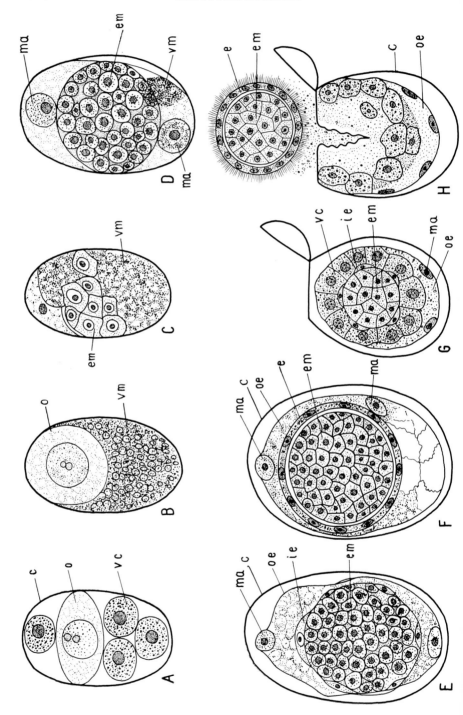

one can only admire the precision of the work done eighty years ago. Schauinsland (1886) studied both groups of pseudophyllideans, one developing in water and the other in the uterus. Although the representatives of the former group were more numerous (*Diphyllobothrium latum, Triaenophorus nodulosus, Ligula simplicissima* and *Schistocephalus dimorphus*), the observations on these were less detailed because of the thick operculate capsule. In this group two or four cells detached early from other embryonic cells and their cytoplasm, together with numerous vitelline cells, surrounded the embryo, forming its outer envelope (Hüllmembrane). These cells, clearly seen in *Ligula*, have large nuclei with conspicuous nucleoli.

A more detailed study was carried out (Schauinsland, 1886) on *Eubothrium rugosum*, which develops inside a delicate, non-operculate capsule. In this species two to three cells become detached from the embryo and surround it with a thick cytoplasmic layer. These cells had extremely large nuclei (Fig. 20D), which seems to indicate that they were the macromeres. The vitelline cells disintegrated relatively early in this species and only some yolk material was found in the embryo, as well as in the outer envelope.

(ii) *Cyclophyllidea.* In Cyclophyllidea, the partial detachment of the macromeres is still noticeable by the end of cleavage. The cytoplasm of these cells surrounds the embryo with a thick layer, forming the outer envelope (Figs. 21 and 22). There are some differences in its formation clearly connected with the cleavage pattern described above. In the first cleavage pattern, three nearly equal macromeres are formed and these three cells form the outer envelope in this group (*Taenia*: van Beneden, 1881; St Remy, 1901a; Janicki, 1907; *Dipylidium*: Rybicka, 1964a; *Baerietta*: Douglas, 1963). Some descriptions of outer envelope formation in this group have been interpreted in different ways, but these interpretations when analysed in detail do not seem to be justified. In *Mesocestoides corti* (see Ogren, 1956a) and *Distoichometra kozloffi* (see Douglas, 1963) only one macromere nucleus was observed in the outer envelope. That only one macromere nucleus occurs in *M. corti* seems to be a misinterpretation, since in drawings presented by Ogren (1956a) himself two or three nuclei in the outer envelope can be seen. As the drawings represent sections of the embryo, it is obvious that three nuclei are not always seen together. The case described by Douglas (1963) seems to need further confirmation, because this careful cytological study shows only an outline of the embryonic envelope formation.

A different interpretation was presented for *Oochoristica symmetrica* where

---

◄—Fɪɢ. 20. The formation of embryonic envelopes in Pseudophyllidea. A–F, *Eubothrium rugosum*. G and H, *Diphyllobothrium latum*. A, Oocyte and vitelline cells surrounded by a capsule; B, vitelline cells forming a yolk mass in the egg; C, cleaving embryo; D, the detachment of macromeres forming the outer envelope; E, the detachment of cells forming the inner envelope; F, late preoncosphere surrounded by capsule, outer envelope and embryophore; G, formation of embryonic envelopes in *D. latum*; H, hatching of coracidium (outer envelope remains within the capsule). *c*, Capsule; *e*, embryophore; *em*, embryo; *ie*, inner envelope; *ma*, macromere; *o*, ovum; *oe*, outer envelope; *vc*, vitelline cell; *vm*, vitelline mass. (After Schauinsland, 1886.)

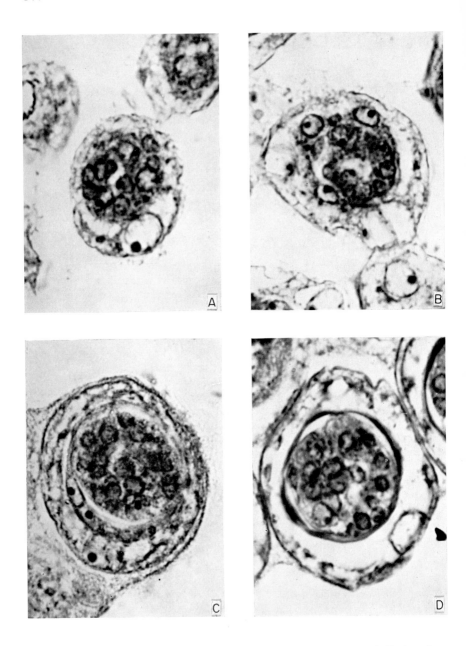

FIG. 21. The formation of embryonic envelopes in *Dipylidium caninum*. A, Early embryo surrounded by the outer envelope; B–D, subsequent phases of formation of the inner envelope, whose prominent nuclei (B) flatten later (C) and finally disappear (D). Prenant's trichrome. (After Rybicka, 1964a.)

a non-cellular origin of the outer envelope was claimed (Ogren, 1957a). However, this writer noticed the presence of large nuclei in the envelope and even explained these originally (Ogren, 1956b) as the blastomere nuclei. When compared with all other studies in tapeworms this original interpretation seems to be more justified than new speculations introduced later (Ogren, 1957a).

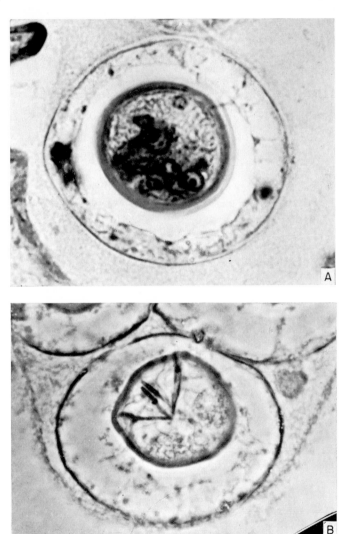

F IG . 22. The oncosphere of *Dipylidium caninum* surrounded by its envelopes. A, Section through the part containing the germinative cells (Prenant's trichrome). B, Section through hooks region and penetration glands; oncospheral membrane draped over the hooks (Feulgen technique, phase-contrast). (After Rybicka, 1964a.)

In the species showing the second cleavage pattern (*Moniezia*: Moniez, 1881; Rybicka, 1964b; *Anoplocephala*: St Remy, 1900; *Diorchis*: Spätlich, 1925; *Paricterotaenia*: Bona, 1957) two equal macromeres were formed and these alone make up the outer envelope (Fig. 17). Three macromeres in first cleavage pattern and two macromeres in the second seem to contain all the yolk supplied with the oocyte. The transformation of these cells into the outer envelope indicates that the function of the latter should be regarded as a store of nutritive material for the embryo. Moreover, in some species of the first cleavage pattern (*Taenia*: van Beneden, 1881; St Remy, 1901a, b; Janicki, 1907; *Dipylidium*: Rybicka, 1964a) the vitelline cell was also extruded to the outer envelope.

(iii) *Proteocephalidae.* Almost nothing is known about the embryonic development of Proteocephalidae. The envelopes observed around the fully formed oncospheres are similar to those of other Cestoda, and it can be supposed that they are formed in the same way. A figure by Ogren (1953, Pl. X, Fig. 238) shows a preoncosphere of *Proteocephalus* sp. Although he interprets otherwise, the macromeres forming the outer envelope as well as mesomeres of the inner one are evident, and this supports the method of formation of embryonic envelopes in Proteocephalidae shown in Fig. 18B.

Smyth (1963) distinguished two types of cestode eggs and included Proteocephalidae in the first group along with Pseudophyllidea, on the basis of the extensive vitellaria in the female reproductive system. It should be pointed out, despite this classification, that the structure of the outer envelope in Proteocephalidae more nearly resembles that of Cyclophyllidea than that of Pseudophyllidea.

(iv) *Cytochemical observations.* The nutritive character of the outer envelope is particularly clear in Pseudophyllidea, where the numerous vitelline cells take part in its formation.

As discussed above, the chemistry of the yolk material supplied by the oocyte and then transported with macromeres to the outer envelope has not been sufficiently studied. Johri (1957) demonstrated the presence of proteins. Although histochemical research on proteins in cestodes has been inadequate, this yolk material can be presumed to be protein. According to von Brand (1952), proteins in the form of cytoplasmic granules form fairly common deposits of reserve materials in parasites. In the outer envelope Ogren and Magill (1962) have revealed the presence of protein conjugated with polysaccharide.

On the other hand, many histochemical observations (Ortner-Schönbach, 1913; Hedrick and Daugherty, 1957; Ogren, 1959b; Pavlova, 1963; Cheng and Dyckman, 1964) indicate that glycogen accumulates in the outer envelope after it is formed, supporting the view that this envelope has a nutritive role in development. The yolk later disappears from the outer envelope, which becomes transparent and filled up with loose cytoplasmic residue. Its surface grows thicker, forming a coat. The heavy accumulation of glycogen in this layer (Bona, 1957; Rybicka, 1964a) may represent a residual glycogen reserve unused by the embryo.

Hedrick (1958) observed a heavy concentration of fat and some phospholipids in this layer of *Hymenolepis diminuta*. As the fat is regarded (Smyth, 1947, 1962; von Brand, 1952) as a metabolic end-product in tapeworms, its presence in the peripheral zone of the old outer envelope may be explained as an accumulation of waste products after the nutritive reserve of the outer envelope has been used by the embryo. The layer hardens to different degrees in various cyclophyllidean species, and in *Moniezia expansa* it forms a very hard coat. Hoy and Clegg (unpublished) demonstrated that in this species a granular secretion deposited on the outer surface by glands in the wall of the uterus, secretion and coat giving a strongly positive reaction for keratin. Rybicka (1964b), using the Mallory-Heidenhein technique (Cason, 1950), observed a yellow staining in the coat of Anoplocephalidae. The same colour was found by this method in the embryophore of Taeniidae, which was shown by Johri (1957) to be keratin (see p. 151).

In the coat of *Hymenolepis diminuta* Ogren and Magill (1962) revealed the presence of simple protein with the amino acids tyrosine and tryptophane. Their study confirms also the findings of Moriyama (1961a) that in this species a thick coat is composed of two layers. Ogren (1959b) claims that the coat of *Dilepis undula* showed positive reactions for sclerotin; the histochemical results obtained by this writer, however, have revealed only the presence of basic proteins.

The hardening of the coat in cyclophyllidean oncospheres suggest that this layer has a protective function.

c. Inner envelope

The degeneration of micromeres and the detachment of macromeres forming the outer envelope indicates that the mesomeres are the cells which multiply and differentiate in the formation of the oncosphere and its inner envelope. The latter is formed by some cells becoming detached from the surface of the developing embryo. Their cytoplasm forms a syncytial layer surrounding the embryo beneath the outer envelope (see Figs. 17–21).

(i) *Pseudophyllidea*. According to Schauinsland (1886), in Pseudophyllidea originally only one cell spreads over the surface of the embryo and there it divides repeatedly to form the inner envelope. Vergeer (1936) confirmed this interpretation, which seems to need some revision. In no other tapeworm so far studied has the division of cells just detached from the embryo been observed. Further, if one cell divides, the new arising nuclei must migrate around the surface of the embryo in order to obtain the final position. Such a migration has never been observed in embryonic cells and its occurrence seems to be unlikely. It is supposed, therefore, that all the cells forming the envelope become detached from the surface of the embryo, but such an event could be easily overlooked by the writers who view developmental stages through the thick wall of the capsule.

The inner envelope subsequently becomes the embryophore. In a pseudophyllidean cestode, developing in water, cilia arise on its surface. The nuclei of the embryophore-forming cells remain in it and they can still be seen in the hatched coracidium (Figs. 18A and 20H). The syncytial cytoplasm becomes vacuolated, resembling a honeycomb, as is clearly visible in *Diphyllobothrium*.

This is then regarded by some writers as a "cellular" structure, although Schauinsland (1886) and Vogel (1929) clearly explained that it is only a specific modification of the syncytial cytoplasm.

The nuclei can be seen in the syncytium, numbering about thirty in *Triaenophorus lucii* (see Michajłow, 1933) and about twenty in *D. latum* (Rybicka, unpublished). The vacuoles may unite (Grabiec *et al.*, 1963a), in which case the number of false cells decreases. In descriptions of the ciliated embryophore in Pseudophyllidea (Schauinsland, 1886; Vogel, 1929; Michajłow, 1933) two membranes (outer and inner) have been distinguished on the surface of the embryophore. The inner membrane was thicker as a rule, and the outer one was covered by cilia.

Some histochemical research (Vogel, 1929; Michajłow, 1933; Grabiec *et al.*, 1962, 1963a) indicates the presence of lipids and phospholipids in the embryophore. According to the last-named writers, these compounds serve as an energy source for moving cilia.

The cilia are usually longer at the pole opposite to the hooks (Vogel, 1929; Michajłow, 1933) and have a thin distal part. Using electron microscopy, Kuhlow (1953) found a thin membrane surrounding each cilium. According to him, contraction of the membrane results in the appearance of this thin distal part. In *Bothriocephalus claviceps*, according to Jarecka (1964), the cilia are of uniform length on the whole surface. In Amphicotylidae the embryophore remains unciliated.

(ii) *Cyclophyllidea*. The formation of the inner envelope by the detachment of some cells has been observed in almost all Cyclophyllidea so far studied. In some cyclophyllideans of first cleavage pattern (*Dipylidium*: Venard, 1938; Rybicka, 1964a; *Mesocestoides*: Ogren, 1956a) the cells forming the inner envelope become detached from the embryo relatively late, after the layer of the outer envelope has surrounded it (Fig. 21B). In others (*Diorchis inflata*: Spätlich, 1925; *Paricterotaenia porosa*: Bona, 1957; *Moniezia expansa*: Rybicka, 1964b) the inner envelope was formed almost simultaneously with the outer one (Fig. 17). A re-examination of slides of *Diorchis ransomi*, already described by Rybicka (1960, 1961a), indicates that this is true in this species. The similarity of cytoplasmic structure of both layers led writers to overlook the cells forming the inner envelope (Rybicka, 1960, 1961a). However, the simultaneous formation of both envelopes can be seen in Fig. 23. The macromeres of the outer envelope are still present in the form of two cells situated on the poles of the embryo. The inner envelope, containing the glycogen, surrounds the whole embryo. It should be pointed out that *D. ransomi* is the only species known in which the distribution of glycogen is clearly different in the outer and inner envelope. The reaction presented in Fig. 23 confirms the earlier observations of Spätlich (1925), who was able to distinguish between the cells forming the two envelopes in a related species, *D. inflata*.

The formation of the inner envelope later than the outer one seems to be typical for the species belonging to the first cleavage pattern, although in *Taenia* (Janicki, 1907) an almost simultaneous formation of both envelopes has been observed which is typical for the second cleavage pattern.

Ogren (1959b, 1962b) did not describe the formation of the outer envelope in *Dilepis undula*, in which the macromeres excluded from the embryo form its inner envelope. A similar picture has been observed in *Drepanidotaenia lanceolata* by Swiderski (1966) and in *Hymenolepis diminuta* by Rybicka (1966). The latter study indicates that five macromeres are detached from the embryo, but among them two types of nuclei can be distinguished. One type participates in the formation of the outer envelope and the second in the formation of the embryophore. The nuclei of the cells forming the outer envelope degenerate

FIG. 23. The formation of the outer and inner envelope in *Diorchis ransomi*. The inner envelope is darkly stained. PAS reaction. (After Rybicka, 1960.)

very quickly after their detachment and hence may be overlooked. Perhaps that is so in *Dilepis undula*, where only the nuclei of the inner envelope have been observed. Indeed, as Ogren (1962b) has pointed out, "almost all developmental problems remain to be investigated in this group".

The detached cells of the inner envelope of Cyclophyllidea undergo a further differentiation. One common feature observed in this group is the degeneration of nuclei in the inner envelope. Around these degenerating nuclei some structural proteins are secreted, leading to the formation of a rigid layer commonly called the embryophore. In some species the remains of degenerating nuclei are visible in the embryophore.

A general schema of the embryophore formation has been presented by Rybicka (1965). More detailed study shows at least three patterns of differentiation of the inner envelope in Cyclophyllidea. These are schematically presented in Fig. 19 as patterns A, B and C.

Pattern A. The nuclei of the inner envelope move towards the inner part and there a rigid embryophore is secreted. The cytoplasmic layer remains around the embryophore. To this group belong *Paricterotaenia porosa* (see Bona, 1957), *Moniezia expansa* (see Rybicka, 1964b) and *Diorchis inflata* (see Spätlich, 1925). It seems justifiable to include here *Hymenolepis diminuta* and *H. nana.* In spite of Ogren's (1955a) conception of the non-cellular origin of the pseudoembryophore in the latter species, the studies of Moriyama (1961a, b) and Rybicka (1966) clearly show a cellular origin of the embryophore in both species. Moriyama (1961a) also described some cells on the surface of the cytoplasmic layer, but these have never been confirmed by other authors. Their structure in the figure by Moriyama (1961a) resembles the false cells seen in the embryophore of the coracidium.

Pattern B. In this group the whole inner envelope contracts during the secretion of the embryophore and no cytoplasmic layer remains. A typical example is *Dipylidium caninum* (see Rybicka, 1964a) (Fig. 21). In this group can be included also *Mesocestoides corti* (see Ogren, 1956a), *Catenotaenia pusilla* (see Joyeux and Baer, 1945) and two species of the family Nematotaenidae studied by Douglas (1963).

Pattern C. This differs from those described above, as the striated embryophore typical for this group does not contain nuclei. The embryophore is secreted in the form of blocks, which originate from the outer membrane of the inner envelope and grow towards the centre. During their growth the nuclei of the inner envelope are pushed down towards the embryo and they eventually degenerate. The rudiment of the inner envelope forms the basement membrane. This pattern is common in the family Taeniidae (see Janicki, 1907; Silverman, 1954b; Lee *et al.,* 1959; Moriyama, 1961c) and it has been recently confirmed by Morseth (1965) in his study of ultrastructure in the developing taeniid embryophore.

In the formation of the embryophore Morseth (1965) observed circular bodies which appear to be focal points around which the dense block substance is deposited. The granular material, closely associated with the developing embryophoric blocks, appears to be incorporated into the block substance.

(iii) *Cytochemical structure.* Studies of the chemical composition of the inner envelope in Cyclophyllidea are few. The cytoplasmic layer in *D. ransomi* stains with pyronin. The presence of RNA in this layer was also noticed in *Infula macrophallus* (Coil, 1963). This seems to be the metabolically inactive RNA remaining in the envelope after the embryophore is secreted. This inactive RNA can be compared with the RNA of "residual bodies" observed in the testes after sperm extrusion (Brachet, 1959).

Glycogen was found in the cytoplasmic part around the embryophore in *Anoplocephala perfoliata* (see Ortner-Schönbach, 1913), *Moniezia expansa* (see Rybicka, 1964b), *Diorchis ransomi* (see Rybicka, 1960, noting the revision mentioned above) and *Hymenolepis diminuta* (see Cheng and Dyckman, 1964). However, it was never observed in the embryophore itself.

The embryophore of *Dilepis undula* (see Ogren, 1959b) stained greenish with bromophenol blue and faintly pink with aniline acid fuchsin. Chemical reactions of the embryophore in *Oochoristica symmetrica* (see Ogren, 1957b) indicated that it was a protein gel and gave positive reactions with xanthoproteic, Millon's reaction and ninhydrin Schiff procedure.

Pavlova (1963) claimed that the typical striated embryophore in *Taeniarhynchus saginatus* is a quinone-tanned protein and the substance cementing its "columns" contains lipoproteins. These results disagree with those obtained by Johri (1957) on another taenid, *Multiceps smythi*. In this species Millon's reaction and bromophenol blue revealed the presence of proteins. As the three structural proteins, chitin, sclerotin and keratin, could be present, tests were made for them. The tests for chitin and sclerotin were negative, only the test for keratin was positive, indicating the presence of -SS- bonds. Johri (1957) pointed out that the term "keratin" is not precise and it is used loosely to include those proteins which contain a high proportion of cystine and give a typical "keratin-type" X-ray difraction pattern. Recently Morseth (1966) carried out some work on infrared studies on the chemical composition of the embryophore in *Taenia hydatigena*, *T. pisiformis* and *T. ovis*, and has shown that the infrared absorption pattern is almost identical with that for keratin; thus confirming the histochemical findings.

In Cyclophyllidea the embryophore is usually formed by the hardening of a cytoplasmic layer due presumably to the inclusion of some structural proteins, judging by the results of chemical studies by Johri (1957), Ogren (1957b, 1959b) and Pavlova (1963). However, observed differences in embryophore formation in various groups suggest possibly that different proteins may be included.

The embryophore of Proteocephalidae (Fig. 18B) resembles that of Pseudophyllidea, particularly of the family Amphicotylidae where it is deprived of cilia. The point of similarity is the presence of nuclei in the embryophore of both groups, as well as the lack of hardening, in contrast to Cyclophyllidea with a hardened embryophore.

d. Oncospheral membrane

At the end of development a thin membrane surrounds the oncosphere beneath the embryophore (Fig. 22B). It is difficult to see, because it lies very close to the embryo and therefore it has seldom been noticed (Bona, 1957; Ogren, 1957b, 1959b; Rybicka, 1961a, 1964a, b). Studies on living cyclophyllidean oncospheres (Sinitsin, 1930; Rendtorff, 1948; Abdou, 1958; Jarecka, 1958, 1960, 1961) show that it is present. The relatively early formation of the oncospheral membrane was noted by Rybicka (1966).

Nothing is known so far about the origin of the oncospheral membrane. It seems to be formed by some kind of secretion. According to Moriyama (1961a, b), it is secreted in *Hymenolepis* by the cells forming the inner envelope, but this interpretation has never been confirmed. According to Ogren (1957b), it is secreted in *Oochoristica symmetrica* by the penetration glands, called by him "epidermal glands". However, our present knowledge of the function of these glands does not accord with this hypothesis.

In Pseudophyllidea, the oncospheral membrane was distinguished by Michajlow (1933) and Thomas (1937). Schauinsland (1886) noticed that the oncospheres of *Diphyllobothrium* and *Ligula* when hatching from the embryophores, were surrounded by a thin membrane which he named the inner membrane of the embryophore. It seems quite probable that it was simply the oncospheral membrane not clearly seen before hatching. The oncospheral membrane has also been clearly seen in the Proteocephalidae (Essex, 1927; Herde, 1938; Jarecka, 1960; Freeman, 1963).

The liberation of the oncosphere from this membrane has been described by Abdou (1958) in *Davainea proglottina*; it is effected by the tips of the hooks which project through this membrane. Many writers (Reid, 1948; Gallati, 1959; Ogren, 1961b) studying the hatched oncosphere noticed a small vesicle adjacent to it, which seems to be the sloughed-off oncospheral membrane. The liberated oncosphere can then use its hooks and glands for penetration.

Not altogether clear are some findings described by Rendtorff (1948) and Ogren (1957b) for the Linstowiidae. The oncospheral membrane was observed around the oncosphere already in the haemocoel of the intermediate host. It may be that perhaps in these species a new membrane is formed in the host haemocoel. However, Ogren (1957b) found the secretion of oncospheral glands present between the membrane and the oncosphere before, as well as after, the penetration of the host's gut. This finding suggests that it was the original membrane preserving the secretion. In this case, however, it is not clear how the oncosphere penetrates the gut wall of the host and further study is required.

3. Development of Hooks and their Musculature

a. Development of hooks. Hook formation has not been studied in detail in the Pseudophyllidea. Schauinsland (1886) noticed that hooks appear at the end of embryonic development, and Michajlow (1933) recorded the presence of hooks in developing eggs of *Triaenophorus lucii* by the 5th or 6th day of development, hatching occurring on the 7th day. Michajlow suggested that the median pair arose first.

Hook development in Cyclophyllidea is known in greater detail, although only three species have been studied: *Oochoristica symmetrica* by Ogren (1957b), *Dilepis undula* by Ogren (1958) and *Hymenolepis diminuta* by Ogren (1961a). In cyclophyllideans hook rudiments appear in the preoncosphere before the embryonic cells have attained their maximal number (Rybicka, 1964a). Each hook arises in a special cell, the oncoblast, and the part first seen is the curved blade (Ogren, 1957b, 1958, 1961a; Rybicka, 1964a) (Fig. 24). According to Ogren, the blade continues to enlarge inside the cell until its base and part of the shank are formed. At this stage the hook begins to project outside the cell and on the cell surface a thickened collar is formed (Fig. 25). The two lateral hook blades appear first (Ogren, 1957b, 1958). A young oncoblast contains RNA in the hook-forming centre, as well as in the nucleolus, but the amount decreases as the hook becomes more complete and the shank appears, i.e. as the total amount of hook protein increases (Ogren, 1961a). Developing hooks give the following reactions: they stain red with safranin O, purple with toluidine blue, yellow with van Gieson's connective tissue stain, red with aniline acid fuchsin and green with bromophenol blue. They also show positive reactions for protein by the xanthroproteic, Millon and ninhydrin Schiff reactions (Ogren, 1958).

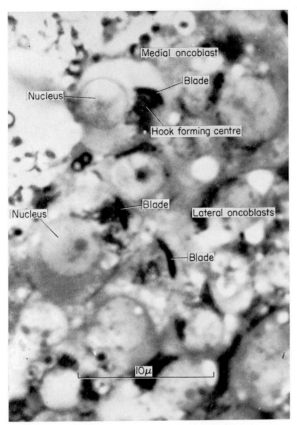

FIG. 24. The oncoblasts with hook rudiments in *Hymenolepis diminuta*. (After Ogren, 1961a.)

b. *Development of muscles.* How the oncospheral muscles are developed in Pseudophyllidea has not been studied. However, there are some descriptions of hook musculature in the coracidium and these will be discussed later.

Some study on the development of muscles in cyclophyllidean embryos was carried out by Ogren (1957a, b, 1958), who distinguished two contractile regions in the embryo: (i) the cells developed in a cortical parenchyma which was associated with constrictions of the body and extension of the hooks, and (ii) a medullary contractile centre forming a contractile system associated with the shortening of the body and retraction of the hooks. According to Ogren (1958) the cortical parenchyma appears to develop from cortical "somatic" nuclei whose cytoplasm become fibrous. The fibres passed to other cells or to

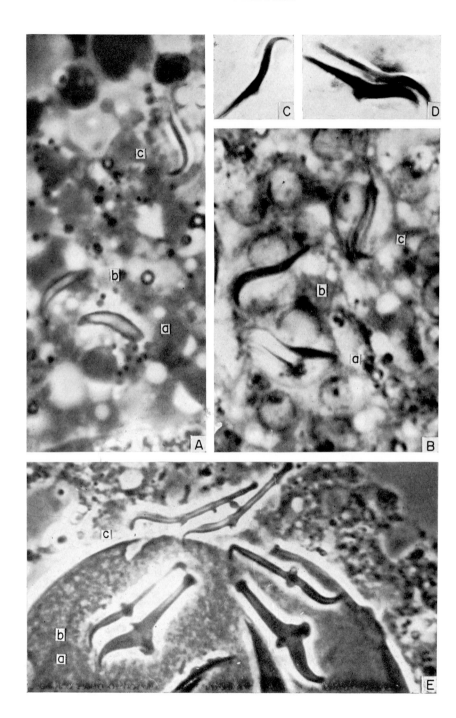

the cuticle. In the late preoncosphere, the cortex produced a much thicker cuticle and more fibres. The nuclei become very small and strongly stained.

The medullary contractile centre arises in the early preoncosphere as a binucleate primordium with relatively larger cells (Ogren, 1956a, 1957b, 1958). This centre appears to be responsible for the formation of intercellular material of a contractile nature. Fibres from the medullary centre make complex associations with cortical fibres and with the hooks. Following completion of the hooks abundant fibres from the centre develop throughout the oncosphere (Ogren, 1958). Figures presented by Ogren suggest that the nuclei of muscle cells are the so-called "somatic" nuclei. The binucleate centre has been observed also in other species (Rybicka, 1964b). It is composed of two relatively large cells, differentiated relatively early in the preoncosphere, and remains unchanged in the oncosphere. It is not yet clear if these cells produce the small muscle cells as Ogren (1958) suggests, because in such a case one would expect to see some changes in the binucleate centre. To clarify this point phases of cellular division in the binucleate centre must be found.

In the hook musculature, two types of muscle strands can be distinguished (Ogren, 1958), those attached to the collar and those attached to the bases of the hooks. According to this writer, the first are derived from special cells in the cortex near the hook and are firmly attached to the cuticle. The second strands are bound to the muscle fibres from the medullary contractile centre and the cortical parenchyma.

The oncosphere muscles have an affinity for collagen stains (Ogren, 1957b).

4. Development of Penetration Glands

The final structure and function of penetration glands will be discussed later. However, there is some information dealing with the development of the glands which can be dealt with here. Ogren (1955a, 1957b, 1959a) has distinguished in developing embryos of *Hymenolepis nana*, *Oochoristica symmetrica* and *Dilepis undula* the bilateral primordia of glands. They appeared simultaneously with hook formation, i.e. in the preoncosphere. These areas developed into a large U-shaped structure. In *H. nana*, chemical changes in the glands were observed during their formation (Ogren, 1955a). The originally acidic granular secretion changed later into an alkaline one. According to Ogren (1957b, 1959a), the glandular areas in *O. symmetrica* and *D. undula* are composed of numerous cells.

Some observations dealing with the formation of penetration glands were also made by Rybicka (1964a, b) in respect of *Dipylidium caninum* and *Moniezia expansa*. In these species, two cells forming the glands are distinguishable during the early stage of hook formation. They have relatively large nuclei and granular cytoplasm. Each gland observed in these species is unicellular.

◄—FIG. 25. Hook development in *Hymenolepis diminuta*. A, Early oncoblast stage, hook blades displaced from the cell; B, early shank formation in oncoblast; C, medial hook with nearly complete shank; D, lateral hooks, nearly complete shank; E, mature hooks forced from mature oncosphere. *a*, Ventral lateral blade; *b*, dorsal lateral blade; *c*, medial blade. (After Ogren, 1961a.)

5. Differentiation of Somatic and Germinative Cells

a. Historical review. Besides the formation of particular "organs" described above, the main mass of the multiplying embryonic cells differentiates in the preoncosphere to form a particular cellular structure in the oncosphere. This structure was originally described in the pseudophyllidean coracidium. Two types of cells were distinguished in the oncosphere of *Diphyllobothrium latum* by Vogel (1929) (Fig. 26A) and *Archigetes* sp. by Wiśniewski (1930). These are the very numerous "somatic" cells, crowded in the hook region, and the not so numerous "plastin" or "germinative" cells, concentrated in the opposite hemisphere. The somatic cells are represented by very small nuclei disposed in the syncytial cytoplasm. The germinative cells contain relatively large nuclei,

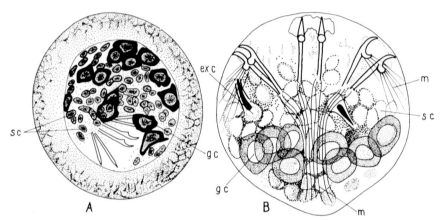

Fig. 26. Oncosphere of *Diphyllobothrium latum*. A, Coracidium (methyl green–pyronin); B, living oncosphere. *exc*, Excretory cell; *gc*, germinative (plastin) cells; *m*, muscle; *sc*, somatic cells. (After Vogel, 1929, 1930.)

surrounded by a well-defined cytoplasmic layer, staining strongly in haematoxylin and pyronin. Although both writers used the term "somatic" cells, their interpretation differed. Wiśniewski (1930) regarded the somatic cells as an "anlage" of the whole somatic part of the future cestode, whereas the germinative cells were supposed to form the future germinative glands only. According to Vogel (1929), the somatic cells represented the somatic part of the oncosphere only and they degenerate in the early procercoid. According to this view, the whole larva and the adult cestode itself develops from the germinative (plastin) cells. A further study (see below) confirmed Vogel's view. Regarding the role of these cells, i.e. the formation of the next developmental stages, the term "germinative" cells will be retained, although in a different sense from that originally introduced by Wiśniewski (1930).

b. Morphological and cytochemical evidence. The number of somatic cells in an oncosphere of the various pseudophyllideans studied is about 100, and germinative ones four to twenty. A study of cyclophyllidean preoncospheres indicates that the maximal number of cells observed during embryonic development approaches the level found in pseudophyllidean oncospheres, but by the end of the preoncosphere phase about two-thirds of the cells degenerate (Fig. 27). As the counting of cells is disturbed by their density, the maximal number found in a preoncosphere has been given for three species only: *Diorchis ransomi* (sixty-five to seventy), *Dipylidium caninum* (about eighty) and *Moniezia expansa* (about sixty) (Rybicka, 1961a, b, 1964a, b, respectively). Most of these cells are somatic ones. In the oncosphere, the number of embryonic cells decreases to twenty-six in *D. ransomi*, twenty-four in *D. caninum*, and fifteen in *M. expansa*. The pycnosis observed in the nuclei of somatic cells indicated that the decrease in number was due to the degeneration of somatic cells. The decrease in number was also observed in *Catenotaenia pusilla* (Joyeux and Baer, 1945), where four cells only remained in the oncosphere.

The study on RNA distribution in the preoncospheral phase indicates its relationship to cellular changes. An accumulation of RNA in the early preoncosphere was noticed in various species (Ogren, 1956a, 1957b; Rybicka, 1961a, b, 1964a, b; Cheng and Jacknick, 1964). This material disintegrates in the somatic cells by the end of the preoncospheral phase and simultaneously it is accumulated in quantity in the cytoplasm and nucleoli of germinative cells (Ogren, 1956a, 1957b, 1958, 1959a; Rybicka, 1961a, 1964a, b; Cheng and Jacknick, 1964). Although the structure has been studied cytochemically in only a few species, it is noteworthy that the somatic cells are commonly characterized as "colourless", and the lack of basophily is due presumably to the absence of RNA. On the other hand, the germinative cells are known to have a strongly basophil cytoplasm, which seems to be due to accumulation of RNA.

These changes of RNA distribution in the embryo become meaningful in our present knowledge of the role of RNA in embryogenesis. Many studies on vertebrate embryos indicate that RNA is associated with protein synthesis (Brachet, 1960). In the early preoncosphere, during intense cell multiplication, protein synthesis occurs in newly arising cells and RNA is simultaneously accumulated in these cells. In the phase of morphogenesis in vertebrates, the protein and RNA gradients superimpose themselves on the morphogenetic gradients and it is found that at later stages the RNA content of every organ rudiment increases just before its differentiation begins (Brachet, 1960).

Although it is difficult to speak of morphogenetic gradients in tapeworm embryos, the cells such as oncoblasts or developing glands are clearly morphogenetic centres, and in these RNA accumulates during the development of hooks and glands (see Section V, B, 4 and 5).

The germinative cells in the late preoncosphere are prepared for further multiplication and differentiation in the intermediate host and this role is confirmed by the RNA synthesis in these cells. The disappearance of RNA in somatic cells indicates that these do not play any morphogenetic role in further development—a conclusion which harmonizes with the degeneration of these cells in the late preoncosphere.

c. Theories on cellular changes. Some of the interpretations placed on the cellular changes in the preoncosphere must be discussed in the light of cytochemical findings. Because the nuclei of somatic cells stained strongly with the

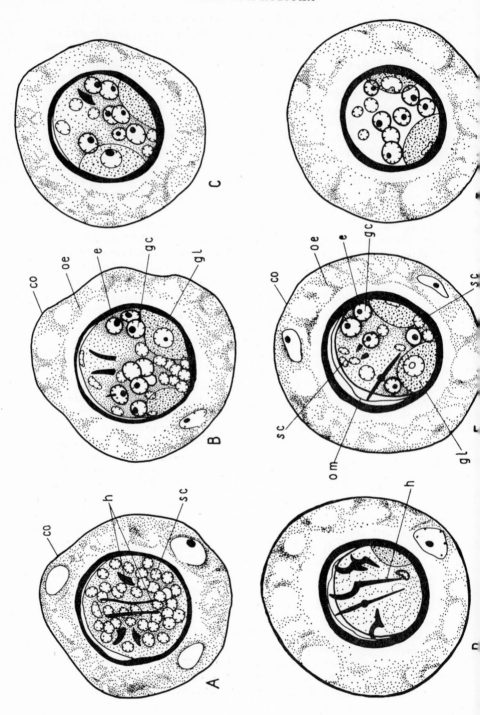

Feulgen technique or methyl green, Silverman (1954b) regarded them as "centres of DNA" around which the germinative cells are formed. This seemed to be confirmed by the simultaneous decrease in density of somatic cells. It is obvious, however, that these DNA centres are simply pycnotic nuclei of degenerating cells. The idea that somatic cells change into germinative ones was accepted by Ogren (1956a), who also noticed the decrease in density of somatic cells. None of these writers counted the total number of cells in the embryo, but this would have revealed whether the decrease in number is due to degeneration or change of cells into another type.

Another idea was presented by Ogren (1959a, 1962a), who considered that germinative cells develop from gland cells. It seems that this confusion is due to the increase of RNA in both types of cells. The differentiation of glands begins earlier than that of germinative cells, so that glands are the first cells to show increase of RNA. The subsequent accumulation of RNA in the neighbouring germinative cells could lead to the erroneous conclusion that the latter are daughter cells of the former. However, no division of gland cells was observed by Ogren and, furthermore (1959a, 1962a), the germinative cells could still be distinguished in an earlier phase before the glands were formed. Even theoretically, it seems unlikely that germinative cells can be formed from gland cells.

c. ONCOSPHERE (HEXACANTH)

The morphology of the oncosphere is quite constant in spite of the fact that earlier developmental phases undergo intense morphogenetic changes. The oncosphere can be defined briefly as a bilaterally symmetrical, spherical or oval embryo, armed with three pairs of hooks, containing a pair of glands and surrounded by embryonic envelopes. The derivation of oncospheral structure has been described above and their final appearance will now be reviewed.

1. Morphology

a. Cellular structure

As described above, two main oncospheral cell types are usually distinguished. The syncytial "somatic" cells are accumulated in the hook region and the "germinative" cells are located in the opposite hemisphere of the larva. The arrangement of oncospheral cells shows bilateral symmetry.

The number of somatic cells present is one of the main differences between pseudophyllidean and cyclophyllidean oncospheres. There are about 80–120 in the former (Fig. 26), whereas in the latter only a few somatic cells remain in the oncosphere after degeneration in the preoncosphere (Fig. 27). In *Catenotaenia pusilla* the degeneration is so remarkable that no somatic cell can be found in the oncosphere (Joyeux and Baer, 1945).

The somatic cells of most cyclophyllidean oncospheres are usually located near the hooks (Vogue, unpublished; Rybicka, 1964b), which suggests that

---

◄—FIG. 27. Degeneration of somatic cells in late preoncosphere of *Dipylidium caninum*. A–C, Subsequent sections of late preoncosphere; D–F, subsequent sections of the oncosphere. *co*, Coat; *e*, embryophore; *gc*, germinative cells; *gl*, penetration glands; *h*, hook; *oe*, outer envelope; *sc*, somatic cells. (After Rybicka, 1964a.)

they are in some way connected with the hooks or their musculature. Apart from the smaller somatic nuclei, two larger ones have been distinguished in numerous species (Ogren, 1957a, b, 1958, 1961a, 1962a; Rybicka, 1964b). These were found near the median hooks and were called by Ogren "the medullary contractile centre". He considered them to be the source of muscle cells, but no direct evidence for this hypothesis was presented.

The classification of oncospheral cells into two groups may be an over-simplification. The fact that some of the somatic cells degenerate, whereas others remain in the oncosphere, suggests that there are at least two different groups. Michajłow (1933) distinguished seven types of cells in the oncosphere of *Triaenophorus lucii* and Voge (unpublished) distinguished five types in *H. diminuta*. It is difficult to generalize at present about these types, particularly as nothing is known about their functional differences.

The germinative cells common in all tapeworm oncospheres are characterized by a large, feebly staining nucleus and a well-differentiated cytoplasmic layer, which stains with pyronin. They contain, as a rule, a prominent nucleolus.

The observations on early larval development (Vogel, 1930; Schiller, 1959; Rybicka, 1961a; Ogren, 1962a) indicate that the larva develops from germinative cells only. This conclusion is supported by the great accumulation of RNA in these cells, as that explains their developmental potentiality (Brachet, 1959, 1960).

b. The hooks

Three pairs of hooks, arranged in a hemisphere, are one of most typical features of the oncosphere or hexacanth. The shape of the embryonic hooks is basically the same in all oncospheres. Each hook has a long handle, a short collar (or guard) and a curved blade. More detailed study, however, reveals differences in the hook form. Fraser (1960), studying the hooks of three species of *Diphyllobothrium*, *D. medium*, *D. ditremum* and *D. dendriticum*, found a different form of hook to be constant for each species studied, and she concluded that the hooks provide a sound basis for specific identification. However, a comparison of hooks in eleven other pseudophyllidean onco-spheres (Hilliard, 1960) revealed that in four of them the hook form is fairly diagnostic, whereas in seven the hook structures are too variable to be of diagnostic value.

Abnormalities in the shape of embryonal hooks were often observed in the coracidium of *Triaenophorus lucii* (Michajłow, 1933).

Kates and McIntosh (1950) and Hwang and Kates (1956) studied embryonic hooks in numerous cyclophyllidean oncospheres. Their conclusions, summarized in the latter paper, were as follows. (i) In some species all hooks are identical and in others they are of either two or three morphological types. (ii) They vary in length from about 7 to 25 μ. (iii) Some hooks are robust in appearance and others are slender. (iv) Guards of hooks vary considerably in appearance and some hooks are without guards. (v) Handles of hooks may or may not terminate in a knob-like enlargement. (vi) Other minor variations have also been detected.

These conclusions are supported by Ogren (1957b, 1958) in a study of

Oochoristica symmetrica and *Dilepis undula*, where different types of hooks are found in the same species. In these species the medial blade is more sharply curved than the lateral blades, the hooks of the lateral pairs differ in shape and the dorsal hooks are more slender than the ventral ones which are the largest.

c. The muscles

Vogel (1930) observed two strands of muscle fibres attached to the hooks in the oncosphere of *Diphyllobothrium latum*; one strand is attached to the collar at one end and to the surface of the embryo near the hook at the other, while the second strand connects the base of the hook shank with the opposite pole of the oncosphere.

Michajłow (1933) has distinguished seventeen separate muscle cells in the hook musculature of *Triaenophorus lucii*. Each cell is pyriform and an elongated fibre is attached to the hook; at the distal end the cell is enlarged and this part contains the nucleus. Some transverse fibres connect the hooks. Some cells were attached to the collar, others to the end of the shank, as described by Vogel (1930) in *D. latum*.

A similar arrangement of muscle fibres was observed in cyclophyllidean oncospheres (Ogren, 1956a, 1958, 1961a, 1962a; Voge (unpublished). There

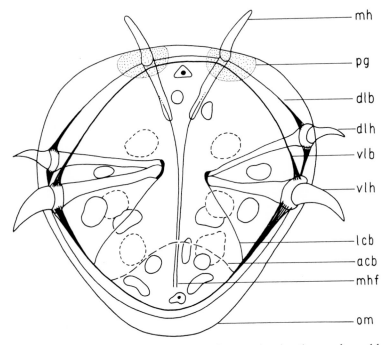

FIG. 28. The oncosphere of *Hymenolepis diminuta* showing the muscles and hooks. *abc*, Anterior connecting band; *dlb*, dorso-lateral band; *dlh*, dorso-lateral hook; *lcb*, lateral connecting band; *mh*, median hook; *mhf*, median hook fibres; *om*, oncospheral membrane; *pg*, penetration glands; *vlb*, ventro-lateral band; *vlh*, ventro-lateral hook. (Courtesy of Dr M. Voge.)

are two continuous bands, ventro-lateral and dorso-lateral, attached to the collars of lateral hooks, the slender median hook-fibres which extend from the shanks of median hooks towards the anterior end, and delicate connexions between the bases of lateral hooks and the anterior loops of the bands (Fig. 28). Ogren (1958) has also observed an irregular network of contractile fibres beneath the cuticle. He claimed that small nuclei are present in the muscle fibres, but these were not described by Voge (unpublished).

Ogren (1961b) and Ogren and Magill (1962) distinguished in oncospheres of *Hymenolepis diminuta* "a strong system of muscle fibres producing extension and another system responsible for retraction of the hooks. The system for extension is located in the cortex and the system of retraction is composed of the germinative cells of the oncosphere gland area." The last statement is based on the particular interpretation of glands and germinative cells proposed by Ogren, which will be discussed elsewhere (see Sections V, B, 2 and 5, and VI).

d. Oncospheral glands

Two types of glands have been described in tapeworm oncospheres: excretory glands found in the coracidia of Pseudophyllidea, and penetration glands found in cyclophyllidean oncospheres.

(i) *Excretory glands.* Excretory glands are composed of two cells, each with a nucleus, placed symmetrically below the lateral hooks. They were described for the first time by Vogel (1930) in the coracidium of *Diphyllobothrium latum* (Fig. 26B). A thin canal originates from the cell, in which an irregularly moving "flame" was seen. The gland duct opens by a pore near the hooks. A granular substance accumulates around the gland cell; granules showing a constant vibration were also observed by Rosen (1918). Excretory glands containing flame cells were also found in *D. decipiens* and *D. erinacei* (see Li, 1929), *Triaenophorus lucii* (see Michajłow, 1933) and *Bothriocephalus rarus* (see Thomas, 1937). Thomas often saw excretory granules in the gland ducts near the pores. Some vacuolate cells appeared near the flame cell.

(ii) *Penetration glands.* Typical secretory glands are found in cyclophyllidean oncospheres. These were noticed by Fülleborn (1922) in *Hymenolepis diminuta* and by Sinitsin (1930) in *Moniezia expansa*, but the first detailed study of such glands was carried out by Reid (1948) on *Raillietina cesticillus, Choanotaenia infundibulum, Hymenolepis* sp. and *Moniezia expansa*. Reid suggested that the secretion of the gland may help to penetrate the intermediate host and he introduced the term "penetration glands", which comprise the two cells located symmetrically behind the hooks and joined together by an isthmus to give a U-shaped mass (Fig. 29). The cells elongate towards the hook region. The pores open between the medial and lateral pairs of hooks. A recent study by Sawada (1961) indicated that there are two canals starting from each gland, thus two ventral and two dorsal canals are present in the oncosphere. Both open in the neighbourhood of the hooks.

These glands have been found in numerous species belonging to various families: Hymenolepididae (by Reid, 1948; Ogren, 1955a, 1961b, 1962a), Dilepididae (by Reid, 1948; Ogren, 1955b, 1959a; Rybicka, 1964a), Davaineidae (by Reid, 1948; Enigk and Sticinsky, 1957; Sawada, 1960, 1961),

Taeniidae (by Silverman, 1954b; Silverman and Maneely, 1955), Anoplocephalidae (by Sinitsin, 1930; Reid, 1948; Rybicka, 1964b), and Linstowiidae (by Rendtorff, 1948; Millemann, 1955; Ogren, 1957a; Gallati, 1959).

The glands are not always easy to distinguish, either in living oncospheres or in fixed materials, although vital staining with neutral red or brilliant cresyl blue and the use of phase contrast microscopy are advantageous. Even in related species striking differences in staining have been observed; in *Raillietina echinobothrium* the glands become stained with neutral red but remain unstained with brilliant cresyl blue, whereas contrary results were obtained in *R. kashiwarensis* (Sawada, 1960). In *Davainea proglottina* the glands remain invisible with the usual stains, but Enigk and Sticinsky (1957) were able to find them by the use of fluorescent microscopy. The oncospheres were stained with acridine orange and, by this method, the glands did not stain and appeared as cells which did not show fluorescence.

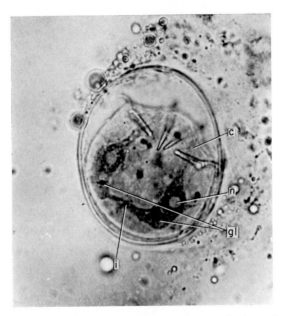

F IG . 29. Penetration glands in *Raillietina cesticillus*. *c*, Gland canal; *gl*, penetration glands; *i*, isthmus; *n*, nucleus of gland cell. (After Enigk and Sticinsky, 1957.)

The glands in *Taenia* (see Silverman and Maneely, 1955) and *Raillietina* (see Sawada, 1960, 1961) show a strongly PAS-positive reaction. The former writers suggest that as the PAS-positive reaction is not destroyed by saliva, glycogen is present.

Silverman and Maneely (1955) demonstrated the proteolytic or cytolytic action of the gland secretion in *Taenia*. The hatched embryos were injected into the lumen of the duodenum or ileum of freshly killed mice. During the process of lysis in the intestine wall chemical changes appear in the gland secretion. It gave a strongly PAS-positive reaction in the early stages of penetration and then appeared to be PAS-negative; this perhaps indicated that the enzymatic polysaccharide complex responsible for lysis of host intestinal cells was breaking down (Silverman and Maneely, 1955). Similar results were obtained by Sawada (1961) in *Raillietina cesticillus*. The oncospheres were studied in the intermediate host (*Tachys lactificus*). The glands showed a strongly PAS-positive reaction in oncospheres remaining in the intestine, but this reaction disappeared in those within the haemocoel of the host. This again indicated that the polysaccharide complex responsible for lysis was breaking down during the penetration process (Sawada, 1961).

Ogren (1957b) observed that gland secretion accumulates around the oncospheres of *Oochoristica symmetrica* covered by the oncospheral membrane. It is remarkable that in this instance the oncospheres found in the haemocoel of the intermediate host did not escape from the oncospheral membranes.

Sawada (1961) also observed the glands during the hatching of *R. cesticillus*. The secretion was discharged twice, during the escape from the embryophore and from the outermost shell membrane; only at this moment were the anterior canals clearly seen. After the oncosphere escaped the secretion was transferred gradually toward the glands. Two substances were distinguished in the secretion; that first discharged consisted of several vesicles, and the other contained many granules showing Brownian movement (Sawada, 1961).

The penetration glands described so far were composed in most cases of two cells. However, in *Davainea proglottina* four gland cells were found (Enigk and Sticinsky, 1957) (Fig. 30). The two relatively large lateral glands

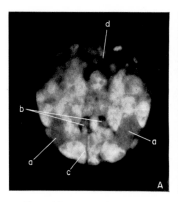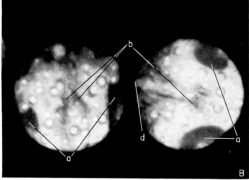

FIG. 30. Penetration glands in *Davainea proglottina* observed by fluorescent microscope. *a*, Lateral glands; *b*, medial glands; *c*, canal of medial glands; *d*, hooks region. (After Enigk and Sticinsky, 1957.)

resembled the penetration glands observed in other species, and from the two smaller medial glands thin ducts arose and were opened by small pores Enigk and Sticinsky did not give any explanation of the glands.

According to Ogren (1961b, 1962a) the glands are composed of numerous cells, "at least four groups of cells having contractile and probably secretory functions". It seems likely that in this instance the gland cells were not clearly distinguished from the neighbouring cells.

The proteolytic nature and cytolytic role of the gland secretion seems to be unquestionable, although the nature of the enzymes involved has not been determined. The secretion appears to take a part in the hatching of the oncosphere, as well as its penetration of the intermediate host.

(iii) *Discussion*. As already mentioned (p. 162), excretory glands, in form of unicellular protonephridia, have been described only in pseudophyllidean oncospheres, whereas in cyclophyllidean oncospheres only secretory penetration glands have been found so far. This difference is surprising, particularly when we consider the general similarity of oncospheres in both groups and also their behaviour in the intermediate host. The protonephridia in their original form are considered to be osmoregulatory rather than excretory in function (Beklemishev, 1952). Possibly coracidia moving freely in water require an efficient osmoregulatory system, whereas cyclophyllidean oncospheres transported passively to the intermediate host do not need one. However, we do not understand why coracidia lack penetration glands when such glands are well developed in cyclophyllidean oncospheres which infect the same kinds of intermediate hosts (e.g. Copepoda). The difficulty of finding the glands in the oncosphere and the different reaction of various species to the same stains, suggests that penetration glands may exist also in Pseudophyllidea, but have not yet been discovered. The functions of the different types of cells observed by Michajłow (1933) in *Triaenophorus lucii* have not been explained and some of the cells may represent penetration glands.

Regarding the lack of excretory glands in cyclophyllidean oncospheres, it is noteworthy that of four gland cells found in *Davainea proglottina* by Enigk and Sticinsky (1957) (Fig. 30), two lateral cells resemble typical penetration glands. However, the smaller size of the medial glands and the presence of thin ducts arising from them bears some resemblance to excretory glands observed in coracidia. Protonephridia are usually difficult to observe and it is likely that they have been overlooked in the cyclophyllidean cestodes studied.

Ogren (1957b) suggested that "epidermal glands" occur in Hymenolepididae and Linstowiidae, differing from penetration glands by the lack of ducts and pores. According to Ogren (1955a, 1957b), the glandular secretion passes through the body surface and the cuticle of the oncosphere, but Sawada (1961) observed that the ducts are visible for a short period when the secretion is being discharged. Voge (see Fig. 28) showed the penetration glands in an unusual location in *H. diminuta*. Comparison of her observation and that of Sawada (1961) suggests that Voge may have observed the secretion at the actual moment of the discharge, when the gland ducts were filled with secretion.

2. Embryonic Envelopes

The ways in which four embryonic envelopes are formed has been discussed above. Two of them (the outer and inner envelopes) undergo the greatest modifications. The schemes represented in Figs. 18 and 19 do not, however. include all the various arrangements. It is well known that in addition to spherical eggs there are oval, spindle-like, hexagonal and other forms. Moreover, the homologous layers of envelopes vary in structure and chemical composition from species to species. For example, *Paricterotaenia porosa* and *Moniezia expansa* both belong to group A (Fig. 19), but the former has a relatively thin, membraneous coat which swells readily in water (Bona, 1957), and the latter an extremely thick coat of specific hexagonal structure and composed of three layers (Sinitsin, 1930), and its hardening is due to the presence of a keratin-type protein (Hoy and Clegg, unpublished). It is noteworthy that Anoplocephalidae are the only Cyclophyllidea known to have a coat containing keratin. In some species the egg surface is spinous, as noted by Calentine and Ulmer (1961) in the caryophylleid *Khawia iowensis* or by Freeman (1949) in the anoplocephalid *Monoecocestus*. Hilliard (1960) found that the egg-shell of some marine Diphyllobothriidae is pitted, but a recent electron micrograph prepared by this writer (personal communication) indicates that the pits are, in fact, cavities, the surface of the egg-shell having a spongy appearance (Fig. 31).

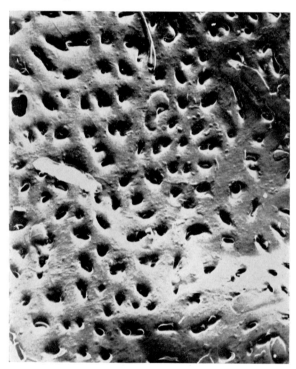

Fig. 31. An electron micrograph of the egg-shell surface in *Diphyllobothrium cordatum*. × 2400. (Courtesy of Dr D. K. Hilliard.)

The embryophore may occur in forms characteristic for families (Taeniidae, Anoplocephalidae), but in some groups it is as a relatively thin membrane. Unfortunately, the term embryophore has not been used consistently in respect of various groups. In Pseudophyllidea, the whole ciliated inner envelope is termed the "embryophore", but in Cyclophyllidea this term is usually reserved for only the hardened part of inner envelope. Another point to note is that in most studies on living oncospheres only the somewhat hardened parts of the envelopes can be distinguished, and these have been termed membranes, shells and coats. The layers between the membrane are often regarded as spaces, although cytoplasm remains and even degenerating nuclei can be seen therein. The ontogenetical description given here serves to clarify the origin of membranes as well as the intervening "spaces". The various terms used by writers to denote particular envelopes or membranes (Table I) must indicate which are comparable from an ontogenetical point of view.

Almost nothing is known about the formation of the embryonic envelopes of Proteocephalidae. The general appearance of the eggs is very similar to that of Cyclophyllidea, and this suggests a similar embryonic development. The coat and the thick outer envelope are invariably seen clearly in this group, and a pair of funnel-like depressions commonly appears in the outer envelope (Meggitt, 1914; Essex, 1927; Magath, 1929; Herde, 1938; Jones et al., 1958). The cytoplasmic layer of the outer envelope was described by Essex (1927) as a gelatinous formation. The inner envelope is relatively less differentiated and it contains the nuclei, as in Pseudophyllidea (Meggitt, 1914; Thomas, 1937; Jones et al., 1958).

The oncospheral membrane in this group is readily observed to enclose the hatching embryo as it emerges from the embryophore, but still remains within the outer envelope.

3. The "Eggs" and their Viability

When pseudophyllidean and cyclophyllidean "eggs" are compared, attention should be paid to the different meaning of the term "egg" in the two groups. In Pseudophyllidea the egg must undergo two developmental phases: (i) embryonation involving cleavage and formation of the preoncosphere, and (ii) perfection of the oncosphere. In Cyclophyllidea the term egg usually implies simply the oncosphere in its envelopes.

a. Pseudophyllidea

The pseudophyllidean eggs embryonate at room temperature within 4–10 days (Vogel, 1929; Michajłow, 1933; Guttowa, 1955, 1961). Then, under suitable conditions (see p. 169), the coracidium usually hatches, although low temperatures delay embryonation. Guttowa (1955) found that at 0–2°C embryonation is inhibited in *Triaenophorus lucii*, but after freezing, eggs embryonate at room temperature in 5–6 days. The duration of freezing determines the numbers of oncospheres which hatch, and a temperature of 0–2°C for 42 days is lethal. However, a temperature of 5–6°C does not inhibit embryonation of the eggs of *T. lucii* (Guttowa, 1958; Watson and Lawler, 1963).

According to Hilliard (1960), the eggs of *Diphyllobothrium ursi* and *D. dalliae* remain viable for 4–5 months at 2°C, but the eggs of *Schistocephalus solidus* will not embryonate when kept at this temperature for a "short" period. Mueller (1959) stored the eggs of *Spirometra mansonoides* at 4°C for 1 month without deterioration. In these instances, low temperature was studied as a factor delaying embryonation, but not the hatching of the oncosphere. The eggs of *Diphyllobothrium latum* require a light stimulus for hatching (Vogel, 1929; Hilliard, 1960; Grabiec *et al.*, 1963b). In this species the formed oncospheres remain viable when eggs are kept in darkness, although according to Guttowa (1961) the oncospheres die within 3–4 weeks. On the other hand, Hilliard (1960) found that at 20°C 60% of the eggs of *D. dalliae* and 20% of the eggs of *D. ursi* hatched after 31 days in darkness.

Coracidia live 1–3 days at room temperature (Vogel, 1929; Michajłow, 1933; Hilliard, 1960; Guttowa, 1958, 1961).

b. Cyclophyllidea

There is little information about the viability of cyclophyllidean eggs. The eggs of species developing in water remain viable for at least 2 weeks at room temperature (Kisielewska, 1957; Jarecka, 1960). Kisielewska noticed that the eggs of *Drepanidotaenia lanceolata* remained viable for about 25 days at 2–4°C. Taeniid eggs are particularly resistant to low temperature. Lucker (1960) stored the eggs of *Taenia saginata* at − 5°C for 76 days, and Schiller (1955) showed that the eggs of *Echinococcus sibiricensis* (= *multilocularis*) can withstand sub-zero temperatures, some eggs remaining infective after 54 days at − 24°C or after 24 h at − 51°C.

Although available data are insufficient for comparative study, the oncospheres of Cyclophyllidea appear to be more resistant than the coracidia and the already formed oncospheres within the egg capsules of Pseudophyllidea.

The physiology of oncospheres is not known, but morphological and cytological stability suggests that this phase has a low metabolic rate. As a rule, the oncosphere does not move within its envelopes. Grabiec *et al.* (1964) pointed out that even within the "swimming" coracidium of *D. latum* the oncosphere remains motionless within the embryophore. Moreover, they suggested that in spite of the developing embryos the coracidia do not use oxygen; this seems to support the idea of low metabolic rate of the oncosphere.

In some cases movement of cyclophyllidean oncospheres has been observed (Venard, 1938; Abdou, 1958); this was, however, concerned with hatching, which in some species occurs spontaneously in water. A similar movement of oncospheres occurs in Proteocephalidae (Essex, 1927; Jarecka, 1960), but according to Herde (1938) and Freeman (1963) movement of proteocephalid oncospheres begins if the outer membranes are ruptured.

4. Hatching

The term "hatching" is commonly used in different senses in Pseudophyllidea and Cyclophyllidea and needs some definition. Pseudophyllidea are believed to hatch in the external world independently of any intermediate host, and Cyclophyllidea within the body of an intermediate host (Smyth, 1963; Clegg and Smyth, 1966). Here two different events are being compared.

The form leaving the operculate capsule in Pseudophyllidea is a coracidium, i.e. an oncosphere surrounded by its inner envelope. For further development it must hatch from this envelope (or embryophore), and this takes place within the intermediate host as in Cyclophyllidea. The comparison is particularly striking when Taeniidae are considered, because in this group the outer envelope is usually lost and the form entering the intermediate host is also an oncosphere surrounded by its embryophore.

Evidently it is difficult to relate exactly similar phases of hatching in the two groups, because different modes of embryonation have resulted in different egg structures and some specificity of hatching mechanisms. It is necessary, however, to indicate the series of homologous events occurring in Pseudophyllidea and Cyclophyllidea. This seems to be the process of hatching of the naked embryo (oncosphere) from its envelopes, which takes place within the intermediate host in all cestodes.

a. Hatching of coracidium

In pseudophyllideans hatching takes place through the opening of their operculate capsule. Nothing is known about the chemical nature of the materials which seal the operculum, but it is considered to be more labile and susceptible to attack by biochemical or mechanical agents than the sclerotin capsule (Smyth, 1963). Some pseudophyllideans require light for hatching (see Vogel, 1930; Smyth, 1955; Mueller, 1959; Hilliard, 1960; Grabiec et al., 1963b), and in these species light may act as a stimulus to release an enzyme which attacks the opercular seal. However, in other species, sometimes belonging to the same genera, the coracidia can hatch in darkness (Hilliard, 1960; Guttowa, 1958).

Hatching in water as described above is restricted to operculate eggs. The eggs of Pseudophyllidea develop within the uterus and are discharged into water. According to Vik (1963), the oncospheres of Eubothrium crassum can live inside the egg capsule for at least 10 days. However, if the capsule is ruptured in water, the oncosphere disintegrates in a few minutes. Similarly, the caryophylleid oncosphere remains alive in an egg capsule for a long time, but does not hatch in water (Sekutowicz, 1934).

b. Hatching of the oncosphere

Factors stimulating hatching of the oncosphere occur in the intermediate host, although hatching can usually be induced by artificial means. Researches on hatching mechanisms and chemistry have been reviewed by Smyth (1963), who recognized two processes in hatching: (i) release of the hexacanth embryo from its membrane, and (ii) activation of the embryo. The two processes are closely correlated, although in some species they occur sequentially. According to Berntzen and Voge (1962), activation of the oncosphere is essential for hatching. The following definition of hatching is tentatively proposed, namely that hatching is the release of the embryo from its envelopes. It appears to occur as a result of three events: (i) the mechanical activity of the embryo, (ii) the lytic action of oncospheral glands, and (iii) the action of the enzymes of the host in stimulating the embryo and perhaps dissolving the embryonic envelopes. The enzyme systems involved in the last two processes have not been precisely identified. Both the mechanical and lytic action of the oncosphere are usually stimulated by some factor or factors in the host, although in some cases spontaneous activity may arise. The same stimuli resulting in these activities may play a different role in different species.

It is well known that proteocephalid oncospheres readily release their embryophores, when the eggs are in water (Herde, 1938) and the hatched embryo remains within the outer envelope. Similar hatching was observed in davaineid oncospheres in various salt solutions (Taylor, 1926; Reid et al., 1949). The detailed study on *Raillietina cesticillus* by Sawada (1961) clearly indicates that the secretion of the penetration glands acts as one of the principal hatching stimuli, additional to the activity of the embryo produced by means of hooks and contractile movements. The oncosphere first releases the embryophore and then the outer envelope.

In *Dipylidium* (see Venard, 1938), *Hymenolepis diminuta* (see Schiller, 1959; Voge and Berntzen, 1961) and *H. citelli* (see Berntzen and Voge, 1962) the first event observed in hatching is the rupture of the outer envelope, clearly facilitated by the action of a digestive substance of the host (Schiller, 1959; Voge and Berntzen, 1961) (Fig. 32). As a result of active movements of the embryo and perhaps of its lytic activity, the oncosphere, surrounded by the embryophore and inner envelope, leaves the outer envelope and then hatches from the embryophore. It is notable that the sequence of hatching in this group resembles that observed in Pseudophyllidea. In *Hymenolepis nana*, two types of eggs are present in the same segment, type A differing from the better-known type B in the absence of polar filaments. It is interesting to note that these types differ in their reactions to hatching solutions as well as in their mode of hatching (Berntzen and Voge, 1962).

In Taeniidae the outer envelope is lost in the uterus as a rule, although Meymarian (1961) observed it around *Echinococcus* eggs. In this species, the outer envelope broke down in physiological saline. Hatching from the taeniid embryophore apparently needs the previous digestion of the cement substance uniting the embryophoral blocks. There are some specific differences in the composition of this substance despite the general resemblance of the embryophore in all Taeniidae. In *Echinococcus granulosus* (see Ross, 1929; Berberian, 1957; Meymarian, 1961), *Taenia pisiformis* (see Silverman, 1954b) and *Hydatigera taeniaeformis* (see Bullock et al., 1934) it could be digested by pancreatin, but not by pepsin, except in *T. saginata* where it was digested by pepsin, but not by pancreatin (Silverman, 1954a).

VI. Discussion

Although most studies on embryogenesis in cestodes have been carried out on species belonging to the Cyclophyllidea, a comparison with fragmentary observations from other groups, and above all from Pseudophyllidea, indicates a common general pattern of embryogenesis in cestodes. This pattern can be briefly summarized as follows:

(1) Spermatogenesis follows the pattern typical of the platyhelminthes, sixty-four spermatozoa arising in each cluster.

(2) Oogenesis begins in the ovary, but is completed in the uterus, where maturation of the oocyte occurs.

(3) Vitelline cells aggregate with the oocyte when entering the uterus.

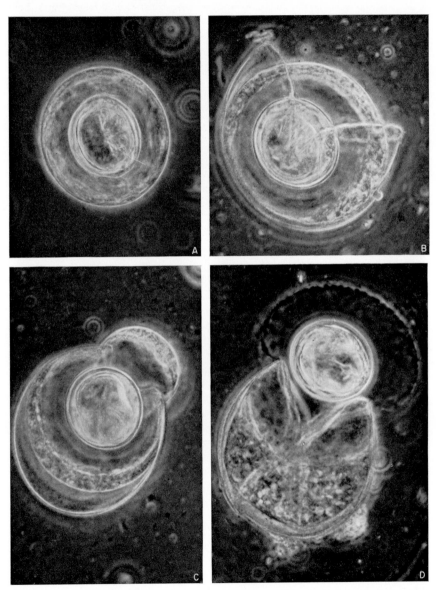

FIG. 32. Hatching of *Hymenolepis diminuta*. A, Intact egg; B, the first step in hatching of the coat; C, the oncosphere in its inner envelope beginning to emerge. D, the inner envelope separate from the coat and outer envelope, the latter is seen as a granular mass within the shell. (After Voge and Berntzen, 1961.)

These cells carry the materials forming the egg capsule and secrete them after the passage through Mehlis's gland.

(4) In cleavage, three types of blastomeres are formed: macromeres, forming the outer envelope; micromeres, degenerating at the early preoncosphere stage; mesomeres, multiplying and differentiating in further development.

(5) In the preoncosphere phase, the cells differentiate into those forming: (a) the inner envelope, (b) hooks and their musculature, (c) glands, (d) somatic and germinative cells. The oncospheral membrane is secreted by the embryo.

(6) The germinative cells of the oncosphere seem to be the only elements from which the future larva and the adult cestode develop.

In spite of morphological and chemical differences observed in various cestode eggs, homologous structures formed according to the described pattern can be found.

Ogren (1953, 1957a) has distinguished some different patterns in cestode embryology and his hypothesis needs a more detailed discussion on the basis of the points considered above. According to this author, the type of the oocyte (see p. 119) determines the early cleavage pattern and therefore:

(1) The "conglomerate oocytes" have a cleavage in which one series of blastomeres is excluded from the embryo, so that only one-half of the zygote takes part in forming the embryo. This pattern would be typical for Cyclophyllidea.

(2) The "granular oocytes" appear to have a cleavage in which all the blastomeres form the embryo, and this would take place in Pseudophyllidea and Proteocephalidae.

It is obvious that the blastomeres excluded from the embryo in Cyclophyllidea are the macromeres forming the outer envelope. Although not many studies exist on the early development in Pseudophyllidea and Proteocephalidae, both the papers of Schauinsland (1886) on the former and of Ogren (1953, Pl. X, Fig. 238) on the latter indicate that in these groups the macromeres are excluded from the embryo and form its outer envelope. Thus at the present state of our knowledge the division of cestode embryos into those developing from a half zygote and those developing from the entire zygote seems to be unjustified.

In a further classification of cestode embryos Ogren (1953) distinguished the following groups:

"(1) An embryophore-stereogastrula is covered by a detached embryophore or epidermis composed of a few squamous cells. This structure is membraneous and surrounds the oncosphere, or inner cell mass bearing six hooks (hexacanth embryo). The oncosphere is composed of ectomesoderm (somatic cells) and contains a few to many large entomesoderm (plastin cells) situated in the presumptive anterior region.

"(2) A ciliafore-stereogastrula consists of a detached, ciliated epidermis. The oncosphere contains two flame cells, ectomesoderm and entomesoderm.

"(3) An oncosphere-stereogastrula is essentially an oncosphere from which the epidermis has not detached to form the embryophore. Epidermal cells become filled with active granules involved in membrane formation and form structures termed granular zones (Reid's glands). Six hooks, ectomesoderm and entomesoderm are present as in other oncospheres."

The main basis for this classification is the mode of embryophore forma-tion. In the embryophore-stereogastrula and ciliafore-stereogastrula the embryophore is formed by detachment of some embryonic cells, which agrees with the general pattern observed in cestodes. The exception would be an oncosphere-stereogastrula. According to Ogren (1953), in this group a non-cellular pseudoembryophore is formed from two membranes arising by the fusion of shell granules. Nuclei from the secondary macromere (i.e. these forming the outer envelope) are incorporated between these granules. Among cyclophyllideans whose embryonic development has been studied in detail, the following species belong to this group: *Hymenolepis nana*, *Dilepis undula*, *Diorchis inflata* and *Oochoristica symmetrica* (see Ogren, 1953). Moriyama (1961a, b) and Rybicka (1966) indicate that the embryophore in *Hymenolepis* is formed from some cells detached from the embryo. Also, Ogren (per-sonal communication) has recently confirmed that in *Hymenolepis* "there are 2 subshell nuclei present (presumably those of the outer envelope, K.R.) and 3–4 nuclei of macromeres in the embryophore (presumably those of inner envelope, K.R.) and the development of a dilepidid tapeworm is like *Hymeno-lepis*". Thus the formation of embryonic envelopes in *Hymenolepis* and *Dilepis* seems to follow the common cestode pattern (see also Section V, C, 2). The same holds good for *Diorchis inflata* as described by Spätlich (1925), whose results are confirmed by re-examination of *D. ransomi* (see p. 148). The case of *Oochoristica symmetrica* is particularly enigmatic. In this species according to Ogren (1953, 1957a, b) neither the macromeres forming the outer envelope nor the cells forming the inner one are detached from the embryo. However, the mature oncosphere is surrounded by the outer and inner envelopes typical for other cestodes. Moreover, Ogren's own drawings of early embryonic phases indicate the presence of nuclei of cells forming these envelopes (see Ogren, 1953, Pl. VII, Figs. 177–182; Ogren, 1957a, Fig. 32; Ogren, 1957b, Figs. 10, 11, 15, 30) (see also p. 145). It seems more than probable that *Oochoristica symmetrica* also follows the same general pattern of the forma-tion of embryonic envelopes.

The other basis for separation of an oncosphere-stereogastrula (Ogren, 1953) was the presence of granulation zones in this group. These zones are clearly the penetration glands. As has been indicated by recent studies, these glands seem to be present in the all-cyclophyllidean oncospheres, although striking differences in their staining have been detected (see Section V, C, 1, d). Thus they are easily visible in some species, whereas in others more com-plicated staining methods are needed. Such differences are as yet an insuffi-cient basis for separating different groups among cestode embryos, particu-larly as the chemical differences in glands are not precisely known.

Ogren's (1953) original suggestion on the role of granulation zones, in forming the embryonic membranes, has been supplemented in subsequent studies by this author. He states that a granulation zone (or epidermal glands) is responsible for the formation of germinative cells (Ogren, 1959a, 1962a) and then that the system of muscle retraction is composed of the germinative cells of the oncosphere gland area (Ogren and Magill, 1962). For the present writer none of the published evidence on the formation of embryonic envelopes in cestodes (see Section V, B, 2), on development and function of the germinative cells (see Section V, B, 5 and C, 1, a), as well as on the development and function of penetration glands (see Section V, B, 4 and C, 1, d) seems to support Ogren's hypothesis on the function of the glands.

Finally, Ogren (1957b) distinguished seven groups among cestode embryos. The basis for this classification is the hypothesis discussed above, as well as the final structure of the embryophore. As has been pointed out by Jarecka (1961), the variety of forms of embryonic envelopes in cestodes seems to indicate some morphological adaptation to the environment rather than a phylogenetical relationship. In this respect, the way in which envelopes are formed seems to be the more important phylogenetic criterion than their final structure. For example, there is a striking similarity in the formation of embryonic envelopes of *Paricterotaenia* (see Bona, 1957) and *Moniezia* (see Rybicka, 1964b), in spite of differences in final structure of the envelopes.

The intention of present writer has been to make clear the general pattern of embryonic development common to all cestodes. It seems possible that many future detailed studies will reveal some criteria for further subdividing this main general pattern. However, at the present time the criteria proposed in Ogren's hypothesis (1953) do not seem to be justified.

Generally, it seems that the changes in the developing embryo are more significant from a phylogenetical point of view than those in its envelopes. When the cellular composition of pseudophyllidean and cyclophyllidean oncospheres is compared, it is clear that there are differences in the number of their somatic cells. A pseudophyllidean oncosphere contains many (over 100) somatic cells. In Cyclophyllidea, a similar increase in number is observed during embryonic development, but at the end of the preoncosphere phase most of these cells degenerate and only a few remain in the oncosphere. Thus, bearing this feature in mind, the pseudophyllidean oncosphere can be compared with the late preoncosphere of Cyclophyllidea; the oncosphere of the latter seems to be a new phase of embryonic development arising in a phylogenetically more recent group.

It should be pointed out that in both groups somatic cells form a syncytial structure in which the cytoplasm is lacking in RNA and contains small pycnotic nuclei. Such a structure indicates that the cells are degenerating. According to Vogel (1930), the somatic cells of *Diphyllobothrium* degenerate in the early procercoid, as do those of Cyclophyllidea in the late preoncosphere. Thus, the point of prolongation of embryonic development in Cyclophyllidea in comparison with that of Pseudophyllidea is that some events occurring in larval development of the latter are included in the embryonic development of the former. From this point of view, the homologous phases of development in both groups can be represented as in Fig. 33.

It is difficult to speculate about the phylogenetic significance of cell degeneration, particularly when nothing is known in this field for other cestode groups. Further study of this process may be useful to elucidate cestode embryology and possible phylogenetic relationships. Of particular interest are the Proteocephalidae, the structure of whose female genitalia resembles that of Pseudophyllidea whereas the oncosphere is rather similar to that of Cyclophyllidea.

Very little is known about the physiological mechanism underlying embryonic development. In this field, an embryologist clearly needs the cooperation of biochemists. It should be pointed out that in the biochemical studies carried out so far on cestodes the embryological problem has been somewhat neglected. This is quite surprising, as the great simplification of most cestode organs, with simultaneous extensive development of their reproductive system, suggests that the latter play a predominant role in these animals and presumably the metabolism of the adult cestodes is influenced to a major degree by the development of its embryos.

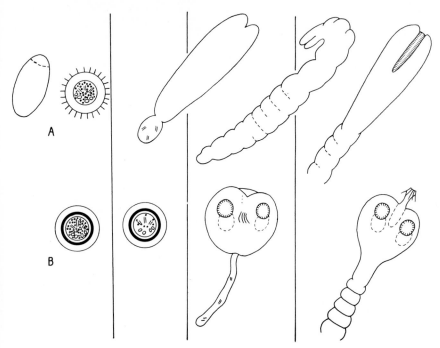

FIG. 33. Diagram of the life cycle of Pseudophyllidea (A) and Cyclophyllidea (B). Vertical lines show possible homologue phases of development.

It is well known from studies on other animals that differences in metabolism occur during the various phases of embryonic development (Needham, 1950; Brachet, 1960). Since the various phases occur successively along the strobila in adult cestodes, one would expect metabolic differences along the strobila. Unfortunately, there exist very few biochemical studies where the separate fragments of strobila have been analysed biochemically.

In this respect, let us briefly review studies which have been made on the role of carbohydrates in cestodes. Most of them have been carried out on

Hymenolepis diminuta and have indicated that in cestodes the lack of utilizable carbohydrates results in a decrease in growth and reproduction which is correlated with a simultaneous decrease in its glycogen content (Read and Rothman, 1957a–c; Read, 1959). In only three papers known to the author has the distribution of glycogen along the strobila been studied (Read, 1956; Daugherty and Taylor, 1956; Fairbairn *et al.*, 1961). Unfortunately, in each of these studies the cestode has been divided in a different manner and, moreover, the description of the particular fragments is inadequate for embryological interpretation. Furthermore, the results of these authors differ. According to Read (1956) and Daugherty and Taylor (1956), there is a maximum glycogen accumulation in the central part of the strobila with a decrease towards the anterior and posterior end. This could be explained by concluding that the most intense glycogen synthesis occurs during early embryonic development, and decreases at the late preoncosphere and oncosphere phases. Such a conclusion seems to be supported by studies on other species. In *H. nana*, a cestode having a limited life-span, the lack of carbohydrates in host's diet was found to influence reproduction only in the early period after infection (Read *et al.*, 1958), presumably, that is, during the early or middle embryonic developmental phases. On the other hand, the lack of carbohydrates did not influence the reproduction of *Schistocephalus*, whose embryonic development occurs in water (Hopkins, 1950, 1952), but in this species the plerocercoid has abundant glycogen reserves. These results support the general conclusion on the significance of carbohydrates for early and middle embryonic development, and thus explain the results of Read (1956) and Daugherty and Taylor (1956) which indicate that in this period the maximum amount of glycogen is accumulated in respective parts of the strobila. However, Fairbairn *et al.* (1961), studying *H. diminuta*, found no essential difference in carbohydrate content between (a) immature proglottids, (b) mature proglottids, and (c) pre-gravid and gravid proglottids. It should, however, be pointed out that in the studies by Read and Daugherty and Taylor glycogen was estimated in relation to the wet weight, but in relation to the dry weight by Fairbairn *et al.* One can assume that the older segments of strobila perhaps contain more water, which results in an apparent decrease in glycogen when compared to the wet weight. On the other hand, Fairbairn *et al.* compared also the "infective" proglottids (the terminal 50 mm of the strobila) where a prominent decrease in glycogen was found, even in relation to the dry weight.

The above review indicates how difficult it is, at present, to draw any conclusions about the physiology of embryogenesis. It seems necessary to correlate closely biochemical with embryological researches, where each part of the strobila could be exactly defined in respect of the phase of embryonic development reached.

VII. Pattern for Further Study

In surveying the embryogenesis of cestodes it is clear that many gaps exist in our knowledge. Even morphogenesis has been studied in a few species only and most of them belonging to one order, the Cyclophyllidea. Some fragmentary information is available about Pseudophyllidea, but nothing is known about cestodes of other orders. It is evident that information about these unknown groups would be of particular value for comparative embryology and consequently for phylogenetic studies on cestodes.

Modern techniques in embryological study include histochemistry. However, in only few studies have histochemical methods been used and further investigation along these lines is clearly needed. Most of the available histochemical information deals with changes in RNA and glycogen during embryonic development, but almost nothing is known about other chemical substances in the embryo. The commonly used term "vitelline material" or "nutritive store" in vitelline cells or oocytes has never been defined in chemical terms. It may be that, in Cyclophyllidea, the role of vitelline cells is reduced mainly to the formation of a thin egg capsule, and the "nutritive material" in this group is accumulated in the oocyte. However, without detailed histochemical study this problem cannot be solved. It is also clear that an increased use of histochemical and perhaps microchemical methods will be necessary to clarify the function of Mehlis's gland.

The form and function of embryonic envelopes represent a separate problem. The variety of their final forms has been commented upon for a long time. As has been indicated in the present review, the various forms of envelopes are comparable from an ontogenetic point of view. The differences in the final forms are undoubtedly connected with differences in their chemistry, but except for the sclerotin capsule in Pseudophyllidea little is known about the chemistry of other envelopes.

The development and physiology of the penetration glands is of particular interest. These glands seem to be common in all Cyclophyllidea, but can they really be absent in pseudophyllidean oncospheres when there exists species from both groups which develop in the same intermediate hosts (e.g. Copepoda)? A similar question arises regarding the osmoregulatory glands found so far only in pseudophyllidean oncospheres.

Besides histochemical methods, cytological studies are useful in embryological research. In this respect early embryos seem to provide the best material for study of chromosome structure in cestodes.

A new field opened for the embryologist is that provided by electron microscopy, which seems to have estimable value in the study of cestode embryos because of their small size, the light microscope being in many cases insufficient. Unfortunately, apart from the studies of Morseth (1965) and some studies on spermatogenesis, electron microscopy has not been used so far in cestode embryology.

The need for co-operation between biochemists and embryologists has already been stressed in Section VI. It seems quite possible to culture some specimens of one species under the same conditions, as is usual in biochemical studies. Two worms cultured in this way can be used, one for biochemical and the other for histochemical analysis, in order to define exactly the various phases of embryonic development.

New prospects for such study seem to arise from recent progress in culture *in vitro*. Berntzen (1961, 1962) has developed a successful system for *in vitro* cultivation. In his study (1962) *Hymenolepis nana* was grown *in vitro* from the cysticercoid stage to adults containing infective eggs. Eggs obtained from worms grown *in vitro* were fed to beetles and normal infective cysticercoids were recovered. Schiller (1965) achieved excellent results by simple methods with *H. diminuta*. The cysticercoids obtained from the eggs of cestodes grown *in vitro* were then fed to rats and gave a second generation of adult cestodes.

Read (1958), in a discussion on physiological and behavioural "resistance", gave a comical but perhaps relevant comparison: "We may feel a bit like Dr E. Racker's drunkard who lost the key to his door and searched for it under the street lamp where the light was more favourable for the search. Dr Racker's friend found a key, but in his drunkenness he could not determine if it was his own. But what a fine time he had, sitting on his doorstep, dreaming of all the castles it might open." Presumably our castles are closed by many keys and perhaps embryology can be regarded as one supplementary key useful for the opening of many castles!

ACKNOWLEDGEMENTS

It is a pleasure to acknowledge my indebtedness to Professor J. D. Smyth (Canberra, Australia) for much help and encouragement and valuable criticism of the work at the manuscript stage. I am grateful to Professor Wl. Michajlow (Warsaw, Poland) for enabling me to carry out this work in his laboratory, and give thanks also to Dr A. Duncan (London, England) for checking the English of this paper.

I am grateful to Dr C. H. von Bonsdorff and Dr A. Telkkä (Finland), Professor H. Enigk (Germany), Dr D. K. Hilliard (Alaska), Dr R. E. Ogren (U.S.A.), Dr B. Rosario (U.S.A.), Dr I. M. Sandeman (Canada), Professor J. D. Smyth (Australia), Professor R. Vik (Norway) and Dr M. Voge (U.S.A.) for their original photographs included in this paper. Thanks are also given to all Editors for permission to use the drawings from their Journals.

REFERENCES

Abdou, A. H. (1958). Studies on the development of *Davainea proglottina* in the intermediate host. *J. Parasit.* **44**, 484–488.

Beklemishev, V. N. (1952). "Osnovy Sravnitelnoi Anatomii Bespozvonochnych." Sovetskaia Nauka, Moscow.

Beneden, E. van, (1881). Recherches sur le développement embryonnaire de quelques Ténias. *Archs Biol., Paris* **2**, 183–210.

Berberian, D. A. (1957). Host specifity and the effect of digestive juices on ova of *Echinococcus granulosus. Rep. Orient Hosp., Beirut* **10**, 33–43.

Berntzen, A. K. (1961). The *in vitro* cultivation of tapeworms. I. Growth of *Hymenolepis diminuta* (Cestoda: Cyclophyllidea). *J. Parasit.* **47**, 351–355.

Berntzen, A. K. (1962). *In vitro* cultivation of tapeworms. II. Growth and maintenance of *Hymenolepis nana* (Cestoda: Cyclophyllidea). *J. Parasit.* **48**, 787–797.

Berntzen, A. K., and Voge, M. (1962). *In vitro* hatching of oncospheres of *Hymenolepis citelli* (Cestoda: Cyclophyllidea). *J. Parasit.* **48**, 110–119.

Bischoff, C. R. (1913). Cestoden aus Hyrax. *Revue suisse Zool.* **21**, 225–284.

Bogomolova, H. A., and Pavlova, L. J. (1961). Zheltonochnye kletki *Fasciola hepatica* i *Diphyllobothrium latum* i ich rol v obrazovanii obolochki iaica i pitanii zarodysha. *Helminthologia* 3, 47–59.

Bona, F. V. (1957). La formazione dei gusci embrionali e la morphologia dell utero in *Paricterotaenia porosa* (Rud., 1810) quali elementi di giudizio per la validita del gen. *Paricterotaenia* Fuhrmann, 1932 (Cestoda, Dilepididae). *Riv. Parassit.* 18, 155–184.

Bonsdorff, C.-H., von, and Telkkä, A. (1965). The spermatozoon flagella in *Diphyllobothrium latum* (fish tapeworm). *Z. Zellforsch. mikrosk. Anat.* 66, 643–648.

Brachet, J. (1959). "The Biological Role of Ribonucleic Acids." Elsevier, Amsterdam.

Brachet, J. (1960). "The Biochemistry of Development." Pergamon Press, New York.

Brand, T. von, (1933). Untersuchungen über den Stoffbestand einiger Cestoden und den Stoffbewechsel von *Moniezia expansa*. *Z. vergl. Physiol.* 18, 562–596.

Brand, T. von, (1952). "Chemical Physiology of Endoparasitic Animals." Academic Press, New York.

Brault, A., and Loeper, M. (1904). Le glycogène dans le développement de certains parasites (cestodes et nematodes). *J. Physiol. Path. gén.* 6, 503–512.

Bullock, F. D., Dunning, W. F., and Curtis, M. B. (1934). Observations on the digestion of the shells of the eggs of *Taenia taenieformis*. *Am. J. Cancer* 20, 390–397.

Calentine, R. L., and Ulmer, M. J. (1961). *Khawia iowensis* n. sp. (Cestoda: Caryophylleidae) from *Cyprinus carpio* L. in Iowa. *J. Parasit.* 47, 795–805.

Cason, J. E. (1950). A rapid one-step Mallory-Heidenhein stain for connective tissue. *Stain Technol.* 25, 225–226.

Cheng, T. C., and Dyckman, E. (1964). Sites of glycogen deposition in *Hymenolepis diminuta* during the growth phase in the rat host. *Z. ParasitKde* 24, 27–48.

Cheng, T. C., and Jacknick, L. (1964). A cytochemical determination of DNA and RNA in *Hymenolepis diminuta* during the growth phase in the rat host. *Z. ParasitKde* 24, 49–64.

Child, C. (1907). Studies on the relation between amitosis and mitosis. III. Maturation, fertilization and cleavage in *Moniezia*. *Biol. Bull. mar. biol. Lab. Woods Hole* 13, 138–160.

Clegg, J. A. (1966). *In* "Symposium on Mucosubstances in Invertebrates." *Ann. N.Y. Acad. Sci.* (In press)

Clegg, J. A., and Smyth, J. D. (1966). Growth, development and culture methods; parasitic platyhelminthes. *In* "Chemical Zoology" (M. Florkin and B. T. Scheer, eds.). Academic Press, New York. (In press)

Coil, W. H. (1963). The genera *Gyrocoelia* Fuhrmann, 1899, and *Infula* Burt, 1939, with observation on the histochemistry of the egg membranes. *Proc. helminth. Soc. Wash.* 30, 111–117.

Daugherty, J. W., and Taylor, D. (1956). Regional distribution of glycogen in the rat cestode *Hymenolepis diminuta*. *Expl Parasit.* 5, 376–390.

Dawes, B. (1940). Notes on the formation of the egg capsules in the monogenetic trematode *Hexacotyle extensicauda* Dawes, 1940. *Parasitology* 32, 287–295.

Dhingra, O. P. (1954). Gametogenesis and fertilization in *Isoparorchis eurytremum*. *Res. Bull. Panjab Univ. Sci.* 44, 21–37.

Douglas, L. T. (1957). The spermatogenesis of two nematotaeniid cestodes. *J. Parasit.* 43, Suppl. 24.

Douglas, L. T. (1962). Experimental studies on morphological variation in the cestode genus *Hymenolepis*. VI. Somatic pairing of chromosomes in normal and mutant strains of *H. diminuta*. *Expl Parasit.* 12, 134–154.

Douglas, L. T. (1963). The development of organ systems in nematotaeniid cestodes. III. Gametogenesis and embryonic development in *Baerietta diana* and *Distoichometra kozloffi*. *J. Parasit.* **49**, 530–558.

Enigk, K., and Sticinsky, E. (1957). Über die Bohrdrüsen der Oncosphäre von *Davainea proglottina* (Cestoidea). *Z. ParasitKde* **18**, 48–54.

Essex, H. E. (1927). The structure and development of *Corallobothrium*. *Illinois biol. Monogr.* **11**, 257–328.

Fairbairn, D., Wertheim, G., Harpur, R. P., and Schiller, E. L. (1961). Biochemistry of normal and irradiated strains of *Hymenolepis diminuta*. *Expl Parasit.* **11**, 248–263.

Franzen, A. (1956). On spermiogenesis, morphology of the spermatozoon and biology of fertilization among invertebrates. *Zool. Bidr. Uppsala* **31**, 355–482.

Fraser, P. G. (1960). The form of the larval hooks as a means of separating species of *Diphyllobothrium*. *J. Helminth.* **34**, 73–80.

Freeman, R. S. (1949). Notes on the morphology and life cycle of the genus *Monoecocestus* Beddard, 1914 (Cestoda: Anoplocephalidae) from the porcupine. *J. Parasit.* **35**, 605–612.

Freeman, R. S. (1963). On the biology of *Proteocephalus parallacticus* Maclulich (Cestoda) in Algonquin Park, Canada. *Can. J. Zool.* **42**, 387–407.

Fülleborn, F. (1922). Über *Hymenolepis diminuta* (Rud.) 1819. *Arch. Schiffs- u. Tropenhyg.* **26**, 193–202.

Gallati, W. (1959). Life history, morphology and taxonomy of *Atriotaenia* (*Ershovia*) *procyonis* (Cestoda: Linstowiidae) a parasite of the raccoon. *J. Parasit.* **45**, 363–377.

Grabiec, S., Guttowa, A., and Michajłow, W. (1962). New data on the ciliated envelope of the coracidium of *Triaenophorus nodulosus* (Pall.) (Cestoda, Pseudophyllidea). *Bull. Acad. pol. Sci. Cl.II Sér. Sci. biol.* **10**, 439–441.

Grabiec, S., Guttowa, A., and Michajłow, W. (1963a). Structure of the ciliated envelope of the coracidium of *Diphyllobothrium latum* (L.) (Cestoda, Pseudophyllidea). *Bull. Acad. pol. Sci. Cl.II Sér. Sci. biol.* **11**, 293–294.

Grabiec, S., Guttowa, A., and Michajłow, W. (1963b). Effect of light stimulus on hatching of coracidia of *Diphyllobothrium latum* (L.). *Acta parasit. pol.* **11**, 229–238.

Grabiec, S., Guttowa, A., and Michajłow, W. (1964). Investigation on the respiratory metabolism of eggs and coracidia of *Diphyllobothrium latum* (L.), Cestoda. *Bull. Acad. pol. Sci. Cl.II Sér. Sci. biol.* **12**, 29–34.

Gresson, R. A. R. (1962). Spermatogenesis of Cestoda. *Nature, Lond.* **194**, 397–398.

Gresson, R. A. R. (1965). Spermatogenesis in hermaphroditic Digenea (Trematoda). *Parasitology* **55**, 117–125.

Gresson, R. A. R., and Perry, M. H. (1961). Electron microscope studies of spermateleosis in *Fasciola hepatica* L. *Expl Cell Res.* **22**, 1–8.

Guttowa, A. (1955). O inwazyjności onkosfer *Triaenophorus lucii* (Müll.) i jej zmienności. *Acta parasit. pol.* **3**, 447–465.

Guttowa, A. (1958). Dalsze badania nad wpływem temperatury na rozwój zarodków tasiemca *Triaenophorus lucii* (Müll.) w jajeczkach oraz inwazyjność powstałych z nich onkosfer. *Acta parasit. pol.* **6**, 367–381.

Guttowa, A. (1961). Experimental investigations on the systems "procercoids of *Diphyllobothrium latum* (L.)—Copepoda". *Acta parasit. pol.* **9**, 371–408.

Hanumantha-Rao, K. (1959). Histochemistry of Mehlis' gland and egg-shell formation in the liver fluke *Fasciola hepatica*. *Experientia* **15**, 464–468.

Hanumantha-Rao, K. (1960a). Studies on *Penetrocephalus ganapatii*, a new genus (Cestoda: Pseudophyllidea) from the marine teleost *Saurida tumbii* (Bloch). *Parasitology* **50**, 155–163.

Hanumantha-Rao, K. (1960b). The problem of Mehlis' gland in helminths with special reference to *Penetrocephalus ganapatii* (Cestoda: Pseudophyllidea). *Parasitology* 50, 349–350.

Hedrick, R. M. (1958). Comparative histochemical studies on cestodes. II. The distribution of fat substances in *Hymenolepis diminuta* and *Raillietina cesticillus*. *J. Parasit.* 44, 75–84.

Hedrick, R. M., and Daugherty, J. W. (1957). Comparative histochemical studies on cestodes. I. The distribution of glycogen in *Hymenolepis diminuta* and *Raillietina cesticillus*. *J. Parasit.* 43, 497–504.

Hendelberg, J. (1962). Paired flagella and nucleus migration in the spermatogenesis of *Dicrocoelium* and *Fasciola* (Digenea, Trematoda). *Zool. Bidr. Uppsala* 35, 569–588.

Herde, K. E. (1938). Early development of *Ophiotaenia perspicua* La Rue. *Trans. Am. microsc. Soc.* 57, 282–291.

Hilliard, D. K. (1960). Studies on the helminth fauna of Alaska. XXXVIII. The taxonomic significance of eggs and coracidia of some diphyllobothriid cestodes. *J. Parasit.* 46, 703–716.

Hopkins, C. A. (1950). Studies on cestode metabolism. I. Glycogen metabolism in *Schistocephalus in vivo. J. Parasit.* 36, 384–390.

Hopkins, C. A. (1952). Studies on cestode metabolism. II. The utilization of glycogen by *Schistocephalus in vitro. Expl Parasit.* 1, 196–213.

Hwang, J. C., and Kates, K. C. (1956). Morphological variations in the embryonic hooks of tapeworms. *J. Parasit.* 42, Suppl. 41.

Janicki, K. (1906). Zur Embryonalentwicklung von *Taenia serrata* Goeze. *Zool. Anz.* 30, 763–768.

Janicki, K. (1907). Über die Embryonalentwicklung von *Taenia serrata* Goeze. *Z. wiss. Zool.* 87, 685–724.

Jarecka, L. (1958). Plankton crustaceans in the life cycle of tapeworms occurring at Drużno lake. *Acta parasit. pol.* 6, 65–104.

Jarecka, L. (1960). Life-cycles of tapeworms from lakes Gołdapiwo and Mamry Północne. *Acta parasit. pol.* 8, 47–66.

Jarecka, L. (1961). Morphological adaptations of tapeworm eggs and their importance in the life-cycles. *Acta parasit. pol.* 9, 409–426.

Jarecka, L. (1964). Cycle évolutif a un seul hote intermédiaire chez *Bothriocephalus claviceps* (Goeze, 1782) cestode de *Anguilla anguilla* L. *Annls Parasit. hum. comp.* 39, 149–156.

Johri, L. N. (1957). A morphological and histochemical study of egg formation in a cyclophyllidean cestode. *Parasitology* 47, 21–29.

Jones, A. W., Cheng, T. C., and Gillespie, R. F. (1958). *Ophiotaenia gracilis* n.sp., a proteocephalid cestode from a frog. *J. Tenn. Acad. Sci.* 33, 84–88.

Joyeux, Ch., and Baer, J. C. (1945). Morphologie, évolution et position systématique de *Catenotaenia pusilla* (Goeze, 1782). *Revue suisse Zool.* 52, 13–51.

Kates, K. C., and McIntosh, A. (1950). The embyronic hooks of some anoplocephalid cestode of mammals. *J. Parasit.* 36, Suppl. 45.

Kisielewska, K. (1957). Wpływ niektórych czynników na przeżywanie i inwazyjność jaj tasiemca *Drepanidotaenia lanceolata* (Bloch) oraz na dalszy rozwój powstałych z nich larw. *Acta parasit. pol.* 5, 585–598.

Kuhlow, F. (1953). Über die Entwicklung und Anatomie von *Diphyllobothrium dendriticum* Nitsch, 1824. *Z. ParasitKde* 16, 1–35.

Lee, H. H. K., Jones, A. W., and Wyant, K. D. (1959). Development of taeniid embryophore. *Trans. Am. microsc. Soc.* 78, 355–357.

Leuckart, R. (1856). "Die Blasenbandwürmer und ihre Entwicklung." Giessen.

Leuckart, R. (1886). "Die Parasiten des Menschen und die von ihnen herrührended Krankheiten," 2nd ed. Leipzig.

Li, H. C. (1929). The life histories of *Diphyllobothrium decipiens* and *D. erinacei*. *Am. J. Hyg.* **10**, 527–550.

Lucker, J. T. (1960). A test of the resistance of *Taenia saginata* eggs to freezing. *J. Parasit.* **46**, 304.

Magath, T. B. (1929). The early life-history of *Crepidobothrium testuda* (Magath, 1924). *Ann. trop. Med. Parasit.* **23**, 121–127.

Meggitt, F. J. (1914). The structure and life-history of a tapeworm (*Ichtyotaenia filicollis* Rud.) parasitic in the stickleback. *Proc. zool. Soc. Lond.* **1**, 113–138.

Meymarian, E. (1961). Host-parasite relationships in *Echinococcus*. VI. Hatching and activation of *Echinococcus granulosus* ova *in vitro*. *Am. J. trop. Med. Hyg.* **10**, 719–726.

Michajłow, W. (1933). Les stades larvaires de *Triaenophorus nodulosus* (Pall.). I. Le coracidium. *Annls Parasit. hum. comp.* **11**, 339–358.

Millemann, R. E. (1955). Studies on the life-history and biology of *Oochoristica deserti* n.sp. (Cestoda: Linstowiidae) from desert rodents. *J. Parasit.* **41**, 424–440.

Moniez, R. (1881). Mémoires sur les cestodes. *Trav. Inst. Zool. Lille* **3**, 1–238.

Moriyama, S. (1961a). Studies on the structure and embryonal development of the ova of Tetrabothridiata. I. On the structure and embryonal development of the ova of *Hymenolepis diminuta* (Rudolphi, 1819) Blanchard, 1891. *Jap. J. Parasit.* **10**, 272–278.

Moriyama, S. (1961b). Studies on the structure and embryonic development of the ova of Tetrabothridiata. II. The structure and embryonic development of *Hymenolepis nana* ova. *Jap. J. Parasit.* **10**, 279–288.

Moriyama, S. (1961c). Studies on the structure and embryonic development of the ova of Tetrabothridiata. III. The structure and embryonic development of *Taenia saginata* ova. *Jap. J. Parasit.* **10**, 289–297.

Morseth, D. J. (1965). Ultrastructure of developing taeniid embryophores and associated structures. *Expl Parasit.* **16**, 207–216.

Morseth, D. J. (1966). Chemical composition of embryophoric blocks of *Taenia hydatigena*, *Taenia ovis* and *Taenia pisiformis* eggs. *Expl Parasit.* **18**, 347–354.

Motomura, I. (1929). On the early development of monozoic cestode, *Archigetes appendiculatus*, including oogenesis and fertilization. *Annotnes zool. jap.* **12**, 104–129.

Mueller, J. F. (1959). The laboratory propagation of *Spirometra monsonoides* as an experimental tool. I. Collecting, incubation and hatching of eggs. *J. Parasit.* **45**, 353–361.

Needham, J. (1950). "Biochemistry and Morphogenesis." Cambridge University Press.

Nez, M. M., and Short, R. B. (1957). Gametogenesis in *Schistosomatium douthitti* (Cort) (Schistosomatidae: Trematoda). *J. Parasit.* **43**, 167–182.

Ogren, R. E. (1953). Concepts of early tapeworm development derived from comparative embryology of onchospheres. Thesis, University of Illinois.

Ogren, R. E. (1955a). Development and morphology of glandular regions in on-cospheres of *Hymenolepis nana*. *Proc. Pa Acad. Sci.* **29**, 258–264.

Ogren, R. E. (1955b). Studies in embryology and histology of the robin tapeworm (*Choanotaenia iola*) Lincicome (Cyclophyllidea: Dipylidiinae) with description of the metachromatic glands in the oncosphere. *J. Parasit.* **41**, Suppl. 31–32.

Ogren, R. E. (1956a). Development and morphology of the oncosphere of *Mesocestoides corti*, a tapeworm of mammals. *J. Parasit.* **42**, 414–428.

Ogren, R. E. (1956b). Embryonic development and morphology of the tapeworm *Oochoristica symmetrica* (Cyclophyllidea: Linstowiidae). *J. Parasit.* **42**, Suppl. 30.

Ogren, R. E. (1957a). Embryonic development of the tapeworm *Oochoristica symmetrica* (Cyclophyllidea: Linstowiidae). *Proc. Pa Acad. Sci.* **31**, 147–160.

Ogren, R. E. (1957b). Morphology and development of oncospheres of the cestode *Oochoristica symmetrica* Baylis. *J. Parasit.* **43**, 505–520.

Ogren, R. E. (1958). The hexacanth embryo of a dilepidid tapeworm. I. The development of hooks and contractile parenchyma. *J. Parasit.* **44**, 477–483.

Ogren, R. E. (1959a). The hexacanth embryo of a dilepidid tapeworm. II. the epidermal glands and post-maturation changes. *J. Parasit.* **45**, 575–579.

Ogren, R. E. (1959b). The hexacanth embryo of a dilepidid tapeworm. III. The formation of shell and inner capsule around the oncosphere. *J. Parasit.* **45**, 580–585.

Ogren, R. E. (1961a). Observations on hook development in the oncoblasts of hexacanth embryo from *Hymenolepis diminuta*, a tapeworm of mammals (Cestoda: Cyclophyllidea). *Proc. Pa Acad. Sci.* **35**, 23–31.

Ogren, R. E. (1961b). The mature oncosphere of *Hymenolepis diminuta*. *J. Parasit.* **47**, 197–204.

Ogren, R. E. (1962a). Continuity of morphology from oncosphere to early cycticercoid in the development of *Hymenolepis diminuta* (Cestoda: Cyclophyllidea). *Expl Parasit.* **12**, 1–6.

Ogren, R. E. (1962b). Embryonic development of a dilepidid tapeworm. *Trans. Am. microsc. Soc.* **81**, 65–72.

Ogren, R. E., and Magill, R. M. (1962). Demonstration of protein in the protective envelopes and embryonic muscle in oncospheres of *Hymenolepis diminuta*, a tapeworm of mammals. *Proc. Pa Acad. Sci.* **36**, 160–167.

Ortner-Schönbach, P. (1913). Zur Morphologie des Glykogens bei Trematoden und Cestoden. *Arch. Zellforsch.* **11**, 413–449.

Pashchenko, L. F. (1961). Rannie stadii spermatogeneza u *Taeniarhynchus saginatus* Goeze, 1782. *Probl. Parasit. Kiev* **1**, 112–122.

Pavlova, L. I. (1963). Sravnitelnoe morfologicheskoe i citochimiceskoe issledovanie gametogeneza, oplodotvorenia i formirovania iaica lentochnych chervey (*Diphyllobothrium latum* i *Taeniarhynchus saginatus*). *Materialy Nauchnoi Konf. Vsesoyuz. Obschest. Gelm.* or *Mat. sci. Conf. Soc. Helm.*, Moscow, 1963, **2**, 34–36.

Pearse, A. G. E. (1953). "Histochemistry." Churchill, London.

Read, C. P. (1956). Carbohydrate metabolism of *Hymenolepis diminuta*. *Expl Parasit.* **5**, 325–344.

Read, C. P. (1958). Status of behavioral and physiological "resistance". *Rice Inst. Pamph.* **45**, 36–54.

Read, C. P. (1959). The role of carbohydrate in the biology of cestodes. VIII. Some conclusions and hypotheses. *Expl Parasit.* **8**, 365–382.

Read, C. P., and Rothman, A. H. (1957a). The role of carbohydrates in the biology of cestodes. I. The effect of dietary carbohydrate quality on the size of *Hymenolepis diminuta*. *Expl Parasit.* **6**, 1–7.

Read, C. P., and Rothman, A. H. (1957b). The role of carbohydrates in the biology of cestodes. II. The effect of starvation on glycogenesis and glucose consumption in *Hymenolepis*. *Expl Parasit.* **6**, 280–287.

Read, C. P., and Rothman, A. H. (1957c). The role of carbohydrates in the biology of cestodes. IV. Some effects of host dietary carbohydrate on growth and reproduction of *Hymenolepis*. *Expl Parasit.* **6**, 294–305.

Read, C. P., Schiller, E. L., and Phifer, K. (1958). The role of carbohydrates in the biology of cestodes. V. Comparative studies on the effects of host dietary carbohydrate on *Hymenolepis* sp. *Expl Parasit.* **7**, 198–216.

Reid, W. M. (1948). Penetration glands in cyclophyllidean oncospheres. *Trans. Am. microsc. Soc.* **67**, 177–182.

Reid, W. M., Nice, S. J., and McIntyre, R. C. (1949). Certain factors which influence activation of the fowl hexacanth embryo of the fowl tapeworm *Raillietina cesticillus. Trans. Ill. St. Acad. Sci.* **42**, 165–168.

Rendtorff, R. C. (1948). Investigation on the life cycle of *Oochoristica ratti*, a cestode from rats and mice. *J. Parasit.* **34**, 243–252.

Retzius, G. (1909). Die Spermien der Cestoden und der Trematoden. B. Die Spermien der Trematoden. *Biol. Unters.* **14**, 72.

Richards, A. (1909). On the method of cell division in *Taenia. Biol. Bull. mar. biol. Lab. Woods Hole* **17**, 309–326.

Rosario, B. (1964). An electron microscope study of spermatogenesis in cestodes. *J. Ultrastruct. Res.* **11**, 412–427.

Rosen, F. (1918). Recherches sur le développement embryonnaire des cestodes. I. Le cycle évolutif des *Bothriocephales. Bull. Soc. neuchâtel. Sci. nat.* **43**, 241–300.

Ross, I. C. (1929). Observations on the hydatic parasite (*Echinococcus granulosus*) and the control of hydatid disease in Australia. *Bull. Coun. scient. ind. Res. Aust.* **40**, 63 pp.

Rybicka, K. (1960). Glycogen distribution during the embryonic development of the cestode *Diorchis ransomi* Schultz, 1940. *Expl Parasit.* **10**, 268–273.

Rybicka, K. (1961a). Morphological and cytochemical studies on the development of the cestode *Diorchis ransomi* Schultz, 1940. *Acta parasit. pol.* **9**, 279–304.

Rybicka, K. (1961b). Cell reduction in the embryonic development of the cestode *Diorchis ransomi* Schultz, 1940. *Nature, Lond.* **192**, 771–772.

Rybicka, K. (1962a). Observations sur la spermatogenèse d'un cestode Pseudophyllidien *Triaenophorus lucii* (Müll., 1776). *Bull. Soc. neuchâtel. Sci. nat.* **85**, 177–181.

Rybicka, K. (1962b). La spermatogenèse du cestode *Dipylidium caninum* (L.). *Bull. Soc. zool. Fr.* **87**, 225–228.

Rybicka, K. (1964a). Gametogenesis and embryonic development in *Dipylidium caninum. Expl Parasit.* **15**, 293–313.

Rybicka, K. (1964b). Embryonic development of *Moniezia expansa* (Rud., 1810) (Cyclophyllidea, Anoplocephalidae). *Acta parasit. pol.* **12**, 313–330.

Rybicka, K. (1964c). Attempt of general approach to the embryology of cyclophyllidean cestodes. *Acta parasit. pol.* **12**, 327–338.

Rybicka, K. (1965). The embryonic envelopes in cyclophyllidean cestodes. *Acta parasit. pol.* **13**, 25–34.

Rybicka, K. (1966). Embryogenesis in *Hymenolepis diminuta*. I. Morphogenesis. *Expl Parasit.* (In press)

St Remy, G. (1900). Le développement embryonaire dans le genre *Anoplocephala*. Contribution à l'étude du développement des cestodes. I. *Archs Parasit.* **3**, 293–315.

St Remy, G. (1901a). Contributions à l'étude du développement des cestodes. 1. Le développement embryonaire de *Taenia serrata* Goeze. *Archs Parasit.* **4**, 143–156.

St Remy, G. (1901b). Sur embryologie du *Taenia serrata. C.r. hebd. Séanc. Acad. Sci., Paris* **132**, 43–45.

Sawada, I. (1960). Penetration glands in onchospheres of the chicken tapeworms *Raillietina cesticillus* and *Raillietina kashiwarensis. Z. ParasitKde.* **20**, 350–354.

Sawada, I. (1961). Penetration glands in the onchospheres of *Raillietina cesticillus*. *Expl Parasit.* **11**, 141–146.

Schauinsland, H. (1886). Die embryonale Entwicklung der Bothriocephalen. *Jena. Z. Naturw.* **19**, 520–578.

Schiller, E. L. (1955). Studies on the helminth fauna of Alaska. XXVI. Some observations on the cold-resistance of eggs of *Echinococcus sibiricensis* Rausch and Schiller, 1954. *J. Parasit.* **41**, 578–582.

Schiller, E. L. (1959). Experimental studies on morphological variation in the cestode genus *Hymenolepis*. I. Morphology and development of cysticercoid of *H. nana* in *Tribolium confusum*. *Expl Parasit.* **8**, 91–118.

Schiller, E. L. (1965). A simplified method for the *in vitro* cultivation of the rat tapeworm, *Hymenolepis diminuta*. *J. Parasit.* **51**, 516–518.

Sekutowicz, S. (1934). Untersuchungen zur Entwicklung und Biologie von *Caryophyllaeus laticeps* (Pall.). *Mém. Acad. pol. Sci.* **6**, 11–26.

Shapiro, J. E., Hershenov, B. R., and Tulloch, G. S. (1961). The fine structure of haematolechus spermatozoon tail. *J. biophys. biochem. Cytol.* **9**, 211–217.

Silverman, P. H. (1954a). Studies on the biology of some tapeworms of the genus *Taenia*. I. Factors affecting hatching and activation of taeniid ova and some criteria of their viability. *Ann. trop. Med. Parasit.* **48**, 207–215.

Silverman, P. H. (1954b). Studies on the biology of some tapeworms of the genus *Taenia*. II. The morphology and development of the taeniid hexacanth embryo and its enclosing membranes, with some notes on the state of development and propagation in gravid segments. *Ann. trop. Med. Parasit.* **49**, 23–38.

Silverman, P. H., and Maneely, R. B. (1955). Studies on the biology of some tapeworms of the genus *Taenia*. III. The role of the secreting gland of the hexacanth embryo in the penetration of the intestinal mucosa of the intermediate host, and some of its histochemical reactions. *Ann. trop. Med. Parasit.* **49**, 326–330.

Sinitsin, D. F. (1930). A glimpse into the life history of the tapeworms of sheep. *J. Parasit.* **17**, 223–227.

Smyth, J. D. (1947). The physiology of tapeworms. *Biol. Rev.* **22**, 213–238.

Smyth, J. D. (1954). A technique for the histochemical reaction of polyphenol oxidase and its application to egg-shell formation in helminths and byssus formation in *Mytilus*. *Q. Jl microsc. Sci.* **95**, 139–152.

Smyth, J. D. (1955). Problems relating to the *in vitro* cultivation of pseudophyllidean cestodes from egg to adult. *Revta ibér. Parasit.*, Tomo Extraordinario, 65–86.

Smyth, J. D. (1956). Studies on tapeworm physiology. IX. A histochemical study of egg shell formation of *Schistocephalus solidus* (Pseudophyllidea). *Expl Parasit.* **5**, 519–540.

Smyth, J. D. (1962). "Introduction to Animal Parasitology." The English Universities Press, London.

Smyth, J. D. (1963). The biology of cestode life-cycles. *Techn. Commun. Commonw. Bur. Helminth.* **34**, 1–38.

Smyth, J. D., and Clegg, J. A. (1959). Egg-shell formation in trematodes and cestodes. *Expl Parasit.* **8**, 286–323.

Spätlich, W. (1925). Die Furchung und Embryonalhüllenbildung des Eies von *Diorchis inflata* Rud. *Zool. Jb.* Abt. Anat. **47**, 101–112.

Swiderski, Z. (1966). Embryonic development of the tapeworm *Drepanidotaenia lanceolata* (Bloch, 1782) (Cyclophyllidea, Hymenolepididae). *Acta parasit. pol.* (In press)

Taylor, E. L. (1926). An observation on the hatching of a cestode egg. *Ann. trop. Med. Parasit.* **20**, 220.

Thomas, L. J. (1937). Environmental relations and life history of the tapeworm *Bothriocephalus rarus* Thomas. *J. Parasit.* **23**, 133–152.

Venard, C. E. (1938). Morphology, bionomics and taxonomy of the cestode *Dipylidium caninum. Ann. N. Y. Acad. Sci.* **37**, 273–328.

Vergeer, T. (1936). The eggs and coracidia of *Diphyllobothrium latum. Pap. Mich. Acad. Sci.* **21**, 715–726.

Vik, R. (1963). Studies on the helminth fauna of Norway. IV. Occurrence and distribution of *Eubothrium crassum* (Bloch, 1779) and *E. salvelini* (Schrank, 1790) (Cestoda) in Norway with notes on their life cycles. *Nytt Mag. Zool.* **11**, 47–73.

Voge, M., and Berntzen, K. (1961). *In vitro* hatching of oncospheres of *Hymenolepis diminuta* (Cestoda: Cyclophyllidea). *J. Parasit.* **47**, 813–818.

Vogel, H. (1929). Studies zur Entwicklung von *Diphyllobothrium.* I Teil: Die Wimperlarve von *Diphyllobothrium latum. Z. ParasitKde.* **2**, 213–222.

Vogel, H. (1930). Studien zur Entwicklung von *Diphyllobothrium.* II Teil: Die Entwicklung des Procercoids von *D. latum. Z. ParasitKde.* **2**, 629–644.

Wardle, R. A. (1937). The physiology of the sheep tapeworm *Moniezia expansa* Blanchard. *Can. J. Res.* D, **15**, 117–126.

Watson, N. H. F., and Lawler, C. H. (1963). Temperature and rate of hatching of *Triaenophorus* eggs. *J. Fish. Res. Bd Can.* **20**, 249–251.

Wiśniewski, W. L. (1930). Das Genus *Archigetes* R. Leuck. Eine Studie zur Anatomie, Histogenese, Systematik und Biologie. *Mém. Acad. pol. Sci.* B, **2**, 1–160.

Yamao, Y. (1952). Histochemical studies on endoparasites. IX. On the distribution of glycogen. *Zool. Mag., Tokyo* **61**, 317–322.

Young, R. T. (1913). The histogenesis of the reproductive organs of *Taenia pisiformis. Zool. Jb* Abt. Anat. **35**, 355–418.

The Structure and Composition of the Helminth Cuticle

D. L. LEE

*The Molteno Institute of Biology and Parasitology,
University of Cambridge, Cambridge, England*

I. INTRODUCTION

The structure and composition of the cuticle of parasitic worms has been studied increasingly during the past few years. There is a demand for information about the role of the cuticle in nutrition, the penetration of anthelmintics, immunology, locomotion and moulting, and the development of a variety of techniques has enabled such studies to be carried out. This contribution deals mainly with recent studies on the cuticle, but earlier findings will be summarized in each section. As a group, helminths are worm-like animals of unrelated kinds, many of which are parasitic. The groups considered include the

Trematoda and Cestoda (Platyhelminthes), the Nematoda and the Acantho-cephala. In its usual connotation the term "helminth" refers especially to parasitic worms, but many nematodes are non-parasitic and the structure of the cuticle of free-living species must be considered in order to reach any firm conclusions about the nature of the nematode cuticle.

II. PLATYHELMINTHES

The phylum Platyhelminthes is divided into three classes: the Turbellaria or free-living flatworms, the Trematoda of flukes, and the Cestoda or tape-worms. The Turbellaria are covered by a cellular or syncytial epidermis, which is usually ciliated, but they are not regarded as helminths and so will be con-sidered only in relation to the origins of the outer covering of the Trematoda and Cestoda. Until recently an epidermis has been considered absent in the Trematoda and Cestoda and the body surface was believed to be a secreted, non-living cuticle. The body surface of those trematodes and cestodes which have been examined with the electron microscope is not covered by a non-living layer, but by a layer of living cytoplasm which is in continuity with large cell-like structures sunk in the parenchyma, and this has led to some confusion in terminology. The term "cuticle", which means an outer skin, is un-fortunately associated in the minds of most biologists with a tough, non-living layer. Threadgold (1963b) suggested that the whole structure should be called a "tegument" and that the cuticle and its sunken portions should be called the outer and inner layers of the tegument. This terminology could lead to con-fusion when describing the outer and inner layers of the outer layer. Burton (1964) called it an "integument" and referred to the cuticle as the distal cytoplasm and the sunken cell-like bodies as the perinuclear cytoplasm, but this assumes that the nuclei of the outer covering are going to be buried in cell-like bodies in the parenchyma in all species and this may not be so. The terms tegument and integument also have non-living implications. The outer covering with its sunken portions conforms with the conception of sunken epidermal cells in free-living turbellarians (Fig. 10; see also Section V), and it is proposed to call the whole structure an epidermis in the trematodes and cestodes. This will be further discussed in Section V.

III. TREMATODA

A. HISTORICAL

Early work on the structure and composition of the "cuticle" of trematodes was summarized by Hyman (1951a) in the following terms.

The trematodes lack an epidermis and are clothed instead with a resistant cuticle. The homology and origin of this cuticle have long been disputed, and several theories have been advanced: (1) that the cuticle is an altered and degenerated epidermis; (2) that it is the basement membrane of the former epidermis; (3) that it is the outer layer of an insunk epidermis, the cells and nuclei of which have sunk beneath the subcuticular musculature; (4) that the cells in question are not epi-dermal but are mesenchmal (parenchymal) cells that secrete the cuticle, and (5) that the cuticle is secreted by the ordinary mesenchyme, not by special cells.

After reviewing the available evidence, Hyman decided that theories (4) and (5) were the most acceptable. It is important to note, however, that nuclei, or bodies resembling them, have been described in the cuticle of some larval and adult Digenea (see Dawes, 1946: 1956). Very little has been done by early workers on the chemical nature of the cuticle, which has been regarded as a scleroprotein.

B. STRUCTURE

The recent advances in our knowledge of the structure of the outer covering came when the electron microscope was applied to the study of digenetic trematodes. Using the light microscope, Alvarado (1951a) distinguished a basal layer (lamina vitrea), a limiting membrane, a cuticular epithelium and a thin epicuticle in *Fasciola hepatica*. The epithelial layer bears the spines and contains structures which were interpreted as vertical, parallel tonofibrils interspersed with chains of radially arranged granules. Alvarado suggested that the spines are formed from compacted tonofibrils, and he also found bodies resembling nuclei in various stages of degeneration, which indicates the existence of an original cellular epithelium. Alvarado (1951b) also showed that the lining of the genital cavities of *F. hepatica* is an extension of the outer layer.

The electron microscope studies of Threadgold (1963a, b) and Björkman and Thorsell (1964) revealed a continuous layer of cytoplasm, 15–21 μ thick, and not an amorphous, non-living cuticle, covering the external surface of *F. hepatica*. The surface of this cytoplasmic layer has a plasma membrane about 10 mμ thick, many invaginations and numerous underlying pinocytotic vesicles which appear to be pinched off from these ingrowths. The outermost part has a dense appearance because of the crowding of vacuoles, vesicles and granules (see Fig. 1). Here and there the external surface is evaginated to form minute balloon-shaped bodies containing finely granular materials and these are pinched off and discarded.

Beneath this dense outer zone there are numerous mitochondria arranged in rows perpendicular to the surface (Fig. 2). These mitochondria, which are probably the chains of granules described by Alvarado (1951a), have a dense matrix and are crossed by only one longitudinal crista. Small ovoid bodies ($< 0{\cdot}1$ μ long) each having a double membrane but lacking internal membranes, are present among the mitochondria. Rough endoplasmic reticulum is sparse, but smooth endoplasmic membranes are orientated parallel to the rows of mitochondria. Numerous small, dense, rod-shaped bodies, 20–30 mμ in cross-section, are present between the mitochondria and are also concentrated close to the surface. Small vesicles, about 150 mμ in diameter, which contain dense granules, and numerous membrane-bounded vacuoles of various sizes are also present.

The epidermis is bounded on its inner surface by a plasma membrane and rests on a thick basement membrane. It is in cytoplasmic continuity with large cell-like cytoplasmic structures in the parenchyma by several processes (Figs. 1 and 2). Each "cell" contains a nucleus, numerous mitochondria, some Golgi vesicles and small vacuoles. As they are in cytoplasmic continuity with the outer cytoplasmic layer they form part of a larger syncytium and thus are

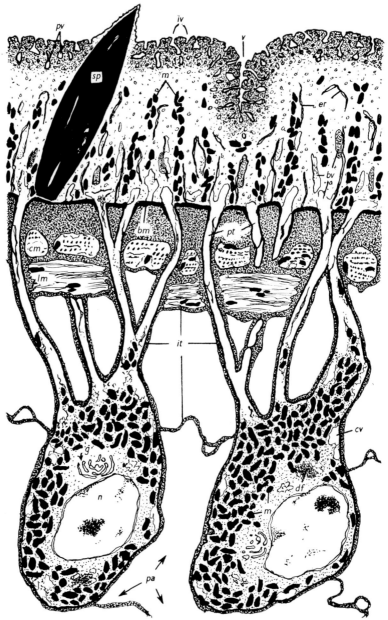

FIG. 1. Diagrammatic drawing of the structure of the epidermis of *Fasciola hepatica*. *bm*, Basement membrane; *bv*, basal vacuoles; *cm*, circular muscle; *cv*, cytoplasmic vacuoles; *df*, diffuse mass; *er*, endoplasmic reticulum; *g*, Golgi bodies; *it*, interstitial material; *iv*, invaginations of plasma membrane; *lm*, longitudinal muscle; *m*, mitochondria; *n*, nucleus; *pa*, parenchymal cell; *pt*, protoplasmic tubes; *pv*, pinocytotic vesicles; *sp*, spine; *v*, valley. (From Threadgold, 1963b.)

FIG. 2. Electron micrograph of the epidermis of *Fasciola hepatica*. *bm*, Basement membrane; *cm*, circular muscle; *m*, mitochondria; *p*, process to sunken portion of epidermis; *pv*, pinocytotic vesicles. (Courtesy of L. T. Threadgold.)

not to be regarded as isolated cells. These structures should be regarded as the sunken portions of the epidermis as in free-living turbellarians (Fig. 10; see also Section V).

Large electron-dense spines project above the general level of the epidermis (Fig. 1) and are always bounded at their tips and bases by the external and internal plasma membranes of the epidermis.

The first study of the ultrastructure of an adult trematode was made by Senft *et al.* (1961) on male and female *Schistosoma mansoni*. According to these writers the worms are covered by an acellular amorphous cuticle which rests on a basement membrane. It contains numerous vesicles and vacuoles, and the suggestion was made that these structures are involved in the uptake of nutriment from the host. The warty protuberances on the body are covered by a thin layer of this acellular covering which is penetrated by hard, acellular spines which extend to the basement membrane. Large cells within the parenchyma were believed to be involved in the production of the outer layer, which was regarded as a secreted covering to the body. These writers were unable to detect any cytoplasmic connexion between these cells and the so-called cuticle. My own (unpublished) study of the ultrastructure of *S. mansoni* has shown the outer covering to be a cytoplasmic layer which has sunken portions within the parenchyma (Fig. 3) and is thus similar to the epidermis of *F. hepatica*. The outer surface of the epidermis is lined by a three-layered membrane. Beneath this are numerous large vacuoles which contain granular materials. Some of these large vacuoles open to the exterior, but others appear to break up into smaller vacuoles towards the base of the epidermis (Fig. 3). Small amounts of fat are present in the middle region of the epidermis and another type of vacuole with different contents occurs near its base. Such vacuoles appear to be formed from the plasma membrane which lines the inner border of the epidermis and is thrown into numerous folds, many of which end in small vesicles, although a few become expanded to form vacuoles. It would appear, therefore, that these vacuoles and their contents are formed at the base of the epidermis and pass to the surface. Small electron-dense rod-shaped bodies, resembling those described in the epidermis of *F. hepatica* by Björkman and Thorsell (1964), are present in the epidermis of *S. mansoni* (Fig. 3). In the males they are numerous and are concentrated in the outer part of the epidermis, although a few are found in the basal regions and in the sunken portions. The epidermis of the female contains fewer of these electron-dense structures. The epidermis contains few mitochondria. The electron-dense spines rest on the fibrous basement membrane and the projecting parts of the spines are covered with the outer membrane of the epidermis.

Burton (1964) found that the ultrastructure of the outer covering of *Haematoloechus medioplexus*, a frog lung-fluke, is essentially the same as that of the other trematodes so far examined. The surface layer of the epidermis is 8–10 μ thick, rests on a basement membrane and has an irregular surface (Fig. 4). Numerous mitochondria are situated near the inner and outer surfaces of the epidermis, which also contains vesicles, fibrous elements and large numbers of dense, membrane-bounded oval bodies. The latter vary in shape and size, but are much larger than the electron-dense bodies found in the

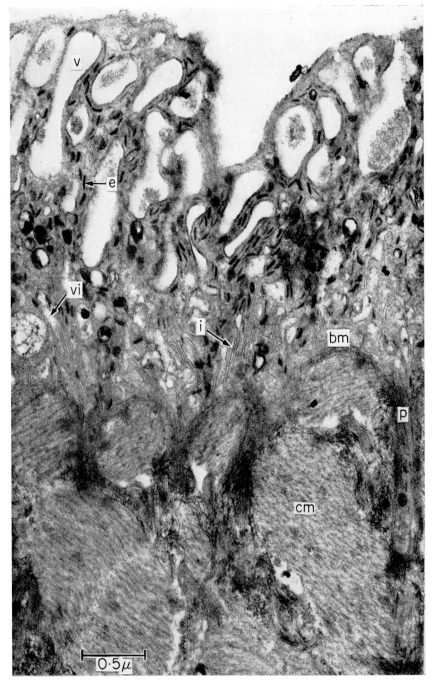

FIG. 3. Electron micrograph of the epidermis of *Schistosoma mansoni* (male). *bm*, Basement membrane; *cm*, circular muscle; *e*, electron-dense rod-shaped bodies; *i*, inner plasma membrane; *p*, process to sunken portion of epidermis; *v*, large outer vacuole; *vi*, small vacuole apparently formed from the inner plasma membrane. (Fixed glutaraldehyde/formalin/osmium tetroxide.)

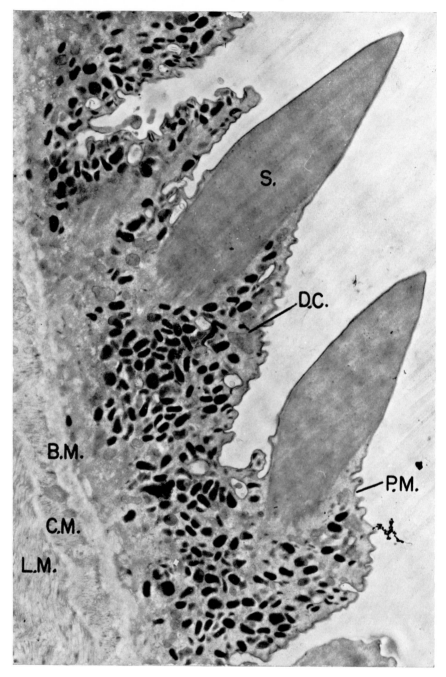

F_{IG}. 4. Electron micrograph of the epidermis of *Haematoloechus medioplexus*. B.M., Basement membrane; C.M., circular muscle; D.C., distal cytoplasm (epidermis); L.M., longitudinal muscle; P.M., plasma membrane; S., spine. (From Burton, 1964.)

epidermis of *F. hepatica* and *S. mansoni* and may not be homologous with them. The irregular outer surface suggests that pinocytosis occurs here, as in these other trematodes. The plasma membrane which covers the external surface is thick (130 Å) and also covers the spines (Fig. 4), which are not so deeply rooted as in *F. hepatica* and *S. mansoni* and apparently consist of a crystalline protein.

The nucleated portions of the epidermis lie in the parenchyma (Fig. 5), but they are connected with the outer cytoplasmic layer of the epidermis by slender cytoplasmic processes, as in *F. hepatica* and *S. mansoni*, and possibly this is a common feature of the epidermis of adult digenetic trematodes. The cytoplasm of the sunken portions of the epidermis contains many dense bodies which are apparently synthesized in association with ribosomes of the endoplasmic reticulum and concentrated in Golgi vesicles. Relatively few mitochondria occur in these sunken portions of the epidermis. The function of the dense bodies is not known. Burton (1964) believed that they are formed in the sunken region of the epidermis and move into the outer region through the cytoplasmic connexions, where they lose their membranes and contribute their substance to the matrix of the epidermis to form the fibrous component and/or the spines. It is possible, on the other hand, that the materials are extruded and form either an excretory product or a secretion. It is also possible that these bodies do not contribute directly to the structure of the epidermis, but contain enzymes which are used in the growth and replacement of the epidermis or in the uptake of substances from the host.

It is apparent from the little work that has been done on the ultrastructure of the outer covering of digenetic trematodes that it is not a secreted sclero-protein structure, but a cytoplasmic layer containing mitochondria, which vary in number from one species to another, and is in cytoplasmic continuity with large cell-like structures, the sunken portions of the outer layer, within the parenchyma. It would seem that theory (3) as outlined by Hyman (1951a) gives the most feasible account of the external layer of digenetic trematodes, allowing for variability as yet undisclosed.

Although no work has been published on the ultrastructure of the Mono-genea, Dr K. Lyons of this Department has unpublished results which show that the outer covering of *Gyrodactylus* sp. and of *Tetraonchus monenteron* is a cytoplasmic layer containing mitochondria and is not a secreted non-living cuticle. It should be regarded as a type of epidermis.

Erasmus and Öhman (1965) studied the ultrastructure of the adhesive organ of some strigeid trematodes. The general body surface of *Cyathocotyle bushiensis* and *Holostephanus lühei* resembles that of other trematodes studied, but the adhesive organ has a highly plastic microvillous surface (Figs. 6 and 7). The outer plasma membrane is elevated to form numerous hollow microvilli up to 2 μ in length which vary in form, sometimes branching or fusing with neighbouring microvilli. The apex of each microvillus may be tapering and rounded or distended to form a bulbous tip containing granular materials (Fig. 7). The cavity of each microvillus is continuous with a lacuna-like space which exists between the basement membrane and the microvillous surface. The basement membrane is perforated by the common ducts from the gland

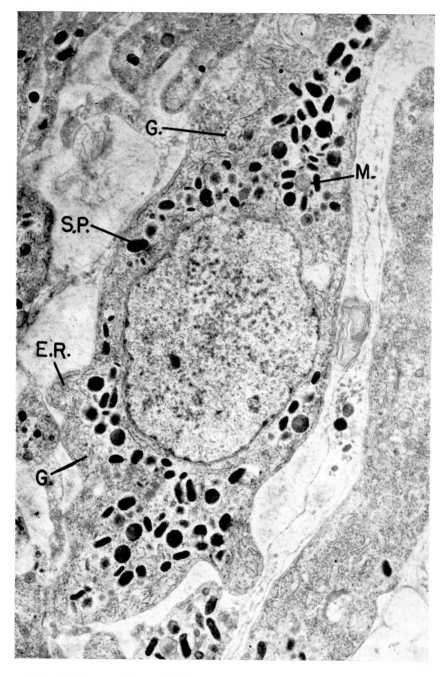

Fɪɢ. 5. Electron micrograph of a "cell" of the sunken portion of the epidermis of *Haematoloechus medioplexus*. E.R., Endoplasmic reticulum; G., Golgi elements; M., mitochondria; S.P., secretory product. (From Burton, 1964.)

cells of the adhesive organ and the secretion from these cells accumulates in the lacunae. The secretion in the ducts and in the lacunae contains mitochondria, electron-dense oval bodies (0·1–0·2 μ diam.) which are referred to as α-bodies, and a fine granular material which also extends into the lumen of each microvillus (Figs. 6 and 7).

Little work has been done on the structure of larval stages of trematodes. Cardell and Philpott (1960) and Cardell (1962) studied the ultrastructure of the cercaria of *Himasthla quissetensis*. The covering of the tail is 1·3 μ thick and has an outer membrane and a double inner basement membrane. Mitochondria are present in this outer covering and are numerous in the region adjacent to the basement membrane. Small vacuoles or tubules are also present. Cardell and Philpott (1960) suggested that the mitochondria supply ATP for the contraction of the muscles which lie beneath the basement membrane. They could not envisage these mitochondria playing a role in the active transport of substances across the epidermis of the tail, but it is possible that the mitochondria are associated with an osmoregulatory function or ion uptake. The body of the cercaria is covered with a layer, 1–4 μ thick, which contains ovoid bodies, but Cardell (1962) stated that they are not mitochondria. The cercaria possesses a collar of triangular spines with sides which are concave in cross-section. The base of each spine rests on the basement membrane of the epidermis.

Work done in this department (V. R. Southgate, unpublished) on the cercaria of *Echinostome* sp. has shown that the outer covering of the cercaria is a living cytoplasmic layer which contains mitochondria and numerous inclusions which appear to be of a secretory nature. The epidermis, including the spines, is covered by a plasma membrane on its external surface.

C. COMPOSITION

The following description of the chemical composition of the epidermis of trematodes will not include the sunken portions of the epidermis, as most work has been carried out only on the covering layer, i.e. what used to be called the cuticle.

Most work on the chemical composition has entailed histochemical methods. Monné (1959b) carried out a histological and histochemical study of the epidermis of several digenetic trematodes before the electron microscope came into use in this field. He decided that the outer covering of trematodes consists of a main inner layer and an external layer which varies in thickness from one species to another. These parts must correspond to the main cytoplasmic part and the outer vacuolated region of the epidermis as revealed by the electron microscope. He did not describe the sunken portions of the epidermis. Monné claimed that the outer region consists of a protein which is associated with polyphenolquinones, but he decided that there was no tanning of the protein. Björkman et al. (1963), by the use of enzymes and histochemical tests, found that the epidermis of *F. hepatica* is proteinaceous. Lee (1962a) showed that most of the epidermis of the metacercaria of *Diplostomum phoxini* contains large amounts of cysteine, which is absent from the lining of the adhesive organ and the lappets (pseudosuckers).

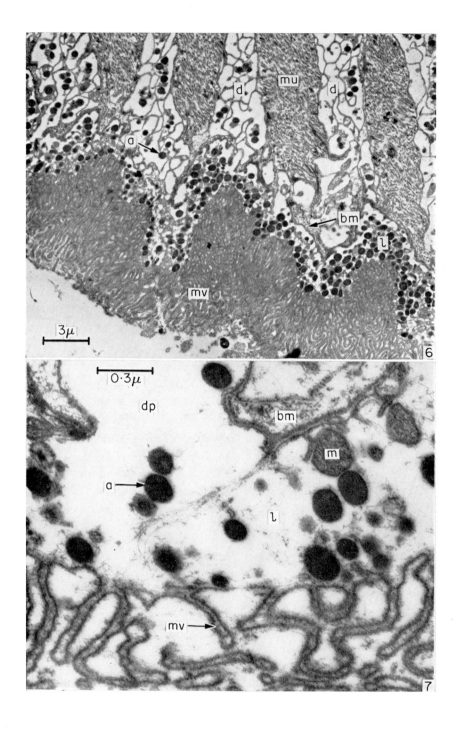

The epidermis of the digenetic trematodes contains a little glycogen, non-glycogen polysaccharides and sometimes some lipid and is covered by acid mucopolysaccharides or mucoproteins (Berthier, 1954; Monné, 1959b; Lal and Shrivastava, 1960; Björkman *et al.*, 1963; Erasmus and Öhman, 1963; Pantelouris, 1964; Öhman, 1965). The outer region contains mucopolysaccharides or mucoproteins which are probably present in the invaginations and vesicles of this part of the epidermis. The mucopolysaccharides are apparently secreted to form the outer layer of mucus. Threadgold (1963b), however, suggested that the evaginated and extruded balloons of cytoplasm of the epidermis of *F. hepatica* may be releasing the mucus. It is known that acid mucopolysaccharides can inhibit various digestive enzymes and the coating of mucopolysaccharide on the trematode probably protects the parasite from the digestive enzymes of the host.

Enzymes have been detected by histochemical techniques in the epidermis of some trematodes. Yamao, in a series of papers, has detected acid and alkaline phosphatases in the epidermis of *F. hepatica* (see Yamao and Saito, 1952), *Dicrocoelium lanceatum* (see Yamao, 1952c) and *Paragonimus westermani* (see Yamao, 1952d); alkaline phosphatase in the epidermis of *Eurytrema coelomaticum* and *E. pancreaticum* (see Yamao, 1952c); and acid phosphatase in the epidermis of *Clonorchis sinensis* (see Yamao, 1952c). Ma (1964) has confirmed the presence of acid phosphatase in the epidermis of *C. sinensis*.

Dusanic (1959) and Lewert and Dusanic (1961) showed that alkaline phosphatase is present in the epidermis of *Schistosoma mansoni*. Robinson (1961) found little alkaline phosphatase activity in the intestinal cells of *S. mansoni*, but noted intense enzyme activity in the cells beneath the epidermis (? sunken portions of epidermis) and suggested that the region of maximum carbohydrate uptake from the host, in *S. mansoni*, is the epidermis. Nimmo-Smith and Standen (1963) located acid and alkaline phosphatases in the epidermis of *S. mansoni*. In female worms these enzymes are evenly distributed in the epidermis, but in male worms they are present only in the dorsal epidermis and are absent from the ventral epidermis, except for small amounts near the ventral sucker.

Alkaline phosphatase is present in both the epidermis and the lining of the adhesive organ in the metacercaria of *Diplostomum phoxini* (see Arvy, 1954; Lee, 1962a). This enzyme is also present in the epidermis which lines the adhesive organ of adult *Cyathocotyle bushiensis* (see Erasmus and Öhman, 1963). According to Erasmus (personal communication), the microvillous membrane of the adhesive organ of *C. bushiensis* is the site of alkaline phosphatase activity and the granular contents of the ducts, lacunae and microvilli

---

◄—FIG. 6. Electron micrograph showing a general view of the surface of the adhesive organ of *Cyathocotyle bushiensis*.

FIG. 7. Detailed view of microvillous surface of Fig. 6.

Key: *a*, α-bodies; *bm*, basement membrane; *d*, ducts from gland cells of adhesive organ; *dp*, duct from gland cell perforating basement membrane to open into a lacuna; *l*, lacunae containing droplets of secretion; *m*, mitochondrion; *mu*, muscle; *mv*, microvilli. (From Erasmus and Öhman, 1965.)

show acid phosphatase activity. The epidermis of *Diplostomum spathaceum* contains alkaline phosphatase, but only the parts which line the lappets and the adhesive organ contain acid phosphatase (Öhman, 1965).

It would appear that phosphatases, chiefly alkaline phosphatases, are associated with the epidermis of adult digenetic trematodes. Cheng (1964) detected alkaline phosphatase in the body wall of the redia and cercaria of *Echinoparyphium* sp. (still within the tissues of the snail), but it is not clear from his description or photographs whether the enzyme is also present in the epidermis. Erasmus (1957a) briefly mentioned that alkaline phosphatase is present in the epidermis of the sporocyst of a strigeid trematode.

Other enzymes which have been detected in the epidermis of trematodes are an aminopeptidase in the adhesive organ of *C. bushiensis* (see Erasmus and Öhman, 1963); and esterase in the epidermis of the metacercaria of *D. phoxini* (see Lee, 1962a), in the lining of the adhesive organ of adult *C. bushiensis* (see Erasmus and Öhman, 1963) and in the epidermis of *S. mansoni* (Lee, unpublished). The distribution of non-specific esterase in *S. mansoni* closely follows that of alkaline phosphatase as described by Nimmo-Smith and Standen (1963) in that there is weak, evenly distributed activity in the epidermis of the female, but in the male the enzyme is almost completely absent from the ventral epidermis, although there is strong activity in the dorsal epidermis. There is one difference, however; there is apparently no esterase activity in the epidermis which covers the warty protuberances of the male (Lee, unpublished).

While nothing is known about the nature of the epidermis of the Monogenea, something is known about the composition of the attachment sclerites of this group. The sclerites are neither chitinous nor are they of epidermal origin; they are composed of scleroproteins. There are, however, two types of skeletal scleroprotein in the Monogenea. The hook-like structures of these trematodes contain and are stabilized by cystine, and X-ray diffraction methods have demonstrated a close similarity between the substance of these hooks and vertebrate α-keratin. The hard framework of the more specialized clamp-like adhesive organs contains no cystine, however, and differs in certain respects from all the scleroproteins with which it was compared, namely, elastin, collagen, reticulin, keratin and sclerotin (quinone-tanned protein) (Lyons, 1964).

D. FUNCTIONAL CONSIDERATIONS

The trematodes were believed to be covered by a thick resistant non-living cuticle which protected the animal from the digestive enzymes of the host. It is now known, however, to be a living cytoplasmic layer. An outer covering of mucopolysaccharide on the worm, apparently secreted by the worm, is believed to inhibit the digestive enzymes of the host and protect the trematode against the host's enzymes (Monné, 1959b; Björkman *et al.*, 1963). Crompton (1963) has suggested that such a covering of acid mucopolysaccharide on intestinal parasites may resist the action of the host's enzymes rather than inhibit the enzymes.

The function of the phosphatase enzymes in the epidermis of trematodes is not known. In vertebrates alkaline phosphatases are present in tissues, such as intestinal mucosa and proximal tubules, where active transport of glucose is known to occur and a functional relationship has been suggested. Whether or not such enzymes are involved in the active transport of glucose through the epidermis of trematodes is not known, but there probably is a relationship. Lewert and Dusanic (1961) found that a symmetrical diaminodibenzylalkane inhibited glycogen uptake *in vivo* and also completely inhibited the alkaline phosphatase activity in the "subcuticle" and gut of *S. mansoni*. Glucose can be taken up through the epidermis of some trematodes, because Mansour (1959) showed that ligaturing the mouth of *F. hepatica* did not prevent the uptake of glucose by the worm and Burton (1962) showed by autoradiography that glucose crosses the epidermis of *Haematoloechus medioplexus*. Similarly, Senft *et al*. (1961) found that "headless" *S. mansoni* survive for several weeks in a nutrient medium and claimed that absorption of nutriment takes place through the epidermis. The distribution of phosphatases in the epidermis of *S. mansoni* is noteworthy. Nimmo-Smith and Standen (1963) did not speculate on the reasons for the lack of phosphatases from the ventral surface of the male, but the lack of the enzyme in the ventral epidermis may be related to the fact that the female is in close contact with this region of the male. It is possible that the ventral surface of the male is not involved in the uptake of nutrients from the host, which would imply that the female is not competing for nutriment with the male. This may be an important factor in the nutrition of the female, which lives partly in the close confines of the gynaecophoric canal, a modification of the ventral surface of the male.

Other substances are known to pass through the epidermis of trematodes. Kuraléc and Ehrlich (1963) showed that there is transfer of amino acids in both directions across the epidermis of *F. hepatica*, and Björkman and Thorsell (1964) showed that particles of ferritin were taken up by the epidermis of this trematode. They incubated adult *F. hepatica* in a solution containing 2% ferritin and examined sections in the electron microscope, and found ferritin not only in the epidermis but also in the tissues beneath it. If the ferritin particles are not broken down during the processes of absorption, incorporation and transport, it means that *F. hepatica* can transport substances of high molecular weight through the epidermis. This is supported by the work of Pantelouris (1964), who found that insulin can be taken in by *F. hepatica* through the epidermis. The mitochondria which are present probably supply energy for the transport of such substances across the epidermis.

The epidermis may also be involved in excretion or in osmoregulation. The arrangement of the mitochondria and endoplasmic reticulum in the epidermis of *F. hepatica* bears some resemblance to that of water-transporting epithelia of other animals and may be involved in water transport (Björkman and Thorsell, 1964). Pantelouris and Gresson (1960) showed that some of the radioactive iron injected into the mouth of *F. hepatica* eventually reappeared in the epidermis and suggested that this region is involved in excretion and/or secretion. This theory was further strengthened when Pantelouris and Hale (1962) found the distribution of vitamin C to be very similar to that of iron in the tissues of *F. hepatica*, that is, in the lumen and walls of the excretory system, in the "myoblasts" (? the sunken portions of the epidermis), and in the epidermis. It is interesting to note that no iron was detected in the epidermis of worms which had not recently ingested iron, but that after the administration of an excess of iron large amounts of it were found there. It is believed that vitamin C incorporates ferric iron into a soluble compound which facilitates excretion of the iron through the excretory system and through the epidermis (Pantelouris and Hale, 1962).

The epidermis of trematodes is often penetrated by the ducts of gland cells which lie beneath the epidermis. Öhman (1965) showed that the cells of the lappets of *Diplostomum spathaceum* terminate in fine processes which penetrate the epidermis as fine ducts. She also showed that enzymes are passed out through these ducts on to the tissues of the host. Lee (1962a) showed a similar arrangement in the lappets of the metacercaria of *D. phoxini*.

The adhesive organ of strigeid trematodes has already been mentioned. As well as containing enzymes, the epidermis which lines this organ is also penetrated by processes from the gland cells of the adhesive organ which secrete enzymes on to the tissues of the host. Erasmus and Öhman (1963) showed that the activities of the adhesive organ are responsible for the extracorporeal digestion of host cells which are then ingested by the mouth and digestion is completed in the caeca of the parasite. Electron microscope observations suggest two routes for the emergence of the enzymes in the adhesive organ. The granular deposit on the outer surface of the microvilli suggests that secretions may pass through the wall. Secondly, the bulbous tips of the microvilli which contain phosphatases may represent a stage in the budding-off of vesicles containing secretion (Erasmus and Öhman, 1965; Erasmus, personal communication).

Thus, the surface of the adhesive organ in strigeid trematodes has become specialized in at least two ways. The presence of microvilli increases the surface area of this region, which is in intimate contact with the host's tissues, and the presence of alkaline phosphatase activity suggests that absorption of nutrients may take place through the surface. In addition, the surface of the adhesive organ represents a region of active secretion and provides a route by which the products of the gland cells of the adhesive organ pass to the exterior of the parasite and on to the tissues of the host (Erasmus and Öhman, 1965; Erasmus, personal communication).

Spines are common in trematodes and probably assist the parasite in retaining its position in the host. This is not their only function in *F. hepatica*, and probably in other trematodes, because Dawes (1963) showed that the spines of adult *F. hepatica* abrade the superficial cells of the hyperplastic bileduct of the host which results from an inflammatory reaction, so that the parasite is provided with a "pasture" of hyperplastic epithelium and connective tissue and utilizes abraded tissue. The sclerites of the Monogenea are used to attach the parasite to the host (Llwellyn, 1957; Kearn, 1964) and usually have a complex associated muscular system. There is strong evidence, however, that these sclerites arise in tissues beneath the epidermis (Llewellyn, 1963; Lyons, 1964).

IV. Cestoda

A. HISTORICAL

Cestodes lack a mouth and an alimentary canal and thus all nutrients must enter the cestode through the surface of the body. For this reason and because living cestodes are not affected by the digestive enzymes of the host, the structure and composition of the surface layer has always aroused interest and controversy. The epidermis has taken on a new significance as a result of work on the uptake of nutrients by tapeworms (see Read and Simmons, 1963), the elucidation of its structure and composition being needed to supplement this aspect of cestode physiology.

The outer layer has been considered by some authors to be a much modified epithelium and nuclei, or structures which resemble nuclei, have occasionally been found therein. Most authors, however, have regarded the outer layer as a tough secreted cuticle which is produced by long-necked cells in the parenchyma (see Wardle and McLeod, 1952). Young (1935) supported the first interpretation as he found progressive degeneration of the epithelium of certain turbellarians from forms in which nuclei are present in the epidermis to forms in which nuclei are absent. He suggested that the "cuticle" of trematodes and cestodes has developed from the epithelium of the Turbellaria by condensation and loss of cellular structure. This topic will be discussed at greater length in Section V.

The "cuticle" of cestodes was known to have three layers, namely, an outer fringe-like comidial layer, a thick homogeneous layer, and a basement membrane. The hooks and spines of the scolex were believed to be specializations of the "cuticle". The fringe-like comidial layer was described by several early workers who also detected pore canals in the "cuticle".

B. STRUCTURE

The most recent advances in elucidating the structure of the external covering of cestodes have come with the application of electron microscopy to the study of these worms. The first such study was by Read (1955), who briefly mentioned that the surface of *Hymenolepis diminuta* and of *Raillietina cesticillus* is covered with projections which strongly resemble the microvilli found on the intestinal mucosa of other animals. Kent (1957) confirmed the existence of these microvilli on *H. diminuta*, *H. nana* and *R. cesticillus*. The microvilli were called microtriches (singular microthrix) by Rothman (1959, 1960, 1963), who studied the ultrastructure of *H. diminuta*. These microvilli or microtriches were also found on *Dipylidium caninum* and *Proteocephalus pollanicoli* by Threadgold (1962, 1965) and they are probably of universal occurrence on the surface of adult cestodes (Figs. 8 and 9). Although Threadgold followed Rothman in calling these processes microtriches, they are referred to here as microvilli.

The microvilli are covered by a limiting membrane which also covers the surface of the worm (Fig. 9). According to Rosario (1962), this limiting membrane is about double the thickness of a typical unit membrane. The distal region of the microvillus is pointed and more electron-dense than the proximal part and is partly separated from the proximal part by a membranous cap which is not continuous with the external plasma membrane (Figs. 8 and 9) (Threadgold, 1962, 1965; McCaig and Hopkins, 1965). Structures which resemble the rootlets of microvilli run down the microvilli and into the general protoplasm at their base (Fig. 9). According to Threadgold (1965), microvilli are always present on the scolex of *P. pollanicoli*. A typical

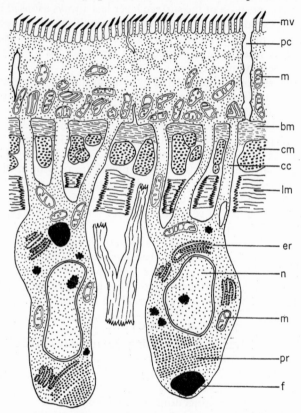

Fig. 8. Diagram of the body wall of *Dipylidium caninum* to show the epidermis and neighbouring structures. *bm*, Basement membrane; *cc*, cytoplasmic connexion between the sunken portion of the epidermis and the outer covering of epidermis; *cm*, circular muscle; *er*, endoplasmic reticulum; *f*, fat droplet; *lm*, longitudinal muscle; *m*, mitochondria; *mv*, microvillus; *n*, nucleus; *pc*, pore-canal; *pr*, protein crystalloid. (Redrawn from Threadgold, 1962.)

microvillous border is found on the entire surface of *H. diminuta* except for the scolex, where the microvilli become smaller and finer (Rothman, 1963). These microvilli even cover the surface of the suckers of the scolex of *H. diminuta* and *H. nana* (Rosario, 1962). The microvilli are absent on localized areas of the external surface of *P. pollanicoli* and in these regions the surface bulges outwards. These evaginations apparently swell further, burst and release their contents, or are cast off as spherical bodies (Threadgold, 1965).

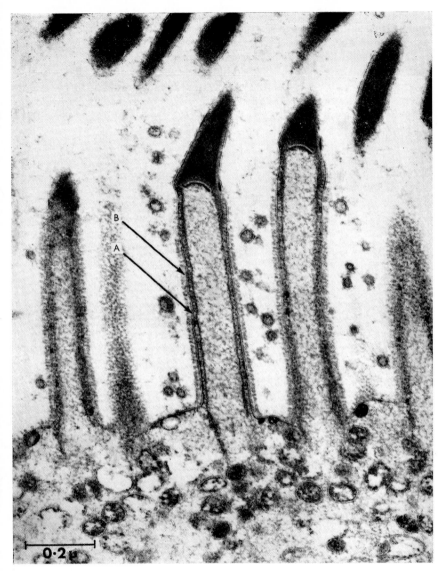

FIG. 9. Electron micrograph of the surface of the epidermis of *Schistocephalus solidus* (after cultivation *in vitro*), to show the characteristic microvilli consisting of a proximal shaft and a terminal electron–dense spine. A, Plasma membrane which covers the epidermis; B, layer of material which covers the epidermis after cultivation *in vitro*. (From McCaig and Hopkins, 1965.)

While the diameter and length of the microvilli do not vary from the immature to the gravid region in the strobila of *H. diminuta*, the number of microvilli per μ^2 of surface does vary, the number increasing from the immature to the mature region and decreasing from the mature to the gravid region. The decrease in number from the mature to the gravid region can be explained by an increase in size of the proglottid without an increase in number of microvilli, but the increase in number from the immature to the mature region can only be explained by an increase in the number of microvilli present, that is, by the formation of new microvilli (Rothman, 1963). It is not known how this occurs. The epidermis is pierced by pore canals, which are bounded by membranes, and these pass from the parenchyma through the epidermis in some species of cestode (Fig. 8) (Threadgold, 1962; Rothman, 1963). Rothman (1963), considering that the pore canals may open to the exterior, thought that they may not be canals at all but globules of the external medium which had been taken up by pinocytosis. Work on the uptake of electron-dense particles, such as ferritin, is required to elucidate this point, which may have an important bearing on the physiology of cestodes.

The epidermis is a syncytium and contains numerous vacuoles, vesicles and scattered mitochondria which tend to be concentrated basally. The outer plasma membrane has both pinocytotic involutions and small evaginations. In *P. pollanicoli* large vacuoles are present immediately beneath the surface and may penetrate to one-third of the depth of the outer layer. These large vacuoles are apparently pinocytotic in origin, because opposed plasma membranes can be observed in the region between the vacuole and the plasma membrane at the surface of the epidermis (Threadgold, 1965). Lipid droplets of various sizes are found in the epidermis of *P. pollanicoli*, but not in any of the other species examined, with the possible exception of *H. nana* and *H. diminuta* (see Threadgold, 1965; Rosario, 1962). In *P. pollanicoli* the smaller droplets are more apical in position than the relatively large droplets. The progressive increase in size of these lipid droplets from the external to the internal parts of the epidermis and to the sunken parts of the epidermis suggests that lipid is taken up through the epidermis (Threadgold, 1965). It is possible that the lipid is being excreted through the epidermis, but this seems unlikely, as the increase in size of the droplets is from without inwards and one would expect lipid excretion to take place through the excretory system as in *Fasciola hepatica* (see Stephenson, 1947) and several cestodes (Smyth, 1947).

Protoplasmic processes, containing mitochondria, extend from the cytoplasm of the covering layer of the epidermis through a thick basement membrane, which contains numerous collagen-like fibrils (Howells, 1965), and through the outer layers of muscle to connect with large "cells" in the parenchyma (Fig. 8). These "cells" are not discrete, but are parts of the general syncytium of the epidermis and are here regarded as the sunken portions of the epidermis, as in the trematodes and the turbellarians. The sunken portions of the epidermis contain a nucleus, endoplasmic reticulum, small numbers of mitochondria, and a number of lipid droplets. Large crystalline bodies, which are probably crystalloids of protein, are also present in the sunken portions of the epidermis of some cestodes (Fig. 8) and are usually associated with strands of endoplasmic reticulum (Threadgold, 1962, 1965). A number of phospholipid-like bodies are also present in these sunken portions in *P. pollanicoli*, which are often connected with one another by means of protoplasmic bridges, and occasionally some are binucleate, having apparently recently undergone mitosis (Threadgold, 1965).

In the structure of its epidermis the proteocephalid cestode, *P. pollanicoli*, is remarkably similar to the cyclophyllidean cestodes which have been studied (species of *Dipylidium*, *Raillietina* and *Hymenolepis*), but minor differences do occur. In *P. pollanicoli* pore canals are absent and lipid droplets are present in the epidermis. The occasional protoplasmic bridges between the sunken portions of the epidermis are not present in the cyclophyllidean cestodes (Threadgold, 1965).

The epidermis of *Moniezia expansa* has been briefly described by Howells (1965). The microvilli which cover the surface of the epidermis are straight and do not have their tips developed as hardened spines, as apparently occurs in the other cestodes examined. Between the microvilli membrane-bounded droplets are extruded from the surface membrane and may be associated with granule-filled, ovoid bodies which concentrate just below the surface of the epidermis. Mitochondria and vesicles are present in the epidermis and a thin membrane, which overlies the basement membrane, is extensively folded and these folds run through the matrix of the epidermis and may act as a supporting framework. The sunken portions of the epidermis lie in the parenchyma.

Timofeev (1964) studied the ultrastructure of the plerocercoid larva of *Schistocephalus pungitii*, and found the epidermis similar to that of the adult cestodes which have been studied with the electron microscope, but it has many finger-like outgrowths which are also covered with microvilli. He believed that the finger-like outgrowths arise in relation to the rapid uptake of nutrients during organogenesis at this stage. The epidermis of the adult worm, whether kept in culture at 41°C or freshly removed from the bird host, has the features seen in other cestodes which have been studied.

Race *et al.* (1965) studied the ultrastructure of the body wall in the coenurus of *Multiceps serialis* removed from cysts in mice and found that the outer covering is essentially the same as that of adult cestodes. Sunken portions were not described, but these apparently do exist, because canals extend from the parenchyma into the outer covering. Race *et al.* also described an external network of fine fibrils connecting the individual microvilli, and suggested that these might co-ordinate movements of the microvilli or play some part in the formation of vacuoles at the surface of the worm. More probably, however, this is mucopolysaccharide lying between the microvilli, as this has a filamentous appearance in electron micrographs. The rostellar hooks are hollow and the root of the hook is surrounded by vacuolated cytoplasm. This supports the suggestion of Crusz (1948) that the rostellar hooks of taenioid cestodes are "cuticular" in origin.

It is apparent, therefore, that the outer layer of cestodes is not a tough secreted cuticle, but is a living, cytoplasmic layer which has sunken nucleated portions in the parenchyma as in the trematodes and the turbellarians.

C. COMPOSITION

The following description of the chemical composition of the epidermis of cestodes will not include the sunken portions of the epidermis, as most work has been carried out only on the covering layer, i.e. what used to be called the cuticle.

Monné (1959b) carried out histochemical tests to determine the composition of the "cuticle" of cestodes. The basal membrane consists of a protein which is very similar to the collagen of mammals. This is consistent with its fibrous appearance in electron micrographs. The main part of the epidermis contains a non-glycogen polysaccharide, acid mucopolysaccharide and proteins. The microvillous border contains a non-glycogen polysaccharide and a protein which is associated with small amounts of polyphenols. Acid mucopolysaccharide is present between the microvilli (Monné, 1959b). The epidermis of *Hymenolepis diminuta, H. nana, Hydatigera taeniaeformis* and *Dipylidium caninum* contains high concentrations of sulphydryl groups, but *D. caninum* has less than the other species. Moderate amounts of lipid are present in the epidermis, but larger amounts are present in the "subcuticular cells". There is no glycogen in the epidermis, but a non-glycogen polysaccharide is present. All species studied, but particularly *D. caninum*, have high concentrations of 1,2 glycols in the epidermis (Waitz and Schardein, 1964).

Various enzymes have been demonstrated, by means of histochemical tests, in the epidermis of cestodes; alkaline phosphatase in the epidermis of *Moniezia expansa* by Rogers (1947), acid and alkaline phosphatases in *Anoplocephala perfoliata, A. magna, Moniezia benedeni, M. expansa* and *Hydatigera taeniaeformis* by Yamao (1952a, b). Acid phosphatase is present in the epidermis of encysted larvae of *Cysticercus bovis* and, together with alkaline phosphatase, in the larvae of *Echinococcus* sp. and *C. fasciolaris* (see Yamao, 1952b). Erasmus (1957a, b) thoroughly investigated the localization and characterization of the phosphatases of *M. expansa* and *Taenia pisiformis*. Acid phosphatase is present in the epidermis of *T. pisiformis*, but there is an uneven distribution along the length of the worm, the greatest activity occurring in the epidermis of the mature proglottides. Gravid proglottides which have been shed are completely negative. The distribution of alkaline phosphatase is more extensive than the acid phosphatase in *T. pisiformis*. The scolex apparently contains no alkaline phosphatase, but the epidermis of the rest of the worm gives a strong positive reaction (Erasmus, 1957a).

In *Moniezia expansa* all acid phosphatase activity is confined to the epidermis, the most active parts of which are the walls of the elaborate system of channels which are present therein (Erasmus, 1957b). There are two alkaline phosphatases in *M. expansa*, one having optimum activity at pH 7·0–8·0 and the other at pH 10·0–11·0. Erasmus (1957b) showed that alkaline phosphatase with optimum activity at pH 7·0–8·0 is confined to the epidermis and the lining of the interproglottidal glands, with greatest activity in mature proglottides. The activity of this enzyme in the mature proglottides is hardly affected by KCN, but there was some inhibition in other regions. An alkaline phosphatase with optimum activity at pH 10·0–11·0 is also found in the epidermis covering the interproglottidal glands, but KCN almost completely inhibits the enzyme (Erasmus, 1957b). Acid and alkaline phosphatases are also present in the epidermis of *Hymenolepis diminuta, H. nana, Hydatigera taeniaeformis* and *Dipylidium caninum* (see Waitz and Schardein, 1964).

Alkaline phosphatase is present in the outer zone of the epidermis of *Anoplocephala perfoliata*, but only on the outer face of the proglottides, which are stacked rather like paper cups so that only this outer face is fully exposed. The coarse microvilli at the posterior margin of the proglottis show intense activity (Lee and Tatchell, 1964).

It seems likely that phosphatases are present in the epidermis of all cestodes, but the distribution of these enzymes varies along the length of the strobila and in the epidermis of individual proglottides from one species to another. This may reflect the mechanisms involved in the uptake of nutrients by the different species of cestode and/or the areas of the worm which are involved in this function. Thus, Lee and Tatchell (1964) postulated that in *Anoplocephala perfoliata* the part of the proglottis which is involved in the uptake of nutrients is that which is not overlapped by the proglottis in front of it, because they found that maximum enzyme activity occurs in the epidermis of this region. They also suggested that the lappets of *A. perfoliata* are involved in the uptake of nutrients from the tissues of the host.

Using histochemical methods, Lee *et al.* (1963) detected non-specific esterase and cholinesterase in the epidermis of *Hymenolepis diminuta*, *H. nana*, *H. microstoma* and *Hydatigera taeniaeformis*. There is weak activity in the epidermis of *Hymenolepis* spp., but strong activity in that of *Hydatigera taeniaeformis*. In this latter species the foremost part of the epidermis of each proglottis in the mature and gravid regions of the strobila stained intensely, but staining intensity gradually declined along the length of the proglottis until at the hind end the stain was present as discrete granules and was not staining the whole epidermis. This was even more noticeable in the immature proglottides. Activity of the esterase progressively decreases in the immature regions of the worm until there is very little activity in the epidermis of the scolex.

Schardein and Waitz (1965) have repeated this work on *Hydatigera taeniaeformis*, *Hymenolepis diminuta*, *H. nana* and *Dipylidium caninum*, and also found that cholinesterase is present in the epidermis of these cestodes, but were unable to find non-specific esterase in the epidermis of *H. nana* and *D. caninum*. This is rather surprising, as cholinesterase should give a result with the methods they used to detect non-specific esterases.

The nervous system of cestodes contains cholinesterase and the nerve endings in the epidermis of these cestodes gave a strong positive result with the histochemical methods used (Lee *et al.*, 1963; Schardein and Waitz, 1965; Wilson, 1965).

Non-specific esterase is present in the epidermis of *Anoplocephala perfoliata*, but the distribution is sparse and is limited to the lateral regions of the foremost face of the proglottides. In this region the epidermis has a different structure; the microvilli are large and the epidermis itself is thicker and has a spongy appearance. Large amounts of non-specific esterase are present in the epidermis which covers the lappets, but the distribution suggests that the enzyme is contained in pore canals which run to the exterior, as well as being more generally scattered in the epidermis. Groups of spherical bodies with a high level of esterase activity are also present in the epidermis of the lappets (Lee and Tatchell, 1964).

Waitz and Schardein (1964) were unable to detect amylophosphorylase, transglucosidase or β-glucuronidase in the epidermis of *Hymenolepis diminuta* and *H. nana*, although there was enzyme activity in the "subcuticular cells".

Rothman and Lee (1963) detected isocitrate dehydrogenase, glutamate dehydrogenase, α-ketoglutarate dehydrogenase, succinate dehydrogenase, malate dehydrogenase and lactate dehydrogenase in the epidermis of *H. diminuta, H. microstoma, H. citelli* and *Hydatigera taeniaeformis*. It is believed that these enzymes are located in the mitochondria of the epidermis. It is interesting to find that the highest concentration of cytochrome oxidase activity in *Hymenolepis diminuta* and *H. nana* is in the epidermis (Waitz and Schardein, 1964). These enzymes are presumably involved in the production of energy, some of which is probably used in the active uptake of nutrients from the external medium.

D. FUNCTIONAL CONSIDERATIONS

The theory that the "cuticle" of cestodes is a tough secretion which protects the worm against the digestive enzymes of the host and permits the absorption of nutrients must be discarded in the light of recent knowledge. The "cuticle" is a layer of living cytoplasm which is involved in the active uptake of nutrients and is well adapted to this function. Microvilli increase the surface area of the worm many times and mitochondria apparently supply the energy which is required for active transport mechanisms. Presumably, tapeworms are protected against digestive enzymes by a layer of mucopolysaccharide and the unbroken plasma membrane of the epidermis. The structure of the microvilli is interesting. In all species examined so far, with the exception of *Moniezia expansa* (see Howells, 1965), the basal part of the microvillus is very similar to the microvilli which line the intestines of other animals, but the cone-shaped, electron-dense cap is peculiar to the microvilli of cestodes. It has been suggested that these parts of the microvilli help the tapeworm to retain its position in the intestine of the host by interdigitating with the microvilli of the intestinal cells; they could also assist in locomotory movements of the strobila in this way, or they may serve to keep the absorptive surfaces of the host and the parasite slightly apart so that nutrients can flow between them.

Erasmus (1957a, b) suggested that the phosphatases in the epidermis of cestodes are involved in the active transport of carbohydrates from the environment into the tissues of the cestode. Phifer (1960), however, has shown that ammonium molybdate, which inhibits the phosphatases of *Hymenolepis diminuta* in macerated tissues of the cestode, does not inhibit the active transport of glucose when *H. diminuta* is incubated in a medium containing ammonium molybdate and ^{14}C-glucose. This would indicate that the phosphatases are not directly involved in the active transport of glucose, at least in this cestode. It is possible, however, that the ammonium molybdate was unable to reach the phosphatases in the living worm, failing thus to inhibit the enzymes.

The function of the non-specific esterases in the epidermis of cestodes is not known. They may be involved in the uptake of nutrients or in the growth of the epidermis or in ion regulation. There is an association between cholinesterase and the active transport of sodium in frog's skin (Kirschner, 1953) and in several other animals, and it is possible that the cholinesterase in the epidermis of cestodes has a similar function. Cholinesterase in the epidermis of *H. diminuta* is not involved in the active transport of glucose, because eserine, which inhibits cholinesterase, does not inhibit the uptake of glucose by this worm (Lee *et al.*, 1963).

Lumsden (1965) has shown that *H. diminuta* takes up labelled proline and leucine, when incubated for 5 min in a solution containing these amino acids, and that activity in radioautographs was restricted to the "subcuticular cells". Following a 2 h "pulse" with unlabelled proline or leucine 66% of the radioactivity was found to have moved from the "subcuticular cells" into the epidermis. Electron microscopy of unnamed mammalian and elasmobranch tapeworms showed that the "subcuticular cells" are synthesizing and elaborating secretory products. Coated vesicles associated with the Golgi apparatus in the "subcuticular cells" are concentrated in the apical cell processes and in the epidermis. These vesicles possess a fine structure which is indicative of quantum protein transport.

The epidermis of cestodes is in many ways similar to that of the digenetic trematodes, but there are several important differences, chief of which is the presence of microvilli and the rarity of spines, other than those on the scolex, in the cestodes. Apparently the epidermis plays some part in the nutrition of both of these groups of platyhelminthes.

V. Origins of the Epidermis of Cestodes and Trematodes

Many theories on the origin of the epidermis of the parasitic platyhelminthes exist and some of them have been discussed by Dawes (1946: 1956), Wardle and McLeod (1952) and Hyman (1951a). Young (1935) considered the external covering to be a much-modified epithelium, because there is progressive degeneration of the epithelium of certain turbellarians from forms in which nuclei are present to forms in which nuclei are absent. He suggested that the so-called cuticle of cestodes and trematodes has developed from the epithelium of the Turbellaria by condensation and loss of cellular structure. All the theories of these early workers were based on the assumption that the external covering is a secreted non-living layer.

The outermost layer of turbellarians is referred to as an epidermis and is usually uniformly ciliated in most groups, but in many species the dorsal surface lacks cilia and in commensal and sand-dwelling species the cilia tend to be lost. For example, the Temnocephalida are ectocommensals and have few, if any, cilia and have a clear, apparently structureless border which resembles a cuticle.

The epidermis of the turbellarians may be cellular or syncytial, and in some species the epidermis is described as sunken, because the nuclei and some cytoplasm of the epidermal cells lie between the muscles or in the parenchyma below them (Fig. 10) (Dorey, 1965). In such an epidermis with sunken portions, the outer layer appears structureless with the light microscope, especially if

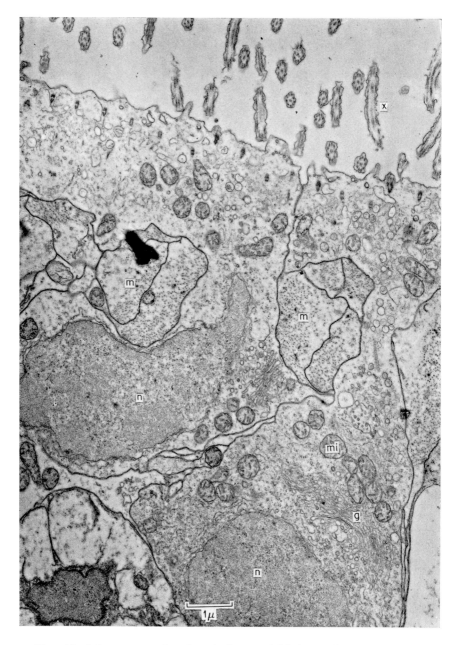

FIG. 10. A transverse section through the superficial tissues of the dorsal surface of *Convoluta roscoffensis* (Acoela). Lobes of two epidermal cells with nuclei are seen to penetrate between the muscle-fibres to form the sunken portion of the epidermis. *g*, Golgi body; *m*, muscle; *mi*, mitochondrion; *n*, nuclei. (From Dorey, 1965.)

the epidermis is syncytial. The epidermis is generally separated from the underlying tissues by a basement membrane, but this is often not present in the Acoela (Hyman, 1951a; Dorey, 1965).

Dorey (1965) studied the ultrastructure of acoelous turbellarians and found that the epidermis consists of a layer of uninucleate cells. The basal parts of these cells are intimately associated with the underlying muscle cells and, through interstices of the muscle network, with the outer portions of the parenchyma. These sunken portions of the epidermis contain the nuclei (Fig. 10). In *Aphanostoma diversicolor* most of the epidermal nuclei lie above the level of the circular muscle layer, but lobes of the epidermal cells penetrate between the muscles.

This type of sunken epidermis is very similar to those of digenetic trematodes and cestodes which have been studied with the electron microscope. It is suggested, therefore, that the cestodes and digenetic trematodes possess a type of sunken epidermis without cilia. The term "sunken" refers to the nucleated portions of the epidermis embedded in the parenchyma beneath the outer muscle network, as in the Turbellaria. It is not suggested that the nucleated portions of the epidermis have descended into the parenchyma; probably it is the surface layer which has risen to the surface. An electron microscope study of the Temnocephalida and further work on the Monogenea should throw more light on this problem.

Skaer (1965) has shown that the epidermis of the triclad planarian, *Polycelis tenuis*, is of parenchymal origin. He showed that the primary epidermis of the embryo is formed by flattened blastomeres, but that all subsequent types of epidermal cell apparently come from the parenchyma by centrifugal migration. Replacement of epidermal cells occurs exclusively by centrifugal migration in both Tricladida and Acoela, but cell division has been reported in the epidermis of a rhabdocoelan turbellarian (Pullen, 1957). Dorey (1965) has shown that the formation of epidermal replacement cells in the parenchyma of *Convoluta* (Acoela) can be provoked by damage to the epidermis. The epidermis, or at least the replacement cells of the epidermis, are thus of mesodermal origin. Work of this nature is urgently needed on the Trematoda and the Cestoda to determine the origins of the epidermis and its replacement or maintenance to make good the effects of wear and tear. The epidermis of cestodes and trematodes may be a secondary epidermis of mesodermal origin. Baer and Joyeux (1961), however, stated that in certain cercaria the cellular epithelium descends and gives rise to the "cuticle" of the adult, suggesting that the epidermis of some trematodes may be a primary epidermis. This observation and the possible presence of nuclei in the outer covering of some larval and adult Digenea (Dawes, 1946: 1956; Baer and Joyeux, 1961) still supports the view that the outer covering of cestodes and trematodes is part of a sunken epidermis.

Wisniewski (1930) found that during development of *Archigetes* there is no epithelium or subcuticle in the early procercoid stage and he believed that the outer covering was a pseudodermis formed from the mesoderm. Vogel (1930) studied the formation of the outer covering in the procercoid stage of *Dibothriocephalus latus* (= *Diphyllobothrium latum*) and believed that the delicate larval "cuticle" is homologous with the basement membrane of the turbellarian epidermis. A definite "cuticle" is then formed beneath the larval cuticle from cells of the parenchyma. Both writers believed that the adult cuticle is a tough secreted layer, but their observations support the theory of a sunken epidermis which probably arises from cells in the parenchyma.

VI. NEMATODA

A. HISTORICAL

Nematodes owe much of their success as a large and ubiquitous group to an organization which includes a cuticle of great ultrastructural complexity and evolutionary plasticity. Much more is known about the structure and composition of the cuticle of Nematoda than about that of other helminths. The cuticle of nematodes is more varied and differences have been of some value in systematics. The subject has been reviewed fully by Chitwood and Chitwood (1950), and the reader is referred to their review for early findings on the structure and composition of nematode cuticles, although some early references will be mentioned here, mainly in discussing layering of the cuticle and its composition. The Chitwoods wrote the first comprehensive review of the cuticle of nematodes, basing this in part on the results of earlier workers, but also on those of their own researches. Their findings are especially valuable because they realized the importance of a comparative study of free-living nematodes as well as forms which are parasitic in plants and animals. They reached the conclusion that all nematodes have a layered cuticle, the layers being essentially the same throughout the group. They presumed that the cuticle of all nematodes is basically a three-layered structure, which is often subdivided to form other layers, and that a fibrous layer or layers are always present. They concluded that the layers were actually a part of living cells at the time of their formation and that the cuticle is a type of connective tissue exoskeleton. They found no convincing evidence to show that the cuticle is a secretion. They also considered the chemical composition of the cuticle, and this has also been reviewed by Hobson (1948), Fairbairn (1957, 1960), Anya (1965) and, more briefly, by Lee (1965b) and de Conink (1965).

B. STRUCTURE

The application of electron microscopy to the study of the cuticle of nematodes has not brought about any great revolution in our knowledge of this structure, as is the case with the trematodes, cestodes and acanthocephalans. Studies on the ultrastructure of the cuticle of nematodes are important in respect of small forms or larval stages, when it is difficult to resolve the various layers using the light microscope, and in following the processes involved in moulting.

The cuticle of *Ascaris lumbricoides* has been most thoroughly studied. Most of the early work was concerned with this nematode and *Parascaris equorum*, and the terminology denoting various layers of the cuticle is based on the terms originally used to describe the cuticle of these nematodes (see Fig. 16).

The body wall of nematodes consists of an external cuticle, a hypodermis and a single layer of longitudinal muscle cells. The cuticle covers the whole of the external surface and also lines the buccal cavity, oesophagus (pharynx), rectum, cloaca, vagina and excretory pore. There are differences in structure and composition between the external cuticle and the cuticle which lines these openings and ducts, but little is known about them.

The external cuticle often has characteristic longitudinal and transverse ridges, and there may be annulations, spines, punctations or inflated areas. Such cuticular markings have some importance in systematics; they have been thoroughly reviewed by Chitwood and Chitwood (1950) and by de Conink (1965) and will not be discussed here except in relation to the layering of the cuticle.

The cuticle of nematodes is basically a three-layered structure and consists of an outer cortex, a middle matrix layer and an inner basal layer. These three layers, which are apparently present in all nematodes, are of varying thicknesses in different species and they are often subdivided. Structures resembling rods, struts and canals are sometimes present in the middle layer and a system of fibres is often, but not always, present in the basal layer or in the outer part of the middle layer. Wieser (1953) found the cyst wall of four species of *Heterodera* to consist of an exo-cuticle and an endo-cuticle and tried to classify the cuticles of other nematodes on the basis of a two-layered structure, but as he did not define the two basic layers they cannot easily be applied to the cuticle of other species. As the cyst wall of *Heterodera* is a highly specialized structure consisting of the swollen body wall of the dead female, it would perhaps be unwise to follow this scheme. Watson (1962), however, considered that the "primitive" cuticle was at least two-layered, and had an outer resistant cortex and an inner layer which corresponds to the matrix and basal layers.

There is some controversy as to which is the "primitive" type of cuticle, but it is probably similar to the relatively simple three-layered cuticle of some of the free-living marine nematodes, e.g. *Cyatholaimus* (Fig. 11), where the cortex has two layers, the outer being a thin refractile layer, and the inner a much thicker layer. The basal layer also has two layers, the inner (basement lamella) being a thin punctate layer marked by longitudinal striations and the outer layer being thicker but apparently homogeneous and without any fibres. The matrix layer appears to be a plastic layer containing a series of transverse rods, radially arranged, which originate from the basal layer and extend to the inner cortical layer (Fig. 11). In surface view these rods resemble punctations (Inglis, 1964a).

There are various modifications of this basic pattern in the Chromadorida. In *Mesonchium*, for example, the matrix layer appears to contain a fluid through which the rods pass (Fig. 12), while in *Chromadorella* the rods are linked to each other transversely at their outer ends to form a ring of material in each annulus (Fig. 13A, B) (Inglis, 1964a).

In *Euchromadora* and in *Longicyatholaimus* (Fig. 14) these rods have become greatly enlarged and elaborated to form double rings (an inner and an outer) in each annulus and are united to each other (Fig. 14). In *Euchromadora* the rods form hexagonal patterns in surface view (Inglis, 1964a).

The cuticle of the anterior end of *Euchromadora vulgaris* differs from that which covers most of the body (Inglis, 1964a). In the region of the oesophagus, as seen with the electron microscope by Watson (1965a), the cuticle has a relatively simple structure unlike the cuticle covering the remainder of the body, described in the light microscope study by Inglis (1964a). The layers

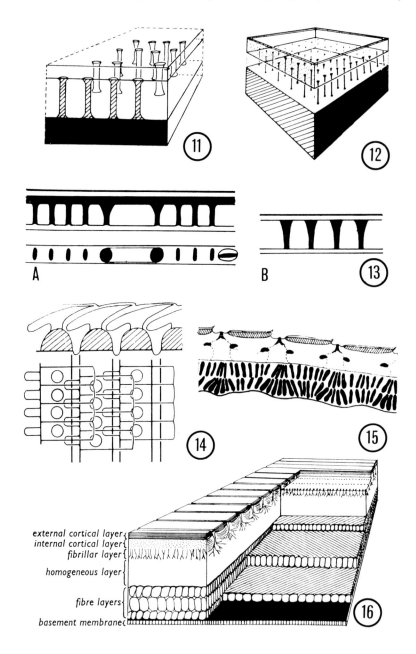

external cortical layer
internal cortical layer
fibrillar layer
homogeneous layer
fibre layers
basement membrane

comprise: (1) an external, electron-dense thin membrane; (2) a cortex (0·4 μ thick) which consists of two layers and forms the surface annulations; (3) a middle layer (1·0–1·5 μ thick) formed from a series of overlapping plates which appear homogeneous in electron micrographs, but are separated by electron-dense material; (4) a basal layer (0·2 μ thick). Canals (0·03 μ in width) pass through the basal layer and the plates of the middle layer and apparently connect the hypodermis with the outer portions of the cuticle (Watson, 1965a) (Figs. 17 and 18). Watson also found groups of hollow structures in localized areas of the middle layer and considered that they are the hexagonal rod-shaped bodies seen under the light microscope. Neither Inglis (1964a) nor Watson (1965a) found any fibre layers in the cuticle of *Euchromadora*.

It will be interesting to study the cuticle which covers the rest of the body of *Euchromadora* using the electron microscope, because there are some differences in the structure of the cuticle as seen by Inglis (1964a) using light microscopy and by Watson (1965a) using electron microscopy.

In *Sigmophora*, *Metachromadora* and *Desmodera* the rods have apparently formed a series of narrow transverse rings lying in a clear matrix. The cortical layer is very thin and the striations of the outer layer correspond with the transverse rings of the matrix layer. These result in the formation of pronounced annuli with a thin strip of less dense material running between each annulus. The importance of this arrangement is discussed later in the section dealing with the function of the cuticle. There is a thin cortical layer and a thin basal layer (Inglis, 1964a).

Thus, the cuticle of the Chromadorida apparently consists of: (1) the outer cortical layer; (2) the middle matrix layer, and (3) the inner basal layer (Inglis, 1964a; Watson, 1965a). Inglis termed the structures embedded in or passing through the matrix layer "punctation canals"; these may be canals, but more probably they are rods with a skeletal function. Inglis gave evidence which indicated that they are rigid structures within a relatively plastic, and sometimes fluid, matrix layer. Watson (1965a) believed that large hollow structures in the middle layer of the cuticle in some regions of *Euchromadora* produce the hexagonal pattern to the cuticle and, as Inglis believed that these originate

◄—FIG. 11. Diagram of a generalized *Cyatholaimus*-type cuticle showing the three basic layers and the transverse rods.

FIG. 12. Diagram of the cuticle of *Mesonchium* showing the three basic layers and the rods.

FIG. 13. Diagrams of the cuticle of *Chromadorella* in oesophageal region. A, Punctation in plan (lower) and transverse section (upper). B, Longitudinal section in same region. Note that the fourth (solid black) layer present in A cannot be seen in B. This is because it forms rings of material around the worm.

FIG. 14. Structure of cuticle at anterior end of body of *Longicyatholaimus dayi*. Longitudinal section above, plan below. Anterior end of body to right of page. Note elaborate rods.

FIG. 15. Longitudinal section through the cuticle of *Toxacara mystax* in the region of the posterior end of the oesophagus showing the two transverse bands in each annulus, and the two fibre layers.

FIG. 16. Diagram showing transverse, longitudinal and tangential sections of the cuticle of *Ascaris*. (Figs. 11–14 from Inglis (1964a); Fig. 15 from Inglis (1964b); Fig. 16 from Lee (1965b) (redrawn from Bird and Deutsch, 1957).)

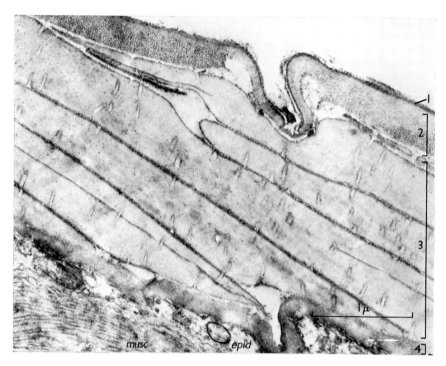

FIG. 17. Electron micrograph of the cuticle of the anterior region of *Euchromadora vulgaris* (longitudinal section) to show the four major layers and the canals in the middle layer. 1, Outer membrane; 2, cortex; 3, middle layer formed from a series of overlapping plates; 4, a basal layer. *epid*, Epidermis (hypodermis); *musc*, muscle. (From Watson, 1965a.)

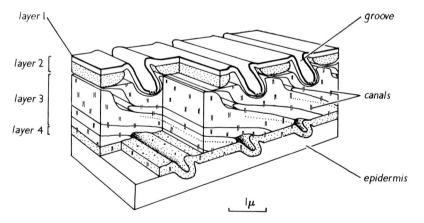

FIG. 18. Three-dimensional reconstruction of the cuticle of *Euchromadora vulgaris* (anterior region) to show the layering. (From Watson, 1965a.)

from the simple rods in the *Cyatholaimus*-type cuticle, these structures possibly are canals. It is necessary to clarify this point because of the controversy about the presence or absence of pore canals in the cuticle of nematodes.

The cuticle of adult *Rhabditis strongyloides* has a thermolabile surface membrane, a cortical layer with canaliculi, a layer with obliquely orientated fibres and a layer with randomly arranged fibrils, which lies directly on the hypodermal membrane. Subcortical, parallel columellae are orientated perpendicular to the hypodermis. The cortex of the early larval cuticle lacks canaliculi (Peebles, 1957).

Watson (1962) found that the cuticle of *Turbatrix aceti* is only 0.2μ thick, but has four layers: (1) an outer thin membrane; (2) a layer about 100 Å in thickness, which is not electron-dense; (3) a layer about 200 Å in thickness, which is very electron-dense, and (4) a layer about 1 600 Å in thickness. In some regions a basal membrane could also be distinguished. The innermost layer contains regularly arranged structures, about 70 Å in diameter, which Watson believed to be rods or canals containing electron-dense material. A similar layer of regularly spaced structures is present in the cuticle of the third-stage larva of *Nippostrongylus brasiliensis* (Fig. 25) (Lee, 1966), and it has been suggested that in this larva these structures are neither rods nor canals, but are indications of very close linkage between the molecules of protein giving a very tough layer. This type of tough protein may also occur in the cuticle of *T. aceti* and possibly in the cuticle of *Rhabditis strongyloides* (see Peebles, 1957) and be responsible for the regularly spaced striations. The cuticle of *T. aceti* is thickened in the region of the lateral cords to form lateral alae. This thickening is due to an extra layer in the cuticle which appears within the innermost layer. The cuticle of the second-stage larva of *T. aceti* shows a structure which is essentially the same as that of the third-stage larva and the adult nematode (Watson, 1962).

The cuticle of *Enoplus communis* has a thin cortical layer, an external layer of oblique fibres, an internal layer of oblique fibres, a punctate layer from which minute "tubes" extend into a thick matrix layer, a thick basal layer and a thin inner basal lamella (Chitwood and Chitwood, 1950; Inglis, 1964a). The cuticle of *Dorylaimus* is very similar to that of *Enoplus* and the cuticles of *Mermis* and *Hexamermis* are similar in layering but much thicker and the matrix layer is stratified (Chitwood and Chitwood, 1950; Inglis, 1964a).

The cuticle of male *Heterodera glycines* has three layers in the mid-body. The outer cortex is an annulated hyaline layer; the matrix layer is a homogeneous layer; while the basal layer appears as a double annulation, two annuli of this layer corresponding to one annulus of the outer layer (Hirschman, 1959, 1960).

When studied in the light microscope the cyst wall of *Heterodera* appears to have two main cuticular layers (exo-cuticle and endo-cuticle) which are apparently divided into several distinct layers (Franklin, 1939; Wieser, 1953). According to Wieser (1953), the exo-cuticle has a cortical layer, a fibre layer, a fibrillar layer, an inner matrix layer and a boundary layer. In *H. rostochiensis* the endo-cuticle is divided into a number of layers which resemble fibre layers (Wieser, 1953).

Ferris (1956) and Ferris and Siegal (1957) found that the cyst wall of *H. rostochiensis* is divided into exo-cuticle and endo-cuticle which show a clear line of demarcation. The exo-cuticle is interspersed with materials of greater electron density, which form irregular layers parallel with the surface of the cyst wall. The proportion of dense to less dense material is greater near the middle of the exo-cuticle than near the line of demarcation, and the amount of dense material increases towards the surface of the cyst wall. The dense area corresponds to that claimed by Wieser (1953) to be fibre and fibrillar layers, but fibres were not observed in the electron micrographs. There is a thin layer of very dense material on the outside of the cyst wall. There are five distinct layers in the endo-cuticle and a basal lamella is present.

Bird (1958b) and Bird and Rogers (1965) have studied the structure of the cuticle of *Meloidogyne* using both light and electron microscopy. The cuticle of the adult consists of an outer osmiophilic cortical layer, an inner cortical layer and a thick fibre layer which appears to be two-layered. This fibre layer merges with the hypodermis and is not separated from it by a basal lamella. There are no vertical striations running from the hypodermis to the outermost layer as originally described by Bird (1958b) by means of light microscopy. There are, however, vertical striae in the external cortical layer which appear to connect with structures in the internal cortical layer. These striae terminate externally just beneath a distinct membrane which covers the external surface of the cuticle.

Wright (1965) has distinguished four zones in the cuticle of the anterior regions of *Xiphinema index* by means of electron microscopy. There is a thin outer zone approximately 30 mμ thick; a thick granular zone which contains basally a palisade-like layer of electron-dense structures; a fibre zone containing two layers of obliquely orientated fibres, each layer being approximately 0·5 μ thick; and an inner lamellar zone consisting of a variable number of layers of material that does not appear fibrous, but does resemble the fibre layers in its reaction with potassium permanganate. Wright suggested that the variability in the number of layers in the inner lamellar zone might be accounted for by the age of the animal. The basal lamellar zone is closely associated with the underlying hypodermis. A series of dense lines extend from the palisade-like layer across the thick granular zone, to the outer surface of the cuticle and appear to be related to the transverse striations on the outer surface of the cuticle. Channel-like or ribbon-like extensions of the inner lamellar zone of the cuticle penetrate deeply into the hypodermal cords and sometimes into large cavities in the anterior region of the body. More posteriorly these invaginations of cuticle are found only in the ventral cord.

Wright (1965) also studied the cuticle lining the stoma of *X. index*. The cuticle anterior to the guide ring is thick (0·5 μ) and is apparently of a similar composition to the innermost zone of the body-wall cuticle, but it is not layered. The outer part of the cuticle has a dense layer 30 mμ thick, which is similar to that which covers the external cuticle. The cuticle of this region is closely associated with the underlying hypodermis. The cuticle posterior to the guide ring is thinner, approximately 0·1 μ thick, and has a strong affinity for potassium permanganate. Unlike the more anterior cuticle it is more loosely associated with the hypodermis.

On the outside of the cuticle of *Capillaria hepatica* Wright (1962, 1963, 1964) recognized three thin electron-dense lines 10 mμ thick, and these follow the contour of the next finely filamentous layer in which deep irregular grooves form transverse striations. The filaments in this layer are longitudinally orientated. The next deeper layer is a dense band 35–50 mμ thick and fine vertical striations appear in some micrographs (see also Watson, 1962; Lee, 1966; Fig. 25). The innermost layer of the cuticle is 300–600 mμ thick, filamentous, and the filaments are orientated transversely (Wright, 1962). The cuticle of *Trichuris* appears to be similar to that of *Capillaria* (Sheffield, 1963).

According to Kagei (1960), the cuticle of *Setaria cervi* has two osmiophilic membranes separated by an osmiophobic membrane, a single cortical layer, a thick middle fibrillar layer, a basal layer and a basal lamella.

Several recent writers agree that the cuticle of *Ascaris lumbricoides* has three layers: the cortex, matrix and fibre layers, which are further subdivided (Fig. 16). An outer osmiophilic layer covers the cuticle (Chitwood and Chitwood, 1950; Bird and Deutsch, 1957; Bird, 1958a; Bogoyavlenski, 1959, 1960; Nagasawa, 1961; Inglis, 1964a; Watson, 1965b). Structures having a characteristic radiating structure arise from the fibrillar layer and extend to the transverse grooves of the cuticle; they have been termed circular lamellae, secretion tracts, canals, fibres and strands of condensed material. Bird (1958a) found that they were hollow after peptic hydrolysis and considered that they are pore canals containing a substance rich in aromatic amino acids. Watson (1965b) also claimed that they are not fibres, but are groups of canals which extend through the matrix layer to the cortex and in young adult worms extend to the inner limit of the matrix layer.

The external cortical layer is divided into a thinner outer layer, which is dense and divided by transverse grooves to give the worm an annulated appearance, and a thicker inner layer, also partly divided into annuli by the fibres or pore canals which extend from the fibrillar layer to the transverse groove. According to Chitwood and Chitwood (1950) the internal cortical layer is continuous with the matrix layer, from which it is separated by the fibrils of the fibrillar layer. Watson (1965b) showed the inner cortex to be a loose network of fibrils, 75–100 mμ in diameter, embedded in material similar to that of the matrix layer.

The fibrillar layer is a network of fibrils between the internal cortical layer and the matrix layer into both of which strands of fibrils or canals extend. The matrix layer appears to be plastic and homogeneous, but Bird and Deutsch (1957) found radial striae in it. The boundary layer is not always distinct and Chitwood and Chitwood (1950) regard it as a condensation layer.

The three fibre layers contain irregular fibres made up of compacted fibrils less than 10 mμ in diameter (Watson, 1965b). The outer and inner fibre layers form spirals in the same direction at 70–75° to the longitudinal axis of the worm, while the middle layer crosses the other two at an angle of 135° (Picken *et al.*, 1947; Harris and Crofton, 1957). The basal lamella is not homogeneous, but is finely fibrillar, and forms a network which joins the spaces between the fibre layers and the hypodermis (Watson, 1965b). This system may facilitate the transport of substances from the hypodermis into the cuticle.

The cuticle of *Parascaris equorum* is similar to that of *Ascaris*. Hinz (1963) recognized an outer membrane, an outer cortex of two layers, an inner cortical layer, a matrix layer, a ribbon-like boundary layer, three fibre layers and a basal lamella.

The outer membrane is about 450 Å thick. The outer cortex has a dense outer layer which is much thinner in the grooves between the annuli of the cuticle than elsewhere (Fig. 19). This outermost layer of the outer cortex is sharply defined and does not merge into the inner layer of the outer cortex. On the other hand, there is no sharp demarcation of the inside zone of the outer cortex from the inner cortex. All three layers are thinner in the region of the grooves between annuli than elsewhere (Fig. 19). Hinz found that the two layers of the outer cortex contain fibres of about 85 Å diameter with dark cross-bands at intervals of about 95 Å. He concluded that the difference in density between the two layers is chemical rather than structural and that impregnation of the outside zone with certain substances, or a chemical change, e.g. quinone tanning (Brown, 1950b; Bird, 1957), occurs. Hinz found no clear definition between the inner cortex, the fibrillar layer and the matrix layer and thus agreed with the findings of Chitwood and Chitwood (1950) and Watson (1965b) on *Ascaris*. The inner cortex contains granular or fibrous materials embedded in the substance of the matrix layer, which extends outwards towards the outer cortex under each external groove (Fig. 19). The so-called fibrillar layer is not a true layer. Fibres of varying diameter arise in the innermost layer of the outer cortex on both sides of the groove between annuli. These fibres branch as they penetrate the cortical layers, and become much more obvious in the matrix layer. With the light microscope these give the impression of a fibrillar layer. Hinz (1963) formed the opinion that the inner cortex and the so-called fibrillar layer are really part of the matrix layer which contains fibres arranged in three main axes, one of these being the fibres which extend from the matrix layer to the outer cortex. Hinz could find no evidence that these fibres are pore canals, although they correspond in position to the pore canals described in the cuticle of *Ascaris* by Bird (1958a) and Watson (1965b).

The matrix layer is 20 μ thick and appears almost entirely homogeneous, although fine fibrils may be present. The boundary layer is in the form of ribbons of material which correspond to the annulations on the external surface of the cuticle. This layer is also embedded in the matrix layer and apparently composed of striated fibrils.

The three fibre layers take up about one-quarter of the thickness of the cuticle. The outer, middle and inner fibre layers are respectively 3·5 μ, 4·5 μ and 2 μ thick. As in the cuticle of *Ascaris*, the fibres run in a spiral, the middle layer crossing the other two at an angle, and they are composed of numerous fibrils and are not enclosed by a membrane. The basal lamella also has a fibrous appearance.

Inglis (1964b) studied the cuticle on the anterior end of a number of nematodes (Ascaridoidea) by means of the light microscope. The cuticle of *Acantho-cheilus* is divided into a thin outer cortical layer (termed by Inglis the epi-cortex), which is not modified by transverse striations, a thick inner cortex, a matrix layer, a basal layer and a thin basal lamella. Fibrils pass from the cortical to the basal layers in some parts of the cuticle and in some regions the

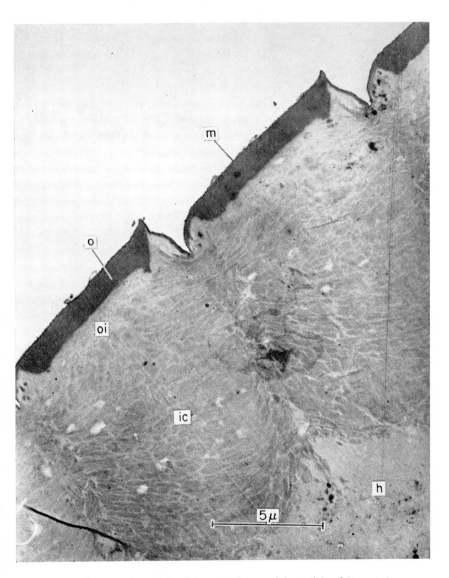

FIG. 19. Electron micrograph of the outer layers of the cuticle of *Parascaris equorum* (longitudinal section). *ic*, Inner cortical layer; *h*, homogeneous or matrix layer; *m*, outer membrane; *o*, outer part of outer cortex; *oi*, inner part of outer cortex. (From Hinz, 1963.)

basal layer appears to form transverse ridges around the body. In *Anisakis simplex* there is a thin outer cortex, an inner cortex, a matrix layer, a boundary layer, two fibre layers and a basal lamella, but no fibrillar layer. At the anterior end of the body the basal layer is modified as a series of transverse continuous ridges which project into the matrix layer. The cortical layer is thick and is marked by narrow striations. More posteriorly the basal layer consists of two thin fibre layers. The outer surface of the cuticle is folded to give the appearance of overlapping annulations (Inglis, 1964b).

According to Chitwood and Chitwood (1950), the cuticle of *Contracaecum spiculigerum* has an outer cortex, an inner cortex, a matrix layer in which are embedded two layers of coarse oblique fibres, a basal layer containing three layers of oblique fibres and a basal lamella. Inglis (1964b) studied the cuticle at the anterior end of this nematode and recognized an outer and an inner cortex, a fibrillar layer, a thin matrix layer, two fibre layers in the basal layer and a thick basal lamella.

In the cuticle of *Amplicaecum* the fibrillar layer appears to form transverse bands; at the anterior end the bands are single structures lying between each annulus, while more posteriorly there are two such bands. Apparently, these bands have arisen by a condensation or compacting of the fibrillar layer. In *Angusticaecum* the fibrillar layer is highly modified; just behind the lips it forms transverse bands which project into the matrix layer as wedges. These enlarge posteriorly until they reach the posterior end of the oesophagus, where the fibrillar layer becomes simple and more like that of other Ascaridoidea.

The cuticle of *Toxocara canis* has the same basic plan as that of other Ascaridoidea, but two transverse bands extend through the matrix layer. These have apparently arisen from a compacting of the fibrils of the fibrillar layer. The two fibre layers of the basal layer are well developed (Fig. 15) (Inglis, 1964b).

Bogoyavlenski (1958a, b, 1960) studied the ultrastructure of the cuticle of *Ascaridia galli* and demonstrated a dense outer cortex, an inner cortex, a membranous layer, an external layer of rods or fibres (fibrillar layer), a matrix layer, two layers of fibres, the outer one being similar to the fibrillar layer, and a basal membrane. He believed that the structures in the fibrillar layer serve a nutritive rather than a supporting function, i.e. that they are canals. His description of the outer layer of the two layers of fibres suggests that the constituent fibrils are not well compacted into fibres. Inglis (1964b) stated that the cuticle of *A. galli* is typical of the Ascaridoidea, but without a fibrillar layer.

The cuticle of *Strongylus equinus* is similar in its layering to that of *Ascaris* (see Chitwood and Chitwood, 1950; Bird, 1958a). It has an external cortical layer, an internal cortical layer, a fibrillar layer containing hollow structures which pass from the matrix layer to the grooves of the external cortical layer, a matrix layer, a boundary layer, an outer fibre layer, an inner fibre layer and a basal layer. The fibre layers cross each other at an angle of 135° (Bird, 1958a).

The cuticle of *Oxyuris equi* has an outer cortex, an inner cortical layer, a fibrillar layer, two fibre layers embedded in a matrix layer and two fibre layers in the basal layer. There is apparently no basal lamella (Bird, 1958a). In the matrix layer beneath the external transverse grooves are two bundles of fibrils; one of them traverses the matrix layer and penetrates the cortical layers to connect with the outer cortex underneath the transverse groove, the other does not penetrate the cortex, but, after traversing the matrix layer, extends between the inner cortex and the outer layer of fibres before connecting with the next transverse groove. There is apparently no trace of any pore canals in the cuticle.

Anya (1965, 1966) studied the cuticle of another oxyuroid nematode, *Aspiculuris tetraptera*, with the aid of the electron microscope. The cuticle is covered with a three-layered membrane which is not seen with the light microscope. There is a rather amorphous outer cortex which is considerably thinner in the transverse grooves which encircle the nematode. The inner cortex is rather more electron-dense and contains an interlacing network of fibrils which are embedded in amorphous material. This layer also contains a number of granules. The next deeper layer is devoid of any obvious structure and the amorphous material appears to be the same as that found in both the inner cortex and in the matrix layer. The matrix layer contains fibrils which are arranged in a series of waves (Fig. 20). In longitudinal section there are 4–12 waves per annulus, the larger number of waves being found in the middle portions of the body. These fibrils are similar to those found in the inner

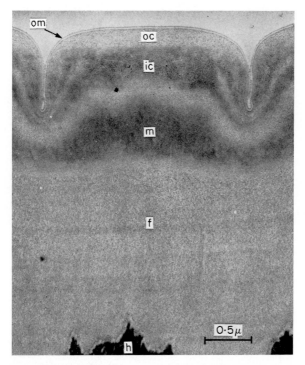

Fig. 20. Electron micrograph of a longitudinal section through the cuticle of *Aspiculuris tetraptera*. *f*, Fibre layers; *h*, hypodermis; *ic*, inner cortex; *m*, matrix layer containing "waves" of fibrils; *oc*, outer cortex; *om*, outer membrane.

cortex, but are more regularly arranged. This layer is followed by the basal layer, which contains three ill-defined layers of fibrils, which are not compacted into fibres (Fig. 20). A system of ramifying spaces is present in this basal layer and the substance in these spaces appears to differ in composition from that of the matrix layer and the inner cortex. A clear zone separates the fibre layers from the hypodermis and may be a basement lamella.

Lee (1965a) has described the ultrastructure of the cuticle of adult *Nippostrongylus brasiliensis*. The cuticle has an outer three-layered membrane, a single cortical layer, a fluid-filled layer containing struts or rods which support the longitudinal ridges of the cuticle, two fibre layers (each layer comprising a number of small fibres formed from compacted fibrils, cross-striated fibrils which are inserted into the cortex, the struts and the fibre layers) and a basement lamella. Apparently fibres also connect the muscles of the body wall with the cuticle. The basement lamella projects into each lateral cord to form a ridge which extends throughout the length of the cords (Figs. 21 and 22).

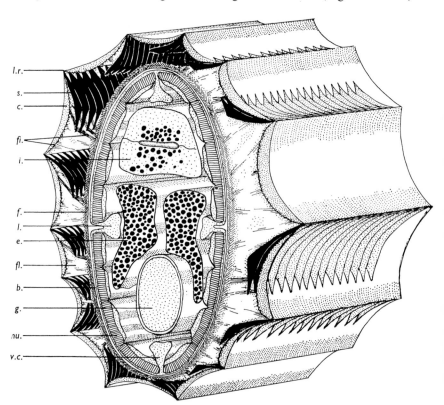

Fig. 21. A stereogram of a section taken from the middle region of *Nippostrongylus brasiliensis* to show the structure of the cuticle. *b.*, Basement lamella; *c.*, cortex; *e.*, "excretory" gland; *f.*, fibre layer of cuticle; *fi.*, fibrils of collagen; *fl.*, fluid-filled layer of cuticle; *g.*, gonad; *i.*, intestine; *l.*, lateral cord; *l.r.*, longitudinal ridge of cuticle; *mu.*, muscle of body wall; *s.*, strut or skeletal rod; *v.c.*, ventral cord. (From Lee, 1965a.)

FIG. 22. Electron micrograph of a transverse section of the cuticle of an adult *Nippo-strongylus brasiliensis* to show the arrangement of the layers of the cuticle. One whole strut and part of the adjacent strut are shown supporting a longitudinal ridge. *c*, Cortex; *f*, fibre layers; *fi*, striated fibrils; *m*, fluid-filled matrix layer (contains haemoglobin); *s*, strut.

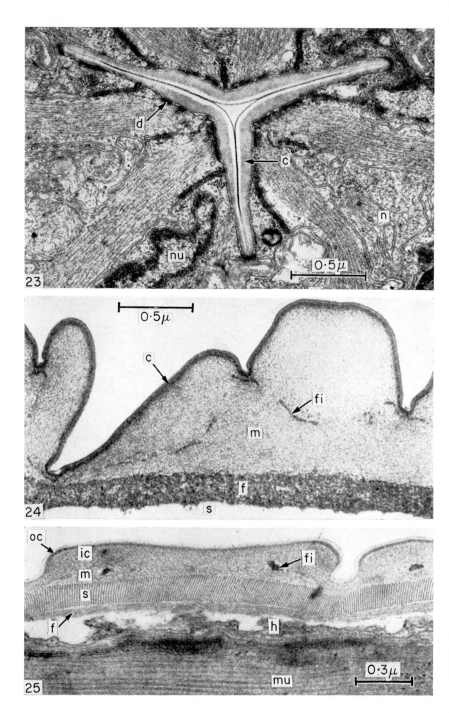

Not much work has been done on the larval stages of nematodes. The cuticle of the encapsulated larva of *Trichinella spiralis*, according to Beckett and Boothroyd (1961), is made up of two definite layers separated by a membrane. The inner layer has an array of very fine fibrils, about 40 Å thick, arranged parallel to the circumference of the larva. There is also a thin external membrane present. Bruce (personal communication) has recognized a three-layered external membrane, a thin external cortex, a thin inner cortex, a rather granular matrix layer which is divided into two parts by a thin electron-dense layer, and a broad basal layer which contains numerous fibrils. Lee (unpublished) has studied the ultrastructure of the cuticle at the final moult of *T. spiralis*. It is very similar to that of the encapsulated larva, but the matrix layer is greatly enlarged and the basal fibril layer is a much more definite layer (Fig. 24). The matrix layer must be quite plastic to allow of the distortion shown.

Lee (1966) has found that the cuticle of the third-stage larva of *Nippostrongylus brasiliensis* is also a multi-layered structure (Fig. 25). There is an outer membrane, a thin outer cortex, an inner cortex, a thin matrix layer, a layer which exhibits regular striations and is rather similar to a layer of regular striations in the cuticle of *Turbatrix aceti* (Watson, 1962), and two layers of fibrils. Two fibres encircle the nematode in the zone between the inner cortex and the matrix layer in each annulus (Fig. 25) and may correspond to similar fibres in the cuticle of *Toxocara* (see Inglis, 1964b). The lateral alae are similar to the rest of the cuticle except that there is a fluid-filled layer, apparently formed from the matrix layer, between the inner cortex and the matrix layer. Strands of material cross this fluid-filled layer and join the cortex to the striated layer. The two fibril layers become much thicker in the lateral alae, but the cortex and striated layers remain about the same thickness.

The cuticle which lines the oesophagus of the third-stage larva of *N. brasiliensis* has a simple structure consisting of two apparently homogeneous zones, one of which is more electron-dense than the other, and a thin membrane which lines the lumen of the oesophagus. The cuticle is closely applied to the tissue of the oesophagus and electron-dense areas, which are probably desmosomes, indicate points of attachment between the muscles of the oesophagus and the cuticle (Fig. 23) (Lee, unpublished).

The later larval stages of *Meloidogyne* appear to have the same structure as the adult nematode (Bird and Rogers, 1965).

◄—FIG. 23. Electron micrograph of a transverse section through the oesophagus of the third-stage larva of *Nippostrongylus brasiliensis* to show the cuticle which lines the lumen of the oesophagus and the attachment of the oesophageal muscles to the cuticle. *c*, Cuticle; *d*, attachment point between muscles and the cuticle (?desmosomes); *n*, nervous material of oesophagus; *nu*, nucleus.

FIG. 24. Electron micrograph of a longitudinal section through the moulted cuticle of the fourth-stage larva/adult moult of *Trichinella spiralis* grown *in vitro*. *c*, Cortex; *f*, fibre layer; *fi*, strand of fibre which links one "annulation" to another; *m*, matrix layer; *s*, space between moulted cuticle and cuticle of young adult.

FIG. 25. Electron micrograph of a longitudinal section through the cuticle of the third-stage larva of *Nippostrongylus brasiliensis* to show the layering of the cuticle. *f*, Fibril layers; *fi*, fibre which runs transversely around the worm; *h*, hypodermis; *ic*, inner cortex; *m*, matrix layer; *mu*, muscle; *oc*, outer cortex layer; *s*, striated layer.

A recent paper describing the ultrastructure of the cuticle of the infective larvae of *Haemonchus contortus*, *Trichostrongylus colubriformis*, *Cooperia punctata*, *Bunostomum trigonocephalum*, *Strongyloides ransomi* and *S. papillosus* must be briefly summarized. The cuticle of the infective-stage larvae has a basement membrane on the hypodermis, above which is a "striped" layer, then a homogeneous layer, and an internal and an external cortical layer. The "striped" layer evidently corresponds to the layer of regularly arranged structures in the cuticle of *Turbatrix aceti*, *Rhabditis strongyloides* and the larva of *Nippostrongylus brasiliensis*. The sheath of the ensheathed larvae of trichostrongylids and *B. trigonocephalum* is structureless, but in some species (*H. contortus* and *T. colubriformis*) an outer and inner zone of electron-dense material was detected (Eckert and Schwarz, 1965).

Watson (1962) has stated that, on the evidence available, the larval cuticle of parasitic nematodes is more similar in structure to the cuticle of free-living adult nematodes than to the complex cuticle of the adult and suggested that the cuticle of the adult parasite may be a comparatively late evolutionary development. This hypothesis is probably correct, but what she did not discuss was the fact that the larvae which have been studied in this respect are the free-living stages of the life cycle and are essentially free-living nematodes, while the adult is usually endoparasitic in other animals or plants, and that the cuticle may be adapted to a free-living and a parasitic existence respectively.

Discussion

The present state of our knowledge indicates that the cuticle of nematodes is basically a three-layered structure with an outer cortex, a middle matrix layer and an inner basal layer. These three layers are often subdivided and it is sometimes difficult to determine their boundaries, especially in electron micrographs; several of the layers of the cuticle are fibrous, differing only in the orientation of the fibrils or degrees of compactness. It may even be difficult to assign any one layer to a particular basic layer.

Inglis (1964a, b) considered that the three-layered cuticle is modified around a canal system, believing that the punctations in the cuticle of the Chromadorida and other nematodes represent canals. There is evidence (Bird, 1958a; Watson, 1965a, b) that such canals occur in *Ascaris lumbricoides*, *Strongylus equinus* and *Euchromadora vulgaris*, but little evidence that they occur in most nematodes, and it is wiser to reserve judgement until more is known about the fine structure of the cuticle of all stages of nematodes. Hinz (1963) could not find such canals in *Parascaris equorum* nor could Wright (1962, 1963) in *Capillaria hepatica*, Sheffield (1963) and Jenkins (personal communication) in *Trichuris suis*, Beckett and Boothroyd (1961), Bruce (personal communication) and Lee (unpublished) in *Trichinella spiralis* larvae, Bird and Rogers (1965) in *Meloidogyne javanica*, Wright (1965) in *Xiphinema index*, Bird (1958a) in *Oxyuris equi*, Anya (1965, 1966) in *Aspiculuris tetraptera*, and Lee (1966) in third-stage larvae of *Nippostrongylus brasiliensis*. The fluid-filled layer of the cuticle of adult *N. brasiliensis* (Lee, 1965a) may be formed by the enlargement and merging of canals in the matrix layer, but more probably this layer is the matrix layer, as the matrix layer has become fluid in a number of species of nematodes (see Chitwood and Chitwood, 1950; Inglis, 1964a).

What appears to be a common feature of the cuticle of nematodes is the presence of fibrils in all the layers to a greater or lesser extent. In some nematodes fibrils are difficult to resolve, even with the electron microscope, and these layers then appear homogeneous. In some nematodes fibrils are compacted basally to form two or three layers of fibres, e.g. (Ascaridoidea), in others the fibrils in the outer part of the matrix have formed fibres (e.g. *Enoplus, Dorylaimus* and *Mermis*), while in *Oxyuris equi* the fibrils have formed layers of fibres in the outer part of the matrix layer and the basal layer. This formation of fibres from the layers of fibrils is usually, but not always, associated with an increase in size of the body and may have mechanical associations in locomotion (see Harris and Crofton, 1957). The struts in the fluid-filled layer of the cuticle of adult *N. brasiliensis* which support the longitudinal ridges of the cuticle may have originated from rod-like structures found in the matrix layer of some free-living marine nematodes, e.g. the Chromadorida.

C. COMPOSITION

Early work on the chemical composition of the cuticle of nematodes has been reviewed by Hobson (1948), Chitwood and Chitwood (1950), Fairbairn (1957, 1960) and Anya (1965) and will not be included in this review.

Bird (1954, 1956, 1957, 1958a, b) has carried out a thorough and extensive study into the chemical composition of the cuticle of nematodes. He found that the sheath of the third-stage larvae (i.e. the uncast cuticle of the second-stage larva) of *Oesophagostomum, Ostertagia, Chabertia, Haemonchus* and *Trichostrongylus* is soluble in water at 105°C. Nine amino acids were identified in hydrolysates of mixed collections of larval sheaths and in pure samples of sheaths from *H. contortus*. These amino acids, in order of the amounts present, were proline, hydroxyproline, aspartic acid, cysteic acid, glutamic acid, alanine, leucine, glycine and valine. Tests for cystine and tyrosine gave negative results (Bird, 1954).

Bird and Rogers (1956) found collagen in the cast sheaths of larval tricho-strongyles such as *Haemonchus*, and Simmonds (1958) found collagen in the cast cuticle of the fourth-stage larva of *Nippostrongylus brasiliensis*. Bird and Rogers (1956) were unable to demonstrate a tanning mechanism in the sheath of these larvae, but Monné (1959a), who described the larval cuticle of *Dictyocaulus* as collagenous, claimed that quinone-tanning occurs in the cuticle of these larvae and that the larval cuticle is more resistant to the action of proteolytic enzymes than is the adult cuticle.

Savel (1955) identified thirteen amino acids in the cuticle of *Ascaris lumbricoides*. He drew attention to the ratio of histidine:lysine:arginine (1:5:13) which is close to the ratio in many keratins (1:4:12–1:5:15) and considered that the cortex is composed of a keratin. This layer is, however, soluble in hot dilute alkali, which is strong evidence against it containing keratin (Fairbairn, 1957).

Bird (1956) found twenty amino acids in hydrolysates of the whole cuticle

of *A. lumbricoides*, *Toxocara mystax* and *Strongylus equinus*. Traces of lipid
and of an aldohexose are also present in the cuticle of *A. lumbricoides* and
S. equinus. The carbohydrate is normally associated with protein in the
cuticle. There is a greater concentration of hydroxyproline in the cuticle of
S. equinus than in the cuticle of *A. lumbricoides* and *T. mystax*, and as Bird
(1954) found large amounts of hydroxyproline in the cast cuticles of infective
strongyloid larvae he suggested that this may be characteristic of the Strongy-
loidea.

The cuticle of *A. lumbricoides* contains about 75% of water and small
amounts of carbohydrates and lipids, as well as the predominating proteins
(Fairbairn, 1956, 1957; Fairbairn and Passey, 1957).

The chemical composition of the individual layers of the cuticle of *A.
lumbricoides* was also studied by Bird (1957), who demonstrated the presence
of lipid on the external surface of the cuticle, thus agreeing with the finding of
an electron-dense layer covering the cuticle (Bird and Deutsch, 1957). Trim
(1949) had already suggested that such a layer might be present in *A. lumbricoides* and Chitwood (1938) found a similar layer in *Ditylenchus* and *Rhabditis*.

The basal lamella and the fibre layers have a similar amino-acid composition, but the external cortex differs in that it does not contain hydroxyproline
and has less lysine but more alanine (Bird, 1957). The protein from the fibre
layers contains cystine and tryptophane, which are absent from vertebrate
collagen, and there is more proline than glycine in this layer of the cuticle, but
less in vertebrate collagen. The external cortical layer has more alanine and
glycine than does vertebrate keratin and 0·5 M thioglycollate, which dissolves
wool keratin, did not break down the external cortical layer, indicating that
keratin is not present. If disulphide linkages are involved in stabilizing this
layer, as suggested by Carbonnell and Apitz (1960), other types of cross-
linkage must also be present. Brown (1950a) stated that keratin is not common
in invertebrates and that they have a collagenous-type of exoskeleton which
may be stabilized by tanning. There is evidence (Brown, 1950b) of quinone-
tanning in the external cortex of *A. lumbricoides*, and Bird (1957) identified
polyphenols and polyphenol oxidase in the external cortex, lending support to
Brown's work. The external cortex dissolved in 10% sodium hypochlorite and
Brown (1950a) regards this as suggesting the occurrence of aromatic tanning.
However, Bird and Rogers (1956) showed that the sheath of the third-stage
larva of *Haemonchus contortus* is dissolved by hypochlorite, but were unable
to find any evidence of tanned proteins.

Polyphenol oxidase and polyphenols are present in the cyst wall of
Heterodera rostochiensis (see Ellenby, 1946, 1963) and in the cuticle of
Meloidogyne hapla and *M. javanica* (see Bird, 1958b), but the cortical layer of
Heterodera glycines and of *Hoplolaimus tylenchiformis* (= *H. coronatus*) is not
dissolved by cold 5% sodium hypochlorite (Hirschman, 1959). Lee (1965a)
could not detect polyphenol oxidase or polyphenols in the cuticle of *Nippostrongylus brasiliensis*, and Anya (1965, 1966) could not find any evidence of
polyphenol-quinone tanning in the cuticle of *Aspiculuris tetraptera* and
Syphacia obvelata.

The amino-acid analyses of the cuticle of *Ascaris lumbricoides* by Watson and Silvester (1959) agreed, on the whole, with those given by Bird (1957, 1958a), and showed conclusively that collagen is present in the cuticle of this nematode and is similar to that found in the cuticle of the earthworm (*Lumbricus*) (Watson, 1958). Bird (1957) and Watson and Silvester (1959) pointed out that the collagen can be divided into two groups; one group gives the typical wide-angle X-ray diffraction pattern of collagen and has the characteristic 640 Å periodicity or cross-banding shown by electron microscopy, and the other group gives a similar X-ray diffraction pattern, but not cross-banding. The second group is generally referred to as a secreted collagen of epithelial or glandular origin, whereas collagen of the first type arises in association with osteoblasts and fibroblasts. Reed and Rudall (1948) suggested that the cuticle of the earthworm contains a secreted collagen. Picken *et al.* (1947) and Rudall (1955) believed that a secreted collagen occurs in the cuticle of *A. lumbricoides*, and this was confirmed by Bird (1957) and Watson and Silvester (1959). Lee (1965a) found that the fibrils which traverse the fluid-filled layer of the cuticle of adult *Nippostrongylus brasiliensis* show cross-striations under the electron microscope and Hinz (1963) found cross-striated fibrils in the cuticle of *Parascaris*; thus, the absence of cross-striations is not a general characteristic of nematode collagen, and banding may reflect only the state of molecular aggregation or association of collagen fibrils.

Nothing is known about the chemical composition of the cuticle of the third-stage larva of *N. brasiliensis*. The regular striations in the middle layer of the cuticle of this larva indicate a very close linkage between the molecules of protein, which suggests that it is a very tough, almost crystalline protein.

Simmonds (1958) studied the cast cuticle of the fourth-stage larva of *N. brasiliensis* and found that the amino-acid composition of the sheath resembles that of typical collagens, as there is a high proportion of non-polar amino acids present, particularly glycine, as well as large amounts of proline and hydroxyproline. Neither cystine nor cysteine were detected, but the tyrosine content was high. The hydrothermal behaviour of the sheath closely resembles that of elastoidin, a collagen-type protein from elasmobranch fish, which also contains large amounts of tyrosine. The sheath is also more soluble in alkali than is collagen, and it contains substantial amounts of polysaccharide and lipid, whereas collagen contains little of these substances. Simmonds concluded that the sheath may be composed of a material resembling reticulin which is a protein–lipid–carbohydrate complex in which collagen or collagen-type protein is the major constituent.

Anya (1965, 1966) found that, with the exception of the outer cortex, the layers of the cuticle of *Aspiculuris tetraptera* are stabilized by electrovalent forces. Bird (1957) reached a similar conclusion for *A. lumbricoides* and also suggested that van der Waal's forces are important in stabilizing all layers of the cuticle except the outer cortex. According to Anya, the outer cortex of *A. tetraptera* is stabilized by the covalent-linked disulphide bond together with another unidentified relatively stable chemical bond; the major structural protein of the cuticle is a secreted collagen, showing no axial periodicity, and it is associated with hyaluronic acid and chondroitin sulphate-containing mucopolysaccharides. Collagen is present in the fibrillar, matrix and fibre layers and possibly in the inner cortex. Phospholipids are present in the outer cortex. One of his most important results is the demonstration of ribonucleic acid (RNA) (Anya, 1965, 1966) as well as ascorbic acid, adenosine triphosphate and acid phosphatases in the inner cortex of the cuticle of *Aspiculuris*, *Syphacia* and *Ascaris*. In *Ascaris* the RNA was removed not only by a solution of ribonuclease, as in the oxyurids, but also by a solution of the enzyme previously heated at 90°C for 10 min (Anya, 1965, 1966), a treatment which destroys any contaminating protease.

Bird (1957) suggested that the cuticle of *A. lumbricoides* is in a state of constant metabolic activity. This has been confirmed by Lee (1961, 1962b), who found esterase in the matrix layer of the cuticle of *Ascaris* and esterase and haemoglobin in the fluid-filled layer of the cuticle of adult *Nippostrongylus brasiliensis* (Lee, 1965a), and by Anya (1965, 1966), who found RNA, acid phosphatase, adenosine triphosphatase and esterase in the cuticle of *Ascaris* and *Aspiculuris*.

Discussion

Apparently, the cuticle of nematodes is composed of a secreted collagen associated with hyaluronic acid, chondroitin sulphate-containing acid mucopolysaccharides and a small amount of lipid. The collagen is usually present as fibrils which are more numerous and more closely associated with each other in some layers (the cortex and the fibre layers) than in others (the matrix layer). The outer cortex contains more sulphur than is found in other layers. This is probably due to disulphide linkages which, together with another type of chemical bond, stabilize the outer cortex, and not to keratin. Polyphenolquinone tanning also seems to play some part in stabilizing the outer cortex of nematodes, but not all of them. The cuticle may contain a number of enzymes, RNA and haemoglobin and is evidently not an inert covering.

D. GROWTH OF THE CUTICLE

It is known that the cuticle of some nematodes grows between moults and after the final moult (Watson, 1962, 1965b; Bird, 1959). Watson (1965b) showed that the cuticle of a small (9 cm) adult *Ascaris lumbricoides* contains the same layers as that of a fully grown worm, but is much thinner. The change in thickness is directly proportional to the change in length of the nematode and all layers of the cuticle increase in size, the matrix layer more rapidly than the fibre layers and these more rapidly than the cortical layers.

It is usually assumed that the proteins and other constituents of the cuticle are synthesized in the hypodermis and then passed into the cuticle. What has never been explained is how relatively large and complex molecules pass from the hypodermis to the various layers of the cuticle. In those nematodes which have pore canals in the cuticle the substances may pass to the outer layers of the cuticle along the canals, but not all nematodes possess such canals. Anya (1965, 1966) has shown that the inner cortex of *Ascaris*, *Syphacia* and *Aspiculuris* contains RNA, which suggests that this layer is involved in the synthesis of proteins in some nematodes. Anya (1965, 1966) identified adenosine triphosphatase, acid phosphatase, ascorbic acid and RNA in both the inner cortex and the hypodermis of these nematodes and suggested that collagen fibrogenesis takes place in these locations. He believed that in some nematodes small molecules (amino acids and sugars) pass between the fibrils of the various layers of the cuticle and are synthesized into collagen fibrils in the outer layers, while macromolecules and fibrils of collagen formed in the hypodermis pass into the basal layers to become incorporated in the fibre layers. Possibly, complete collagen molecules are formed in the hypodermis and then extruded into the cuticle, where they polymerize into fibrils. Polymerization is a slow process and would give the soluble collagen molecules time to move through the cuticle before fibrogenesis occurred. Substances in the cuticle may also serve to regulate the rate of polymerization. The suggestion has been made that the arrangement of the fibre layers in the cuticle of *Ascaris* is related to mechanical forces acting on the cuticle during secretion (Picken *et al.*, 1947; Picken, 1960).

E. FUNCTIONAL CONSIDERATIONS

The cuticle of nematodes has several functions, notably to protect the body against possible injury and to isolate the tissues of the body from the external environment, thus allowing nematodes to regulate their internal environment. As a result, they have been able to invade almost every type of ecological niche. Another important function of the cuticle is related to locomotion. The cuticle imposes a restraint on changes of bodily shape, but its structure is such that restraint produces those changes in shape that can and must be made (Clark, 1964).

Harris and Crofton (1957) have shown that the functions of the cuticle in *Ascaris lumbricoides* are highly specialized. The lattice of fibres of the fibre layers are inclined at an angle of 75° to the longitudinal axis of the body and contraction of the muscles of the body wall, which are all longitudinally arranged, tends to increase the angle of the fibres and to reduce the volume enclosed by the fibres and the muscles. The pseudocoele is full of incompressible fluid, however, and the effect of contraction of the muscles is to increase the hydrostatic pressure of the body fluid. It is increase in hydrostatic pressure which acts against the longitudinal muscles and restores them to their resting length. Relaxation of the muscles decreases the hydrostatic pressure and results in elongation of the nematode to the elastic limit of the cuticle. Harris and Crofton (1957) suggested that the lattice-work of fibres, together with the elasticity of the cuticle and the high turgor pressure of the body cavity, can be regarded as the key to nematode locomotion and to the uniformity of structure in nematodes. This is probably true of the larger nematodes which possess a system of fibres in the cuticle, and possibly of those smaller nematodes and nematode larvae which do not possess a system of fibres, but do have a basal layer or layers of fibrils in the cuticle. However, some nematodes do not possess a system of fibres or fibrils in the cuticle, and both Watson (1962) and Inglis (1964a) have suggested that in such forms a different type of system must be operative. The critical feature of all these systems is the necessity for the cuticle to resist diametrical rather than longitudinal stretch. Some larvae and small adults possess such a system in the

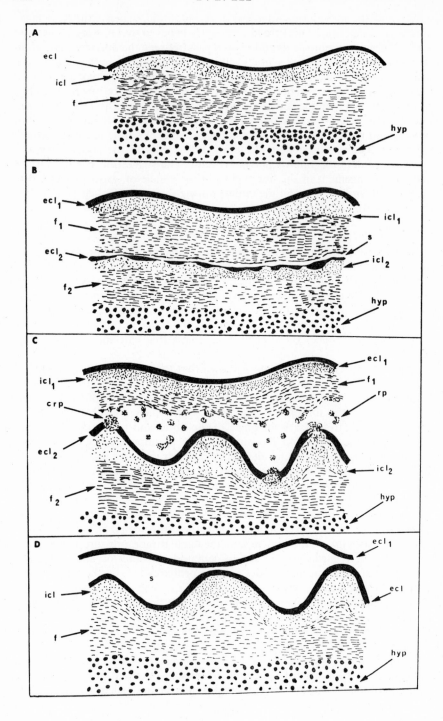

toughened parts of the external cortical layer which form rings or annuli. These annuli are united by rings of soft cuticle which act as joints between the annuli. Other small nematodes have, in the middle layer of the cuticle, a system of plates or rods united transversely to form a toughened ring of material in each annulus, as described by Inglis (1964a) for the Chromadorida (see Figs. 11–14). Such systems will permit longitudinal extension of the body by virtue of the softer rings of cuticle, but will oppose diametrical extension. The rings of fibres in the cuticle of the third-stage larva of *Nippostrongylus* may have this function (Lee, 1966). Coupled with a high hydrostatic pressure in the body cavity and the action of the longitudinal muscles, these two kinds of cuticle could function in the manner suggested by Harris and Crofton for *Ascaris* (Watson, 1962; Inglis, 1964a). Watson indicated that the efficient working of these systems depends on closely spaced annuli to minimize diametrical distortion and hardened or toughened annuli to provide resistance and elasticity.

The cuticle of nematodes plays an important role in osmoregulation and ion regulation (see Lee, 1965b), but its role in nutrition is still disputed.

F. MOULTING

All nematodes moult four times during development to the adult stage, but little is known about the moulting process. Watson (1962), Bird and Rogers (1965) and Lee (unpublished) have studied moulting in nematodes by means of the electron microscope.

Watson (1962) found that at an early stage in the moult of *Turbatrix aceti* the hypodermis retracts from the cuticle, leaving a space which may be filled with liquid. The new cuticle is then secreted by the hypodermis. At a later stage, when all the layers of the new cuticle have appeared, very little of the old cuticle has been dissolved, although the layer containing the regularly spaced rods or striations has disappeared. The newly formed cuticle is not folded, but within a few hours after ecdysis the surface is extensively folded. Folding of the new cuticle coincides with rapid increase in length of the body after ecdysis. In *T. aceti*, ecdysis occurs before the secretion of the new cuticle has been completed and the rapid secretion, folding and increase in surface area, followed by elongation of the worm, all occur after ecdysis.

The moulting cuticle of *Rhabditis strongyloides* separates beneath the columellae and ecdysis is preceded by the formation of a new cuticle (Peebles, 1957).

At the inception of moulting in *Meloidogyne javanica* (Fig. 26) the hypodermis becomes granular, probably because of an increase in the number of ribosomes, and thicker (Bird and Rogers, 1965). The amount of RNA and

◄—FIG. 26. Diagram illustrating the stages which occur during moulting of the cuticle of *Meloidogyne javanica*. A. Larval cuticle before moulting showing external cortical layer (*ecl*), internal cortical layer (*icl*), fibre layer (*f*) and the hypodermis (*hyp*). B. The onset of moulting showing the two cuticles inner (2) and outer (1) and space (*s*) between them. C. A later stage of moulting showing reabsorption of the innermost layers of the outer cuticle as particles (*rp*) through the cortical layer (*crp*). D. Moulting completed with only the external cortical layer of the old cuticle (*ecl*) remaining. (From Bird and Rogers, 1965.)

protein also increases in the hypodermis. The fibre layer of the cuticle then begins to separate from the hypodermis which forms an interrupted osmio-philic line, the future external cortical layer of the new cuticle. Unlike *T. aceti*, the new cuticle in *M. javanica* is laid down in convolutions, allowing for rapid growth after completion of the moult (Fig. 26). A stage is reached when old and new cuticles are of equal thickness and are separated by large spaces which become filled with particles believed to be concerned with the breakdown and reabsorption of the inner layers of the moulted cuticle. The external cortex is not reabsorbed and is the only part of the cuticle which is cast off. The old cuticle is apparently absorbed through regions in the newly formed cuticle where the external cortical layer has not been formed (Fig. 26). After ecdysis the new cuticle continues to increase in thickness.

Lee (unpublished) has shown that most of the cuticle of the fourth-stage larva of *Trichinella spiralis* is shed at the final moult, and only the basal lamella appears to be dissolved (Fig. 24). The cuticle of the young adult nematode is much thinner at this stage than that of the fourth-stage larva, which is being shed. The external surface forms small waves or folds, but is not extensively folded. Thus in the final moult *T. spiralis* more closely resembles *Turbatrix aceti* than *Meloidogyne javanica*.

Watson (1962) and Inglis (1964a) both suggested that moulting may be associated with the difficulty of increasing the diameter of the toughened parts of the cuticle beyond a certain amount. Watson (1962) suggested that in some nematodes softening of the cuticle permits cuticular growth independently of moulting, but this is incompatible with the function of the cuticle of providing an elastic return mechanism for the muscles. However, the larger nematodes have used the collagen fibrils, an important component of the cuticle in all nematodes, to form a system of fibres which has taken over the function of the elastic annuli and the stiffening structures in the matrix layer and can be added to during growth. With the development of the lattice-work of fibres the outer layers of the cuticle have become less extensively toughened, thus allow-ing only limited growth to occur. Watson claims, therefore, that instead of being the key feature of locomotion in nematodes, the addition of a system of fibres to the cuticle has led to greater diversification and increase in size of nematodes.

Neurosecretory cells may play an important part in controlling moulting in nematodes (Rogers, 1962; Rogers and Sommerville, 1963), but there is no experimental evidence that this is so.

In some nematodes parasitic in animals third-stage larvae retain the cuticle of the second-stage larva as a sort of sheath which completely encloses the third-stage larva as the mouth, anus and excretory pore become occluded. When the larva is ingested by the host certain stimuli (see Rogers and Sommer-ville, 1963) bring about exsheathment of the larva in the alimentary tract of the host. The larvae are stimulated to secrete an exsheathing fluid, an important constituent of which is leucine aminopeptidase (Rogers, 1965). This enzyme attacks a weak ring in the sheath at the anterior end, causing a cap to be released, and the larva escapes from the open sheath (Lapage, 1935; Rogers and Sommerville, 1963).

VII. ACANTHOCEPHALA

A. HISTORICAL

The nomenclature of the various layers of the body wall of the Acantho-cephala is somewhat confused. According to Meyer (1933), the body wall of the Acanthocephala has essentially the same structure in all species and consists of a thin cuticle, a striped layer, a felt layer, a radial layer and a base-ment membrane. Hyman (1951b) referred to all the layers beneath the cuticle as the epidermis. According to Baer (1961) the body wall of the Acantho-cephala consists of a cuticle of two layers and a complex hypodermis which is also divisible into two layers. The thin outermost layer of the cuticle is homo-geneous and corresponds to the cuticle as described by Meyer. The second layer of the cuticle was said to have fine striations perpendicular to the surface and corresponds to the striped layer in Meyer's terminology. The two layers of the hypodermis correspond to the felt and radial layers.

Some writers consider the radial layer to be the epidermis and all the remaining layers parts of the cuticle (see Crompton, 1963). Because of this controversy it is necessary to consider the entire body wall in this article (see Fig. 27).

A system of fluid-filled canals, the lacunar channels, lies within the radial and, to a lesser extent, the felt layers of the body wall. The entire body wall contains a number of large nuclei and is a syncytium. On the inner surface there is a layer of circular muscles, followed by a layer of longitudinal muscles (Fig. 27).

B. STRUCTURE

Rothman and Rosario (1961) studied the surface layers of *Macracantho-rhynchus hirudinaceus* with the electron microscope and published a short abstract of their findings. The periphery of the worm is said to have two distinct types of structure. The first has a spongy appearance and the second the appearance of a palisade. These presumably correspond to the cuticle and the striped layer described by other workers using the light microscope.

Crompton (1963) and Crompton and Lee (1965) studied the structure of the body wall of *Polymorphus minutus* by means of histological and electron microscopical techniques and their findings are summarized in Fig. 27. The body wall is covered by a thin layer of mucopolysaccharide which Crompton (1963) called the epicuticle and which is probably secreted on the surface of the worm. In electron micrographs this layer is seen as an irregular deposition of electron-dense material (Fig. 28), and it was also seen on *M. hirudinaceus* by Crompton and Lee (1963), but Stranack, Woodhouse and Griffin (un-published) were unable to find an epicuticle at the surface of *Pomphorhynchus laevis*.

The external layer of the metasoma (trunk region) of *Polymorphus minutus* is a thin cuticle having an outer three-layered membrane and a homogeneous layer (Fig. 28), and numerous pores which are the openings of canals passing through the striped layer (Figs. 27 and 28) (Crompton and Lee, 1965). The cuticle of *Pomphorhynchus laevis* is similar in that it has an outer three-layered membrane, a middle layer of medium electron-density and an inner narrow

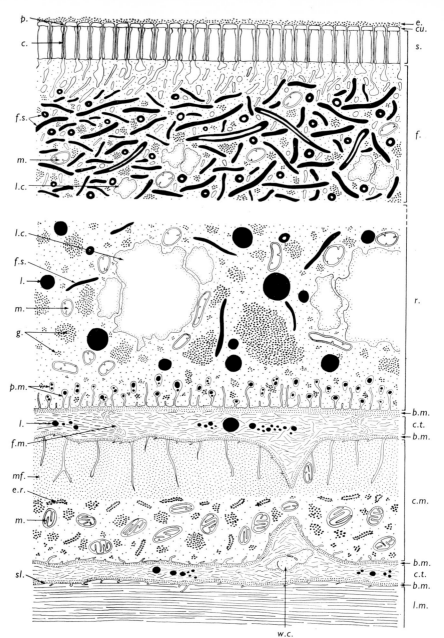

FIG. 27. A diagrammatic representation of the metasomal body wall of *Polymorphus minutus*. *b.m.*, Basement membrane; *c.*, canal; *c.m.*, circular muscle; *c.t.*, connective tissue; *cu.*, cuticle; *e.*, epicuticle; *e.r.*, endoplasmic reticulum; *f.*, felt layer; *f.m.*, fibres attaching muscles to body wall; *f.s.*, fibrous strands; *g.*, glycogen; *l.*, lipid; *l.c.*, lacuna channel; *l.m.*, longitudinal muscle; *m.*, mitochondrion; *mf.*, myofilaments; *p.*, pore; *p.m.*, folded plasma membrane; *r.*, radial layer; *s.*, striped layer; *sl.*, sarcolemma; *w.c.*, wandering cell. (From Crompton and Lee, 1965.)

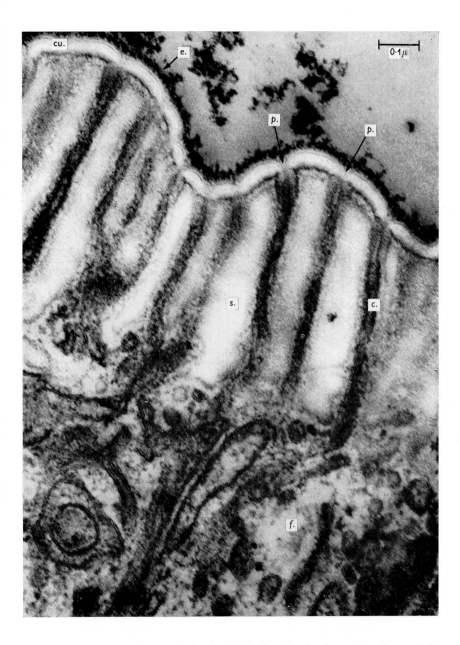

Fig. 28. Electron micrograph of a longitudinal section in the trunk region of *Polymorphus minutus* showing the three-layered membrane of the cuticle, the pores which penetrate the cuticle, and the canals of the striped layer. *c.*, Canal; *cu.*, cuticle; *e.*, epicuticle; *f.*, felt layer; *p.*, pore; *s.*, striped layer. (From Crompton and Lee, 1965.)

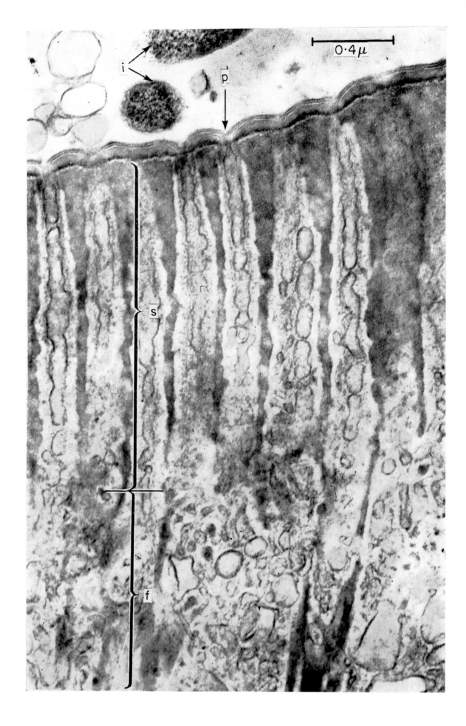

band of greater electron-density. This cuticle is also pierced by many pores which communicate with channels or canals in the striped layer (Fig. 29) (Stranack *et al.*, unpublished). The striped layer of these two species appears to consist of a homogeneous material surrounding canals which pass from the felt layer to the cuticle and open by pores in the cuticle. The canals, many of which are filled with some electron-dense substance, give this layer its characteristic striped appearance under the light microscope. The opening or pore through the cuticle is narrower than the rest of the canals (Figs. 28 and 29). The three-layered membrane of the cuticle also extends into and lines the lumen of the canals.

The cuticle on the praesoma (neck region and proboscis) of *Polymorphus minutus* is similar to that on the metasoma, but is penetrated by fewer canals. The contents of the canals in the striped layer of the neck region are very electron-dense and have the appearance of lipid (Fig. 30).

The felt layer of the metasoma of *Polymorphus minutus* and of *Pomphorhynchus laevis* contains many fibrous strands extending in various directions (Figs. 27 and 31). The fibres in *Polymorphus* appear to be hollow or to have a less electron-dense core. Mitochondria with few cristae are present in this region of the body wall and numerous vesicles are also present in this layer, some of them apparently connected to the canals of the striped layer, while others may be a kind of endoplasmic reticulum (Crompton and Lee, 1965; Stranack *et al.*, unpublished).

The radial layer of *Polymorphus* contains fewer fibrous strands than the felt layer, but large thin-walled lacunar channels are present. Mitochondria are much more numerous in the radial layer than in the felt layer and are often arranged around the lacunar channels. Large amounts of lipid are present in this layer in large and small droplets.

On the inner surface of the body wall of *Polymorphus* and of *Pomphorhynchus* there is a greatly folded plasma membrane, the ends of the folds often forming small vesicles which in *Polymorphus* contain droplets of electron-dense material, possibly lipid. These folds and vesicles resemble pinocytotic vesicles (Crompton and Lee, 1965; Stranack *et al.*, unpublished).

A fibrillar basement membrane covers the inner surface of the body wall. The circular muscles are attached to the body wall by aggregations of fibrils which pass from the basement membrane through fibrous connective material to the membrane enveloping the muscles.

The felt and radial layers of the praesoma of *Polymorphus* are similar to those of the metasoma but thinner. There is apparently no radial layer in the proboscis. The plasma membrane adjacent to the basement membrane is folded as it is in the metasoma, but the folds are more open and do not contain lipid droplets.

◄—FIG. 29. Electron micrograph of a section through the body wall of *Pomphorhynchus laevis* showing the cuticle pores (*p*) piercing the cuticle and opening into the radial canals of the striped layer (*s*). Supporting columns of the striped layer alternate with the canals. *f*, Felt layer; *i*, intestinal contents of the host. (Courtesy of F. R. Stranack, M. A. Woodhouse and R. L. Griffin.)

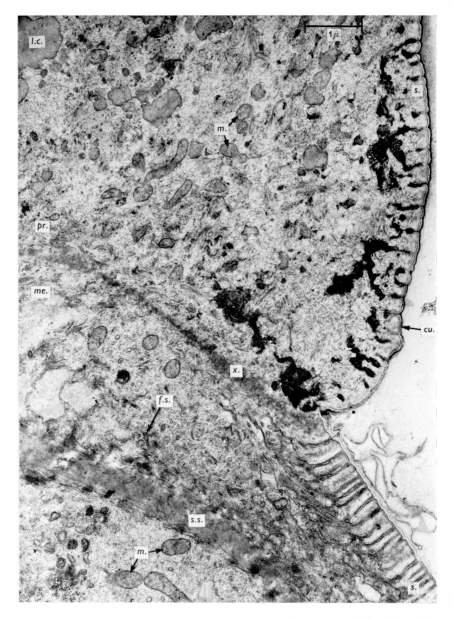

FIG. 30. Electron micrograph of a longitudinal section through the junction of the praesoma and metasoma of *Polymorphus minutus*. Note the difference in appearance of the striped layer and the nature of the contents of the canals in the two regions. *cu.*, Cuticle; *f.s.*, fibrous strands; *l.c.*, lacunar channel; *m.*, mitochondria; *me.*, metasoma; *pr.*, praesoma; *s.*, striped layer; *s.s.*, skeletal fibres of trunk spine; *x.*, partition separating the neck from the trunk. (From Crompton and Lee, 1965.)

The hooks of the proboscis consist of hard, non-living material surrounding an inner core of cytoplasm in *Polymorphus*. The trunk spines, on the other hand, are formed from the general body wall and are covered with the thin outer cuticle and the striped layer, but the latter becomes thinner and has fewer canals towards the apices of the spines. Compacted fibres of the felt layer form a hollow cone which is the skeletal element of each spine (Crompton and Lee, 1965).

Nicholas and Hynes (1963) published an electron micrograph (taken by Dr A. F. Bird) of the outer layers of the body wall of *Moniliformis dubius* and gave a brief description of it. Nicholas and Mercer (1965) have now given a detailed description of the ultrastructure of the body wall of *M. dubius* which shows that there is little difference between it and the body wall of *Polymorphus* and *Pomphorhynchus*. However, they interpreted their findings rather differently from Crompton and Lee (1965) and Stranack *et al.* (unpublished).

Nicholas and Mercer (1965) termed the outer layer of mucopolysaccharide (the epicuticle) "layer I" of the body wall, and consider that it should be called cuticle. To regard a replacement layer of mucopolysaccharide, which is not an integral part of the body wall, as part of the cuticle is misleading. A similar layer of mucopolysaccharide covers the surface of trematodes, cestodes and the surface of the microvilli in the intestine of most animals and probably provides resistance to the action of the host's digestive enzymes. This coating of mucopolysaccharide should therefore be regarded as an epicuticle and not a structural part of the body wall of the Acanthocephala.

The epicuticle is separated from the body wall of *M. dubius* by a plasma membrane 80 Å thick, and adjacent to it there is another membrane, the subplasma membrane. This region of the body wall corresponds to the cuticle of *Polymorphus* and *Pomphorhynchus*. Nicholas and Mercer do not name the various layers of the body wall, which they call the tegument, but number them instead. The epicuticle is layer I and the layers between the outer plasma membrane and the basement membrane are layers II to V and are intracellular.

Below the subplasma membrane (cuticle) in layer II they describe a dense meshwork with long, tapering interstices which extend to the surface. In longitudinal sections at right-angles to the surface this layer appears to consist of branching septa lying perpendicular to the body surface, interspersed with pores which taper as they approach the body surface. This layer corresponds to the striped layer described by other workers and in *Polymorphus* and *Pomphorhynchus* there is a system of canals running through a homogeneous material to open by pores in the cuticle (Crompton and Lee, 1965; Stranack *et al.*, unpublished). Nicholas and Mercer interpret this and the vesicles below the striped layer in *M. dubius* as evidence of pinocytotic activity at the outer surface of the body wall, but this does not occur in the other two species.

In layer III, between the striped layer (II) and the felt layer (IV), and in layer V (the radial layer) fibres extend mainly in a radial direction. In layer IV the fibres are more numerous and form a feltwork. The mitochondria in layers III–V have poorly developed cristae. Lipid droplets of varying size, glycogen and ribosomes are also present in these layers.

There is a plasma membrane and a basement membrane at the base of the

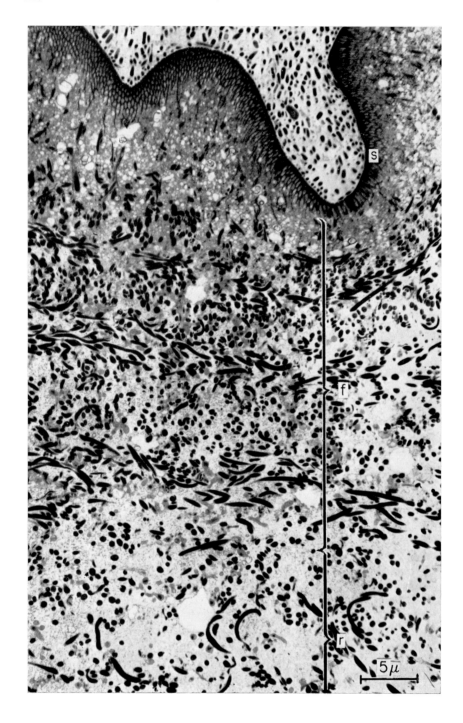

body wall. The radially arranged fibres of the body wall appear to attach to the plasma membrane. Vesicles line the distal surface of the plasma membrane and sometimes this membrane is drawn out to form an incompletely enclosed vesicle. Nicholas and Mercer decided that the vesicles are either pinched off from the plasma membrane, as Crompton and Lee (1965) suggested occurs in *Polymorphus*, or coalesce with it.

Discussion

The body wall of the Acanthocephala is basically the same in all species. In *Polymorphus minutus*, *Pomphorhynchus laevis* and *Moniliformis dubius* the main differences are matters of interpretation. The striped layer and the thin outer cuticle should perhaps be regarded as two layers of the cuticle, which would then consist of an outer layer covered by a three-layered membrane, as in the nematodes (see Section VI), and perforated by numerous pores, and a basal striped layer through which canals pass from the hypodermis to the pores in the outer layer of the cuticle. The layers of the body wall beneath the striped layer should be regarded as the hypodermis.

C. COMPOSITION

The epicuticle appears to consist of acid mucopolysaccharide (Monné, 1959b; Crompton, 1963; Crompton and Lee, 1963; Nicholas and Mercer, 1965). The outer layer of the cuticle of *Polymorphus minutus* consists of a lipoprotein containing -SH groups and -SS- linkages (Crompton, 1963). Crompton decided that more than 4% sulphur is present in the cuticle of this worm, but Mueller (1929) found that the "cuticula" of *Macracanthorhynchus hirudinaceus* contained only 0·564% sulphur. It is possible that the "cuticula" examined by Mueller consisted of more than the outer layers of the cuticle and the striped layer and that the other layers contain little sulphur. It is probable that the disulphide linkages serve to toughen the cuticle of the Acanthocephala.

Monné (1959b) states that the cuticle is keratinized but according to Brown (1950a) keratin does not normally occur in invertebrates. Monné (1959b) believed that the cuticle is stabilized by polyphenol-quinone tanning, but this assumption was based solely on the reduction by the cuticle of ammoniacal silver nitrate and the fact that it recolorized Schiff's reagent. The only significance which can be attached to this is that some components of the cuticle have reducing properties.

Crompton (1963) was of the opinion that the fibres of the felt and radial layers are of a similar composition to that of the cuticle and the homogeneous material of the striped layer.

The hypodermis of the body wall of acanthocephalans contains large amounts of glycogen and lipid and the distribution of these substances appears

---

◄—FIG. 31. Electron micrograph of the body wall of *Pomphorhynchus laevis* showing the main layers of the body wall. The cuticle cannot be resolved at this magnification. Intestinal contents of the host lie outside of the body wall. The strands of electron-dense material (fibres) are well shown. *f*, Felt layer; *r*, radial layer; *s*, striped layer. (Courtesy of F. R. Stranack, M. A. Woodhouse and R. L. Griffin.)

to be similar in most species which have been studied (von Brand, 1939, 1940; Bullock, 1949b; Crompton and Lee, 1965; Nicholas and Mercer, 1965; Crompton, 1965).

The epicuticle and the outer layer of the cuticle apparently show no enzyme activity, but alkaline phosphatase is present in the hypodermis and in the striped layer of the cuticle of most acanthocephalans which have been studied (Bullock, 1949a, 1958; Crompton, 1963). However, none of eight species of the Neoechinorhynchidae gave any evidence of alkaline phosphatase activity, and it is apparently not present in *Acanthocephalus* sp. and *Leptorhynchoides thecatus* (see Bullock, 1958). The enzyme activity in the striped layer is probably confined to the canals, but no special research effort has been made to determine this.

Lipase is present in the inner and outer layers of the body wall, but not in the cuticle, the middle layer or in the body wall of the praesoma of those Acanthocephala which have been studied (Bullock, 1949a).

Non-specific esterase is present in all layers of the body wall of *Polymorphus minutus* except the epicuticle and the cuticle (Crompton, 1963); it is also found in the striped felt and radial layers of *Moniliformis dubius* and is especially concentrated in the proboscis (Crompton and Lee, 1963). However, hardly any esterase has been detected in the body wall of *Macracanthorhynchus hirudinaceus* (see Crompton and Lee, 1963).

Leucine aminopeptidase is present in the striped layer, presumably in the canals, and in the felt layer of the body wall of *Polymorphus minutus* (see Crompton, 1963).

D. FUNCTIONAL CONSIDERATIONS

Monné (1959b) considered that an outer coating of acid mucopolysaccharide will protect parasites against the digestive enzymes of the host by acting as enzyme inhibitors. Crompton (1963) suggested that such a covering may serve equally well if the host's enzymes are unable to split the mucopolysaccharide. Thus, the epicuticle of some Acanthocephala may protect the parasite against the digestive enzymes of the host. Presumably, the mucopolysaccharide is produced in the hypodermis and passed to the surface through the canals in the striped layer.

The striped layer may facilitate the absorption of nutrients into the body wall by means of a series of components whose ends are separated and supported by a thin, inert cuticle (Crompton, 1963). In *Polymorphus minutus* and *Pomphorhynchus laevis* these components are canals which open to the exterior through pores in the cuticle, and nutrients may pass through these pores and canals into the worm (Crompton and Lee, 1965; Stranack *et al.*, unpublished). The presence of electron-dense material, possibly lipid, in the canals of the striped layer in the neck region (Crompton and Lee, 1965) (Fig. 30) supports the hypothesis that some acanthocephalans are able to absorb lipid through the body wall (Pflugfelder, 1949; Bullock, 1949b). This region of the worm is in close contact with the tissues of the host, being enclosed in a nodule of the host's tissues, and apparently absorbs lipid from the tissues of the host. Small particles of carbon and thorium dioxide are taken up through the cuticle of *Moniliformis dubius* and electron micrographs reveal such particles in the canals of the striped layer (Edmonds and Dixon, 1966).

Nicholas and Mercer (1965) suggested that a form of pinocytosis occurs across the body surface of *Moniliformis dubius*, but they may have misinterpreted the structure of the surface layers and canals and pores may be present.

Crompton and Lee (1965) suggested that the matrix of the striped layer and the fibres of the hypodermis have a skeletal function. The radial layer is apparently the main metabolic centre of the body wall and the main storage organ of the body (Crompton, 1963). Von Brand (1939) and Bullock (1949b) both suggested that the lacunar channels serve to transport nutrients from one part of the worm to another.

Crompton and Lee (1965) suggested that the folds and vesicles of the plasma membrane lining the inner surface of the body wall of *Polymorphus minutus* represent pinocytotic activity and that nutrients, including lipid droplets, are transferred from the body fluid to the tissues of the body wall in this way. Accordingly they suggested that the body fluid is also important in the storage and transport of nutrients.

VIII. GENERAL SUMMARY

The last few years have brought renewed interest in the structure and composition of the external covering of helminths. Various modern techniques have been applied to the study of the cuticle and have improved our knowledge of the structure and function of the outer covering of the parasitic Platyhelminthes and the Acanthocephala. All the available evidence indicates that the three major groups of helminths, viz. the parasitic Platyhelminthes, the Nematoda and the Acanthocephala, have fundamentally different outer coverings.

The "cuticle" of the digenetic trematodes and the cestodes is a syncytial cytoplasmic covering continuous with nucleated portions of the cytoplasm situated in the parenchyma beneath the muscle layers and is to be regarded as an epidermis, as in the Turbellaria. The epidermis of cestodes is covered with numerous microvilli which greatly increase the absorptive surface of the worm; it also contains numerous mitochondria and enzymes which are presumably associated with the active transport of materials. The epidermis of the digenetic trematodes is devoid of microvilli, but it contains mitochondria and enzymes and also numerous vacuoles and vesicles which appear to be associated with the uptake and/or excretion or secretion of materials across the epidermis.

It has often been suggested that the Acanthocephala are closely related to the cestodes because of the lack of a gut and because they possess a proboscis. The main body of evidence is against this theory, however, and the body wall of the Acanthocephala has a completely different type of structure from that of other helminths. The presence of pores and canals in the cuticle and striped layer of the body wall of the Acanthocephala indicates that nutrients are absorbed through these openings in the body wall, rather than through the general body surface.

The nematode cuticle has a complex and varied structure with basically three main layers which are usually subdivided into further layers. There are marked differences from one genus to another and much more work needs to be done on the ultrastructure before it is possible to generalize about this structure. Other results may be expected to appear during the next few years, together with information on the changes which occur during moulting.

The cuticle of nematodes seems to be composed of collagen plus small amounts of carbohydrate and lipid, and the outer layer is usually toughened or strengthened in some way. The presence of enzymes and RNA in the cuticle of nematodes shows that it is not an inert secretion but is a metabolically active structure.

Clearly, the ultrastructure of the epidermis of the trematodes and cestodes, and the cuticle of nematodes requires further investigation. Studies on ultrastructure in the Monogenea, the Temnocephalida, the larval stages of Platyhelminthes, and the free-living nematodes will provide much-needed information. The application of cytochemistry and autoradiography, along with electron microscopy, will undoubtedly lead to new and important discoveries in this field of study.

ACKNOWLEDGEMENTS

I wish to thank many willing helpers. Dr A. O. Anya, Mr R. G. Bruce, Dr K. M. Lyons, Mr V. R. Southgate (all of this department), Dr P. R. Burton, Dr A. F. Bird, Dr D. A. Erasmus, Dr A. E. Dorey, Dr F. R. Stranack, Dr L. T. Threadgold, Dr B. D. Watson and Dr K. A. Wright generously lent originals of their published figures or permitted the use of unpublished results. Dr P. Tate criticized the manuscript, Professor C. F. A. Pantin and Dr L. E. R. Picken advised about the terminology of the external covering of trematodes and cestodes and Mr A. Page assisted in electron microscopy and the preparation of the illustrations. A grant from the Agricultural Research Council is gratefully acknowledged.

REFERENCES

Alvarado, R. (1951a). *Trab. Inst. Cienc. nat., Madr.* 3, 1–90.
Alvarado, R. (1951b). *Boln R. Soc. esp. Hist. nat.* 49, 159–162.
Anya, A. O. (1965). Ph.D. thesis, University of Cambridge.
Anya, A. O. (1966). *Parasitology* 56, 179–198.
Arvy, L. (1954). *Annls Parasit. hum. comp.* 29, 510–520.
Baer, J. G. (1961). "Traité de Zoologie. IV (1), Plathelminthes, Mésozoaires, Acanthocéphales, Némertiens." Masson, Paris.
Baer, J. G., and Joyeux, C. (1961). "Traité de Zoologie. IV (1), Plathelminthes, Mésozoaires, Acanthocéphales, Némertiens." Masson, Paris.
Beckett, E. B., and Boothroyd, B. (1961). *Ann. trop. Med. Parasit.* 55, 116–124.
Berthier, L. (1954). *Archs Zool. exp. gén.* 91, 89–102.
Bird, A. F. (1954). *Nature, Lond.* 174, 362.

Bird, A. F. (1956). *Expl Parasit.* **5**, 350–358.
Bird, A. F. (1957). *Expl Parasit.* **6**, 383–403.
Bird, A. F. (1958a). *Parasitology* **48**, 32–39.
Bird, A. F. (1958b). *Nematologica* **3**, 205–212.
Bird, A. F. (1959). *Nematologica* **4**, 31–42.
Bird, A. F., and Deutsch, K. (1957). *Parasitology* **47**, 319–328.
Bird, A. F., and Rogers, G. E. (1965). *Nematologica* **11**, 224–230.
Bird, A. F., and Rogers, W. P. (1956). *Expl Parasit.* **5**, 449–457.
Björkman, N., and Thorsell, W. (1964). *Expl Cell Res.* **33**, 319–329.
Björkman, N., Thorsell, W., and Lienert, E. (1963). *Experientia* **19**, 3.
Bogoyavlenski, Y. K. (1958a). *Dokl. Akad. Nauk SSSR* **120**, 1119–1121.
Bogoyavlenski, Y. K. (1958b). *Biofizika* **3**, 626–628.
Bogoyavlenski, Y. K. (1959). *Helminthologia* **1**, 243–247.
Bogoyavlenski, Y. K. (1960). *Trudy gel'mint. Lab.* **10**, 58–67.
Brand, T. von (1939). *J. Parasit.* **25**, 329–342.
Brand, T. von (1940). *J. Parasit.* **26**, 301–307.
Brown, C. H. (1950a). *Nature, Lond.* **165**, 275.
Brown, C. H. (1950b). *Q. Jl microsc. Sci.* **91**, 331–339.
Bullock, W. L. (1949a). *J. Morph.* **84**, 185–199.
Bullock, W. L. (1949b). *J. Morph.* **84**, 201–225.
Bullock, W. L. (1958). *Expl Parasit.* **7**, 51–68.
Burton, P. R. (1962). *J. Parasit.* **48**, 874–882.
Burton, P. R. (1964). *J. Morph.* **115**, 305–318.
Carbonnell, L. H., and Apitz, R. (1960). *Expl Parasit.* **10**, 263–267.
Cardell, R. R. (1962). *Trans. Am. microsc. Soc.* **81**, 124–131.
Cardell, R. R., and Philpott, D. E. (1960). *Trans. Am. microsc. Soc.* **79**, 442–450.
Cheng, T. C. (1964). *Parasitology* **54**, 73–79.
Chitwood, B. G. (1938). *Proc. helminth. Soc. Wash.* **5**, 68–75.
Chitwood, B. G., and Chitwood, M. B. (1950). "An Introduction to Nematology",
    2nd ed. Monumental Printing Co., Baltimore.
Clark, R. B. (1964). "Dynamics of Metazoan Evolution." Clarendon Press, Oxford.
Conink, L. de (1965). "Traité de Zoologie. IV (2), Némathelminthes." Masson, Paris.
Crompton, D. W. T. (1963). *Parasitology* **53**, 663–685.
Crompton, D. W. T. (1965). *Parasitology* **55**, 503–514.
Crompton, D. W. T., and Lee, D. L. (1963). *Parasitology* **53**, 3–4P.
Crompton, D. W. T., and Lee, D. L. (1965). *Parasitology* **55**, 357–364.
Crusz, H. (1948). *J. Helminth.* **22**, 179–198.
Dawes, B. (1946:1956). "The Trematoda—with special Reference to British and
    other European Forms." Cambridge University Press.
Dawes, B. (1963). *Parasitology* **53**, 123–133.
Dorey, A. E. (1965). *Q. Jl microsc. Sci.* **106**, 147–172.
Dusanic, D. G. (1959). *J. infect. Dis.* **105**, 1–8.
Eckert, J., and Schwarz, R. (1965). *Z. ParasitKde* **26**, 116–142.
Edmonds, S. J., and Dixon, B. R. (1966). *Nature, Lond.* **209**, 99.
Ellenby, C. (1946). *Nature, Lond.* **157**, 302.
Ellenby, C. (1963). *Experientia* **19**, 256.
Erasmus, D. A. (1957a). *Parasitology* **47**, 70–80.
Erasmus, D. A. (1957b). *Parasitology* **47**, 81–91.
Erasmus, D. A., and Öhman, C. (1963). *Ann. N.Y. Acad. Sci.* **113**, 7–35.
Erasmus, D. A., and Öhman, C. (1965). *J. Parasit.* **51**, 761–769.
Fairbairn, D. (1956). *Can. J. Biochem. Physiol.* **34**, 39–45.
Fairbairn, D. (1957). *Expl Parasit.* **6**, 491–554.

Fairbairn, D. (1960). *In* "Nematology. Fundamentals and Recent Advances with Emphasis on Plant Parasitic and Soil Forms" (J. N. Sasser and W. R. Jenkins, eds.). University of North Carolina Press, Chapel Hill.

Fairbairn, D., and Passey, R. F. (1957). *Expl Parasit.* **6**, 566–574.

Ferris, V. R. (1956). *Phytopathology* **46**, 12.

Ferris, V. R., and Siegal, B. M. (1957). *Nematologica* **2**, 16–18.

Franklin, M. T. (1939). *J. Helminth.* **17**, 127–134.

Harris, J. E., and Crofton, H. D. (1957). *J. exp. Biol.* **34**, 116–130.

Hinz, E. (1963). *Protoplasma* **56**, 202–241.

Hirschman, H. (1959). *Proc. helminth. Soc. Wash.* **26**, 73–90.

Hirschman, H. (1960). *In* "Nematology. Fundamentals and Recent Advances with Emphasis on Plant Parasitic and Soil Forms" (J. N. Sasser and W. R. Jenkins, eds.). University of North Carolina Press, Chapel Hill.

Hobson, A. D. (1948). *Parasitology* **38**, 183–227.

Howells, R. E. (1965). *Parasitology* **55**, 20–21P.

Hyman, L. H. (1951a). "The Invertebrates: Platyhelminthes and Rhynchocoela. The Acoelomate Bilateria", Vol. II. McGraw-Hill, New York.

Hyman, L. H. (1951b). "The Invertebrates: Acanthocephala, Aschelminthes, and Entoprocta. The Pseudocoelomate Bilateria", Vol. III. McGraw-Hill, New York.

Inglis, W. G. (1964a). *Proc. zool. Soc. Lond.* **143**, 465–502.

Inglis, W. G. (1964b). *Bull. Soc. zool. Fr.* **89**, 317–338.

Kagei, N. (1960). *Acta med. Univ. Kagoshima* **2**, 142–149.

Kearn, G. C. (1964). *Parasitology* **54**, 327–335.

Kent, H. N. (1957). *In* "Premier symposium sur la spécificité parasitaire des parasites de vertébrés." Université de Neuchâtel.

Kirschner, L. B. (1953). *Nature, Lond.* **172**, 348–349.

Kuraléc, B., and Ehrlich, I. (1963). *Expl Parasit.* **13**, 113–117.

Lal, M. B., and Shrivastava, S. C. (1960). *Experientia* **16**, 185–186.

Lapage, G. (1935). *Parasitology* **27**, 186–206.

Lee, D. L. (1961). *Nature, Lond.* **192**, 282–283.

Lee, D. L. (1962a). *Parasitology* **52**, 103–112.

Lee, D. L. (1962b). *Parasitology* **52**, 241–260.

Lee, D. L. (1965a). *Parasitology* **55**, 173–181.

Lee, D. L. (1965b). "The Physiology of Nematodes." Oliver and Boyd, Edinburgh.

Lee, D. L. (1966). *Parasitology* **56**. (In press.)

Lee, D. L., and Tatchell, R. J. (1964). *Parasitology* **54**, 467–479.

Lee, D. L., Rothman, A. H., and Senturia, J. B. (1963). *Expl Parasit.* **14**, 285–295.

Lewert, R. M., and Dusanic, D. G. (1961). *J. infect. Dis.* **109**, 85–89.

Llewellyn, J. (1957). *Parasitology* **47**, 30–39.

Llewellyn, J. (1963). *In* "Advances in Parasitology" (B. Dawes, ed.), Vol. 1, pp. 287–326. Academic Press, London and New York.

Lumsden, R. D. (1965). *J. Parasit.* **51** (Suppl.), 41–42.

Lyons, K. M. (1964). *Parasitology* **54**, 12P.

Ma, L. (1964). *J. Parasit.* **50**, 235–240.

Mansour, T. E. (1959). *Biochim. biophys. Acta* **34**, 456–464.

McCaig, M. L. O., and Hopkins, C. A. (1965). *Parasitology* **55**, 257–268.

Meyer, A. (1933). "Acanthocephala. Bronn's Klassen und Ordnungen des Tierreichs." Leipzig.

Monné, L. (1959a). *Ark. Zool.* (*Ser.* 2), **12**, 99–122.

Monné, L. (1959b). *Ark. Zool.* (*Ser.* 2), **12**, 343–358.

Mueller, J. F. (1929). *Z. Zellforsch. mikrosk. Anat.* **8**, 362–403.

Nagasawa, T. (1961). *Archvm. histol. jap.* **21**, 469–489.

Nicholas, W. L., and Hynes, H. B. N. (1963). *In* "The Lower Metazoa. Comparative Biology and Phylogeny" (E. C. Dougherty, Z. N. Brown, E. D. Hanson and W. D. Hartman, eds.). University of California Press, Berkeley.

Nicholas, W. L., and Mercer, E. H. (1965). *Q. Jl microsc. Sci.* **106**, 137–146.

Nimmo-Smith, R. H., and Standen, O. D. (1963). *Expl Parasit.* **13**, 305–322.

Öhman, C. (1965). *Parasitology* **55**, 481–502.

Pantelouris, E. M. (1964). *J. Helminth.* **38**, 283–286.

Pantelouris, E. M., and Gresson, R. A. R. (1960). *Parasitology* **50**, 165–169.

Pantelouris, E. M., and Hale, P. A. (1962). *Res. vet. Sci.* **3**, 300–303.

Peebles, C. R. (1957). *J. Parasit.* **43** (Suppl.), 45.

Pflugfelder, O. (1949). *Z. ParasitKde* **14**, 274–280.

Phifer, K. (1960). *J. Parasit.* **46**, 145–153.

Picken, L. E. R. (1960). "The Organization of Cells and other Organisms." Clarendon Press, Oxford.

Picken, L. E. R., Pryor, M. G. M., and Swann, M. M. (1947). *Nature, Lond.* **159**, 434.

Pullen, E. W. (1957). *J. Morph.* **101**, 579–621.

Race, G. J., Larsh, J. E., Esch, G. W., and Martin, J. H. (1965). *J. Parasit.* **51**, 364–369.

Read, C. P. (1955). *In* "Some Physiological Aspects and Consequences of Parasitism" (W. H. Cale, ed.). Rutgers University Press, New Brunswick.

Read, C. P., and Simmons, J. E. (1963). *Physiol. Rev.* **43**, 263–305.

Reed, R., and Rudall, K. M. (1948). *Biochim. biophys. Acta* **2**, 7–18.

Robinson, D. L. H. (1961). *Nature, Lond.* **191**, 473–474.

Rogers, W. P. (1947). *Nature, Lond.* **159**, 374–375.

Rogers, W. P. (1962). "The Nature of Parasitism." Academic Press, New York and London.

Rogers, W. P. (1965). *Comp. Biochem. Physiol.* **14**, 311–321.

Rogers, W. P., and Sommerville, R. I. (1963). *In* "Advances in Parasitology" (B. Dawes, ed.), Vol. 1, pp. 109–177. Academic Press, London and New York.

Rosario, B. (1962). *In* "Fifth International Congress for Electron Microscopy", LL–12. Academic Press, New York.

Rothman, A. H. (1959). *J. Parasit.* **45** (Suppl.), 28.

Rothman, A. H. (1960). *J. Parasit.* **46** (Suppl.), 10.

Rothman, A. H. (1963). *Trans. Am. microsc. Soc.* **82**, 22–30.

Rothman, A. H., and Lee, D. L. (1963). *Expl Parasit.* **14**, 333–336.

Rothman, A. H., and Rosario, B. (1961). *J. Parasit.* **47** (Suppl.), 25.

Rudall, K. M. (1955). *Symp. Soc. exp. Biol.* **9**, 48–71.

Savel, J. (1955). *Revue Path. gén. comp.* **55**, 52–121; 213–279.

Schardein, J. L., and Waitz, J. A. (1965). *J. Parasit.* **51**, 356–363.

Senft, A. W., Philpott, D. E., and Pelofsky, A. H. (1961). *J. Parasit.* **47**, 217–229.

Sheffield, H. G. (1963). *J. Parasit.* **49**, 998–1009.

Simmonds, R. A. (1958). *Expl Parasit.* **7**, 14–22.

Skaer, R. J. (1965). *J. Embryol. exp. Morph.* **13**, 129–139.

Smyth, J. D. (1947). *Biol. Rev.* **22**, 214–238.

Stephenson, W. (1947). *Parasitology* **38**, 140–144.

Timofeev, V. A. (1964). Electron and fluorescence microscopy of the cell. *Tsitologiya*, Suppl. 1, 50–60. (In Russian.)

Threadgold, L. T. (1962). *Q. Jl microsc. Sci.* **103**, 135–140.

Threadgold, L. T. (1963a). *Expl Cell Res.* **30**, 238–242.

Threadgold, L. T. (1963b). *Q. Jl microsc. Sci.* **104**, 505–512.

Threadgold, L. T. (1965). *Parasitology* **55**, 467–472.

Trim, A. R. (1949). *Parasitology* **39**, 281–290.
Vogel, H. (1930). *Z. ParasitKde* **2**, 629–644.
Waitz, J. A., and Schardein, J. L. (1964). *J. Parasit.* **50**, 271–277.
Wardle, R. A., and McLeod, J. A. (1952). "The Zoology of Tapeworms." University of Minnesota Press, Minneapolis.
Watson, B. D. (1962). Ph.D. thesis. University of Cambridge.
Watson, B. D. (1965a). *Q. Jl microsc. Sci.* **106**, 75–81.
Watson, B. D. (1965b). *Q. Jl microsc. Sci.* **106**, 83–91.
Watson, M. R. (1958). *Biochem. J.* **68**, 416–420.
Watson, M. R., and Silvester, N. R. (1959). *Biochem. J.* **71**, 578–584.
Wieser, W. (1953). *Meddn. St. VäxtskAnst.* **65**, 3–15.
Wilson, V. C. L. C. (1965). *J. Parasit.* **51** (Suppl.), 20.
Wisniewski, L. W. (1930). *Mém. Acad. pol. Sci. B*, **2**, 1–160.
Wright, K. A. (1962). Ph.D. thesis. Rice University, Houston, Texas.
Wright, K. A. (1963). *J. Morph.* **112**, 233–259.
Wright, K. A. (1964). *Can. J. Zool.* **42**, 483–490.
Wright, K. A. (1965). *Can. J. Zool.* **43**, 689–700.
Yamao, Y. (1952a). *Zool. Mag., Tokyo* **61**, 254–260.
Yamao, Y. (1952b). *Zool. Mag., Tokyo* **61**, 290–294.
Yamao, Y. (1952c). *J. Coll. Arts Sci. Chiba Univ.* **1**, 9–13.
Yamao, Y. (1952d). *Jikkon Seibutsugaku Ho* **2**, 159–162.
Yamao, Y., and Saito, A. (1952). *Jikkon Seibutsugaku Ho* **2**, 153–158.
Young, R. T. (1935). *Trans. Am. microsc. Soc.* **54**, 229–239.

Dynamics of Parasitic Equilibrium
in Cotton Rat Filariasis

D. S. BERTRAM

*Department of Entomology, London School of Hygiene
and Tropical Medicine, London, England*

I. INTRODUCTION

Filariasis, the first human disease shown by Manson and his colleagues, nearly ninety years ago, to be conveyed from man to man by a blood-sucking insect, is widely distributed throughout tropical and subtropical territories and has long since been found to comprise a group of diseases caused by several different species of filarial worm, each with its own particular type of vector insect, including mosquitoes, *Chrysops* flies, *Simulium* flies and *Culicoides* midges. Experimental studies with these infections in the human subject have seldom, for obvious reasons, been practicable. Since they are not acute killing infections, investigations of host–parasite relationships in the vertebrate host have depended largely on limited opportunity for observations on human post-mortem or biopsy material, and on surveys of clinical manifestations of filarial disease—elephantiasis, hydrocoele, cutaneous swellings and pruritis, ocular defects and so on, depending on the parasite concerned—and, in particular, of the incidence of people with microfilariae in their blood, or skin in onchocerciasis, and of the densities of microfilariae in the positive individuals. The need for animal infections for experimental research in filariasis long remained recognized but unsatisfied, although ever since the earliest days sporadic use was made of mosquito-borne filariases in dogs by various workers.

Intensive search for other filarial species in animals convenient for laboratory maintenance and experiment is one of several interesting developments in filariasis research in the past twenty years or less. Animal, including avian, filariae of comparable biology so far as known to the human filarial parasites belong to the Family Onchocercidae within the Superfamily Filaroidea of the Order Spirurida, following the classification of Chabaud (1954) and Chabaud and Anderson (1959) as modified by Nelson (1964). About 300 species (Nelson, 1964), in about fifty genera, are grouped in this Family Onchocercidae, but, in fact, little is known of the biology and nothing of the vectors for most of them, and a vector is essential if a filarial infection is to be maintained as a laboratory strain. Recent years have, however, witnessed some progress. Thus, twelve years ago intermediate hosts could be listed for only twenty-nine species by Chabaud (1954), but for thirty-five, thirty-nine and fifty species, respectively, by Lavoipierre (1958b), Hawking and Worms (1961) and Nelson (1964). More recently, Niles *et al.* (1965) reported on a new filarial species, and its mosquito vector, from fowl in Ceylon; the list continues to grow.

Few of these host–parasite–vector combinations have become practicable models for experimental research. Progress in understanding host–parasite relationships in filarial infections has been particularly with a mite-borne filarial infection in cotton rats, and, more recently, also with mosquito-borne filariases in cats and *Chrysops*-transmitted loiasis in mandrill monkeys, which, respectively, closely simulate the important widespread mosquito-borne filariases of man, due to *Wuchereria bancrofti* or *Brugia malayi*, and human loiasis due to the worm, *Loa loa*, of equatorial west-central Africa.

Cotton rat filariasis, which in certain respects bears resemblance to infections of *Culicoides*-transmitted *Dipetalonema perstans* of man, is the central theme of this contribution. It has, since the vector mite was discovered by Williams and Brown (1945, 1946), proved not only of immense value in several laboratories in the U.S.A. and Great Britain for the evaluation of filaricidal drugs but also for quantitative experiments on host–parasite relationships, and in particular on the influence of repeated reinfections on the expression of the infection in the cotton rat host.

II. Host Susceptibility

The cotton rat, *Sigmodon hispidus*, is commonly enough naturally infected with the filarial worm, *Litomosoides carinii*, in southern states of the U.S.A. (Culbertson and Rose, 1944; Scott, 1946). As many as 43% of them trapped in one area of Florida where the mite vector, *Ornithonyssus bacoti*, was common were blood-positive for microfilariae and others developed a microfilaraemia after capture (Williams, 1948). Bertram (1950a, 1953a) showed that the susceptibility of cotton rats was such that, at least up to infections of twenty worms, all infective larvae transmitted during a single day by the bite of the vector developed to adult worms. That cotton rats may well show little resistance to much heavier transmissions on a single occasion is suggested by infections of 87, 98 and 563 adult worms in cotton rats exposed once only to the bites of 41, 42 and 740 mites of an infective group of which some, in fact, would have been negative individuals. The adult worms parasitize mainly the pleural cavity of the host (Fig. 1A and B). Strain differences in host or parasite appear to have little influence on susceptibility of the rodent to infection. Comparative studies on infections, and reinfections, in two subspecies of cotton rat, *S. h. hispidus* from Alabama and *S. h. texianus* of Texas, with *L. carinii* from both regions, indicated that, although a worm strain was possibly slightly better adapted to the cotton rat with which it was naturally associated geographically, differences in the development of primary infections and in effects of a pre-existing infection on the growth of a subsequent infection were slight (Scott *et al.*, 1957, 1958b). Other records for natural hosts include *Sciurus* squirrels and *Neotomys* rats in Brazil, *Mus* in Venezuela, and *Holochilus* in Argentine (Vaz, 1934).

The laboratory white rat, although a less hospitable host than the cotton rat, has been quite extensively used by several workers particularly concerning the nature of its resistance to infection (Briggs, 1957, 1963; Olson, 1959a, b; Scott, 1958). Strain differences in susceptibility appear, however, to be appreciable in white rats (Singh and Raghavan, 1962; Ramakrishnan *et al.*, 1962). Hamsters and white mice are susceptible (Hawking and Burroughs, 1946; Westbrook and Scott, 1955, for mice only), but infection is brief. Zein-Eldin (1965) reports good development of adult worms in Mongolian gerbils, possibly better than in cotton rats. In general, however, the cotton rat has remained, although a difficult animal to manage in certain respects, the host of choice for most work on this filarial parasite and sources of supplies of clean laboratory-bred cotton rats were variously developed for research and cultures of the vector mite established for transmission purposes (e.g. Bertram *et al.*, 1946; Williams, 1946; Scott *et al.*, 1947; Hawking and Sewell, 1948).

It has long been appreciated that cotton rats, whether infected in nature or in the laboratory, may contain a few or several hundred adult worms and that the microfilariae to which they give rise in the blood-stream (Fig. 5A) may also be few or numerous, but not necessarily in densities obviously commensurate with the numbers of adult worms in the host. The present paper considers, together with relevant studies by others, a series of about 200 cotton rats infected in the laboratory in the course of several years' work by the

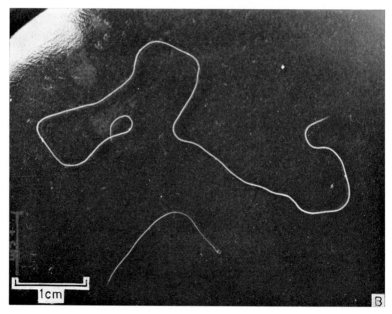

FIG. 1. A. Coil of adult worms of *Litomosoides carinii* in the pleural cavity of a cotton rat, *Sigmodon hispidus*, as exposed by dissection.

B. Female, and smaller male, worm of *L. carinii*. Note spiral at hind extremity of male.

author, from which some guidance as to factors controlling the variable relationship between microfilarial densities and adult worm numbers emerges, in particular the influence of superinfection on this relationship.

In the series, the number of adult worms per cotton rat ranged from one male, or one female, worm in a few unisexual infections, which never exceeded four to five worms altogether, to at least 1007 worms in bisexual infections in which both sexes of the worm were well represented. In mature infections the long female is distinctive from the smaller, finer, male worm, which is, more-over, readily recognized by its coiled posterior end (Fig. 1B). From Fig. 2,

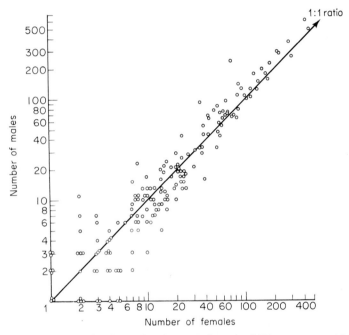

FIG. 2. The numbers of male and female worms in each of 173 cotton rats with bisexual infections of the filarial parasite, *Litomosoides carinii*. Each symbol (o) represents one cotton rat. Plotted on logarithmic scales.

plotted on logarithmic scales, the numbers of male and female worms per cotton rat may be read off directly for the bisexual infections. Many more infected animals would be required to clarify various problems which this series embodies, but the range of infections is reasonably representative of the different worm burdens previously reported from cotton rats. Thus, Wharton (1947) lists infections of five to more than 450 adult worms in naturally infected cotton rats, and Scott *et al.* (1946) record a total infection, following reinfection of a cotton rat in a mite-infested artificial nest, of 1004 worms (106 adults + 898 immature worms). About half of the present series were exposed to infection more than once and most of the heavier infections, in-cluding that of 1007 worms, are the result of reinfection.

Table I brings out the point that both male and female cotton rats harboured slight, moderate or heavy infections, and Table II shows that cotton rats of both sexes are quite susceptible from infancy to at least 8 months of age. Westbrook and Scott (1955) found that the rate of growth of worms was rather greater in male than in female rats and in cotton rats over 1 year of age than in 6- to 12-month-old animals. These graphical and tabular summaries

TABLE I

Numbers of live female and male adult worms of the filarial parasite, L. carinii, *in 109 female and 59 male cotton rats infected in the pleural, and peritoneal, cavities*

No. of adult worms (excluding encapsulations)	No. of ♀ cotton rats	No. of ♂ cotton rats
1–30	61 (55·9 %)	31 (52·5 %)
31–200	37 (33·9 %)	19 (32·2 %)
201–1007	11 (10·1 %)	9 (15·3 %)
Maximum adult worm infection	976 + encap.	1007 + encap.
Total rats	109 ♀♀	59 ♂♂

TABLE II

Numbers of live female and male adult worms of the filarial parasite, L. carinii, *in female and male cotton rats exposed to a single primary infection, or to the first infection in a series of reinfections, at birth and up to an age of 226 days*

Age of cotton rat at exposure (days)	Sex of cotton rat	No. of rats	No. of adult worms per rat (excluding encapsulations)
At birth	♀	3	10–125
	♂	2	137–160
11–40	♀	2	3–41
	♂	1	240
41–60	♀	16	2–220
	♂	15	3–298
61–80	♀	14	6–1007
	♂	8	3–25
81–100	♀	19	4–346
	♂	6	17–976
101–150	♀	11	2–341
	♂	3	5–505
151–200	♀	9	7–503
	♂	4	17–407
201–226	♀	2	67–70
	♂	1	40

do not allow, for some of the rats, for encapsulated formations or calcified fragments of dead worms. This is so for the infection of 1 007 live worms, so that even this is not the upper limit of infection which a cotton rat may tolerate.

As regards microfilarial infections of the peripheral blood-stream, well known to those familiar with this infection to be variable but often of several hundred microfilariae per mm³ (Fig. 5A), the level of microfilaraemia ranged in this series of cotton rats from less than 50 microfilariae per mm³ in some animals to 1 000–3 000 in others, with one extremely heavy microfilaraemia of nearly 10 000 microfilariae per mm³. Microfilaraemias persisted for less than 3 months or up to the limit of observations about a year or more after initial transmission.

III. EARLY DEVELOPMENT OF ADULT WORMS

Infection of the cotton rat begins with transmission by the feeding vector of infective third-stage larvae (Fig. 3A–C) developed from microfilariae, or first-stage larvae, ingested by the mites when they fed about 2 weeks previously on a microfilaria-positive animal. An intermediate second-stage larva occurs during development in the mite. Infective larvae have a mean length of 0·8 mm (Scott *et al.*, 1951; Westbrook and Scott, 1955) within a range of about 0·5–1 mm which Williams (1948) suggested may denote the sexual difference in size which becomes more apparent later. They migrate to the pleural cavity. It seems generally agreed that the migrations of the infective larva involve some tissue invasion and penetration. Kershaw (1953) traced them in the pleural cavity of cotton rats as soon as 18 h after transmission by mites engorging on the tail; possibly, they had delayed some hours in tissues near the site of transmission. When infective larvae are dissected from mites and are then inoculated into a subcutaneous incision, some reach the pleural cavity within 2 days, but most of them take 4–6 days (Scott and Macdonald, 1953). Zein-Eldin (1965) successfully infected cotton rats by intravenous inoculations of infective larvae.

Scott (1946) and Webber (1954a) studied the subsequent growth and development of infective larvae in cotton rats exposed for 10 days or more in the laboratory to transmission in artificial mite-infested nests. Scott *et al.* (1951) and Westbrook and Scott (1955) provide further observations, the latter from animals infected on a single occasion by subcutaneous inoculations of infective larvae. Despite the concise timing of transmission and statistical design of this last study, considerable variation in the rate of growth and time of moulting could not be wholly eliminated, but the salient events in the early development of an infection are clear (Fig. 4, curve *W*).

Infective larvae change little or not at all in their passage to the pleural spaces and their mean size when first located there is still 0·8 mm. Morphological development begins, but there is no appreciable growth until 8–10 days later, when there is a moult to a fourth-stage larva in the process of which a sharp increase of 25 % in length takes place to a mean of 1·2 mm. During the fourth stage, growth continues as well as further morphological differentiation

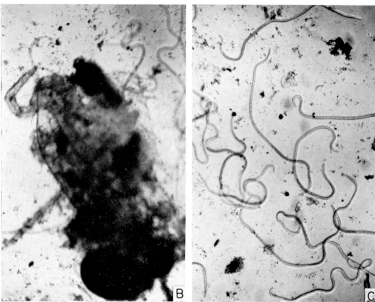

FIG. 3. A. Adult females of the vector-mite, *Ornithonyssus bacoti*, about 1 mm long, feeding in groups on the blood of a white rat exuding from a scarification along its tail.

B. Infective third-stage larvae of *L. carinii* escaping from an adult female mite partially teased out in normal saline.

C. Some of fifty-three infective third-stage larvae of *L. carinii*, mean length 0·8 mm, in normal saline after release from one vector-mite by teasing it apart in saline on a slide.

(Cross and Scott, 1947) and, about 2 weeks later, the immature male worms are 7·0–7·5 mm long and the immature female 9·0–9·5 mm (Westbrook and Scott, 1955). A final moult into adult worms now happens, about 24 days after transmission, during which there is a further increase in length of 1 or 2 mm, so that the young male worm is about 8·8 mm long and the young female worm about 10·9 mm.

All males over 26 days old are sperm-positive and all females are inseminated before the 33rd day (Webber, 1954a). Repeated insemination is not essential to maintain a microfilaraemia (Webber, 1954b). Growth of the worms continues after this final moult and, within a further 3 or 4 weeks, the male worm approaches its maximum length of 2·0–2·5 cm, while, in this same period, females lengthen to 6·0–6·5 cm. The maximum length to which female worms grow is influenced by various factors, which will be considered later below; suffice here to say that females may later attain lengths of 10–12 cm

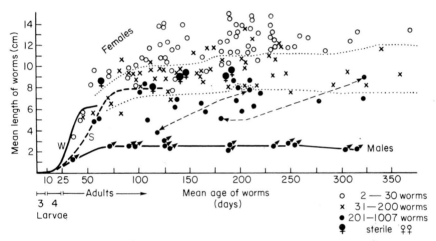

FIG. 4. The growth of female, and male, worms of *L. carinii* in the pleural cavity of cotton rats.

Mean length of male worms in fourteen cotton rats related to the age of the worms (•').

Mean length of female worms in bisexual infections in 144 cotton rats related to the exact age of the worms in primary infections and to their mean age in reinfected cotton rats (o, x or •), these symbols denoting, as shown in the key, the total infection of live worms (♀ + ♂) in each cotton rat.

• denotes sterile female, not exceeding 5 per cotton rat, in unisexual infections.

Curve *W* (after Westbrook and Scott, 1955) and curve *S* (after Scott, 1946) show the rate of growth of female worms from infective third-stage larvae to adult worms in the early phase of an infection, curve *W* being based on mean female lengths for primary infections of known age, and curve *S* on approximations to female age in reinfected cotton rats and on the largest female per cotton rat.

Two dotted lines are arbitrary limits for three zones of mainly light (o), moderate (x) or heavy (•) infections.

Two broken arrow-headed lines connect the first and second populations of female worms for two cotton rats reinfected at the interval represented by the distance apart of the paired observations. The symbols • denote the total infection present in these cotton rats, not the number of worms in each of the two populations.

and more (Fig. 4). There appears to be scanty information about the time required for microfilariae to develop in the females and pass to the pleural fluid. Hawking (1954) suggests that this takes about 5 or 6 days, so that a few microfilariae might be expected in the pleural fluid about 35–40 days after transmission. In a few observations by the writer, there were no microfilariae in females only 36 days old, but they were formed, although still coiled within a membrane, in 46-day-old females. There is ample evidence by various workers that microfilariae are sufficiently numerous to begin to appear in the peripheral blood-stream on or about the 50th day after transmission. Kershaw (1949a) showed that they may pass from the pleural cavity to the blood within a day of parturition and, Williams (1948) concluded, probably mainly by penetrating the lung wall and heart muscles. The fully gravid female produces large numbers of embryos which, in smears of females (Fig. 5B), show a range from ova and morulae to well-formed microfilariae coiled, or extended, within a vitelline membrane; large numbers of these straight microfilariae may be packed longitudinally along a considerable length of the uterus. Details of embryogenesis are discussed by Kershaw (1948) and McFadzean and Smiles (1956).

IV. THE MATURE ADULT WORMS

The adult worms commonly survive for much of a year, and rather longer in some cases. During this time the female may continue to produce microfilariae, although it is probable that fecundity is greatest about 4–6 months after transmission (Kershaw and Bertram, 1948; Williams, 1948). In the present group of cotton rats an infection of sixteen live worms (7 ♀ + 9 ♂) transmitted on a single day by infective mites still included productive females 300 days later, the pleural fluid was positive for microfilariae, and the circulating blood-stream had also still been microfilaria-positive a few days previously; several other adult worms, however, were dead and encapsulated. Hawking (1954) calculated that a mature female, 90 days old, may produce 15000 microfilariae per day. Since Kershaw (1949a) has shown that microfilariae transfused into clean cotton rats are, at least in small numbers, still present in the peripheral circulation weeks or months later, it is clear that the potentialities for heavy microfilaraemias are immense, and not surprising that microfilarial densities are often high in this infection and that the blood may remain positive for a year or more. The total population of circulating microfilariae in cotton rats infected with seven to eight females may well exceed 1 million, or several million in the presence of "very many active worms" (Hawking et al., 1950).

In light infections, individual worms may be found separate, or in copula; in heavier infections they tend to become coiled together and entangled and, in time, adhesions along their lengths and with the pleural surfaces develop (Fig. 6A). Both sexes may live for many months, but ultimately, and it seems within 1–1½ years after transmission, deaths begin to occur and they become embodied in compact lobulate masses of encapsulation of a creamy-white colour which may be small, consisting of probably one, or a few, worms, but up to several millimetres across (Fig. 6B), with, or without, loops and ends of

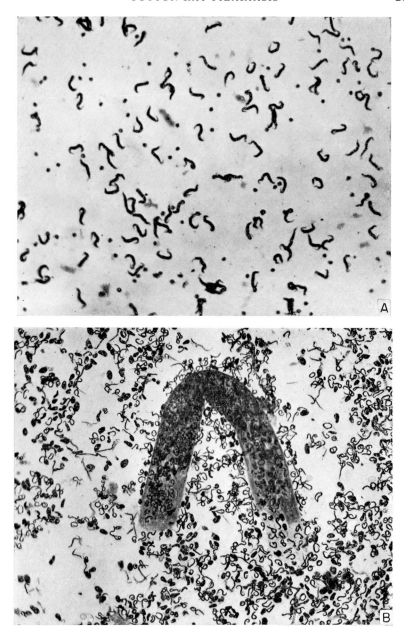

FIG. 5. A. Microfilariae of *L. carinii* in a smear of the peripheral blood of a cotton rat. Length of microfilariae about 70–90 μ.

B. Small portion of smeared gravid female of *L. carinii* showing various stages in embryogenesis up to fully formed microfilariae, and indicating the copious reproduction of which the female worms are capable. Length of microfilariae about 70–90 μ.

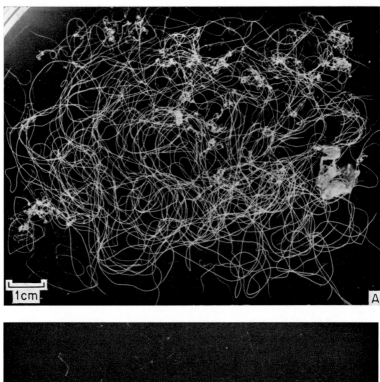

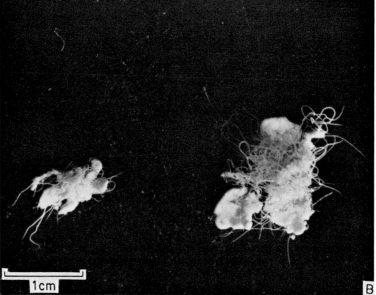

FIG. 6. A. Tangle of female, and male, worms of *L. carinii*, together with slight encapsulations and numerous adhesions of worms, removed from the pleural cavity of a cotton rat about 8 months after transmission.

B. Advanced encapsulations of female, and male, worms of *L. carinii* with protuberant loops and ends of worms, some still alive, from the pleural cavity of a cotton rat about 1 year after transmission.

worms, some of which are still alive, protruding from the mass. These certainly involve numerous worms. Small fragments of calcified worms may be all that remain of some worms. The slow onset of this encapsulative process may be apparent as early as about the 200th day in some cotton rats, but there is much variation in this from one host to another and between worms in the same host (Kershaw, 1949b). An early stage of deterioration is seen in worms active at one extremity but stiff and of opaque chalky appearance at the other. In the present series, in cotton rats infected on a single day with up to ten worms, a female was occasionally already dead and encapsulated by the 190th day, but this was more frequently observed in 250- to 315-day-old infections, although never involving all the worms in one rat. Thus, one infection 258 days old consisted of two live males and five females, two of the females being dead and coiled in encapsulation and, in the 315-day-old case, one encapsulated female was present besides three live females and two live males. With infections of up to thirty worms encapsulated individuals were also unusual up to 217 days, but some worms were involved, and dead, in a 300-day-old infection in which seven females and nine males were, however, still alive. In yet heavier infections of thirty-two to 563 worms, all also transmitted on a single day, there was no obvious evidence of more rapid deaths and encapsulation of worms in relation to the larger numbers present. Thus, in infections 167–170 days old a single coiled encapsulated female was found besides 20 ♀♀ + 19 ♂♂ and 23 ♀♀ + 15 ♂♂ all alive in each of two rats; only slight or no encapsulations occurred in infections of eighty-seven worms 131 days after transmission, of seventy worms 142 days old, fifty-four worms 211 days old, ninety-eight worms 245 days old and sixty-seven worms at 260 days. The 563 worms (306 ♀♀ + 257 ♂♂) in a 135-day-old infection were all alive and no encapsulations were seen (Table III). Macdonald and Scott (1958) record dead worms only in cotton rats infected 14–22 months previously with 16–25 infective larvae. In other cotton rats infected with 150–285 of these larvae 12–19 months before the hosts were autopsied, both dead and live worms, the latter varying from three only to 199 per rat, were found. All these animals had been exposed to a reinfection 24 days before autopsy, but it is doubtful if this affected the condition of the 12- to 22-month-old primary infections. It was not the purpose of the experiments to compare the final state of the primary infections in relation to initial dosage, and it is well simply to view these data as informative on the variability, 1 year to 18 months or so after transmission, between cotton rats in the time required before all worms which they harbour are dead. The male worm appears to die less quickly and be less readily embodied in encapsulation, but does not, in the long run, escape this fate.

The ultimate endpoint of death and encapsulation appears to be absorption of the worm material until no visible trace of them may remain, but how long this may take, and in relation to the numbers of worms present, is not at all clear. In three cotton rats exposed only on a single day, no trace of adult worms was found in one 17 months, and only three to four small compact encapsulations of worm tissue in the others 17 and 21 months, after transmission.

The pathology of this infection and of encapsulation receives cursory comment by several authors. Wharton (1947), Williams (1948) and Kershaw (1949b) may be usefully consulted for more detailed observations.

What we are concerned to note here is that numerical description of the adult worm load is quite practicable in the early months of an infection, but becomes progressively with time more difficult and qualitative as, first,

TABLE III

Parasitization by L. carinii *of only the pleural cavity of cotton rats until pleural infection is of the order of* 400 *worms, or more, when invasion of the peritoneal cavity begins to take place*

(See text for comments on sex ratio and encapsulations.)

Sex of cotton rat	Exposure period (days)	Pleural infections					Maximum age of worms (days)
		Total no. of worms	♀♀	♂♂	Encaps.	Sex ratio	
♀	1	67	34	33	1 ♀ enc.	0·97	260
♀	1	70	37	33	Nil	0·89	142
♀	6	84	51	33	?	0·65	208
♂	1	87	43	44	Slight	1·02	131
♀	8	90	38	52	Slight	1·37	144
♀	1	98	56	42	Slight	0·75	245
♀	18	125	49	76	?	1·55	111
♂	18	129	56	73	Nil	1·30	135
♀	18	136	60	76	Nil	1·23	169
♂	18	139	68	71	1 worm	1·04	135
♀	12	142	75	67	Nil	0·89	238
♀	12	147	78	69	Nil	0·88	51
♀	18	167	88	79	?	0·89	169
♀	12	202 + 6 < 3 cm	102	100	Slight	0·98	194
♀	18	206 + some < 3 cm	100	106	Fine dead worms	1·06	111
♀	18	222	86	136	+ +	1·58	229
♀	18	341	167	174	Nil	1·04	111
♂	36	407	183	223	Slight	1·2	157
		Peritoneal	—	1	Slight	—	
♀	1	563	301	255	Nil	0·81	135
		Peritoneal	5	2	Nil	0·4	

adhesions and, later, encapsulations develop. Removal from the pleural cavity and subsequent separation of the worms intact is hindered by adhesions which lead to damage and breakage of worms, while advanced forms of encapsulation and calcified fragments of worms prevent quantitative statement of the worms involved. As in Bertram (1953a, 1958) a qualitative score of *slight* to + + + + provides a broad differentiation of amounts observed.

Clearly, the longer one follows the microfilarial infection in the blood-stream, the more difficult in the end is the interpretation of the adult worm infection which produced it. This is especially true of superinfections in which transmission recurs over some weeks, or months, and more than one adult worm population has been, or is, present. The solution to this quandary would seem merely to be quantitative transmission, i.e. to transmit known numbers of worms on any occasion when an animal is exposed, but this, as we shall consider briefly later, is unfortunately so far an elusive perfection more easily advocated than accomplished.

V. Distribution of Adult Worms

There is frequent comment by different workers that adult worms occur usually in the pleural cavity, including the mediastinum, and some may at the same time be present in the pericardial cavity, but that parasitization of the peritoneum is less frequent and usually associated with heavy pleural infection.

The relative predilection of the adult worms is seen in a cotton rat which, besides some encapsulations of worms in the lateral pleural spaces, had 222 live worms (86 ♀ + 136 ♂) disposed as follows:

Lateral pleural cavities	75 ♀ + 121 ♂
Mediastinum	10 ♀ + 13 ♂
Pericardial cavity	1 ♀ + 2 ♂
Peritoneal cavity	Nil

Differentiation, in this paper, of the source of worms from the three thoracic spaces is not further made, and infections designated as of the pleural cavity include pleural and mediastinal worms besides such specimens as may also have been removed from the pericardial cavity. However, infections of the pleural cavity in this broad sense and worms from the peritoneal cavity are always distinguished.

What stimulates peritoneal infection and what density of pleural worms may be critical in promoting it are problems which have received little attention. In the present series, the peritoneal cavity was negative in all cotton rats with bisexual infections in the pleural cavity of under 100 worms, regardless of whether the rats had a primary infection only or had been reinfected. All of fifty-five worms (39 ♀ + 16 ♂) in a cotton rat exposed twice at an interval of 110 days were in the pleural cavity and these pleural worms clearly belonged to two populations with mean female lengths of 7·2 and 11·4 cm in a bimodal distribution. Reinfection is not, then, of itself a predisposing factor to peritoneal invasion. Table III summarizes the distribution of worms in moderate to heavy infections for cotton rats exposed on a single day, or up to 18 days— in one case, 36 days—in a mite-infested nest. Up to infections of 341 worms (167 ♀ + 174 ♂) the pleural cavity only was parasitized. However, slight invasion of one to seven worms occurred with heavy pleural infections of 406 (183 ♀ + 223 ♂) worms and 556 (301 ♀ + 255 ♂) worms, the latter animal being particularly informative, since its infection was a primary one only, transmitted on a single day 135 days before autopsy. These few data suggest that the critical pleural infection promoting peritoneal invasion is of the order of 400–500 worms. In other cotton rats to be considered below which were subject to much longer or more complex experiences of recurring transmissions this numerical relationship is not always apparent; peritoneal infection is evident, although the pleural infection of live adult worms is only, for example, 126 worms (Fig. 16a). To some extent, this is explicable by uncountable worms, embodied in encapsulations. Wharton (1947) notes up to twelve females and fifteen males, all alive, in the peritoneal cavity of naturally infected cotton rats with total infections, mainly in the pleural spaces, of 200 and 275 live worms. These rats could be presumed to have experienced reinfections in the wild.

There is little doubt that the pleural cavity is a preferred primary site of infection and that the peritoneal cavity is a secondary situation for these worms, usually invaded only after the pleural cavity has accommodated an infection of a few hundred worms. This is emphasized further from the recovery of worms mainly from the pleural cavity in cotton rats inoculated intra-abdominally with infective larvae, or ruptured infective mites, by Scott and Macdonald (1953); the animals were autopsied 28–170 days after inoculation. It seems possible that invasion of the peritoneum, in the case of heavily infected hosts, is by infective larvae soon after transmission rather than by older worms, as Scott and Macdonald (1958) found that even 7-day-old worms were relatively reluctant to migrate after transplant into the abdominal cavity of cotton rats.

VI. The Microfilaraemia and Transmission

The microfilariae of *L. carinii* are non-periodic, occurring in the peripheral blood of the cotton rat without appreciable cyclical change in density by day or night, although wide random fluctuations in numbers occur even in 4-hourly blood films (Bell and Brown, 1945). In direct observations by special microscopy methods on the flow of microfilariae in the capillaries of the liver of an anaesthetized cotton rat, whose microfilaraemia was about 2000 microfilariae per mm^3, Taylor (1960) describes how they are straight in larger vessels and flow with the blood, offering little resistance, but that they may move against the flow to escape restraints within a fine capillary. As already noted, densities may commonly be of the order of a few hundred microfilariae per 1 mm^3 of peripheral blood, which is considerably more than is usual to find with other animal filariae, or the human filariases. The fate of most microfilariae in the cotton rat, indeed in all filarial infections, must be to die off in the host. In loiasis of mandrills massive destruction of microfilariae takes place in the spleen (Duke, 1960b), but this was not found to be the case in cotton rat filariasis, nor for filariae in dogs or birds (Hawking, 1962); few microfilariae were seen in the spleen of cotton rats by Williams (1948) or Wharton (1947), although the latter observed splenomegaly to be a feature of infected cotton rats.

Periodically, however, some microfilariae are taken into the gut of the blood-sucking vector-mite (Fig. 3A). Many undergo disintegration there even within half an hour (Freer, 1953). Some survive to leave the gut and develop in the fat-body (Hughes, 1950; Scott et al., 1951; Lavoipierre, 1958b), to become, after moulting through a second larval stage, the active third-stage infective larva which escapes from the mite when next it feeds and establishes infection in the host animal, in the way outlined above. This extrinsic cycle in the vector lasts, at 25°C, only 2 weeks, and there is no doubt that transmission happens as the vector feeds, although the exact manner in which the infective larvae escape from the mite remains unknown (Bertram, 1947). Infective mites swallowed by rats do not cause infection (Williams, 1948; Scott and Macdonald, 1953). The infective larvae are remarkably large (mean length = 0·8 mm) in view of the small size of the adult female vector-mite, which is not much longer (Fig. 3B and C). Yet, one mite may contain nearly eighty larvae, although infections are usually much less (Bertram, 1949). It is a fascinating sight to see, under the microscope, infective larvae wriggling freely about in the haemocoele of an undamaged mite lightly restrained in water under a coverslip, bumping the gut and other organs aside as they pass from end to end of the mite, including even up to the extremity of a palp. In heavily-infected mites many of the worms are tightly coiled and not, on the contrary, readily seen like those which are active.

VII. Quantitative Transmission

Early studies with cotton rat filariasis were required to ensure above all else that strains of the parasite were maintained by serial passage from infected to clean hosts by the feeding vector, and use was made of artificial mite-infested nests in which the infected and clean hosts were interchanged or accommodated together (e.g. Scott and Cross, 1946; Bertram et al., 1946; Williams, 1948; Scott, 1948; Hawking and Sewell, 1948). The recipient rats remained a few days, or perhaps about 1 month, in a nest. Such methods still have value for stock maintenance of this parasite.

Two approaches were soon, however, being explored with a view to controlling the dosage of infective larvae to accurately known numbers and also the time at which they were transmitted and so placing transmission and infection on a quantitative basis. This seemingly simple aspiration is not yet fully met and the nature of the problem and of the techniques devised to deal with it, with partial success, deserve some attention.

A. BY THE MITE-VECTOR

Bertram (1949) sought to obtain transmission of known numbers of infective larvae by natural transmission through the feeding mite-vector. For this, small numbers (ten to twenty) of mites—adult females are the stage normally used—for which a mean number of infective larvae per mite was known from a sample of about forty dissected to give this information, would be released for 24 h on a cotton rat. The original hope was that a basically simple calculation of the *number of mites engorging* × the *arithmetic mean number of infective larvae per mite* would provide a closely accurate estimate of the numbers transmitted. The difficulty was, and remains, that there tends to be wide variation in the number of infective larvae in the individual mites of a group even though, as in this work, all have the same opportunity to take up microfilariae from the same donor rat 2 weeks previously. In preliminary observations, most positive mites contained one infective larva, and others usually less than five, but a few mites would harbour more, up to nearly eighty infective larvae. Broadly, the lower the overall percentage infection rate for infective larvae in a batch of mites, the less likely were these heavily infected individuals to be encountered. Something less than a 50% infection rate was necessary. By infecting mites initially on cotton rats with a microfilaraemia of less than 200 microfilariae per mm^3, the level of mite infections with infective larvae 2 weeks later was kept low enough to avoid heavily infected individuals. In this way, some quantitative transmissions of reasonable accuracy were accomplished, estimated transmission agreeing quite well with the number of worms subsequently found in the pleural cavity of the recipient cotton rats (Kershaw and Bertram, 1948; Kershaw, 1949b; Bertram, 1950a, b, 1953a). Otherwise, this was less assured if percentage infection rates were high and one, or more, mites containing large numbers of infective larvae happened to be included in the small batch used for release on a cotton rat to infect it. Certainly, if larger numbers of mites were used for each cotton rat the discrepancy would be less marked, but the need at the time was to achieve transmission of small numbers of worms. Later, over the years, these troublesome heavily infected mites began to turn up even if engorgement initially was on cotton rats with low microfilarial counts. It is not yet clear why this should have happened, but it is possible that there was a gradual shift to increased susceptibility to infection in the mite colony.

Bertram (1949), with Armitage, shows that this distribution of infective larvae in mites, skew to low infections, did not conform to a Poisson distribution, but rather, although only partially, to a negative binomial distribution. The implication from this of a proneness of some mites to be heavily infected has more recently been further substantiated; in a re-examination of the same data, Irwin (1963) obtained a better fit to the Waring distribution, due to Irwin, a mathematical description for data skew to small values, but incurring also a long tail with a few high, or very high, values. This proneness to heavy infections in a few individuals could be a manifestation of genetic factors controlling infectivity in the mites, and it might be profitable to the problem of quantitative transmission to attempt selection for a strain of low susceptibility in which heavily infected mites would, perhaps, not occur or be very unusual. Genetic control of infections of human and certain animal filariae in a mosquito vector is one of the interesting findings in this field in recent years (Macdonald, 1962a, b; Macdonald and Ramachandran, 1965; Macdonald and Sheppard, 1965).

The matter is complicated by the fact that fewer infective larvae develop than the intake of microfilariae would lead one to expect (Bertram et al., 1946; Freer, 1953). For example, in mites engorging on a cotton rat with 348 microfilariae per mm^3, the intake per mite ranged from 21 to 695 microfilariae in twenty-five mites smeared for counts after engorgement. Two weeks later the infection rate for infective larvae was 94·7% of fifty mites dissected: 56% of the positive mites contained five or fewer larvae, 26 % had six to ten larvae and 8 % more, up to a maximum of forty-two infective larvae in the most heavily infected individual. It may be reasonable to suppose, although hardly possible to prove directly, that the higher infections of infective larvae in some mites are the result of their heavier intakes of microfilariae. Biological factors in the feeding behaviour of the mites which might, at least in part, account for this range in microfilarial intake are considered in Bertram (1949) and include the fact that they take several partial blood meals while roaming freely for 24 h on the donor cotton rat before becoming replete; some may feed directly from capillaries, while others on blood exuding from scratches and scars to which these mites are readily attracted (Fig. 3A). Whether proneness to heavy infections of infective larvae in some mites is due to a predisposition to feed in a manner resulting in a large intake of microfilariae or to a greater suscepti-bility to ingested microfilariae developing to infective larvae seems arguable; conceivably, either or both attributes could be under genetic control. Various aspects of the intake of microfilariae by mosquitoes and other dipterous vectors of other animal, and human, filariae have been intensively investigated by numerous workers: e.g. Kershaw et al. (1953, 1955) for a canine filaria in mosquitoes; Kershaw and Duke (1954) for *Loa* worms in *Chrysops*; Nicholas and Kershaw (1954) and Duke (1956) for *Dipetalonema* infection in *Culicoides*; Duke (1962a, b) for *Onchocerca* in *Simulium*.

The writer's preference has been for natural transmission by infective mites free to feed at will during a 24-h period on its host. It is known, as seen in Fig. 3A, that they will engorge within 1 h, or less, on the scarified tail of a rat (Bertram et al., 1946) and indeed transmit the infection (Kershaw, 1953). In all probability, scarification causes no real abnormality of transmission. But cotton rats do not take kindly to the restraint needed for this technique and can readily shed the skin, later the bone, of the tail during such processes. One would be unlikely to repeat this technique with one of these animals very often and, if it is a question of repeated re-exposures to infection in the elucidation of superinfections, the solution seems to be a short period, conveniently 24 h, in which mites may engorge in a normal way on a cotton rat confined com-fortably in a small cage.

Thus, precise quantitative transmission by the naturally feeding vector has proved rather elusive for the statistical and biological reasons briefly outlined. Moreover, but not here elaborated, the technical procedures involved are sufficiently laborious to be impracticable to carry out repeatedly with that frequency which would be necessary for studies on prolonged exposures to recurring superinfection; it was tried. Recourse was made, as a compromise, to mite-infested nests, but of a special design (Bertram, 1953b), in which reinfections could be imposed on cotton rats and, indeed, in which cotton rats could be kept at risk to continuous reinfection for several months con-tinuously.

B. BY INOCULATION OF INFECTIVE LARVAE

Inoculation into cotton rats of infective larvae freshly dissected from mites was first reported as a possible method for quantitative transmission by Scott

(1947). Later, Scott and Macdonald (1953) compared the efficiency of inoculation by various routes and found the most practicable and successful to be the introduction of counted numbers of the larvae into a subcutaneous incision in the skin of the recipient host. The agreement between numbers inoculated and adult worms subsequently found in the pleural cavity a month or so later was, however, rather disappointing. Recovery rates varied from 14% to 80% in different cotton rats. For example, in one experiment, recovery rates were 30% of 77, 35% of 87, 37% of 75, 50% of 73, 59% of 85 and 65% of 80 infective larvae inoculated into separate cotton rats in this way (Scott et al., 1958a). Zein-Eldin (1965), of the same laboratory and using gerbils, obtained 34–52% recovery after intravenous inoculations. Nevertheless, this subcutaneous inoculative method, together with certain variations in the route for particular purposes, has proved immensely informative in an extensive series of experiments with cotton rats, white rats and mice by Scott and his colleagues in America, particularly concerning the rate of growth of worms in the pleural cavity and on the effects of a pre-existing infection on the worms transmitted in a reinfection. To this we return later. The method has not been pursued to a study of the effect of reinfection on the microfilaraemia in the blood-stream, but it would appear to have a good deal to offer as a technique in this respect. At least it places a known ceiling to transmission on any occasion, which is less easy to feel confidence about in natural transmission by the feeding mite, for the reasons discussed above. A disadvantage which hardly outweighs its worth is the problem of the extent to which the delay, about 4–6 days, before most infective larvae reach the pleural cavity is entirely on account of natural migration or due in part to the artificial element in the technique, and how much of the loss which occurs is from natural causes. However, these matters are by no means overlooked in the analyses by the American workers of the fascinating results they obtain using this method of transmission.

VIII. PRIMARY INFECTIONS

We may turn now to consider the relationship of the density and duration of a microfilaraemia to the numbers of adult worms in the infected host, particularly in the case of cotton rats with a primary infection transmitted by infective mites feeding on a rat during a single 24-h period. Throughout, the age of developing or adult worms is expressed as the interval between transmission and final dissection of the host to remove the worms.

A. UNISEXUAL INFECTIONS

Unisexual infections occurred infrequently—eighteen cotton rats in the present series—and were always of small numbers of worms from one male, or one female, up to four males or five females. Microfilarial infections never developed, nor was embryological development taking place in unmated females up to 184 days old. Sterile females were never more than about 9 cm in length, even when nearly 200 days old, by which time fertile productive females in comparably light bisexual infections were often 11–15 cm long (Fig. 4). The worms were in the pleural cavity except for one instance, in which one of five females, aged 148 days, was in the peritoneal cavity, suggestive of migratory activity in search of a mate, since, as already noted, peritoneal invasion in bisexual infections appears to be associated with much heavier worm loads in the pleural cavity.

B. BISEXUAL INFECTIONS

The fertile female of a single pair of worms in the pleural cavity suffices to produce a microfilaraemia (Fig. 7). The microfilaraemia, already patent at the first blood film taken 64 days after transmission, is low, barely 50 micro-filariae per mm³ at its maximum and, in this rat, persisted for about 9 months before microfilariae finally disappeared from the peripheral blood. The female worm had died and become encapsulated, but not the male, by autopsy 314 days after transmission. In another cotton rat with one female and three males in the pleural cavity, none encapsulated, at autopsy 97 days after transmission, microfilarial densities never exceeded 7 microfilariae per mm³ and the blood was erratically positive in three of eight examinations up to autopsy. Low fluctuant counts lasting considerably less than a year, with the blood negative on occasions, can be expected in single pair infections (Kershaw, 1949b).

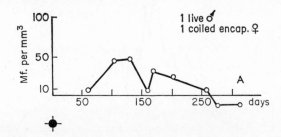

FIG. 7. The density and course of the microfilaraemia (Mf.) of *L. carinii* in a cotton rat with a primary infection of one pair of worms in the pleural cavity, transmitted by the bite of the vector-mite during a single day, at +. Autopsy at *A*.

Occasionally also, the blood may be negative in infections of several fertile females. In three of 229 cotton rats (1·3 %) with bisexual infections, circulating microfilariae were not found between 70 and 107 days after transmission, although their pleural infections were 4 ♀♀ + 4 ♂♂; 5 ♀♀ + 2 ♂♂, and 8 ♀♀ + 23 ♂♂. Yet microfilariae were active in the pleural fluid of these animals and smears of females included all stages of embryo up to extended microfilariae. In one of these rats, four microfilariae were found in 10 mm³ of auricular blood. Thus, at least a few cotton rats, although not insusceptible to infection with adult worms, may present a barrier to invasion of the blood-stream by microfilariae. This individual variability, however, is not acceptable as an adequate explanation for the widely different microfilarial counts which different cotton rats may display.

As the worm load in the pleural cavity is increased a positive correlation with a higher microfilaraemia, and more prolonged, can be discerned. This was described for infections up to about 22 ♀♀ worms (Kershaw, 1949b). Figures 8 and 9 illustrate other examples: microfilaraemia rose to a plateau-type density of 75–100 microfilariae per mm³ for 2 ♀♀ + 1 ♂, to 100–150 microfilariae per mm³ for 4 ♀♀ + 3 ♂♂. Still heavier infections of 6 ♀♀ + 5 ♂♂ (calculated, Bertram, 1950a, b), 12 ♀♀ + 7 ♂♂ and 19 ♀♀ + 12 ♂♂ (Fig. 9) assumed a peaked pattern of, respectively, about 500, 1000 and 1300 microfilariae per mm³ 200 days or so after transmission. Microfilariae had first appeared in their peripheral blood-stream about the 50th day and were still numerous, although the peak had subsided or was declining, before autopsies 200–250 days after transmission; there was little or no encapsulation evident at this time. In the cotton rat with an estimated adult infection, a low terminal infection persisted up to autopsy about the 460th day, although all adults were by then dead and encapsulated. The relationship of microfilarial and adult worm densities in these animals is, then, roughly proportional.

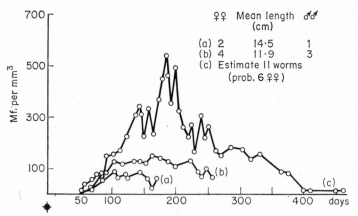

FIG. 8. The density and course of the microfilaraemia (Mf.) in cotton rats with primary infections of 3, 7 and 11 (estimated) worms in the pleural cavity, transmitted by the bite of the vector-mite during a single day, at +. (Infection of 11 worms after Kershaw, 1949b; Bertram, 1950a, b.)

However, it appears that with rather heavier infections of adult worms this relationship begins to fail. Thus, a 131-day-old infection of eighty-seven worms (43 ♀ + 44 ♂) had developed a microfilaraemia of only 214 microfilariae per mm³. Figure 9 illustrates an infection of ninety-eight worms (56 ♀ + 42 ♂) in which counts were not higher than about 700 microfilariae per mm³ in a rather early peak about day 140, and this declined sharply to below 150 microfilariae per mm³ by autopsy on the 245th day. The adult worms, entirely in the pleural cavity of the cotton rats of Fig. 9, were alive and still fecund at autopsy; encapsulations were slight. If proportionate to female worms, the peak microfilaraemia of the last animal should have been of the order of 3000–4000 microfilariae per mm³. Thus, there is indication that quite moderately low adult worm numbers induce a suppression of the potential microfilaraemia, and a premature peak. This could arise from rapid destruction of circulating microfilariae, but there is no direct proof for this for these rats. On the other hand, although the lengths of female worms are highly variable, as Fig. 4 shows, there is a trend towards shorter worms in heavier infections. In three of the foregoing cotton rats, for which the age of the adult worms was between 212 and 245 days, mean female lengths (measured to the nearest 0·25 cm) were

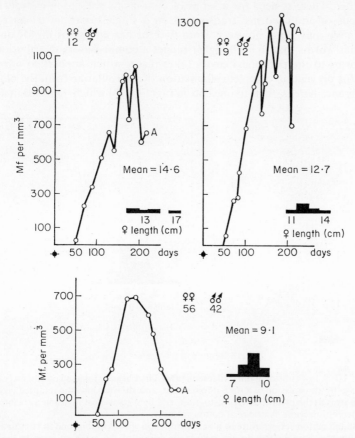

FIG. 9. The density and course of the microfilaraemia (Mf.), and the mean and distribution of female lengths (histograms), for primary pleural infections in cotton rats of 19, 31, and 98 worms transmitted by the bite of the vector-mite on a single day, at +. Autopsy of cotton rats at *A*.

Sex ratio shows a slight preponderance of female worms. (Infection of 98 worms, after Bertram, 1953a.)

14·6 cm for 12 ♀♀, 12·7 cm for 19 ♀♀ and, notably, only 9·1 cm for 56 ♀♀; the compact range in lengths (histograms) suggests a normal distribution of variation; the 17 cm worm seems exceptionally long. It seems reasonable to conclude that at least some part of the suppression of microfilaraemia results from a lowered reproductive potential in the shorter worms of heavier pleural infections.

One could suppose that with worm load increasing further above fifty to sixty female worms, their lengths and fecundity would be further curtailed, so that the peak of microfilarial density would happen sooner and the general level of microfilaraemia be generally lower; that this converse relationship at some upper limit could lead to the microfilaraemia being suppressed altogether. There is need for a series of cotton rats with progressively larger infections of adult worms, transmitted on a single occasion, to clarify this matter. We may note, however, from two further infections of 407 and 563 live adult worms that in such higher ranges a compensatory distribution of a few worms to the peritoneal cavity takes place, which appears to offer provision for preventing complete elimination of microfilariae from the blood.

Reference here is, first, to one cotton rat (Fig. 10) which, exposed in a mite-

Pleural cavity	Peritoneal cavity
183 ♀♀	1 ♂
223 ♂♂	Encap. slight
Encap. slight	

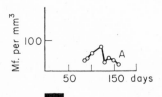

Mean = 6·9 cm

Total infection 407 worms + encap.

FIG. 10. A low subsiding microfilaraemia (Mf.) in a heavily infected cotton rat, exposed for 36 days to transmission in a mite-infested nest, and showing also the retarded growth of female worms in the pleural cavity (histogram) and light peritoneal invasion associated with heavy pleural infection. Autopsy of cotton rat at A.
(Note. Stated periods of exposure to nest transmission shown in this, and in later figures for other superinfections, by ▆▆ do not include the period of the extrinsic cycle in the vector before transmission could take place between a donor and recipient cotton rat, or before self-reinfection could occur.)

infested nest for 36 days, cannot be viewed as comparable to a primary infection induced by transmission on a single day, but, at the same time, it does not follow that it was subject to reinfection daily. The distribution of female lengths suggests that the bulk of the considerable transmission may well have occurred in the course of a few days only. A retarding effect on the growth of worms in reinfection (Macdonald and Scott, 1953) and on their microfilarial output (Bertram, 1953a) cannot be excluded for this cotton rat. But the points for consideration at the moment are that despite a total infection, together with additional slight encapsulations, of 407 live worms (183 ♀ + 224 ♂) the microfilaraemia was very low, less than about 75 microfilariae per mm³, and was declining from a peak which occurred as early as 120 days after transmission could first have happened. The females at a mean female length of 6·9 cm for a mean age of 135 days at autopsy are small compared to those of most lighter infections of corresponding age (Fig. 4). Moreover, besides some slight encapsulation, one male was in the peritoneum.

The other cotton rat is less complicated in that it developed an infection of 563 worms (306 ♀ + 257 ♂) following a single primary exposure to infection by over 700 mites on a single day; all worms were alive and no encapsulation was observed at autopsy 135 days later. Although, unfortunately, only one blood film was examined, it showed this cotton rat to be quite reasonably blood-positive by the 67th day after transmission, at 350 microfilariae per mm³. It is interesting that, at a mean female length of only 6·2 cm for the 301 females in the pleural cavity (Fig. 11), these worms confirm the adverse impact

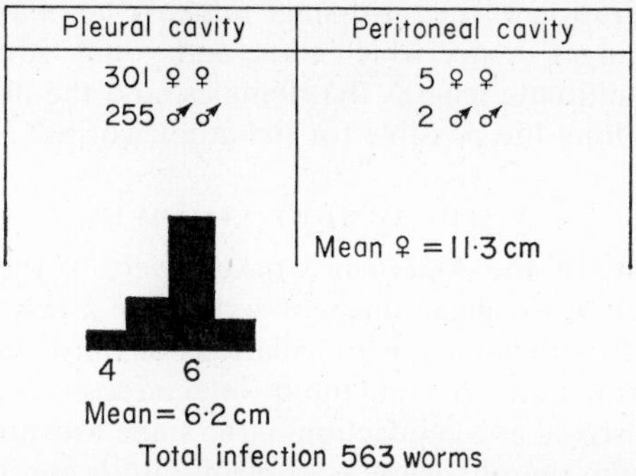

Pleural cavity	Peritoneal cavity
301 ♀ ♀	5 ♀ ♀
255 ♂ ♂	2 ♂ ♂

Mean ♀ = 11·3 cm

4   6

Mean = 6·2 cm

Total infection 563 worms

FIG. 11. A heavy primary infection showing retarded growth of the numerous female worms in the pleural cavity of the cotton rat, but normal growth in the few worms in the peritoneal cavity.

on growth of heavy infection of the pleural cavity. This influence of worm numbers on growth is further corroborated by the five females in the peritoneal cavity, of exactly the same age, which attained a mean length of 11·3 cm (range 10·5–11·75 cm). We may note, again, the compact histogram approximating to a normal distribution for the variability of female lengths in the thoracic population. Both pleural and peritoneal females were fecund, producing microfilariae.

The suggestion that a massive pleural worm load might eliminate a microfilaraemia completely is not confirmed by the two infections just discussed, but rather that, before this happens, worms begin to invade the secondary site, the peritoneal cavity, where they can independently develop to a quite normal length and productivity, observed in the five robust peritoneal females to be much more copious than in the stunted pleural worms. Peritoneal females may thus supplement the restricted flow of microfilariae to the blood-stream from the worms crowded in the pleural cavity. That microfilariae injected into the peritoneal cavity of clean cotton rats subsequently appear in the peripheral blood and persist for nearly 80 days was shown by Kershaw (1949a); there is no reason to suppose, therefore, that those produced by worms in this cavity need fail to do so or to make a substantial contribution to the microfilaraemia.

IX. WORM DEVELOPMENT AND IMMUNITY

Cotton rats are not only highly susceptible to primary infection with *L. carinii* but to reinfection. We shall be looking later at the suppression, or augmentation as the case may be, of the microfilaraemia in superinfected cotton rats in relation to the adult worm infection which they develop as a result of recurring transmissions, but it is of interest to take note first of the findings of Scott and his colleagues (Macdonald and Scott, 1953 *et seq.*) on the influence of a primary infection on the early development of further worms subsequently transmitted as a reinfection. Figure 4 illustrates, and curve *W* particularly for females in the early primary infection (Westbrook and Scott, 1955), the brief duration of the third-stage infective larva and the fourth-stage larva, and the changes in size which these and young adult worms undergo in relation to the ultimate lengths that females, and the much smaller males, may attain in the long life possible for the adult worms.

A. THE IMMUNE STIMULUS

The experiments by the American workers were of the type in which an immunizing infection was given once, or serially on a few occasions at about weekly intervals, by subcutaneous inoculations of third-stage infective larvae freshly dissected from mites. About 1 month later a second inoculum of infective larvae was administered as a reinfection in the same way and clean cotton rats infected at the same time likewise as controls. Both controls and reinfected animals were allowed to develop their infections for, usually, a further 24 days and autopsies were then carried out. Criteria of a protective response in the reinfected cotton rats were (1) lengths of the females and males of the re-infection population, and (2) percentages of these worms which had moulted finally to adult worms compared with corresponding data for the primary infections of the same age in the controls. Throughout, these studies are notable for their statistical design and analyses, which cannot be adequately represented in the brief review which follows.

By this approach, Macdonald and Scott (1953) showed that a pre-existing infection caused retardation of the growth and moulting rate of the worms of the second, or challenge, infection in the reinfected animal. Thus, in non-immunized cotton rats, mean lengths of females and males on the 24th day were 10·9 mm (1·1 cm) and 8·8 mm, respectively, and 54–83% had moulted finally, while, for worms of the reinfecting population in the immunized host, the lengths of worms were only 4·9 mm ($♀♀$) and 4·0 mm ($♂♂$) and as few as 1–3% had undergone the final moult. When autopsy was delayed to 35–38 days after challenge and control transmissions, the females of the reinfection population in rats immunized once with 30–46 larvae were still shorter by a difference of 1·3 mm than control females, which, by this time, were 3·5 cm long. The small male worms of the two populations in reinfected hosts could no longer be distinguished at this age. Further, if immunization was of five serial inoculations amounting in all to 181–227 infective larvae, this difference was greater, at 2·4 mm. It could not be determined from these observations, however, whether the repetitive sequence of inocula or total heavier dosage mattered most.

It was shown by Bertram (1953a) and in this article for primary infections (Figs. 9 and 11) and, generally (Fig. 4) that, despite great variability in the lengths of female worms, the total pleural worm load when heavy leads to worms being smaller than when fewer worms are present. One may suppose that this could be, at least, a contributory factor to retardation of growth in reinfections. For example, in one comparison in the above studies on re-infections the mean pleural infection in eight control cotton rats was 24 adult worms at autopsy when the worms were 35–38 days old, and their mean female lengths ranged from 3·2 to 5·0 cm in the different hosts. Following single immunization of five cotton rats and their subsequent reinfection, the total pleural worms numbered 41 per rat, on average, with mean female lengths of 2·3–4·3 cm for the reinfection females, while for three cotton rats given five serial immunizing inocula and afterwards a reinfection the total pleural load was about 99 worms. With this heaviest total infection the mean female lengths for reinfection females were least at 0·6–1·6 cm. Thus the total bulk of live worms in the pleural spaces may not be wholly irrelevant to the observed retardations.

Whilst this may be so, other comparisons suggest that retardation of growth, irrespective of numbers, is certainly also involved. Thus, Scott and Macdonald (1958) immunized cotton rats with about 200 infective larvae each. These were inserted into the abdominal cavity. The recovery rate follow-ing this unusual route was in due course very low, 34 of 384 larvae. Nearly three-quarters of these had migrated to the pleural cavity, but, even so, this meant that the immunizing infection in the pleural cavities of these animals was represented by only nine or ten growing worms. Reinfections given about 1 month later were of 75–83 infective larvae administered by the most success-ful route, subcutaneously, which could be expected to give although not full at least good recoveries, and from the pleural cavity. In the event, 42–59 of these reinfecting larvae were recovered at the conclusive autopsies 24 days later. Total pleural infections were thus of the order of 50–70 worms per rat, immunizing and reinfection populations combined, in the reinfected cotton rats. In the appropriate controls, the pleural infections were 30–60 worms. There was, again, retardation of the growth and moulting of the worms of the reinfection population in the immunized hosts; in particular, growth of both sexes and their moulting rates were statistically significantly less for the re-infection population in an immunized rat than in a control with such similar densities of worms as, respectively, 68 and 60 worms. It is an important point which appears to be further substantiated in related observations on induction of immunity by intraperitoneal transplants to cotton rats of 7-day-old larvae (i.e. late third-stage larvae) removed from the pleural cavity of other cotton rats. Of 415 of these older larvae inserted intra-abdominally into altogether four recipient cotton rats, only 164 were ever found; but all were still in the abdomen, except two which had successfully migrated to the pleural cavity. As a result, when the subsequent reinfection of infective larvae was given subcutaneously it amounted to about fifty-six worms in the pleural spaces of these immunized cotton rats, hardly more crowded than in the control density of sixty growing worms. Yet, statistically significant retardation of mean lengths of females and males of the reinfection worms, and of their moulting rates, occurred in the reinfection population. Results of this kind appear to demonstrate that, independent of worm numbers, a pre-existing infection stimulates an immune response in the host which, albeit slight or partial, curtails the rate of growth and moulting of worms of a subsequent reinfection.

As regards the capacity of different stages of worm to induce this immune response, it appears that 7-day-old third-stage larvae, fourth-stage larvae and young adult worms are much less effective than equivalent numbers of younger third-stage larvae (Scott et al., 1956, 1958a; Scott and Macdonald, 1956, 1958). Consideration of various aspects of quite intricate experiments leads to the view (Scott and Macdonald, 1956, 1958) that the more intensive stimulus promoted by young infective larvae, i.e. the form transmitted by the vector, may reside in their greater migratory activity in reaching or, for some of them, trying to reach the site of choice, the pleural cavity, for development. In consequence, there is a more intimate association with the tissues of the host than is the case with the 7-day-old or older worms, which seem, for the most part, to remain usually localized in the pleural cavity once there in normal infections and, if transplanted artificially to the peritoneal cavity, tend to remain there, indicating a relative inability or reluctance to migrate from a coelomic space in which they have become established. The immune stimulus of older worms is more effective with greater numbers. Retardation of a reinfection was not apparent after an immunizing dose of 140 7-day-old larvae, but apparent after about 200 of these worms per rat were given (Scott and Macdonald, 1958), while, for 15- to 28-day-old worms, i.e. fourth-stage and young adults, retardation of a reinfection followed immunization of cotton rats with 69–86 of these worms but not with fewer, 18–51 (Scott et al., 1958a).

B. PERSISTENCE OF IMMUNE RESPONSE

How long immune response may persist is investigated by Macdonald and Scott (1958) for cotton rats which were reinfected by subcutaneous inoculations of 74–134 infective larvae per rat in the 12th to 22nd months of primary infections given originally as 79–285 infective larvae by the same route. All but one of these animals, which had received 132 larvae initially, had become blood-positive for microfilariae, but only one was still so at the time of reinfection. They were, in general, good typical primary infections. At autopsies 24 days after the reinfections, the worms of the primary infections were much involved in tissue reactions. All were dead in three of the cotton rats and some only in five of them. Counts were necessarily imperfect and ranged from 3 to 199 live worms, the last in a rat autopsied 1 year after initial transmission of unknown numbers of worms by infective mites during a single day. Mean lengths of worms in control infections, i.e. in five cotton rats infected by subcutaneous inoculations of 79–130 infective larvae on the same day as the reinfections were given to the other cotton rats with long-standing primary infections, were between 8·7 mm and 11·8 mm (♀♀) and 5·0–7·7 mm (♂♂) on the 24th day after transmission. Retardation of growth was particularly evident in the reinfection population of worms in cotton rats still harbouring live as well as dead worms of the 12–19 months old immunizing infection, viz. mean lengths of 4·0–5·4 mm (♀♀) and 2·7–4·4 mm (♂♂). Retardation was, however, less marked if all primary worms were dead (at 14–22 months), mean lengths then being 5·2–11·2 mm (♀♀) and 4·4–7·6 mm (♂♂). Moulting percentages were low for females, but high for males in the controls, and the latter only permit of comparisons. In controls, 61 % of male worms had completed the final moult, but only 20 % in cotton rats with long-standing pre-existing infections and, by inspection, this moulting by males was least in the presence of living worms and more successful, up to 96 % in one case, if all the worms of the primary infection were dead.

The degree of retardation seemed thus essentially the same a year or more after transmission of a primary immunizing infection, more especially if live worms were still present, as it was a month or so after this event. But it remained uncertain whether this was due solely to a persistence of the immunity initially stimulated in these prolonged infections by the original immunizing infective larvae, or whether this was fortified by a response of the host to the adult worms in the course of the several months of the evolution of the infection in these cotton rats (Scott, 1958; Macdonald and Scott, 1958). Reinforcement by transient late third-stage larvae or fourth-stage larvae, in view of their low efficiency in stimulating immunity, must have been negligible, but the continuous reproductive and metabolic activities of adults over months could well have a considerable cumulative effect compensating for any inherently weaker capacity to stimulate immunity.

One point seems to deserve note here. In subcutaneously induced primary infections all, or most, of the immunizing worms would reach the pleural cavity. But, one understands, this would probably not be the case for most of the 15- to 28-day-old worms, such as were recovered, transplanted into the abdominal cavity in the other experimental series concerned with their lesser potentialities in inducing immunity (Scott et al., 1958a). One rather gathers that recoveries were largely from the abdominal cavity to which they were transplanted, although this is not certainly stated. Such a difference between natural and abnormal distribution may matter greatly in interpreting the year-long persistence of immune response under discussion, since the infective larvae of the reinfections entered a pleural cavity already containing considerable worm matter—3, 6, 39, 79 and 199 live plus dead worms in five immunized cotton rats. The cause of the retardation of the reinfection population might be a sustained fortification of immunity by these living worms, but, possibly, after many months of parasitization, the pleural cavity was physiologically less favourable to the growth of the new infective larvae. There may have been a crowding effect also; the greatest retardation was in twenty-six reinfection worms developing with 199 old live worms plus dead worms of the immunizing infection; one of the least retarded was, on the other hand, eighteen reinfection worms developing in association with an immunizing infection of only three live and forty dead worms. It seems extremely difficult to differentiate, in these long-standing infections, between impacts on newly transmitted infections which may be due to immunity of an antigen-antibody nature, a physiological inadequacy of the long-parasitized pleural environment, and a curb on growth imposed by heavy total infection of the pleural spaces. All three may play a part. The retardation observed could express an integration of the interactions of these factors one with the other and a combined effect on the development of a new population of young larvae transmitted in a reinfection.

The virtually negligible to slight retardation of reinfection worms in the presence of dead worms only in a long-standing primary infection suggests that their antigenic properties are minimal and, indeed, whether they possess this faculty to an extent significant in promoting immunity still stands in need of further investigation (Scott, 1958; Macdonald and Scott, 1958). Some data suggest that dead worm material has little or no antigenicity. Infective larvae killed by freezing failed to stimulate, even in inocula four times numerically the dose effective with live infective larvae, a suppressive response against reinfections; treatments with dead dried, or recently dead adult worms, from 22 to 100 per cotton rat, were at most only very slightly effective (Macdonald and Scott, 1953). It seems likely that with dead worms compactly encapsulated in late natural infections, no matter how many are involved, the physiological condition of the pleural cavity thus relieved of active parasitization could be more hospitable to reinfections and conducive to their normal development than when some live worms still exist.

C. OTHER EFFECTS IN REINFECTIONS

Fewer larvae of a reinfection succeeded in developing in a cotton rat with a pre-existing infection than in a cotton rat not previously infected, recovery rates being 48% of challenge worms in hosts infected already about 1 month earlier and 61% for primary infections in controls (Macdonald and Scott, 1953). Two cotton rats (Table III) exposed for 12–18 days in mite-infested transmission nests contained, at autopsy 194 and 111 days later, 202 live worms (mean ♀ = 8·9 cm) and 206 live worms (mean ♀ = 8·4 cm), but also some very stunted worms (< 3 cm, and not ♂♂) and, in one rat, numerous fine small dead worms. These may represent instances of worms in a stage of abortive development in reinfected hosts. The appreciable encapsulation (+ +) in a third cotton rat, 229 days after 18 days of exposure, which contained 222 live worms (mean ♀ = 7·5 cm) might be a later phase in the disposal of unsuccessful worms. Absence of such features in other cotton rats of Table III, also exposed for 18 days, may mean that transmission was largely only during a day, or two, of the total period, so that reinfection effects were negligible. This, together with absence of encapsulation in the case of a heavy infection of 341 live pleural worms (mean ♀ = 8·0 cm) after a similar exposure period and of 556 pleural worms (mean ♀ = 6·2 cm) after only a single day of transmission, carries again the implication that reinfection, apart from mere numbers of worms, induces a condition, an immune response, which causes interference with the development of a secondary infection.

Scott *et al.* (1958c) show that the suppression of growth of the worms of a reinfection is not dependent on a continuing presence of the immunizing, pre-existing, infection. Larvae which are allowed to grow for their first 7 days in an immunized cotton rat and which are then transferred to a clean cotton rat were still found retarded in growth 17 days later. A critical irreversible impact is imposed on the recently transmitted migratory larvae, possibly an inter-ference in enzyme production (Scott, 1958), which persists at least for 17 days and this only happens, it seems, during the first few days of larval life in the host. Thus, it was also shown that larvae allowed to grow for the first 7 days in a previously uninfected cotton rat attained normal growth when trans-planted to continue their development for 17 days more in an immunized cotton rat.

D. THE NATURE OF THE IMMUNE RESPONSE

Sufficient has been said of the possibility of mere numbers of pleural worms and, in advanced living infections, of physiological conditions in the pleural environment as factors contributing to the check a cotton rat may impose, by partial suppression of the growth of worms of reinfections, on the load of infection it harbours. It is generally suspected, however, that an antigen-antibody mechanism must be involved in this low-grade immunity manifest as retarded growth of reinfections. McFadzean (1953) reported complement-fixing antibodies in cotton rats infected with *L. carinii*, but concluded for this, and certain other filarial species in dogs and monkeys, that difficulty in demonstrating, or apparent absence of, various immunological reactions could be related to the low level of immune response which these essentially non-pathogenic filariae stimulated in their hosts.

The stimulus to immune reaction in cotton rats by *L. carinii* arises, it would seem, particularly during the migratory early phase of the infective larvae following transmission and before they reach the pleural cavity, possibly (Scott, 1958; Briggs, 1957) because of their active secretion of enzymes to assist migration or because the absorption of these is facilitated by the intimate contact between the larvae and the tissue they traverse. It is, too, the infective migratory larvae which seem to be most exposed to, and crucially affected by, the reactions of the host in reinfections. Antigenic mechanism is deduced, too, from oral precipitates on infective larvae *in vitro* in sera from infected cotton rats, and proportionately most apparent for sera from cotton rats infected with large numbers, or repetitive inocula, of infective larvae (Scott, 1952). In other studies with white rats (Olson, 1959a, b; Briggs, 1957, 1963), highly resistant to *L. carinii* when mature but less so when young, serum precipitates were related to the size of the larval inoculum and not to the few worms, if any, which may develop in the older rats. Cortisone, an inhibitor of antibody formation, suppressed inflammatory reactions against developing pleural worms and their early encapsulation in young white rats (Olson, 1959b), diminished without eliminating entirely the natural resistance of mature white rats to the invasive phase of migratory infective larvae and suppressed their serological precipitate reaction (Briggs, 1963). Furthermore, in discussing conservatively the case for antigen-antibody mechanisms in the retardation of a reinfection of *L. carinii* in cotton rats, Scott *et al.* (1958a) express the view that, if indeed antigens are involved—and they could be metabolic products of living worms—the lesser capacity which they observed of 7-day-old third, or fourth, larvae and young adults to stimulate immune response compared to infective migratory larvae was not necessarily a matter of different antigen, but of less production of the requisite antigen by the later larval and adult stages of the parasite. Immunity to infection in cotton rat filariasis awaits much further elucidation, but there seem grounds for accepting that an antigen-antibody mechanism is concerned, apart from numerical or physiological factors, in providing some slight protection for the cotton rat host against unrestricted superinfection with adult worms.

X. SUPERINFECTIONS

The term "superinfection" is used to denote that the infection harboured by a cotton rat is the result of transmission on two or more separate occasions and does not necessarily imply, as we shall see, that unusually large numbers of adult worms or of circulating microfilariae are present.

It has just been described how the worms of a reinfection of *L. carinii* which succeed in reaching the pleural cavity of the cotton rat—and probably not all of them necessarily always do—grow and moult to adult worms more slowly than worms of a primary infection, and how, if reinfection occurs about 1 month after the initial primary transmission, the female worms of the second transmission are still distinguishable as shorter worms for at least 5 further weeks. Researches by the American investigators of the kind just outlined on adult worm development in reinfections have not, as yet, dealt with the consequences of reinfection for the microfilarial output of the female worms and for the microfilaraemia in the blood-stream. We now turn to this not less complex aspect which has already received some attention in Bertram (1953a, 1957) and, briefly, in Bertram (1958). With few exceptions, the superinfected cotton rats available for consideration were, for reasons already discussed of biological and technical difficulties in obtaining precise quantitative transmission by the feeding vector-mite, exposed to reinfections in mite-infested nests for various periods of time. It is convenient to consider first under the heading of double exposures cotton rats which were exposed during two widely separated periods, each of about 2–3 weeks or less, together with two cotton rats exposed twice, but only for a 24-h period on each occasion.

A. DOUBLE EXPOSURE

Figure 12 illustrates the adult worm infection and microfilaraemia in two cotton rats exposed to natural transmission in the laboratory by the bites of a few infective mites (less than thirty) on an initial occasion and 85 days later, on a second occasion, transmission being during a single 24-h period each time. Autopsies were at 230 days after the first and 145 days after the second transmission (*A*, on the charts). Total adult worms, all in the pleural cavity, were 27 (10 ♀ + 17 ♂) and also 27 (16 ♀ + 11 ♂). Encapsulation of three females in one animal appears to be bound up with individual characteristics of these worms, or the rat, rather than with factors of reinfection or worm load which are almost identical for both hosts. There is some slight indication of two populations of adult worms in each rat, with mean female lengths about 11 cm and 13 cm in one (overall mean = 12·3 cm), but of 8 cm and 10–11 cm in the other (overall mean = 10·2 cm). Certainly, the more compact distribution of a unimodal curve as in primary infections (e.g. Fig. 9) is not obvious, although one might have expected this if the two populations had attained similar lengths in the considerable time of 145 days they had for growth after the reinfection. This suggests that the early retardation of growth of reinfection worms imposed during the first few days on the infective larvae (Scott *et al.*, 1958c) is never quite overcome.

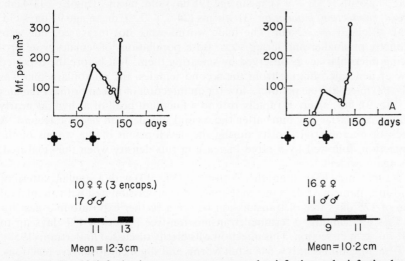

Fig. 12. Double infection in two cotton rats exposed to infection and reinfection by the bite of mites on separate days at +, showing suppression of microfilaraemia (Mf.) during development of the second population of worms to maturity and the rapid rise in microfilaraemia when these females began to produce microfilariae. Total number of worms per rat, mean and distribution of female lengths are also shown, all worms being in the pleural cavity. Autopsy of cotton rats at *A*.

The microfilarial infection due to the primary transmission was already patent at the first blood examinations made of each rat about 60 days after transmission. These continued to rise as would be expected for primary infections of, probably, five to eight fertile females by inspection of the histograms, but as soon as reinfection happened the microfilaraemia began to decline in a way not characteristic at this age of infection for prolonged plateau- or peak-type microfilaraemias of light, primary infections (Figs. 8 and 9). By the time, however, that the second population worms had time to mature and be productive, 50 days after their transmission, the microfilarial density began again to rise, and very rapidly. This rise may include not only a flow to the blood of new microfilariae from the younger worms but also a reconstitution of the level of microfilaraemia which the primary infection would have created had there not been a check on this by the imposition of re-infection. Although one cannot differentiate the contribution of the two populations of adults to the sharp rise in microfilaraemia, it is of particular interest that this occurred and, also, that reinfection caused a suppression of the prevailing microfilaraemia which persisted until the reinfection worms had themselves become productive adults.

A similar effect was observed in another cotton rat, not here illustrated, exposed in a mite-infested transmission nest for 9 days and again, 110 days later, for 20 days. At autopsy 82 days later, its infection, entirely in the pleural cavity and in which encapsulative processes were barely evident, amounted to fifty-five worms distinguishable as two populations, viz.: *first, primary, popula-tion*: 24 worms (15 ♀ + 9 ♂), mean age 195 days old, mean ♀ length = 11·4 cm; *second, reinfection, population*: 31 worms (24 ♀ + 7 ♂), mean age 92 days old, mean ♀ length = 7·2 cm. The male worms were not measured, but were distinctly of smaller and larger sizes. Both populations of females were pro-ducing microfilariae, as observed by smearing them. Just before the expected flow of new microfilariae from the second females, the microfilaraemia was only 450 microfilariae per mm^3, low for an infection of fifteen primary females (cf. Fig. 9), but, again, it rapidly rose to a fluctuant peak of as high as nearly 1400 microfilariae per mm^3 after the second females had become fecund. A check of microfilarial density during the development of the worms of the reinfection, followed by a rapid increase in this density when they matured, was again evident.

We may now look at another cotton rat (Fig. 13) with a similar pattern of exposure, namely 12 days in a mite-infested transmission nest with an interval then of 125 days free of transmission before a further exposure in a nest for 17 days and, finally, a terminal transmission-free period of 171 days up to post-mortem dissection. This infection was briefly discussed in Bertram (1958).

Total infection is heavy, 646 adult worms and slight encapsulative reactions, not enough to prejudice the count of worms, although not all could be measured because of some breakage. Of the total worms, 505 (200 ♀ + 305 ♂) were in the pleural cavity and 141 (88 ♀ + 53 ♂) formed a peritoneal infection. Of 127 measurable females of the pleural worms, 15 had a mean length of 9·0 cm and 112 a mean length of 5·2 cm, respectively, the first and second populations of worms from the two 12- and 17-day periods of exposure. If one assigns half of the seventy-three unmeasured females to each group and allocates the males on a 3:2 basis, an approximation of the worms in each population is *first population*: 129 (51 ♀ + 78 ♂); *second population*: 376 (148 ♀ + 228 ♂). From this, the initial population was not heavy enough to promote peritoneal invasion and the 88 ♀♀ + 53 ♂♂ in that cavity would appear to be part of the much larger transmission during the 17-day second episode of transmission. At a mean female length of 10·4 cm, they are much longer than the pleural worms of this transmission (mean ♀ = 5·2 cm), but this is quite consistent with earlier findings from the heavy primary infec-tion, transmitted on a single day, of 563 worms (Fig. 11).

At post-mortem, microfilariae occurred in good numbers in smears of females from both pleural populations and in very substantial numbers in the long robust females from the peritoneum, also in the fluids of both pleural and peritoneal cavities. A microfilaraemia clearly results from the first population females (Fig. 13). If produced by 15 ♀♀ it should have climbed to 1000 microfilariae per mm³, or more (cf. Fig. 9) or, alternatively, if by 51 ♀♀, an

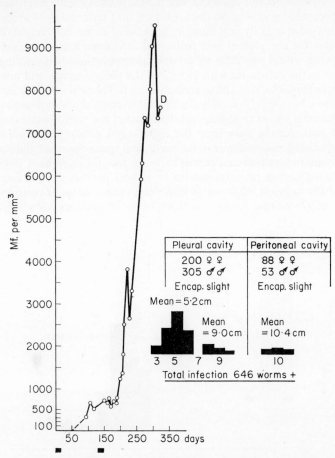

FIG. 13. Double infection in a cotton rat exposed to infection and reinfection for two widely separated short periods in mite-infested nests, showing, in particular, the extremely high microfilaraemia (Mf.) following the maturation of the second population of worms due largely to the heavy infection of adult worms in the peritoneal cavity. Details of distribution of worms and female lengths shown as in previous figures. Black blocks (■) below scale of days show time of exposures in the mite-infested nests. Post-mortem dissection of cotton rat at *D*. (After Bertram, 1958.)

early peak of perhaps 600–700 microfilariae per mm³ would be possible about the 150th day with a sharp decline before the 200th day (cf. Fig. 9). Neither event is apparent. A plateau-like microfilaraemia persists at 600–700 between the 150th and 200th day until the remarkably rapid rise in micro-filaraemia occurs at the time when increments from the second population worms could be expected. There is some indication, again, of suppression of potential microfilarial levels whilst new worms are developing in the coelomic spaces of a reinfected cotton rat.

The rise in microfilaraemia when the second population of adults became fecund is both rapid and immense, reaching a count of 9505 microfilariae per mm³ before what seems to be the beginning of a terminal decline just before the rat died—not directly, it is thought, because of its heavy infection (Bertram, 1958). How far the pleural and peritoneal infections were responsible is of interest. One would conclude by comparison with the low-subsiding micro-filaraemia in the cotton rat with 183 ♀♀ in the pleural cavity and none in the peritoneum (Fig. 10), that the contribution of the pleural infection of this rat, now at 200 ♀♀ + 305 ♂♂, mostly stunted individuals of the reinfection, to the microfilaraemia would be slight, and that most of the microfilariae composing the huge peak density were from the eighty-eight robust peritoneal females. As already noted, microfilariae in the peritoneal space can reach the peripheral blood-stream in numbers and persist there for months (Kershaw, 1949a).

Two other cotton rats exposed for two short periods at wide intervals in nests had the heaviest adult worm infections of this series of cotton rats. An infection of 976 worms, together with slight encapsulations, shown in Fig. 14,

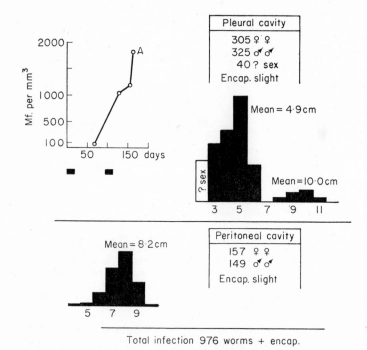

Total infection 976 worms + encap.

FIG. 14. Double infection in a cotton rat with a similar history of infection and reinfection, and resultant parasitic pattern to that of the infection of Fig. 13, although total adult worm load is much heavier.

resembles closely, although worm numbers are greater, the foregoing animal in the history of its exposure and in the characteristics of its worm and micro-filarial infection, so far as this was followed. Two pleural populations are evident and a yet heavier peritoneal infection which can be attributed, as before, to the second episode of transmission and which is of considerably longer females than the stunted females of the heavy pleural infection from the same episode. The microfilaraemia began to rise sharply at the time when the second population worms had matured; it may have risen to very high densities had it been followed for longer.

The rat (Fig. 15) with 1007 live worms together with considerable pleural encapsulations ($++$) is interesting for its low microfilaraemia, whenever

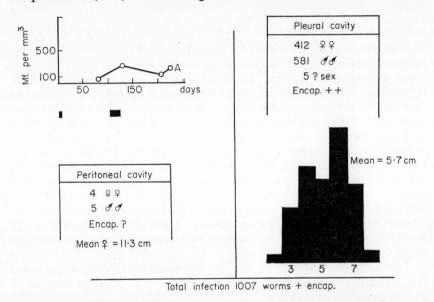

FIG. 15. Double infection in a cotton rat with a similar history of infection and re-infection in mite-infested nests as for the cotton rats of Figs. 13 and 14. The adult worm infection of the pleural cavity is very heavy and associated with a low microfilaraemia (Mf.) which is attributable to the light peritoneal infection.

examined. The encapsulations may represent early death of the worms trans-mitted during the 3 days of initial exposure. These were probably few in view of this short exposure period and the low microfilarial count about 80 days later. It remains unexplained, if all or the bulk of the 998 pleural worms were transmitted in the second 18-day exposure 99 days later, why so few migrated to the peritoneal cavity. Nevertheless, a few were found and, again, they were robust and long (mean ♀ = 11·3 cm) compared to corresponding females in the massively infected pleural cavity for which severe retardation of growth from sheer numbers, as well as a reinfection effect, can be deduced from the short mean female length (5·7 cm) and wide spread of variability in their lengths.

The rat lived long enough to have developed a heavy microfilaraemia, but the density of microfilariae was only about 200 microfilariae per mm³ at its highest. It seems that the intense parasitization of the pleural cavity virtually eliminated this population as a source of microfilariae for the circulation and that the four large fertile females in the peritoneal cavity could maintain only a moderate microfilaraemia, indeed not dissimilar from that for only four fertile females in the pleural cavity of a primary infection (Fig. 8, cotton rat b).

These superinfected animals with their particularly heavy pleural infections include, in this cavity, a few or numerous very small worms, none of which were males with characteristic spiral extremities, suggesting, as previously observed, that they were worms particularly severely retarded by the influence of immune responses and worm load on reinfections.

B. INTERMITTENT EXPOSURE FOR BRIEF PERIODS AT LONG INTERVALS

In nature in a region endemic for filariasis, whether an animal or a human infection, transmission in the course of the life of the host must occur on numerous occasions. Indeed, the combinations and permutations of re-infection are immense, with limitless possibilities in the frequency with which transmission may occur and in terms, too, of how many infective larvae are transmitted at any one instant of time. We go on now to cotton rats which were exposed in mite-infested transmission nests on three or four fairly short occasions with considerable intervals between each of these episodes. More so than those just described, which experienced only two such episodes, the cotton rats now to be considered simulate superinfection which might well happen in the wild if the abundance of the vector, or at any rate contact between vector and host, fluctuated appreciably for seasonal or other reasons, so that transmissions to the host recurred, but only intermittently at considerable intervals. As for the previous cotton rats, observations on worm lengths are limited to female worms.

This aspect is illustrated by the parasitological condition of three cotton rats exposed for three, or four, short periods (9–32 days) at intervals of 56–134 days (Fig. 16a–c).

The first period of transmission established an initial microfilaraemia. Thereafter, microfilarial densities rose, with various fluctuations, to between 1 500 and 3 000 microfilariae per mm³ and continued, even still rising in two of the rats, about this level until final dissection of the host about 400–450 days after first exposure. One can attribute these sustained high blood infections to a cumulative augmentation of the circulating microfilariae by the adult worms of successive episodes of transmission. Primary infections without succeeding reinfections could be expected to have declined after a peak about the 200th day to low microfilarial densities (Figs. 8 and 9), or to a negative condition, when 400 or more days old (Williams, 1948; Kershaw, 1949b; Macdonald and Scott, 1958). Despite the high, sustained blood infections, the total for countable, discrete live worms per rat is moderate, viz. 126 (35 ♀ + 91 ♂), 220 (94 ♀ + 126 ♂) and 298 (173 ♀ + 125 ♂) worms, but the considerable encapsulations (+ to + + + +) certainly involved substantial numbers of other large worms which were formerly alive and, we have no reason to

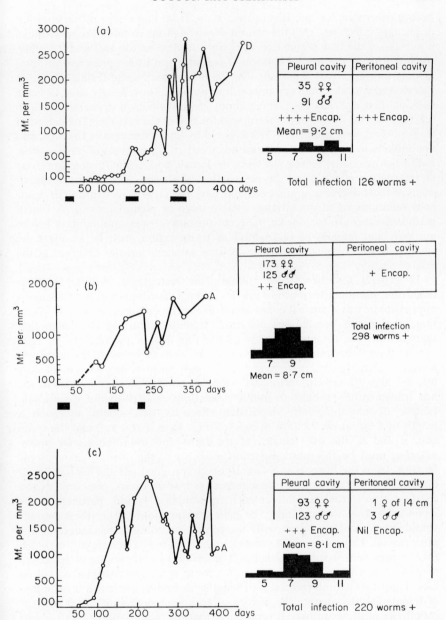

FIG. 16. Persistingly high microfilaraemias (Mf.) in three cotton rats exposed to transmission at long intervals for three, or four, periods of short to moderate duration in mite-infested transmission nests. Details of adult worm infection shown as in previous figures; also periods of exposure (■). (*a* and *c* after Bertram, 1958.)

believe otherwise, fecund. It is fairly certain, from knowledge of the duration of primary infections, that the pleural encapsulations embody probably most, if not all, of the first population of worms in these cotton rats and, possibly, some worms of the second episode of transmission which preceded autopsy, or post-mortem, by 8–9 months. On the other hand, some female worms of this second episode could certainly still be amongst those finally alive, as is the case, at their age, say on average about 250 days old, in primary infections (cf. Fig. 9). The worms of the third, and for two of the rats their last period of transmission, were about 178–190 days old by final dissection of the host, and are unlikely to be included amongst advanced encapsulations of large worms, but rather as smaller female worms of the female population (histograms), due to retardation effects from the pre-existing infections; less successful individuals of these different populations may have been lost to recognition in minor encapsulations or at an extremely early stage of pleural growth. A fourth period of exposure for one of these cotton rats (c) was only 60 days before autopsy, and females of this period of transmission must be amongst the smaller, if not composing entirely the very smallest, females observed at the final dissection.

In general for these three animals, the histograms indicate by their departure, particularly in two of the rats, from a distribution of female lengths approximating to a normal curve to a wide erratic distribution over 4–16 cm, that overlapping populations occurred. It may be further concluded that retardation, due to immune responses acting within populations of each of the several episodes of transmission as well as between them, played a part in creating this pattern and the overall mean female lengths of only 8·1, 8·7 and 9·2 cm. In cotton rat c it is inconceivable that females of the last transmission—subject to immune reactions, and probably some quantitative or physiologically depressive effect as well—could approach a length of 8 cm at 60–78 days of age (cf. Fig. 4). For this rat, and the other two, a and b, the live females of the third and even the second transmissions must be the most important elements of the overall means. Some females, from the histograms, were 10 or 11 cm, good lengths for females of about 250 or 180 days old, of these respective transmissions; one could expect the first transmitted females of each transmission period, particularly the second, to grow well enough. The later transmissions within these periods would be particularly retarded by the recent preceding transmissions of the same period. Thus, the overall means are not what might be normally expected for the prevalent worms, whether 180 or 250 days old, viz. about 10–12 cm (Fig. 4), but are consistently lower at 8–9 cm in these superinfected cotton rats. These low overall mean female lengths, as well as the broad distribution of female lengths, denote the history of complex reinfection which was the experience of these animals. It is probable that the trend to a low mean female length is accentuated by the deaths of the original, largest worms involved in encapsulation and, although without quantitative transmission throughout one cannot be sure, to a suppressive effect on worm growth of sheer numbers of pleural worms which existed at some intermediate stage of these superinfections before encapsulative processes began to eliminate any appreciable part of the infection. The considerable quantities of pleural encapsulations suggest that deaths and encapsulations were happening in these cotton rats unusually early under pressure of adverse factors in heavily infected, and superinfected, pleural spaces. There is, then, a possibility that in intermittent transmissions of this order there is a slow turnover of the active, fecund, worm population which eventually tends to be a population of somewhat stunted worms. Regardless of size of females, they were fecund in these animals although, qualitatively, less prolific, it appeared, than larger robust worms seen in less complex infections; pleural fluids were microfilaria-positive.

Coupled with the interpretation of heavy cumulative pleural infection during the evolution of these superinfections is the evidence, as encapsulations ($+$ to $+++$) or as 1 ♀ + 3 ♂♂ alive, of peritoneal invasion. Since *total* pleural infections at final dissections were either considerably fewer, or at least well below the critical level which seems important in promoting peritoneal invasion, it would follow that the numbers of worms entering the pleural spaces in the last transmission episode were even fewer and peritoneal invasion unlikely during that period. Thus, the encapsulated peritoneal worms were transmitted, it is thought, during one or other of the preceding periods of transmission. We can be more precise about the single 14 cm long peritoneal female in cotton rat *c*, which could hardly be so long (cf. Fig. 4) at an age of only 60–78 days if transmitted during the fourth period of exposure; it must surely belong to the preceding episode at least. All this supports the concept that, in all these cotton rats, populations of microfilariae from peritoneal females contributed, before the death of these females, to the creation and maintenance of the high, persisting microfilaraemias observed. Indeed, if pleural worm burdens were as heavy as is postulated, the peritoneal females may have made the predominant contribution.

These reinfections may not, at first glance, appear to suppress the microfilaraemias, but, except for an inexplicable rise during early development of the worms of the second transmission period of cotton rat *a*, it is possible, even in these complicated infections, to relate the period of growth of reinfection worms to fecund adults with a probable check on rising microfilarial densities (*a*, *b* or *c*, second transmissions; *a*, third transmission; *c*, fourth transmission) or a sharp fall to a fluctuant rather lower level (*b* and *c*, third transmission). It seems of some importance to the maintenance of these prolonged high microfilaraemias that the intervals between transmission episodes were usually longer, 70–134 days, than the time required (50 days) for worms to grow and become productive of microfilariae. Thus, the worms of each new population, and particularly peritoneal worms if the pleural infection was heavy, were enabled, before reinfection again supervened, to contribute further microfilariae to the blood infection. One has to envisage, too, some augmentation due to relaxation of the check on a microfilaraemia caused during the growth to maturity of a reinfecting population. Conversely, with only 56 days between the second and third transmission episodes (Fig. 16, cotton rat *b*), a sharp fall in microfilarial density occurred during the start of the onslaught of the third transmission period, the time at which, otherwise, the microfilarial output to the blood from the pre-existing females could have just begun to supplement the microfilaraemia. Finally, relief from the adverse impact of further reinfection allowed the microfilaraemia in cotton rats *a* and *b* to rise steadily after the worms last transmitted had matured and, although this is not evident for cotton rat *c*, only 10–28 days were available before autopsy in which this could have been displayed in this animal.

C. INTERMITTENT EXPOSURE FOR LONG PERIODS AT SHORT INTERVALS

This significance of the length of transmission-free intervals between exposures seems to be borne out further, apart from further aspects of the influence of reinfection, in the apparently anomalous infection of the cotton rat illustrated in Fig. 17. Interpretation of this infection is unusually diffi-

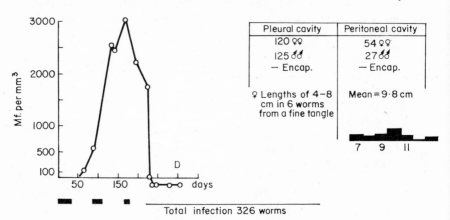

Pleural cavity	Peritoneal cavity
120 ♀♀	54 ♀♀
125 ♂♂	27 ♂♂
— Encap.	— Encap.
♀ Lengths of 4–8 cm in 6 worms from a fine tangle	Mean = 9·8 cm

Total infection 326 worms

FIG. 17. Rapid subsidence of a high microfilaraemia (Mf.) to a persistent negative state in a cotton rat exposed to heavy reinfection (see text) in the course of three exposures to transmission in mite-infested nests. Intervals between transmission episodes barely longer than the time required (50 days) for each new population of female worms to become fecund. Other details of infection shown as in previous figures.

cult because the rat died during a week-end and post-mortem condition was poor at dissection. It experienced three transmission episodes of 35, 26 and 15 days in mite-infested nests with transmission-free intervals of only 51 and 56 days. Post-mortem dissection was 105 days after the last exposure. The microfilaraemia is, essentially, of a broad peaked form up to 3000 microfilariae per mm³ about 170 days after transmission first began in the initial 35-day episode, with a puzzling rapid decline thereafter to a negative condition as early as the 227th day; the blood persisted negative for the remaining 61 days up to the death of the rat. It had not during this time been obviously unfit. No encapsulations were seen and the total live worms (326) were disposed as 245 pleural worms (120 ♀ + 125 ♂) and, notably, a large peritoneal infection (54 ♀ + 27 ♂). One might dismiss this infection as one with a particularly high peak microfilaraemia due to the worms transmitted during the initial 35-day exposure, and that this ran its course to a rather early terminal phase of negative blood with little or no transmission occurring in the two later exposure periods. However, in both these later exposures this rat was alone in the nest as the sole host of the mites. Repeated reinfections from itself were, so far as the empirical nature of such nests can ensure, inevitable. Indirect evidence that this was probably, on both occasions, on a substantial scale is available in total transmissions to several clean cotton rats, which were substituted for a few days in the nest when the rat in question was removed, of 187 (86 ♀ + 101 ♂) worms (second nest) and 275 (128 ♀ + 147 ♂) worms (third nest).

The pleural worms were, in the rat under discussion, too much damaged, or broken, to measure except for 6 ♀♀ of 4–8 cm, so that a histogram pattern is not available to assist in confirming this view. However, the small size of these females indicates that they were much too small to be those of the first transmission episode, which would be 263–288 days old at post-mortem, but must be either of one or both of the subsequent episodes, the worms of which would have a mean age of 189 and 112 days, respectively. Even so, females of 4 cm are very stunted individuals if they are of the latter age, more so if 189 days old (cf. Fig. 4). Thus far, adverse immunity effects on reinfections, perhaps also numerical or physiological suppression, during these later episodes of transmission can be deduced for the pleural worms.

The microfilaraemia peak at 170 days is remarkably high for transmissions during the initial 35 days, and one may ask how it could have come about. There is evidence for its validity in another cotton rat, not here illustrated, which was exposed in a nest for 28 days and its microfilaraemia by the 166th day was 3 078 microfilariae per mm³. At autopsy 1 month later its infection, entirely in the pleural cavity, was only 52 (31 ♀ + 21 ♂) worms, but these were clearly of two populations, one probably transmitted about the beginning and the other towards the end of the 28 days, with female lengths in a bimodal distribution as a first population of 26 ♀♀ (mean ♀ = 12·3 cm) and a second of 5 ♀♀ (mean ♀ = 9·4 cm); males were not compared. Its heavy microfilaraemia, one can conclude, was due to the moderate primary infection of 26 ♀♀, numbers likely to give a high microfilaraemia (cf. Fig. 9), supplemented in due course by further increments to the blood-stream from the five younger females when they had also matured (cf. Fig. 12). A similar reinfection pattern and overall lightness of worm load probably occurred for the cotton rat of Fig. 17 during its first 35-day nest transmission.

The peak microfilaraemia and a history of recurring transmissions in the three main episodes of exposure for this animal seem, then, acceptably explicable.

The most anomalous feature of this infection, however, is the final rapidly subsiding microfilaraemia and, particularly, persistently negative blood in the presence of heavy peritoneal infection (54 ♀ + 27 ♂) with mean female lengths of 9·8 cm (range 7–13 cm). Why, as in previous animals so infected, did these not flood the blood-stream with microfilariae? Three factors may be concerned. First, with only 56 days transmission-free between the second and third nest exposures, worms of the former episode had little opportunity to contribute to the microfilaraemia before the third transmission and its maturation supervened to suppress this process. Secondly, the total load of reinfection may well have been so very heavy as to stimulate an immune response in this animal intense enough to curb the microfilarial increments to the blood from the peritoneal cavity, as well as from the pleural cavity. Here one is accepting the concept that immune response is stimulated by infective larvae which fail to reach the pleural cavity apart from those which do and develop, even if always stunted. Thirdly, the distribution of female lengths for the peritoneal females is wide, without a central, sharp, mean value. This suggests that reinfection of the peritoneum occurred rather frequently, at least during both second and third episodes of 26 and 15 days, rather than on a single short occasion as indicated by the compact distributions for other animals with heavy peritoneal infections, but high or rising microfilaraemias associated with that, as in Figs. 13 and 14.

We appear to witness in this cotton rat, from its second exposure period onwards, a suppressive effect of repeatedly recurring transmission and reinfection on not only pleural worms and the microfilaraemia but also on peritoneal worms. Clearly, by comparison with Figs. 13 and 14, the mere number of peritoneal worms cannot be an adequate explanation for their apparent incompetence; the facts are more in favour of a subtler effect from a strong, generalized immune response in the host to intensive superinfection

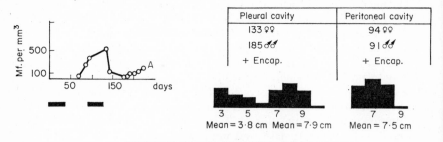

FIG. 18. Low microfilaraemia (Mf.) in a heavily infected cotton rat exposed for two long periods of reinfection in a mite-infested nest, the interval between the two episodes of transmission being only 52 days. A trend towards recovery of the microfilaraemia is apparent, attributable to the considerable peritoneal infection as the suppressive influence of the last period of reinfection relaxes. Other details of infection shown as in previous figures.

unrelieved except for a period of 56 days. This interval barely allows for relaxation of the adverse influence of developing reinfections on existing parasites and their potentialities to maintain, or supplement, a prevailing microfilaraemia.

Whether, given longer, microfilariae from these peritoneal worms—together with lesser numbers from the pleural infection—would have appeared in the peripheral circulation of this host is an open question. But this might be so. Figure 18 illustrates a similar infection of 503+ worms following exposure periods of 39 and 36 days, separated by only 52 days, and with 99 days between the last possible transmission and autopsy. Two quite substantial pleural populations, of the order, respectively, apart from males, of

74 ♀♀ and 59 ♀♀ and a peritoneal infection (94 ♀ + 91 ♂) together with additional worms encapsulated in each colemoic situation, indicate a quite intensive experience of transmission. The live peritoneal worms, at a mean age of 117 days, seem of appropriate length to be of the second episode (Fig. 4) and all the encapsulations are, it is thought, more those of the first population on the basis of ages of the worm populations. It is of interest to note the check, again, of microfilarial increase during the second period of reinfection, the persistent decline as it developed, and the slow, as opposed to a dramatically rapid, refortification of the microfilaraemia from about 50 days and onwards after the last possible reinfection had happened. Such a recovery may have been operating slowly in the preceding cotton rat, but one cannot be certain what fluctuations or density changes were going on in a blood infection so low as to be negative for microfilariae in the standard samples taken of 2 mm³ of peripheral blood.

In Bertram (1953a), but also illustrated here (Fig. 19), a cotton rat exposed

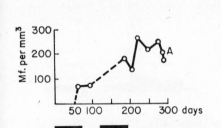
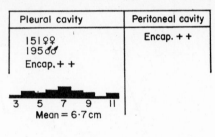

FIG. 19. Low microfilaraemia (Mf.) in a heavily infected cotton rat exposed for two long periods of reinfection in mite-infested nests, with a short interval between the two episodes of transmission. No recovery of microfilaraemia latterly, in view of encapsulation of peritoneal infection. Other details of infection shown as in previous figures. (After Bertram, 1953a.)

for 72 and 70 days with a transmission-free interval between of only 48 days, failed to attain more than a microfilarial density of about 260 per mm³ in the 97 days after the last possible reinfection occurred; indeed, latterly, the microfilaraemia was falling. Undoubtedly from the total pleural infection of 151 ♀♀ + 195 ♂♂, a mean female length of 6·7 cm for a variable distribution from 3 to 11 cm, together with much encapsulation (+ +) in both this and the peritoneal cavity, this animal had been intensively and quite persistently reinfected. As pointed out in Bertram (1953a), this result suggested strongly that peritoneal worms, subsequently subjected to effects of prolonged continuing reinfection of the host as a whole, i.e. to intensified generalized immune response, were liable to die prematurely and become encapsulated quickly. On the other hand, if peritoneal invasion occurred at or near the end of a period of transmission and the worms were then free of the influences of a further onslaught of reinfection, peritoneal worms, thus less inhibited, could grow quite successfully with a good microfilarial output which would flood the blood-stream to produce a high microfilaraemia, This (Bertram, 1953a) was deemed to be the case for a cotton rat (Fig. 20) in which a pre-existing high microfilaraemia (1 000 per mm³) from an initial light primary infection was rapidly suppressed to about 130 per mm³ during subsequent prolonged re-infection (116 days exposure, with a 13-day respite at one stage). However, 70 days, not 50, after transmission had ceased, a rapidly rising microfilaremia developed which must largely have been due to the 11 ♀♀ of the peritoneum. A peak of 1040 microfilariae per mm³ was reached just before the rat was autopsied.

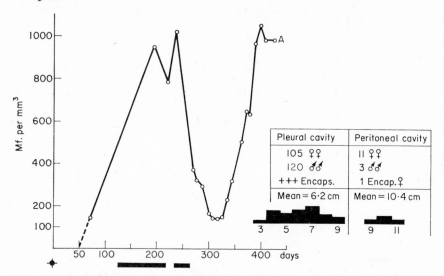

FIG. 20. High microfilaraemia (Mf.) due to initial primary infection, transmitted at ✦, suppressed by prolonged period of reinfection in mite-infested nests (■), interrupted by minor transmission-free period of 13 days. Recrudescence of the microfilarial density occurs on relaxation of further reinfection, and is attributable largely to the female worms in the peritoneal cavity. Other details of infection shown as in previous figures. (After Bertram, 1953a.)

The superinfected cotton rats so far considered have variously demonstrated a suppression of microfilarial density during the onslaught of further trans-missions and the development to maturity and fecundity, even if of stunted growth, of such worms as do reach the coelomic cavities. It remains obscure whether this result is an interference with the microfilarial output of the pre-existing infection of adults, obstruction of the passage of microfilariae from coelomic cavities to the blood-stream, a destruction of microfilariae once they have passed to the blood or, possibly, in part, some redistribution of circulat-ing microfilariae tending to concentrate and localize many of them in the vascular system of internal organs. The last is a capacity well enough known in relation to cyclical rhythms of a 24-h periodicity for certain other filaria species. In simian loiasis, massive microfilarial destruction by the spleen, which appears to be the principal mechanism limiting microfilarial den-sities in that host-parasite association (Duke, 1960b), although not in cotton rat filariasis or other experimental filarial models (Hawking, 1962). This whole problem stands in need of further research in which pathological findings are closely correlated in a representiative range of superinfected hosts, with different conditions of parasitic load, and parasitic expression in terms of microfilaraemia.

D. CONTINUOUS EXPOSURE

It is appropriate now to consider superinfections in cotton rats exposed to continuous risk of reinfection indefinitely without respite. This has not been done for the entire life of a cotton rat, but for up to 153 consecutive days using specially designed nests suitable for such prolonged associations of cotton rat, parasite and vector (Bertram, 1953b). Superinfections resulting from such exposures were described by Bertram (1953a) and a few of these are briefly discussed here.

One cotton rat which died in a nest after 124 days of exposure harboured 552 worms (222 ♀ + 283 ♂ + 47 very small and unsexed). No encapsulations were observed, and there was no infection of the peritoneal cavity. Lengths of females ranged from 10 to 3 cm, the smaller worms being progressively much more numerous, indicative not only of recurring reinfection but of retarded growth due to the earlier transmissions represented by the larger worms. The day before the death of the rat the microfilaraemia was only 83 microfilariae per mm³. This appeared to be a result less of failure of microfilariae to reach or survive in the blood-stream than to the curtailed reproductive life of the few larger 9–10 cm long worms whose gonads were empty, and a low potential output in the smaller worms, from 8 to 3 cm, in which numbers of embryos and microfilariae were only moderate or, particularly in the smallest worms, few or sparse.

Rapid loss of female fertility leading to a low transient microfilaraemia, less than about 50 microfilariae per mm³, which lapsed to a negative condition within 150 days of the first possible transmission and persisted so for 175 days up to the autopsy of the host, was particularly clear in another cotton rat (Fig. 21a) exposed to transmission for 140 consecutive days. Autopsied 180 days after the end of this exposure, it contained only 125 live worms (58 ♀ + 67 ♂), but considerable encapsulations (+ +) in the pleural cavity, while the peritoneum was uninfected. Lengths of females again indicated superinfection, in a wide range from 4 to 9 cm, and with a mean of only 7·5 cm. Of 26 ♀♀ representative of all sizes, twenty contained no embryos at all, and six only a few microfilariae or a few early stages. No microfilariae were found in the pleural fluid.

A rather similar type of infection followed exposure for 65 consecutive days (Fig. 21b) and in a third cotton rat exposed for 153 consecutive days (Fig. 21c). For the latter, autopsied 48 days after removal from the nest, the pleural infection was not only, again, of relatively fewer worms than one might have expected (79 ♀ + 109 ♂)—no encapsulations were observed—in the circumstances but of females of 3–10 cm, with a mean female length of only 6·5 cm. If reinfections had not occurred, even the youngest possible females (48 days) should have been 6 cm long (Fig. 4, curve W). Few embryos were present in 15 ♀♀ of 5–10 cm, although other 22 ♀♀ were reasonably fecund. The microfilaraemia, examined during continuing exposure, never exceeded 32 microfilariae per mm³. Up to autopsy the blood continued positive, but only just, and may have been so because of six slightly fecund females in the peritoneal cavity. It is impossible to decide if these were, at 6–7 cm. stunted or not as, at 48 days of age, they could be this length. It remains a puzzle why, with a comparatively light infection of mostly stunted worms in the pleural

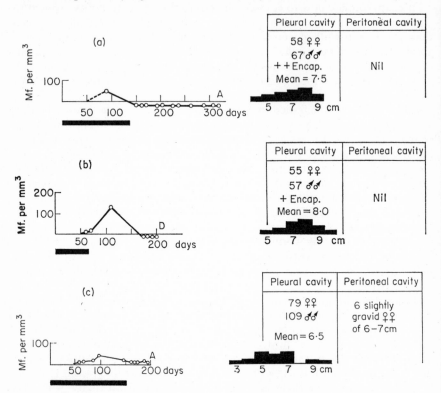

Fig. 21. Very low, transient (a) and (b) or low, persisting (c) microfilaraemias (Mf.) in cotton rats exposed continuously to reinfection for up to 153 days in mite-infested nests. The persistence of the microfilaraemia of cotton rat (c) is probably due to microfilariae contributed to the blood-stream by the few, short worms in the peritoneal cavity. Other detail of infections shown as in previous figures. (After Bertram, 1953a.)

cavity, peritoneal invasion occurred at all, since it did not happen with fairly comparable infections in the other cotton rats subject to prolonged continuous exposure.

In this, and other cotton rats of similar history and infection, cyst-like bodies, ovoid to spherical and about as long as a microfilaria, were common in the pleural fluid, but what these represent is unknown; possibly, an eliminative phase of microfilariae of suboptimal vigour from parent worms severely retarded sexually as well as in growth.

It seems that under conditions of prolonged, virtually uninterrupted transmission, few female worms other than those first transmitted attain normal lengths. Those of the successive reinfections are not only severely retarded in growth but their microfilarial output is curtailed in time and severely diminished in potential. In these conditions of protracted superinfection, a low, transient microfilaraemia followed by a continuing negative condition of the blood is likely to ensue, and does. Inadequacy of reproduction of microfilariae by the parent worms appears to be the important mechanism here in the suppression of the microfilaraemia. In contrast, in intermittent transmissions, other factors militate against the maintenance, or augmentation, of the microfilaraemia, although, as already commented, it is less clear whether these factors have direct effect on reproduction by parent worms or on the microfilariae already in the coelomic spaces or on those in the blood.

It may be noted that respite from further transmissions, even for 180 days, did not enable the prevailing moderate-sized population of stunted, poorly productive worms in the rats just discussed to recover normal capacity for growth, or normal fecundity. This suggests that an immune reaction of a particularly intense degree was stimulated during prolonged recurring transmissions. Either this persisted, as Macdonald and Scott (1958) seemed to show, or the immediate impact on successively transmitted infective larvae under conditions of persistently activated, and fortified, immune reaction in the host experiencing months of reinfection—most of which failed to become patent as growing coelomic infections—imposed not only changes in larvae, particularly in their first few sensitive days (Scott et al., 1958c), but irreversible changes deleterious to their potentialities for normal growth and reproduction. Finally, although it is difficult to eliminate the physiological condition of the coelomic environment as a factor in the parasitic balance these cotton rats established, their quite low to moderate loads of developed worms, many of them small worms, can hardly be as important in these rats in sustaining the suppressed condition of the infection, adult worms and microfilaraemia, as an immunological state conferred on them in virtue of their long continuous subjection to frequently repetitive transmissions.

XI. The Length of Female Worms

The foregoing account of primary infections and superinfections of L. carinii in cotton rats has brought out frequently how variable is the length to which the female worms may grow. Some aspects of the lengths of females merit further consideration. Figure 4, already often referred to, brings together observations on the early growth of females in cotton rats by Scott (1946), curve S, and by Westbrook and Scott (1955), curve W, besides data, represented by various symbols, for the worms from the numerous cotton rats studied by the writer in which infections were, for the most part, older than those represented by the two curves. The researches referred to on early growth dealt with both females and males. The males need not be discussed further here except to comment that the writer's observations on male lengths, as charted on Fig. 4, are in general accord with those of Scott, and of Westbrook and Scott. That males of reinfections are, like females, retarded in growth and moulting rate has been demonstrated repeatedly by Scott and his colleagues; the writer has on occasion taken note of larger and smaller males representing separate populations in superinfected animals, but without actually measuring specimens.

A. GROWTH CURVES FOR PRIMARY INFECTIONS

There appears to be considerable disparity between the two growth curves, W and S. The more rapid growth shown by W is, undoubtedly, the more accurate, as it is based on the mean length of females in cotton rats infected once only with infective larvae, inoculated subcutaneously. The age of the worms was thus known with considerable precision, and the mean length (arithmetic) is a satisfactory measure of the average female length in primary infections, as shown by histograms in other figures. In the earlier preliminary study (Scott, 1946) which provided curve S, the cotton rats were exposed in mite-infested nests to transmission for not less than 10 days. Transmission may, or may not, have happened at once. The compromise adopted to meet the problem of the age of these infections was that of basing the curve on the maximum possible age of the worms, that is, immediate transmission was assumed, and also on the length of the longest female in an infection. This avoided calculating mean lengths which, in view of the possible presence of later small worms of reinfections, subject, too, to retardations of their growth, could well be illogical and unrepresentative of the lengths of the worms first transmitted. Deficiencies of this sort were acknowledged at the time by Scott. A correction for any point on this curve towards rather smaller female lengths to reflect more accurately mean length for the first worms transmitted, and to younger females on an assumption of other than immediate transmission, would not be unreasonable and lead to a closer agreement between the rather dissimilar growth rates shown by the two curves. It is interesting that the three observations (open circles) for young worms lying close to curve W were all transmitted on a single day by mites.

The upper limit of curve W suggests that a maximum growth of females at a little over 6 cm is reached when they are about 50 days old. The curve was derived by Westbrook and Scott (1955) theoretically on the basis of primary infections of 4–74 ♀♀ (with males, total infections of 13–128 worms) available up to only 38 days of age. A maximum growth of 6 cm or so appears to reflect inadequately the potentialities for growth up to nearly 15 cm indicated for the writer's observations by the various symbols, each of which denotes, as for curve W, a mean female length for females from a single animal. Closely comparable with curve W are fifty-three primary bisexual infections of 2–556 pleural worms, aged 50 days or older, transmitted on a single day by infective mites. Of these, forty-two (67%) are amongst the sixty-three light infections of two to thirty total worms (open circles) and they vary in age from 50 to 315 days. One may thus conceive the mean female length for primary infections of thirty or fewer worms increasing further after the rapid growth phase of curve W to, say, a mean of 12 cm by 125 days after transmission.

It is, however, of further relevance that calculation of the upper limit of curve W was based on young infections of 13–128 worms, that is, on heavier infections than the infections of two to thirty worms represented by open circles. Infections, 50 days and older, of 31–200 worms (symbols x) could be expected to have mean female length values closer to those indicated as theoretically attainable by curve W. This tends, indeed, to be so (Fig. 4).

The two heaviest of ten primary infections of this group (x) are comparable, at eighty-seven and ninety-eight worms, with the heavier of the infections involved in the computation of curve W and, for these, mean female lengths were, respectively, 6·8 cm (at 131 days) and 9·1 cm (at 245 days). The only primary infection in the group of heaviest infections (closed circles) was of 556 pleural worms with a mean female length of only 6·2 cm when 135 days old. These data suggest that for primary pleural infections of about, say, 100 worms, mean female lengths would be, at the end of the initial rapid period of growth, about 6 cm or so, as in curve W, with potentialities for further growth to about 9 cm in the course of developing full reproductive output. Thus, the calculated maximal mean female length of females of a primary infection indicated by curve W as a little over 6 cm about 50 days after transmission is less at variance than seems at first with the writer's observations on female lengths from 50 days onward, provided account is taken of the numbers of worms present in an infection.

It would seem to follow that the rate and limit of growth of female worms in primary infections of *L. carinii* is less fully described by a single curve than it could be, in view of this influence of worm load on growth, by a fan of growth curves, each curve leading to a particular maximal mean length. It would be interesting as an example to construct a curve on data for primary infections, 10–100 days old, of about 250–300 worms.

B. GROWTH IN SUPERINFECTIONS

The disposition of superinfections of 50 days of age, or older, in Fig. 4 is a much more complex matter. About one-third of the sixty-three light infections (2–30 worms; open circles) are superinfections following exposure in mite-infested nests for less than 1 week, or for longer periods in nests of low transmission efficiency; some are, in effect, not much different from light primary infections, but this group does include, for example, the two double infections each of twenty-seven worms of Fig. 12 with means of 10·2 cm and 12·3 cm at a mean age of 187 days. Worms of light superinfections are usually large.

As regards the fifty infections of intermediate density (31–200 worms, x), forty are nest superinfections, although, again, this includes a number exposed for only 6–18 days which are relatively more like primary infections than others continuously exposed for up to 153 days (Fig. 21a–c), or intermittently at wide intervals over about 300 days (Fig. 16a). For Fig. 4, each symbol represents, except those joined by arrowed broken lines, the mean female length for the whole pleural population of a superinfection, and the age is calculated from the mean day of transmission, i.e. half the period of time between first and last possible exposure, whether continuous or intermittent, *plus* the transmission-free interval up to dissection of the cotton rat. This compromise has, indeed, considerable limitations, but it is hardly practicable to do otherwise for Fig. 4.

The effect of this choice may be noted for the superinfection of 125 worms with a mean female length of 7·5 cm at a mean age of 250 days, due to exposure for 140 consecutive days in a nest (Fig. 21a). (The mean age of the female worms of 250 days is derived as 70 days *plus* 180 days for the vector-free interval to autopsy.) Any other age, from minimum (180 days) to maximum (140 + 180 = 320 days) would not, in fact, much alter the disposition of this observation in Fig. 4 in relation to others plotted on the same basis. Even if one were to adopt a compromise in this problem by alternatively, or additionally, plotting the smallest female (3 cm) against the youngest possible age (180 days) or the largest female (9 cm) against the oldest age (320 days), this whole population of live worms is still certainly of undersized, stunted individuals, especially the smaller ones of later reinfections.

Turning now to the seventeen observations on heavy infections of 201–1 007 worms (closed circles) within the zone of lowest mean female lengths, 7·5 cm or less: sixteen are superinfections, the one exception being the very heavy primary infection of 556 pleural worms already discussed. The superinfections include the ten already examined in some detail in correlating microfilaraemias with live and encapsulated worms in the pleural, or peritoneal, cavities and are representative of widely spaced double exposures of brief duration with pleural infections of 505–993 live sexable worms (Figs. 13–15); widely intermittent exposures on three or four occasions yielding 216–298 such worms (Figs. 16b, c, and 17); more intensive intermittent transmissions for which 225–346 worms could be sexed (Figs. 18–20); and a 36-day exposure resulting in 406 pleural worms (Fig. 10). Thus, heavy superinfections resulting from widely different experiences of recurring transmission lead to low mean female lengths.

It has not been thought practicable to discuss, or represent on Fig. 4, all superinfections with reference for each to the validity of choice of mean age and mean female length. However, the mean female lengths for two distinctive pleural populations following two separate periods of exposure are linked by arrowed broken lines for two of these superinfections. These were discussed earlier in some detail (Figs. 13 and 18). The cotton rats in question had total infections of 646 and 503 live worms, but we are here mainly concerned with their respective pleural infections of 505 (200 ♀ + 305 ♂) worms and 318 (133 ♀ + 185 ♂) worms.

The overall mean female length for the pleural infection of 505 worms is 7·1 cm at a mean age of 248 days (range 171–325 days). This is not shown in Fig. 4, but, instead, the mean female length of 9·0 cm for the estimated first population of about 129 worms, aged 313–325 (mean = 319) days, is linked to that of 5·2 cm for the second population of 376 worms which is 171–188 (mean = 179) days old. The other superinfection of 318 pleural worms with an overall mean female length of 6·5 cm at a mean age of 162 days (range 99–226 days) is likewise differentiated in Fig. 4 into a first population of 177 worms (74 ♀ + 103 ♂—on a 1:1.4 ratio) aged 187–226 (mean = 207) days with a mean female length of 7·9 cm, together with a second population of 141 worms transmitted later having a mean female length of only 3·8 cm at an age of 99–135 (mean = 117) days. Thus, both populations in both superinfections were, as Fig. 4 shows well, of rather small to very small worms for their ages. At pleural densities for the first population worms of 129 and 177 worms an effect of crowding can be invoked as contributory to their limited growth. This would be especially effective against the second populations. It does seem significant, however, that the second population of only 141 worms in the overall lighter total infection of 318 pleural worms (lower mean female length value of the left-hand paired observations of Fig. 4) is as stunted as it is, at 3·8 cm. A numerical, or physiological, cause seems hardly adequate to account for such severe suppression. This suggests that retardation of growth due to an immune response by the host, stimulated by the initial episode of transmission, played an important role in suppressing the growth of this second population, apart from retardation also imposed on worms of reinfections transmitted within this second episode itself. The skew distribution of the second population histogram (Fig. 18) indicates this latter influence. Encapsulations in this cotton rat would seem to compel the assumption that loss of some larger worms from the measurable live populations lowered the mean female values, but more likely of the first than the second population. It is to be recalled that this cotton rat had other evidence of sustained heavy transmission which could be conceived to promote a particularly effective immunity, viz. exposures for 39 and 36 days with only a 52-day vector-free period between these, a peritoneal infection of 185 live worms with additional encapsulation besides the pleural infection, and a microfilarial count in the blood barely exceeding 500 microfilariae per mm³ which almost reverted towards a negative condition in spite of the worm infections in both the pleural and, particularly, peritoneal cavities.

C. OTHER ASPECTS OF FEMALE GROWTH

The fourth symbol of Fig. 4 shows the mean length for sterile females in unisexual infections of up to 5 ♀♀ and their moderate lengths at about 9 cm, even when nearly 200 days old. In contrast, females of bisexual infections of two to thirty worms are, on average, from 10 to nearly 15 cm long. This indicates an additional growth, perhaps some stretch, which fertile females undergo in the course of developing their copious reproductive activity to the full.

Westbrook and Scott (1955) submitted primary infections from forty-six cotton rats, comprising altogether 1550 worms (808 ♀♀ + 742♂♂) aged 12–38 days, to intensive statistical analysis; some of this has been discussed above. The present writer's researches cover primary infections and a variety of superinfections in about 200 cotton rats yielding nearly 14000 worms (almost 7000♀♀ and over 7000♂♂) within an age range of about 40–400 days. Both sexes of cotton rat harboured light to heavy infections (Table I) and transmission was successful to infant cotton rats and older animals up to 226 days of age (Table II). Scrutiny, but not statistical analyses, of sex and age of host, also sex ratio of worms in view of the relative shortness of sterile females (Fig. 4, ♀) failed to elicit any consistently convincing reason for differences, sometimes of a few cm, in the mean female lengths of primary infections of similar age and worm numbers, nor for unusually long worms in moderately heavy infections. These are represented in overlaps in Fig. 4. Nevertheless, a slight effect of host sex and age (Westbrook and Scott, 1955) in controlling worm growth is certainly not disputed. It is important to note their observation that, although the influences of host sex and age were not taken into account by Macdonald and Scott (1953), these would be too slight to render invalid the marked differences they observed in growth rates of worms in immunized and non-immunized rats. On the other hand, standardization of host sex and age is advocated as a proper refinement of technique for the further study of parasitic development in the immunized filarial host. It is thought, finally, that the case is made here for an effect generally by which greater worm loads progressively reduce female lengths apart from the curb of immune response by the host in superinfections.

XII. Sex Ratio

That the ratio of the sexes of *L. carinii* in cotton rats is rarely 1:1 is clear from Fig. 2. For light to moderate infections in sixty-six primary infections—mean infection 9·5 ♀♀ + 8·4 ♂♂ and a maximum infection of 70 (37 ♀ + 33 ♂) worms—it was shown (Bertram, 1953a) that a slight preponderance of females over males at a sex ratio of 0·88 was, in fact, statistically significant; even an infection of 8 ♀♀ + 23 ♂♂ was not outwith the range of chance variation. One could expect variability to be less in heavier infections than, as Fig. 2 shows, is so marked in the lightest, since larger numbers of worms would tend to cancel out chance differences in the sex of worms transmitted. This becomes apparent at infections of about sixteen worms altogether. There is, however, also a trend with total worm numbers of about seventy to eighty per rat and higher for the sex ratio to shift towards and beyond a 1:1 ratio. About two-thirds of these heavier infections show, in fact, a preponderance of male worms over females. Three primary infections, transmitted by mites on a single day, of 87, 98 and 563 worms with sex ratios of, respectively, 1·02, 0·8 and 0·8 indicate that heavy worm load, at least in infections of 135–245 days of age, is not of itself the cause of this shift.

The shift to an excess of males, in the pleural cavity, is much more consistent (19 out of 20 infections) in the more complex heavy superinfections, whether of 126–1007 worms (Table IV) as a result of intermittent transmissions of varying degree or of 112–552 worms (Table V) following continuous exposures for up to 153 consecutive days. There is only one instance of an excess of females (sex ratio = 0·8; Table V) and that particular animal died 3 days after 140 days of continuous exposure. The sex balance may have been representative in this infection of 151 worms of transmissions latterly acquired, i.e. not greatly differing from a primary infection in this particular respect. In like manner, since it died on the last day of 124 consecutive days of transmission, the sex ratio of 1·3 for the infection of 552 worms may well be no more than a random variation from the mean of 0·88 previously calculated as characteristic for primary infections.

There appears to be, however, one important factor causing an excess of males in the other superinfected cotton rats. As noted earlier, females tend to

Distribution of worms, L. carinii, in the pleural and peritoneal cavities of 11 cotton rats exposed to 2–4 separate periods of transmission in mite-infested nests, and harbouring infections up to 520 days of age

(See text for discussion of excess of male over female worms in the pleural cavity following prolonged experience of intermittent transmission, and, conversely, an excess of female over male worms in the peritoneal cavity when this is heavily infected).

| Cotton rat | | Total separable worms | Pleural cavity | | | | Peritoneal cavity | | | | Maximum age of worms of each exposure period (days) |
Sex	Total exposure in days (no. of separate periods)		No. and sex of worms	Mean♀ length (cm)	Sex ratio	Encaps.	No. and sex of worms	Mean♀ length (cm)	Sex ratio	Encaps.	
♂	44 (3)	126	35♀ + 91♂	9·2	2·6	+++	—	—	—	+++	448 / 295 / 190
♀	66 (4)	220	93♀ + 123♂	8·04	1·3	+++	1♀ + 3♂	14·0	3·0	—	396 / 206 / 183 / 78
♂	117 (3)	240	105♀ + 120♂	6·2	1·1	+++	11♀ + 3♂	10·4	0·25	1♀	405 / 276 / 171
♂	64 (3)	298	125♀ + 173♂	8·7	1·4	++	—	—	—	Slight	391 / 255 / 178
♂	27 (2)	306	73♀ + 233♂	7·0	3·2	++++	—	—	—	—	520 / 337
♀	76 (3)	326	120♀ + 125♂	5·8	1·04	—	54♀ + 27♂	9·8	0·5	—	288 / 202 / 120
♀	142 (2)	346	151♀ + 195♂	6·7	1·3	++	—	—	—	++	287 / 167
♀	75 (2)	503	133♀ + 185♂	7·9 / 3·8	1·4	+	94♀ + 91♂	7·5	0·97	+	226 / 135
♂	29 (2)	646	200♀ + 305♂	9·1 / 5·2	1·5	Slight	88♀ + 53♂	10·4	0·6	Slight	325 / 188
♂	33 (2)	976	305♀ + 325♂ + 40 unsexed	10·0 / 4·8	1·1	Slight	157♀ + 149♂	8·2	0·95	Slight	162 / 70
♀	28 (2)	1007	412♀ + 581♂ + 5 unsexed	5·7	1·4	+++	4♀ + 5♂	11·3	1·3	—	218 / 131

die and become encapsulated sooner than males (see also Williams, 1948; Kershaw, 1949b; Macdonald and Scott, 1958). A selective survival of pleural males is evident in sex ratios of 1·04–3·2 for long-standing infections (e.g. maximum ages of 287–520 days; Table IV) in which considerable encapsulations have occurred, and also for some of the continuously exposed animals (Table V), as early as 205–272 days after first exposure, in which encapsulations and calcifications also occur.

Bearing in mind the greater physiological demand of growing and fecund females, and that their greater lengths must incur more contact with the surfaces of their coelomic environment and more risk of injury and involvement in host reactions than for the small males, it is not surprising that male survival is better and that an excess of males tends to accumulate with time. Wharton (1947) comments that a high proportion of worms in cotton rat filariasis in nature are always males; in wild-caught cotton rats, one might well expect that circumstances of natural reinfection in the wild would lead to a preponderance of this sex.

It is interesting to note (Table IV) that where substantial numbers of peritoneal worms were found in total infections of 240, 326, 503, 646 and 976 separable worms, the pleural sex ratio was from 1·04 to 1·5, but the peritoneal sex ratio was from 0·25 to 0·97, closer to the statistically significant ratio of 0·88 for uncomplicated primary pleural infections. This suggests that the infective larvae of later transmissions respond about equally, regardless of sex, to the incompatibilities of a heavily superinfected pleural environment by migrating to the peritoneal cavity. The light peritoneal infections of 1 ♀ + 3 ♂, and 4 ♀ + 5 ♂, are not at variance with this point of view, their ratios of 3·0 and 1·3 being not more remarkable than that of many light, primary infections of the pleural cavity (Fig. 2).

XIII. TRANSMISSION EFFICIENCY AND PATHOGENICITY

Microfilaraemias may, it is clear, vary very considerably from one cotton rat to another, but also during the course of an individual infection, depending especially on the host's experience of superinfection. This prompts the question of how effective different microfilaraemias may be in infecting the vector.

Bertram (1950a) showed, for forty-four feedings of mites on twenty cotton rats with primary infections, that infection rates for infective larvae ranged from 14·9% (mean number of larvae per mite = 0·2; maximum number per mite = 2) when mites engorged on blood containing as few as 10 microfilariae per mm^3 to as high as 86·4% (mean larvae per mite = 4·1; maximum per mite = 13) when fed on a cotton rat circulating 1 150 microfilariae per mm^3. Furthermore, for microfilaraemias up to about 200 microfilariae per mm^3 infection rates rose rapidly to about 60%, but thereafter for mites engorging on the denser microfilaraemias the level of infection increased relatively slowly to the heaviest rate of 86%. Subsequent observations show that this suppression of the infection of the vector with infective larvae to below a level which would happen if it were proportionate to the microfilaraemia of the donor host also occurs with the much denser microfilaraemias of superinfected

TABLE V

Distribution of worms, L. carinii, in the pleural cavity mainly, of 9 cotton rats exposed for up to 153 consecutive days in mite-infested nests (See text for discussion of excess of male over female worms in the pleural cavity of most of these animals.)

Cotton rat		Total separable worms	Pleural cavity			Encaps.	Maximum age of worms (days)
Sex	Duration of single period of exposure (days)		No. and sex of worms	Mean ♀ length (cm)	Sex ratio		
♀	65	112	55♀ + 57♂	8·0	1·04	+	221
♀	140	125	58♀ + 67♂	7·5	1·2	++	320
♂	112	137	53♀ + 84♂	8·1	1·6	++	272
♀	140	151	82♀ + 65♂ + 4 unsexed	6·4	0·8	+ (Calcification)	143
♂	31	160	65♀ + 95♂	8·1	1·5	—	306
♂	153	194	79♀ + 109♂ Peritoneal cavity 6♀	6·5 / 6·3	1·04 / —	— / —	201
♀	140	287	142♀ + 145♂	6·5	1·02	+ (Calcification)	205
♂	36	407	183♀ + 223♂ Peritoneal cavity 1♂	6·9 / —	1·2 / —	Slight / Slight	157
♂	124	552	222♀ + 283♂ + 47 unsexed	(<3–10)	1·3	—	124

cotton rats. Thus, on four occasions, infection data for infective larvae in mites fed on the very dense microfilaraemia of the cotton rat of Fig. 13, in the period between the 209th and 310th day after initial transmission, ranged from 91·3% (mean larvae per mite = 19·9; maximum per mite = 59) to 100% (mean larvae per mite = 24·2; maximum per mite = 70) for microfilaraemias prevailing at the time of 2555–7382 microfilariae per mm³. In the super-infections of Fig. 16*a* and *c*, the microfilaraemias were less remarkably heavy, but it is interesting to record that, as in the foregoing heavy primary infection of 1150 microfilariae per mm³, these superinfected cotton rats were about the time of their third and fourth episodes of transmission, and when they had microfilarial counts of, respectively, 1810 and 994 per mm³, just about as infectious for the vector (87·5–95·9% infected with infective larvae; mean larvae per mite = 6–7; maximum infections in a mite = 21 and 28). Again, the mites were, although well infected, less heavily infected than the numerical density of microfilariae in the blood of the cotton rats might lead one to expect.

It is remarkable how many mites can survive (60–70%) after engorging on cotton rats with such heavy microfilaraemias, even 2000 to over 7000 micro-filariae per mm³. Neither Bertram (1950a) nor Williams and Kershaw (1961) found consistent evidence of infections of *L. carinii* larvae in the mite being lethal to the vector, although the latter authors, infecting mites from a cotton rat with only about 50 microfilariae per mm³ of peripheral blood, obtained some indication that mortalities may occur when the vector is damaged at the end of the intrinsic cycle when the infective larvae escape finally during trans-mission, an event shown to cause mortality during *Chrysops* transmission of infective larvae of *Loa* (Kershaw *et al.*, 1954; see also Lavoipierre, 1958a) and with a mosquito-borne filariasis of dogs (Kershaw *et al.*, 1953). In the latter vector–parasite association mortality was also evident about the time micro-filariae were escaping from the gut and occurring in the haemocoele; but this is not a conspicuous consequence for the mite infected with *L. carinii*. There may be subtle factors limiting actual intake; this we do not know. But two protective mechanisms limit the risk of lethal infections for the mite. First, rapid disintegration takes place of many microfilariae, even within half an hour or less of being taken up in the blood meal (Freer, 1953). Secondly, and this is particularly apparent in mites feeding on heavy microfilaraemias, a suppression of larval development so that mites contain all stages of larvae from active infective forms to small larvae which, although alive, have developed little beyond the microfilarial stage at which they were taken up 2 weeks earlier. Rather as for heavy infections of growing worms in the pleural cavity of the vertebrate host, interference with normal growth and develop-ment of at least some microfilariae within the vector enables the vector to survive potentially lethal intakes of microfilariae.

Apart from these limitations to levels of infection in mites engorging from heavy microfilaraemias, the infectivity for the vector of heavily infected bloods in superinfected cotton rats is apparently not impaired; they are as infectious as similar densities in heavy primary infections. On the other hand, Bertram (1950a) was concerned to understand why two cotton rats, infected when wild-caught in America and subsequently again in mite-infested nests for a while after shipment in 1946 to the laboratory in this country, induced infection rates for infective larvae of only 7·9%, 21·1%, 21·7% and 39·3% (mean larvae per mite = 0·09–1·0; maximum per mite = 1–5) with micro-filarial densities of 1000–3000 per mm^3. This suggested that in certain circumstances of repeated reinfection considerable numbers of circulating microfilariae may be abnormal and incapable of developing in the vector. So far, however, such low infectivity of dense microfilaraemias has not been confirmed with laboratory-induced superinfections.

Cotton rats exposed to heavy continuous transmission may die off quickly, particularly infant and young rats. Williams (1948) indicates that, in nature, infected cotton rats seem less fit than uninfected cotton rats. Bertram (1953a, 1958) records how cotton rats at continuous risk to reinfection for weeks and months in the laboratory (e.g. those of Fig. 21) or to frequent long periods of reinfection (e.g. those of Figs. 19 and 20) were thin, 79–117 g as compared to weights of up to 220 g for lightly infected and uninfected cotton rats of similar age and sex. They would sit hunched with fur raised on top of their wool nests, an unusual attitude suggestive of pyrexia, for as long as several weeks before autopsy. It seems improbable that such animals could survive in the wild. The cotton rat of Fig. 18, likewise, was latterly in poor condition, trembling and with shallow respiration. In contrast, none of the superinfected cotton rats exposed to less prolonged transmissions (Figs. 10, 12–16) had weights or clinical condition at autopsy notably abnormal, even though adult worm infections and microfilaraemias were, in some of these, very heavy. The pathology and clinical consequences of different types of superinfection stand in need of more intensive investigation, but it seems that the filarial worm, *L. carinii*, is not so innocuous for the cotton rat as is often supposed and that it is pathogenic for the host if sufficiently heavy continuous transmission prevails.

XIV. CONCLUSIONS

From laboratory investigations of primary infections and superinfections of the filarial worm, *L. carinii*, in cotton rats, several mechanisms appear to come into play to maintain in a cotton rat community microfilaraemias consistent with efficient transmission even though the animals of the community may be subject, as must happen in the fluctuant complexities of their natural environment, to reinfection varying from time to time within a wide range of possibilities from slight, when transmission is infrequent and light, to severe when transmission is continuous and heavy.

First, increasing worm numbers in the preferred site of parasitization, the pleural cavity, lead to inhibited growth of and lesser microfilarial output by the adult worms (Figs. 9 and 10), but the trend towards inadequate micro-filaraemia which this may cause is counteracted by secondary parasitization of the peritoneal cavity in which worms mature and reproduce more successfully to augment the microfilaraemia (Figs. 11, 13–15). This happens for both primary and subsequent reinfections. In the case of reinfections, an immune response by the already infected host also imposes a retardation in the growth and development of new populations of worms, particularly in the pleural cavity, and may also diminish the proportion of infective larvae in reinfections which succeed in reaching any coelomic cavity. Provided transmission is intermittent and infrequent (Figs. 12–16), successive populations of worms in the pleural or peritoneal cavity mature, however, to fecundity and produce microfilariae to maintain, or augment, an existing microfilaraemia which may be of several hundred or more microfilariae per mm³. The density of an existing microfilaraemia is, however, subject to some suppression while re-infection is happening and during the 50 days or so while a new worm population is maturing to fecundity. This results in a microfilaraemia, under circumstances of infrequent intermittent transmission, being held in check periodically by each successive exposure to reinfection. But as the suppression due to each transmission episode relaxes, the microfilaraemia tends to increase again and a high and slowly rising microfilarial density can persist indefinitely in such circumstances (Fig. 16). Older worms die and become encapsulated as a cotton rat grows older, but its adult worm infection is periodically re-plenished by the new worms of the successive populations transmitted in reinfections and these, albeit stunted in development, maintain the micro-filaraemia. Thus, slowly, there can be a gradual change, or turnover, from old to younger worms throughout the life-span of the cotton rat, so that the animal remains an adequate or good source of microfilariae, ensuring that transmission of the parasite continues to be possible through the vector.

The prospects of this are less if frequency of reinfection increases such that reinfections recur before the most recent worm population has had oppor-tunity to reproduce and contribute microfilariae to the blood-stream. When this happens, as well as generalized suppression of the existing blood infection while reinfections are taking place and maturing, productive pleural, and even peritoneal, worms may fail to maintain a high, or ultimately any, micro-filaraemia (Figs. 17–20). Failure in transmission would, however, then be prevented from proceeding to its extreme evolution by a corresponding trend towards a period again of more intermittent and lighter transmission as sources of mite infection became less abundant and the positive rats infected the vector rather less heavily than they did in their preceding phase of high microfilaraemia.

Cotton rats exposed from their first infection onwards to intensively con-tinuous reinfections are affected rather differently (Fig. 21). Judging from the relatively light pleural infections, and seldom peritoneal infections, found in animals with histories of this kind, a particularly high proportion of infective larvae die off in the early migratory or developmental phase. Of those which do begin to develop in the pleural cavity, the first few may attain normal growth, but others are severely retarded by the intensified immune response of the host; reproduction may be sparse in amount or curtailed in time for all worms in such superinfections. Microfilaraemia is consequently very low and likely to be of brief duration. Intensive superinfection of this order is patho-genic and likely to lead to the premature death of these ineffectual hosts.

The ebb and flow of transmission is less influenced by infection levels in the vector-mite, but rapid destruction of most microfilariae in the gut of the vector and, when very heavily infected, delayed development of some micro-filariae help to reduce the probability for the cotton rat of lethally intense superinfection, or of reinfection sufficiently severe to eliminate, or prevent, a microfilarial infection of the blood-stream.

The variability of the equilibrium which a cotton rat is capable of maintaining with its filarial parasite, both as an adult worm infection and as a microfilaraemia, and particularly the sensitivity of the microfilaraemia to changes in incident transmission, together with the capacity of the vector for efficient transmission whether feeding on low or high microfilarial infections, are adaptations of this parasitic system well suited to perpetuate an overall incidence of infection in the cotton rat community, in the transmissible form of the microfilaraemia, sufficing to ensure continuing transmission of the parasite despite such fluctuations as may occur seasonally, or for other reasons, in host–vector contact in the natural environment. The consequences of this highly adaptable host–parasite equilibrium for the sensitivity of immuno-logical tests, and on their meaning and interpretation, deserve careful experimental study in terms of the mathematical concepts underlying helminthic diseases and their immunological expression as recently propounded by Elsdon-Dew (1965).

In conclusion, a few comparisons with other experimental filarial models, and some wider implications from this synthesis of cotton rat filariasis, may be briefly considered.

It is well known, especially for the filariae affecting man and domesticated animals, that different species of filarial worm have specific predilections as adult worms for particular tissue systems of the host they parasitize and, also, that while the microfilariae of many species circulate in the blood-stream their location for others, as in onchocerciasis, is in the skin. It is hardly to be expected that host–parasite relationships in cotton rat filariasis could be precisely applicable to other species of parasite in other hosts. Nevertheless, the present synthesis of researches with cotton rat filariasis has led to some understanding of how the cotton rat is able to cope with the considerable amount of transmission and reinfection which it may recurringly experience in the wild during a life-span of at least two or three years, and exactly this problem must confront the host of any filarial species in nature. Passage through the vector, whatever kind of arthropod it may be, must filter off some of the potential burden of superinfection by selective development of limited numbers of ingested microfilariae, or deaths amongst the vector from heavy infection, while mortality from adverse environmental conditions, besides abnormal feeding or flight behaviour, possibly vision defects, from patho-logical effects of developing worms within the vector may well be concerned from time to time in reducing the total impact of transmission which the vertebrate host is called upon to absorb (Lavoipierre, 1958a, b). We are more concerned for the moment with mechanisms which come into play within the vertebrate host.

Of several experimental filarial models, other than cotton rat filariasis, now available, e.g. mosquito-borne filariases in cats (Edeson and Wharton, 1957, 1958; Nelson et al., 1962), in dogs (Webber and Hawking, 1955) and in monkeys (Hawking and Webber, 1955) or *Chrysops*-transmitted loiasis in mandrill monkeys (Duke, 1960a, b), most have been studied as primary infections. Occasionally, reinfections are given with the hope of ensuring successful development of a microfilarial infection in the blood-stream. However, purposeful experiments on the effects of recurring reinfection on the microfilaraemia of loiasis in mandrills have also been carried out by Duke (1960a). Reinfections on three occasions at intervals about, or rather longer than, the incubation period before a primary infection would produce a microfilaraemia, are shown to cause a slight and transient increase in circulating microfilariae. In contrast to the cotton rat infection, the spleen of the drill in loiasis is active in removing microfilariae from the circulation (Duke, 1960b) and, indeed, in the first place, reduces the considerable initial microfilarial peak of a primary infection to a very low level, the "suppressed" infection. This splenic mechanism also checks and suppresses the increases of microfilaraemia resultant from new populations of adult worms of reinfections, so that a microfilaraemia tends to remain at a level in the reinfected host as low as, or only slightly higher than, that which would have prevailed in the "suppressed" condition of the unmodified primary infection. Thus, substantial suppression of a microfilaraemia as a means of curbing the hazard to a host community of excessive transmissions is well proven experimentally for two quite different filarial models, although the exact manner by which this comes about is not identical for the two systems.

It has yet to be shown with models of mosquito-borne filariases that microfilaraemias are suppressed by reinfections. One cat exposed to five transmissions of *Brugia malayi* at monthly intervals amounting to 285 infective larvae (Edeson and Wharton, 1958) developed a microfilaraemia 81 days later, rising rapidly and much higher than year-long blood infections in other cats which were exposed once only. This cat received considerably more larvae than those with primary infections and a direct numerical relationship may be a valid explanation. It may be possible, however, in mosquito-borne filariases of this kind that a predilection of adult worms to develop in relatively small foci like lymph glands could incur retardation of their growth and productivity, as observed in heavy pleural infections of the cotton rat filaria, and that the main, or sole, contribution to the microfilaraemia would be from a few worms which happened to develop in one, or more, other situations in the lymphatics where parasitization happened to be light. But we do not know what the distribution was of adult worms for this superinfected cat, nor the numbers of worms recovered, so that this concept remains conjectural. A variable distribution of worms of this nature may, however, account for the experience of other workers (Laurence and Pester, personal communication) who, with *Br. patei*, a natural infection in dogs in East Africa, found that 7% of twenty-nine cats failed, after experimental transmissions in a London laboratory, to develop a microfilaraemia although inocula were from 66–116 infective larvae (mean = 99) per cat as against comparable transmissions of 14–250 larvae (mean = 88) per cat in the animals which successfully developed a microfilaraemia. It is conceivable that the unsuccessful infections resulted from a chance localization of all larvae in one lymphatic gland, or similar limited situation in the lymphatics, with severe inhibition of their development, while in the positive animals at least some worms developed adequately in less heavily parasitized situations. It is bound to be very difficult in such relatively large hosts to find worms in the lymphatics weeks or months after one or more exposures; few data of this sort are available. But it may well be, if intensive suppression in heavily infected localized sites is, in fact, a reality in this type of filariasis, that many infective larvae fail to develop enough, or survive long enough, to be recognizable, or indeed exist, at subsequent autopsy, and only those are found as developed worms which were fortunate in developing in a less competitive situation. This interpretation has yet to be proved. It is suggested here as an indication of a possible explanation for puzzling results arising during the practical management of this type of experimental filarial infection. If valid, control of the level of microfilaraemia to be induced in the experimental host could be extremely difficult. Further clarification of the problem could come from a series of primary infections ranging from a few to numerous infective larvae.

Finally, it is seen that not only the amount but the frequency of reinfection markedly affects the host–parasite equilibrium in the cotton rat model, and this must have its counterpart in nature for any filarial species, whether a parasite of man or other vertebrate, depending on seasonal or other factors which cause host–vector contact to be perennial or intermittent. It is, of course, important to determine quantitatively the characteristics of the primary infection of any experimental filaria, but the wider problem of the influence of superinfection on host–parasite relationships and all that may stem from this in terms of pathological conditions, clinical sequelae and immunological manifestations of infection must surely also be an important, if not essential, facet for the future progress of experimental filariasis and for its application to the understanding of the epidemiology of human filariases and the chronic ill health and incapacitation which, in its several forms, it causes mankind in tropical territories widely throughout the world.

REFERENCES

Bell, S. D., and Brown, H. W. (1945). *Am. J. trop. Med.* **25**, 137.
Bertram, D. S. (1947). *Ann. trop. Med. Parasit.* **41**, 253.
Bertram, D. S. (1949). *Ann. trop. Med. Parasit.* **43**, 313.
Bertram, D. S. (1950a). *Ann. trop. Med. Parasit.* **44**, 55.
Bertram, D. S. (1950b). *Ann. trop. Med. Parasit.* **44**, 107.
Bertram, D. S. (1953a). *Trans. R. Soc. trop. Med. Hyg.* **47**, 85.
Bertram, D. S. (1953b). *Ann. trop. Med. Parasit.* **47**, 371.
Bertram, D. S. (1957). *In* "Biological Aspects of the Transmission of Disease", pp. 113–122. Institute of Biology. Oliver and Boyd, Edinburgh and London.
Bertram, D. S. (1958). *Proc. VIth int. Congr. trop. Med. Malar.*, Lisbon, **2**, 437.
Bertram, D. S., Unsworth, K., and Gordon, R. M. (1946). *Ann. trop. Med. Parasit.* **40**, 228.
Briggs, T. N. (1957). *Am. J. trop. Med. Hyg.* **6**, 387.
Briggs, T. N. (1963). *J. Parasit.* **49**, 225.

Chabaud, A. G. (1954). *Ann. Parasit.* **29**, 42, 206 and 358.
Chabaud, A. G., and Anderson, R. C. (1959). *Ann. Parasit.* **34**, 64.
Cross, J. B., and Scott, J. A. (1947). *Trans. Am. microsc. Soc.* **66**, 1.
Culbertson, J. T., and Rose, H. M. (1944). *Science, N.Y.* **99**, 245.
Duke, B. O. L. (1956). *Ann. trop. Med. Parasit.* **50**, 32.
Duke, B. O. L. (1960a). *Ann. trop. Med. Parasit.* **54**, 15.
Duke, B. O. L. (1960b). *Ann. trop. Med. Parasit.* **54**, 141.
Duke, B. O. L. (1962a). *Ann. trop. Med. Parasit.* **56**, 130.
Duke, B. O. L. (1962b). *Ann. trop. Med. Parasit.* **56**, 255.
Edeson, J. F. B., and Wharton, R. H. (1957). *Trans. R. Soc. trop. Med. Hyg.* **51**, 366.
Edeson, J. F. B., and Wharton, R. H. (1958). *Trans. R. Soc. trop. Med. Hyg.* **52**, 25.
Elsdon-Dew, R. (1965). *Nature, Lond.* **208**, 696.
Freer, P. (1953). *Ann. trop. Med. Parasit.* **47**, 13.
Hawking, F. (1954). *Ann. trop. Med. Parasit.* **48**, 382.
Hawking, F. (1962). *Ann. trop. Med. Parasit.* **56**, 168.
Hawking, F., and Burroughs, A. M. (1946). *Nature, Lond.* **158**, 98.
Hawking, F., and Sewell, P. (1948). *Br. J. Pharmac. Chemother.* **3**, 285.
Hawking, F., and Webber, W. A. F. (1955). *Parasitology* **45**, 378.
Hawking, F., and Worms, M. J. (1961). *A. Rev. Ent.* **6**, 413.
Hawking, F., Sewell, P., and Thurston, J. P. (1950). *Br. J. Pharmac. Chemother.* **5**, 217.
Hughes, T. E. (1950). *Ann. trop. Med. Parasit.* **44**, 285.
Irwin, J. O. (1963). *Jl R. statist. Soc.* **126**, 1.
Kershaw, W. E. (1948). *Ann. trop. Med. Parasit.* **42**, 377.
Kershaw, W. E. (1949a). *Ann. trop. Med. Parasit.* **43**, 96.
Kershaw, W. E. (1949b). *Ann. trop. Med. Parasit.* **43**, 238.
Kershaw, W. E. (1953). *Ann. trop. Med. Parasit.* **47**, 68.
Kershaw, W. E., and Bertram, D. S. (1948). *Nature, Lond.* **162**, 149.
Kershaw, W. E., and Duke, B. O. L. (1954). *Ann. trop. Med. Parasit.* **48**, 340.
Kershaw, W. E., Lavoipierre, M. M. J., and Chalmers, T. A. (1953). *Ann. trop. Med. Parasit.* **47**, 207.
Kershaw, W. E., Chalmers, T. A., and Duke, B. O. L. (1954). *Ann. trop. Med. Parasit.* **48**, 329.
Kershaw, W. E., Lavoipierre, M. M. J., and Beesley, W. N. (1955). *Ann. trop. Med. Parasit.* **49**, 203.
Lavoipierre, M. M. J. (1958a). *Ann. trop. Med. Parasit.* **52**, 103.
Lavoipierre, M. M. J. (1958b). *Ann. trop. Med. Parasit.* **52**, 326.
Macdonald, E. M., and Scott, J. A. (1953). *Expl Parasit.* **2**, 174.
Macdonald, E. M., and Scott, J. A. (1958). *Am. J. trop. Med. Hyg.* **7**, 419.
Macdonald, W. W. (1962a). *Ann. trop. Med. Parasit.* **56**, 368.
Macdonald, W. W. (1962b). *Ann. trop. Med. Parasit.* **56**, 373.
Macdonald, W. W., and Ramachandran, C. P. (1965). *Ann. trop. Med. Parasit.* **59**, 64.
Macdonald, W. W., and Sheppard, P. M. (1965). *Ann. trop. Med. Parasit.* **59**, 74.
McFadzean, J. A. (1953). *Am. J. trop. Med. Hyg.* **2**, 85.
McFadzean, J. A., and Smiles, J. (1956). *J. Helminth.* **30**, 25.
Nelson, G. S. (1964). *In* "Host–Parasite Relationship in Invertebrate Hosts", pp. 75–119. Blackwell, Oxford.
Nelson, G. S., Heisch, R. B., and Furlong, M. (1962). *Trans. R. Soc. trop. Med. Hyg.* **56**, 201.
Nicholas, W. L., and Kershaw, W. E. (1954). *Ann. trop. Med. Parasit.* **48**, 201.
Niles, W. J., Fernando, M. A., and Dissanaike, A. S. (1965). *Nature, Lond.* **205**, 411.
Olson, L. J. (1959a). *J. Parasit.* **45**, 182.

Olson, L. J. (1959b). *J. Parasit.* **45**, 519.

Ramakrishnan, S. P., Singh, D., and Krishnaswani, A. K. (1962). *Indian J. Malar.* **16**, 263.

Scott, J. A. (1946). *J. Parasit.* **32**, 570.

Scott, J. A. (1947). *Science, N.Y.* **105**, 437.

Scott, J. A. (1948). *Am. J. trop. Med.* **28**, 481.

Scott, J. A. (1952). *J. Parasit.* **38** (Suppl.), 18.

Scott, J. A. (1958). *Proc. VIth int. Congr. trop. Med. Malar.*, Lisbon, **2**, 401.

Scott, J. A., and Cross, J. B. (1946). *Am. J. trop. Med.* **26**, 849.

Scott, J. A., and Macdonald, E. M. (1953). *Expl Parasit.* **2**, 129.

Scott, J. A., and Macdonald, E. M. (1956). *J. Parasit.* **42** (Suppl.), 16.

Scott, J. A., and Macdonald, E. M. (1958). *J. Parasit.* **44**, 187.

Scott, J. A., Sisley, N. M., and Stembridge, V. A. (1946). *J. Parasit.* **32** (Suppl.), 17.

Scott, J. A., Stembridge, V. A., and Sisley, N. M. (1947). *J. Parasit.* **33**, 138.

Scott, J. A., Macdonald, E. M., and Terman, B. (1951). *J. Parasit.* **37**, 425.

Scott, J. A., Macdonald, E. M., and Olson, L. J. (1956). *Am. J. trop. Med. Hyg.* **5**, 380.

Scott, J. A., Macdonald, E. M., and Olson, L. J. (1957). *Expl Parasit.* **6**, 594.

Scott, J. A., Macdonald, E. M., and Olson, L. J. (1958a). *Am. J. trop. Med. Hyg.* **7**, 70.

Scott, J. A., Macdonald, E. M., and Olson, L. J. (1958b). *Expl Parasit.* **7**, 418.

Scott, J. A., Macdonald, E. M., and Olson, L. J. (1958c). *J. Parasit.* **44**, 507.

Singh, D., and Raghavan, N. G. S. (1962). *Indian J. Malar.* **16**, 193.

Taylor, A. E. R. (1960). *Trans. R. Soc. trop. Med. Hyg.* **54**, 450.

Vaz, Z. (1934). *Ann. trop. Med. Parasit.* **28**, 143.

Webber, W. A. F. (1954a). *Ann. trop. Med. Parasit.* **48**, 367.

Webber, W. A. F. (1954b). *Ann. trop. Med. Parasit.* **48**, 375.

Webber, W. A. F., and Hawking, F. (1955). *Expl Parasit.* **4**, 143.

Westbrook, M. G., and Scott, J. A. (1955). *Tex. Rep. Biol. Med.* **13**, 537.

Wharton, D. R. A. (1947). *J. infect. Dis.* **80**, 307.

Williams, R. W. (1946). *J. Parasit.* **32**, 252.

Williams, R. W. (1948). *J. Parasit.* **34**, 24.

Williams, R. W., and Brown, H. W. (1945). *Science, N.Y.* **102**, 482.

Williams, R. W., and Brown, H. W. (1946). *Science, N.Y.* **103**, 224.

Williams, P., and Kershaw, W. E. (1961). *Ann. trop. Med. Parasit.* **55**, 217.

Zein-Eldin, E. A. (1965). *Tex. Rep. Biol. Med.* **23**, 530.

Some Tissue Reactions to the Nematode Parasites of Animals

D. POYNTER

Research Division, Allen and Hanburys Ltd, Ware, Herts, England

I. INTRODUCTION

The tissue reactions to nematode parasites have probably not been studied as extensively as the reactions to other infective agents. Many parasitologists have no facilities for histological examinations and many pathologists are not concerned with worms. The subject is in a state where the purely descriptive stage is giving way to one where the lesions are gradually being appreciated and the pathogenesis of some of the diseases understood. This is sometimes due to the fact that workers from different disciplines are associated together on definite topics and consequently provide much fertile stimulation each to the other.

An attempt is made here to deal with the nematodes under the main organs they infect, but no apology is made in also discussing other aspects of the pathology of a given nematode under its initial heading. The account is concerned primarily with domestic animals. A glance at the references will show that much has been contributed during the last few years; although an effort has been made to cover the important works, this account does not pretend to be exhaustive and no attempt has been made to deal with changes in the blood.

II. GASTROINTESTINAL NEMATODES

During the past ten years the reactions of the alimentary tract to nematode parasites have been more closely studied, and our appreciation of the lesions concerned and their significance is gradually being rationalized. One interesting recent observation is that various nematode infections of the small intestine may result in the appearance of a typical malabsorption syndrome such as is seen in non-tropical sprue or idiopathic steatorrhoea.

Sheehy *et al.* (1962), in a paper on hookworm disease (*Necator americanus*) and malabsorption, described the appearance of intestinal biopsies taken from patients. The villi of the jejunum were usually shorter and broader than normal, with widening club-like tips. The natural convolutions of the sides were lost, the columnar cells were frequently disorientated, but nuclei were well preserved and the brush border seldom broken. Vacuolation of the columnar cells was sometimes apparent, but none of the biopsies showed obliteration of the glands. These epithelial changes were apparently secondary to the inflammation of the underlying lamina propria as denoted by marked infiltration with lymphocytes and polymorphs, with some eosinophils, mononuclear cells and plasma cells. In several specimens the lamina propria was denser than normal and a fibrous proliferation was present. However, oedema was not a prominent finding. Mild to moderate thinning of the zone containing the crypts of Lieberkühn was seen, indicating mild mucosal atrophy.

Some thirty years ago Porter (1935) and Taliaferro and Sarles (1939) described the jejunal pathology of *Nippostrongylus brasiliensis* infections in detail. Lately, Symons and Fairbairn (1963) gave a comprehensive account of the biochemical pathology of the jejunum of rats parasitized by *N. brasiliensis*. The jejunum was greatly enlarged as a result of mucosal hyperplasia and hypertrophy of the muscularis externa. The lumen was filled with much fluid, as had already been reported by Symons (1957). The extent of the histopathological changes depended upon the severity of the infection, which varied from one animal to another. In the 10-day infection, the villi were short, irregularly shaped and fused with one another and there was marked hyperplasia of the lamina propria. The brush borders stained normally with periodic acid–Schiff (PAS). In severe infections the changes were intensified and some of the villi disappeared, the crypts becoming abnormally deep. In these cases the brush borders of the epithelial cells were thin and stained poorly or not at all with PAS. In places the epithelial cells were cuboidal rather than columnar, but these formed a continuous sheet except where occasionally interrupted as a result of acute inflammation. There were also indications of an increase in the number of mitotic figures in the crypt cells and the general picture was that of a malabsorption syndrome.

At 5 days the histopathological changes were slight, although at this time the parasites were nearly mature. There was some oedema, but PAS sections showed the brush borders to be unaffected by the disease. Hyperaemic changes were seen in the villi. At 21 days the configuration of the villi was again essentially normal, but there was still some enlargement of the jejunum with some hyperplasia and oedema. The gross hypertrophy of the muscularis externa remained.

The malabsorption syndrome is also seen in the experimental infection of guinea-pigs with the larvae of the sheep nematode *Trichostrongylus colubriformis* (Fig. 1A). In these infections the glands of the small intestine may become cystic (Fig. 1B, C) and dilate into the submucosa.

At present it is generally held that there is a continuous replacement of the intestinal epithelium and that the absorptive cells have their origin in the crypts from which they migrate up the villi, being extruded at the tip. Whilst undergoing migration the cells become differentiated. The absorption of fat seems greatest in the oldest cells. Amino acids and sugars are in greatest concentrations in cells in the upper third of the villus. Padykula (1962) has shown that there is much support for the concept of a progressive differentiation of epithelial cells as they migrate upwards. In non-tropical sprue it seems as though the major part of the intervillus is lined by epithelial cells normally found in the crypts. The cause of non-tropical sprue is unknown, but a constant feature is the presence of a chronic inflammatory process in the lamina propria (Ashworth and Chears, 1962) and such inflammation is known in gastrointestinal nematodiasis.

Gardiner and Fraser (1960) investigated a severe outbreak of hookworm disease in a kennel of hounds in south-west Australia. The livers of infected dogs showed mild centrilobular fibrosis and deposition of reticulin. There was an intense proliferation of Kupfer cells which were packed with haemosiderin granules and there was also some haemosiderosis of the hepatic cells. Haemosiderin was present in the reticulum of the sinuses of the mesenteric lymph nodes and there was a marked increase in the number of plasma cells. A moderate congestion of the kidneys was seen and the macroscopic subcapsular foci seen on post-mortem examination were found to consist of lymphocytes, fibroblasts and numerous plasma cells. The most significant renal lesions were seen in the glomeruli, in which many basement membranes of the capillary tufts were thickened with extensions to the capsule of Bowman. Albuminous material often filled the spaces of Bowman and the tubular lamina. There was desquamation of cells in the proximal convoluted tubules and this was associated with cellular regeneration. The small intestine was markedly damaged. There were focal areas of fibroblasts and round cells in the lamina propria in which the normal mucosa was altered or destroyed. The lamina was heavily infiltrated with lymphocytes and plasma cells and the mucosal surface was covered with mucin containing desquamated epithelium, cellular debris and the cross-sections of parasites. The species concerned with this outbreak were *Uncinaria stenocephala* and *Ancylostoma caninum*. The authors consider that the continued activity of these hunting dogs during a period of steady depletion of blood produced a state of relative anoxia in the liver and kidney with the development of the lesions seen. The haemosiderosis was produced by accumulation of hepatic iron under conditions characterized by chronic protein depletion within both the reticulo-endothelial cells and the hepatic cells.

Gibbs (1958), working with *Uncinaria stenocephala* in puppies, found only small amounts of haemorrhage at the point of attachment of the adult worm. In the lungs the larvae evoked a polymorph rather than an eosinophilic reaction. The worms were not as effective blood suckers as *Ancylostoma*

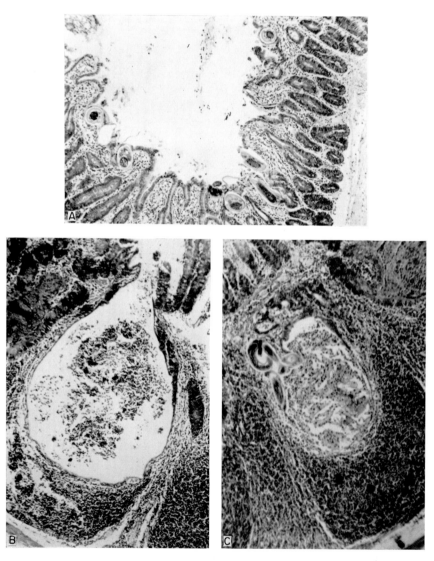

FIG. 1. *Trichostrongylus colubriformis* in the small intestine of the guinea-pig. A, Stunting and fusion of villi, such as occurs in the malabsorption syndrome. B, Reaction; the glands are now cystic and dilated into the submucosa. C, Larva in a dilated mucus-producing gland near a Peyer's patch.

caninum. The inflammatory response Gibbs found in the skin and lungs was marked, and he thought it might possibly be due to a secondary bacterial infection.

Turner (1959) found that in experimental strongyloidiasis in sheep and goats the tissue damage was usually confined to severe enteritis with fluid catarrhal exudate, leucocytic infiltration and oedema of the duodenum and jejunum. The adults and larvae did not penetrate beyond the muscularis mucosa.

Turner *et al.* (1960) studied the migration of *Strongyloides papillosus* in lambs and the pathological changes which followed percutaneous infection. Larvae were placed on the skin of susceptible lambs in doses of 25000 and biopsies were performed at varying intervals of time. Similar observations were made on resistant lambs. No dermatitis was found in susceptible lambs which were exposed to single infections, and larval penetration occurred within 15 min, but was not seen to involve the lymph channels. After 24 h there was some neutrophilia in the vicinity of invading larvae, but tissue destruction was negligible. In immune lambs a slight erythema resulted after the fourth exposure and a pustular erythematous dermatitis developed after the fifth and subsequent exposures. After eleven exposures, active phagocytosis of the larvae was seen. The inflammatory reaction consisted of a fluid exudate and infiltration of the tissue with eosinophils, neutrophils, lymphocytes and giant cells. Nearly every larva was surrounded by such cells. In the highly immune animal the intense inflammatory reaction in the dermis was destroying most if not all of the larvae observed therein.

Using doses of approximately 2 million infective larvae, it was found that they could be recovered from the circulating blood 12–72 h after infection. Maximum numbers were found 12 h after infection, the highest concentration of larvae being seen in the jugular vein.

No worms were recovered from the heart, liver, kidney, spleen, gall-bladder, urinary bladder or spinal cord. Worms were, however, found in the gracilis muscle, the loin muscle, diaphragm, lungs, trachea, oesophagus, abdominal cavity, pleural cavity and in the contents of the abomasum and small intestine. On one occasion one worm was found in the pericardial sac.

The first pathological changes were seen in the lungs of a lamb killed 48 h after infection. A slight haemorrhage and some oedema of the upper portion of the apical and diaphragmatic lobes was seen. Sixty-eight hours after infection petechial haemorrhages were concentrated in the upper portion of the left lung. Eighty-eight hours after infection many subpleural, petechial and ecchymotic haemorrhages were present over the surfaces of both lungs. Maximum lung haemorrhage was seen 113 h after infection. Only scattered petechiae were seen 9 days after infection and 15 days after infection the lungs appeared normal.

No severe damage was noticed in the small intestine during the first 15 days. The general aspects of the pathological changes in the intestine in patent infections were extensive erosion of the mucosa of the small intestine with oedema and leucocytic infiltration. Parasites were present deep in the intestinal glands, but there was no penetration of the muscularis mucosa.

This study showed that larvae were able to penetrate the skin or enter the host through the epithelial tissues of the sebaceous glands and hair follicles. The larvae traversed the epidermis and underlying components perpendicularly and took advantage of the sebaceous glands and the hair follicles in entering the subcutis. Oshio and Furata (1955) made similar observations in respect of *S. ransomi*. Oshio (1956) reported that *S. stercoralis* and *S. ransomi* utilized the lymphatics as well as the blood vessels in the migration, but Turner and his colleagues did not find *S. papillosus* in the lymph channels of the skin of their lambs.

In general the larvae of *S. papillosus* in the numbers employed caused little reaction in the skin of susceptible lambs. Oshio and Furata (1955) also found little damage in the pigs they exposed to *S. ransomi*. Tomita (1941), however, noted that vesicles appeared on human skin after the application of *S. papillosus* larvae. Man is not normally a host of *S. papillosus* and this may account for the difference in reaction. After repeated infections, pustular dermatitis and intense inflammatory reactions occurred in the skin, representing a defence mechanism.

Goldgraber and Lewert (1965) carried out some experiments in mice using *Strongyloides ratti*. Mice were rendered immune by repeatedly injecting them with filariform larvae and other mice were used as controls. The authors were particularly interested in mast cells and in the possibility that these cells degranulate more in the sensitized than in the unsensitized animal, when meeting the appropriate antigen. In observations on connective tissue it was found that the percentage of degranulating cells in sensitized mice stimulated with *S. ratti* antigens was appreciably increased.

Several workers have investigated the pathological effects of *Trichostrongylus axei* in a variety of hosts. Leland *et al.* (1959) used larvae of equine origin to infect calves. The LD_{50}, i.e. the dose required to kill 50% of the animals receiving it, was about 500000. The calves were in extremely poor condition, with little body fat and breakdown of omental fat. In acute fatal cases the abomasal mucosa showed hyperaemia with scattered flecks of necrotic debris adherent to the surface. The more chronic abomasal response showed that a thick layer of cells, debris and necrotic material covered the mucosa to form a diphtheritic membrane.

In the horse Leland *et al.* (1961) found that the pathology of the stomach lesion began with hyperaemia which progressed to lymphocytic and catarrhal inflammation, necrosis, erosion of the mucus epithelium and thence to chronic proliferative inflammation. An eosinophilia of the gastric mucosa occurred.

Leland (1963), using *Trichostrongylus axei* in Mongolian gerbils, produced similar gastroduodenal lesions to those seen in rabbits, ruminants and horses. These commenced as hyperaemia with a progression to catarrhal inflammation, necrosis and chronic proliferative inflammation.

In sheep Leland *et al.* (1960), using 50000 *T. axei* larvae per host produced scattered, mildly hyperaemic areas in the abomasum. With doses of 250000 or more the lesions progressed to erosion of the mucosa, and in one case ringworm-like lesions similar to those already seen in horses were noted. There was an infiltration of the abomasal mucosa and submucosa with lymphocytes. At very high doses (50000 or more) the omental fat was hard, dull, gritty and leathery and gave the general appearance of extensive dehydration. At this level fatty degeneration of the liver was reported, but this may have been related to the typical fatty change seen in the liver during anorexia.

Kates and Turner (1960) also infected lambs with *T. axei* and reviewed recent research on the disease in ruminants. Working with larval administrations of 50000–500000, it was found that the parasite produced enlargement, oedema and hyperaemia of the abomasum and duodenum. The obvious histological changes were localized in the abomasum and, to a variable extent, in the duodenum. These were similar to those reported by Doran (1955) in calves. Sections of the affected areas of abomasum and duodenum showed ample erosion of the superficial mucosa, oedema in the submucosa and muscle layers, variable small ulcerated areas in the mucosa, hyperaemia and considerable cellular infiltration, which was mainly lymphocytic, in the mucosa.

Tromba and Douvres (1958) infected swine with *Trichostrongylus colubriformis* and found that even with doses above 1 million, the pathological changes associated with the parasite were relatively slight.

The changes in the alimentary tract of the sheep undergoing self-cure from *Haemonchus contortus* and *Trichostrongylus axei* were studied by Stewart (1953). During self-cure the abomasum showed oedema of the mucosa. The superficial epithelial cells were swollen and in some preparations a superficial aggregation of eosinophilic cells was also present. There did not seem to be an increased secretion of mucin and the oedematous changes were paralleled by rises in the blood histamine concentration.

During the last few years attention has been given to the pathological changes associated with infections of cattle and sheep with species of the genus *Ostertagia*. In cattle the nematode *Ostertagia ostertagi* is a common cause of parasitic gastritis. Ross (1963) found that a previous infection was necessary to produce severe lesions in the abomasum. He noted severe inflammation of the abomasum as well as reactions in the duodenum which he believed might be concerned with the intermittent scouring associated with the disease. Ross and Dow (1965a) provided an account of field and experimental infections with the nematode in which they described the abomasal changes. The mucosa of the fundus was thickened and mucoid metaplasia was apparent, especially around dilated glands which had been, or still were, occupied by *Ostertagia* larvae. The epithelium lining the glands occupied by larvae was of the mucin-secreting type and ranged from cuboidal to columnar. Cystic glands vacated by larvae tended to persist as nodules of hyperplastic acinar structures. Peptic cells were absent in areas of mucoid metaplasia. Larvae within dilated glands provoked little infiltration of the surrounding mucosa by inflammatory cells. Submucosal oedema was consistently present at least to some degree. Similar changes were also seen in the pyloric mucosa. Ross and Dow (1965b) went on to study the development of the abomasal lesions in calves experimentally infected with *O. ostertagi*. Using single infections of 100000 larvae, they found that after 1 week discrete white nodules containing fourth-stage larvae covered the entire mucosa. By the 2nd week the nodules had coalesced, but the larval cysts were considerably enlarged and the glands showed mucoid metaplasia with a loss of parietal and zymogen cells. During weeks 2–8 the larvae left the mucosa and the nodules disappeared, but the glandular metaplasia persisted.

Anderson *et al.* (1965) observed outbreaks of parasitic gastroenteritis in the west of Scotland, where *O. ostertagi* was the predominant parasite. They divided the disease into three phases, two of which (types I and II) were clinically apparent. The type I disease corresponded to the classical description of clinical parasitic gastritis and was associated with the vast majority of ingested larvae developing to maturity in the expected period of 3 weeks. Pre-type II was clinically non-apparent and about 80 % of the larvae were then inhibited in the early fourth stage. When these larvae eventually matured, even 6 months later, they caused the clinical condition characterized by weight loss and diarrhoea.

In the type I cases five main lesions were noted in the abomasum—nodules, diffuse irregular epithelial hyperplasia, epithelial cytolysis, oedema of the abomasal folds and congestion. The main pathological features of the pre-type II cases which show virtually complete inhibition are the minimal nature of the reaction to the larvae and the absence of gross damage to the mucosa. The inhibited fourth-stage larvae lie in glands and these become lined by mucous-type epithelium. There is almost no reaction in surrounding glands. In some cases lymphoreticular foci are found related to inhibited larvae. In other cases old "emerged" lesions are found, which consist of empty mucous cell-lined glands associated with a larval reaction in the lamina propria, consisting of lymphoreticular hyperplasia, plasma cell aggregates, eosinophil infiltration and the presence of globular leucocytes.

The type II disease develops as a result of the emergence of large numbers of previously inhibited larvae. Consequently, lesions of the inhibited phase are found together with lesions due to larval development and emergence. Nodules are produced as in type I and after emergence these are surrounded by areas of epithelial hyperplasia and lining of the glands by undifferentiated cells. Confluence of these leads to the "morocco leather" appearance. Epithelial cell sloughing over these areas can be marked and diphtheresis, superficial inflammation and congestion are apparent. Globular leucocytes are numerous and lymphoreticular and plasma cell activity may be marked. Typical lesions are shown in Fig. 2A–D.

The real pathogenic stage of the disease is associated with the emergence of larvae, when epithelial cell sloughing occurs and there is a conversion of surrounding functionally differentiated cells to undifferentiated cells. Confluence of the pits means that large areas of mucous membrane lose their specialized secretory function. When confluence is extensive, the pH rises and pepsinogen is not activated. It seems that the cell junctions and integrity of the epithelial sheet are seriously disturbed, so that pepsinogen can leak back into the blood and macromolecules leak out into the stomach. Mulligan *et al.* (1963) showed an increased plasma albumen loss into the gastrointestinal tract in this disease.

Further experiments on *O. ostertagi* in calves have been carried out by Ritchie *et al.* (1966), who investigated the parasitology and pathogenesis of a single infection. Using 100000 larvae, they found that even 2 days after infection the epithelium of a gland containing a larva had lost clarity of delineation of mucous, parietal and zymogen regions. By day 4 the lining was of the relatively undifferentiated cuboidal type and, where larvae did not directly touch, it was sometimes hyperplastic and was differentiating into mucous cells.

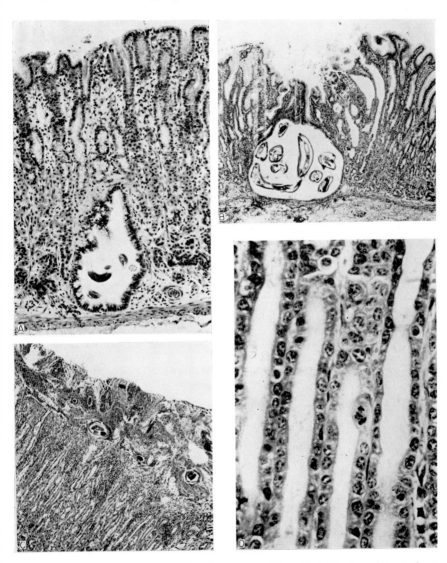

Fig. 2. *Ostertagia ostertagi* in the abomasum of the calf. A, Early nodule at about day 8. B, A pre-emergent nodule at about day 16. C, Epithelial cytolysis associated with the post-emergent stage. D, Cell conversion in non-parasitized glands, showing non-differentiation of the epithelial layer.

At day 21, when the fifth-stage larvae were emerging and there was a change in the lesion pattern, the coalescence of nodules and epithelial hyperplasia were responsible for the naked eye "morocco leather" or "crazy paving" effect. At this time there was also a cytolysis and sloughing of the superficial epithelial cells. By day 28, when emergence was almost complete, globular leucocytes became prominent, particularly between the epithelial cells in the superficial areas of the pits. On day 60 most of the epithelium had returned to its normal differentiation, although the glands which had formerly contained larvae were obvious because of their mucous cell lining. By day 90 the mucosa was almost normal, but globular leucocytes persisted and plasma cell foci remained.

During the course of the infection the abomasal lymph nodes showed the expected changes. After the 1st week there were reactive changes in the germinal centres which became marked by day 21, when many plasmocytes were seen packing the medullary cords.

Similar work was carried out on *Ostertagia circumcincta*, a parasite of sheep, by Armour *et al.* (1966), who first clarified the pathogenesis of this condition. The sequence of pathological changes was similar to that seen in calves. There was a stretching of parasitized glands due to the growth of the developing larvae together with epithelial hyperplasia and a replacement of the functional cells lining the gland by undifferentiated cells. A consequent elevation of abomasal pH and a leakage of pepsinogen into the plasma occurred. At day 16 of the infection a marked cytolytic reaction of the superficial epithelial cells occurred, leading to areas of mucosal sloughing which coincided with the loss of the adult worm population. By day 60 the lesions had regressed and abomasal function had returned to normal.

Changes in the glands surrounding that occupied by a larva occur, so that circular lesions are formed. These coalesce to produce a thickened undifferentiated epithelium lacking in secretory function which is also probably unable to prevent the leakage of large molecules between the cells as the junctional complexes are disturbed (Halliday *et al.*, 1966).

No work has yet been reported on the nature of the stimulus responsible for cell hyperplasia and the replacement by undifferentiated cells. Armour *et al.* (1966) suggested that the stimulus may be physically induced by the stretching of the gland or by a chemical product from the larva. The epithelial cytolysis, which is similar to that seen in *O. ostertagi* in the calf, is also of obscure origin, but might be related to an immune reaction associated with sensitized cells. The lymphoreticular reaction to *O. circumcincta* can be seen at 4 days, after which it becomes progressively more marked. This local immune reaction begins near glands containing larvae and in this region plasmoblasts and plasmocytes are present. Globular leucocytes were seen at 21 days infiltrating the epithelium of the superficial layer of the mucosa.

The work carried out on ovine and bovine ostergiasis has made it obvious that the foreign body giant cell granulomas often seen in the mucosa are produced by the abnormal break-out of larvae into the lamina propria instead of the lumen.

Cystic glands were also observed by Bogdanovich (1958), who infected rats with larvae of *Ascaris* spp. and found that the crypts of the glands of the intestinal mucosa underwent such a change. Oedema of the submucosa was also seen and once the larvae attained this layer they were surrounded by an abundant cellular infiltrate rich in eosinophils.

The reaction of the alimentary tract of the horse to invasion by nematodes is in many ways different from those reactions already discussed. Müller (1953) described the reactions in the intestines of horses infected with *Trichonema* spp. larvae, noting the encapsulation of larvae and an eosinophilic infiltration of the mucosa. Descriptions were also given by Poynter (1958). The infective larvae enter the epithelial cells and are soon encapsulated by the host reaction (Fig. 3A, B). There is little inflammatory response and as the

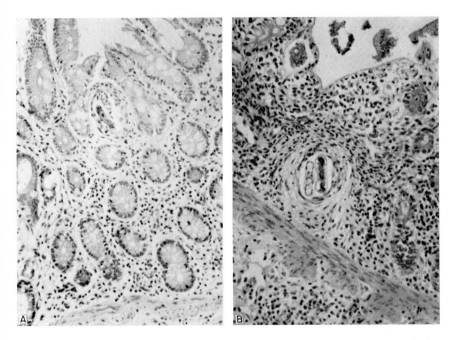

FIG. 3. *Trichonema* sp. in the large intestine of the horse. A, Third-stage larva in the epithelial layer. B, Larva encapsulated by fibrous tissue produced by the host.

larvae grow the cysts around them also increase in size. Larvae may reach the submucosa (Fig. 4). In these cysts the larvae may remain for long periods of time. On re-entry into the gut lumen the capsule breaks down and at this time a marked inflammatory response in which eosinophils are common may occur. Pout (1964) described lesions observed in association with a severely damaged epithelium and numerous encysted small strongyles. The cell population consisted mainly of eosinophils, small round cells and macrophages, which were often arranged in tracts with a few plasma cells, fibroblasts and mast cells in the vicinity. In the large colon of a mare it was found that large areas of mucosa were necrotic and desquamated with a massive exudation containing eosinophils. The submucosa was thickened with collagen fibres and many eosinophils and small round cells were present as well as aggregates of plasma cells. Pout (1964) also observed granulomata of parasitic origin in the lymph nodes and liver. In one case *Strongylus edentatus* was found. An account of the nodules and burrows in the liver of horses infected with *S. edentatus* was given by Wetzel and Kersten (1956).

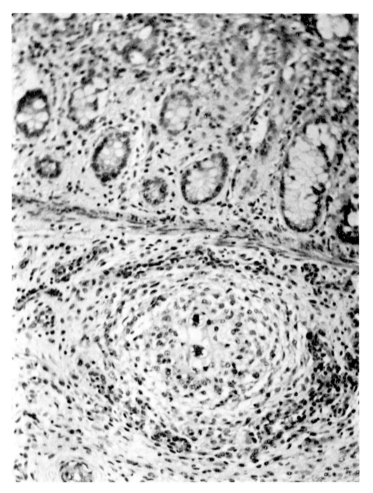

Fig. 4. *Trichonema* sp. in the large intestine of the horse. The larva has invaded the submucosa.

Rai (1960) states that larval members of the genus *Trichonema* in the horse cause a thickening of the caecal wall with dilatation of the blood vessels and endarteritis. Erosion, hypertrophy and inflammation of the mucosa is also seen.

Liu (1965a) studied the effects of *Nematospiroides dubius* in mice infected orally with 200 larvae each. After 4 h the larvae had entered the gastro-intestinal mucosa, where they provoked a local gastritis. Within 36 h the larvae left the mucosa, producing necrosis and thrombi in the lumen of damaged vessels. On the 3rd day the larvae encysted in the muscularis externa. The subsequent emergence of the larvae provoked more pronounced lesions which were repaired within 21 days after infection.

Liu (1965a) assumed that the lymphadenitis and hyperplasia of reticulo-endothelial tissue in the mesenteric lymph nodes, the non-specific hepatitis and splenomegaly were due to mechanically produced tissue damage in the intestines resulting from larval invasion, and to the allergenic factor of the substances released by the parasite. The focal non-specific hepatitis, although attributed to the nematodes, is not unlike the lesion seen in rats infected with JHM virus.

In a subsequent paper Liu (1965b) described the pathology seen in re-infection. In general more severe lesions were seen. Parasitic nodules were seen on the intestinal wall which were similar to those produced by *Oesopha-gostomum*. These were believed to be connected with the development of resistance and were still present 90 days after reinfection.

Whur (1966) in recent experimental work has produced evidence showing there is no longer any doubt that the globule leucocyte may be related to the presence of helminth parasites. Sections from the abomasum and small and large intestine of parasitized and worm-free sheep showed the globule leucocyte to be common in the parasitized animals, but almost totally absent from the worm-free sheep. Experimental primary infections of rats with *Nippostrongylus brasiliensis* produced a marked globule leucocyte response on the 12th day of infection which coincided with self-cure and increased until the 18th day. The actual function of the globule leucocyte still awaits elucidation.

Some observations on the role of the small intestine in nematode immunity were made by Larsh *et al.* (1962) working with *Trichinella spiralis* and mice. They utilized immunized mice, immunized mice irradiated at 450 r and control mice. In the control mice there was a mild inflammatory reaction with a few polymorphonuclear leucocytes in the mucosa. Immunized, non-irradiated mice showed a general inflammation of the mucosa with infiltration of plasma cells and lymphocytes and a few polymorphs. In immunized mice irradiated 8 days before challenge the inflammatory response was even less than in the controls; the mucosa contained some lymphocytes and plasma cells, but very few polymorphs. If immunized mice were irradiated 12 days before challenge the inflammatory response was of an intermediate type with extensive lymphoid proliferation. It was concluded that the acquired immunity to *T. spiralis* in mice was due firstly to specific antibodies and secondly to cells responsible for eliminating the worms. Irradiation apparently damaged the haemopoietic system so that a cellular response did not result or was diminished. Without this response the worms remained in spite of an unchanged antibody titre.

It is apparent that during the last few years our knowledge of the changes in the alimentary tract in response to nematode parasites has markedly increased. Old concepts whereby worms were regarded as being in direct competition with their hosts for nutritional sources have been largely discarded and replaced by newer concepts of a more subtle nature. Some of the advances made have been stimulated by an increased knowledge of the pathological processes operating in the human intestine and the refined biopsy techniques which may now be employed. Thus, an understanding of the malabsorption syndrome in nematodiasis is related to work carried out on human non-tropical sprue. The observation of certain histological features may suggest certain biochemical or physiological upsets and the converse is, of course, true. The work on *Ostertagia* has made an appreciation of the clinical disease easier and well illustrates the immense advances which may be made by various specialists working together.

III. PULMONARY REACTIONS

Many nematode parasites inhabit the lung; some are merely temporary but others reside there as adults. Jubb and Kennedy (1963) succinctly summarized the position when they stated that "the lungs are at the cross roads of parasitic migrations, and the many parasites that pass that way leave behind, for a short time at least, traces of their passage".

A. *Dictyocaulus viviparus*

The essential features of bovine parasitic bronchitis were clarified by the workers at the Glasgow Veterinary Hospital and the whole topic recently reviewed by Poynter (1963). Since the publication of this review Jarrett and Sharp (1963) have compared the course of infections with normal and irradiated *D. viviparus* larvae in calves. Three days after infection with irradiated larvae lesions were present in the mesenteric lymph nodes. These consisted of small necrotic tracts surrounded by a narrow zone of macrophages and eosinophils. After 7 days lesions of the type associated with the breakthrough of larvae into the alveoli were discovered. These foci usually involved four or five alveoli in which were present fibrin and erythrocytes. Often small fibrinoid necrotic centres were found surrounded by a light infiltration of neutrophils, eosinophils, macrophages and one or two foreign body type giant cells.

With infections of 250000 larvae, differences were noted according to whether the larvae were normal or irradiated. With irradiated larvae, the eosinophilic infiltration seemed to be more marked and there were a large number of lesions present which represented the first stage of a process designated the lymphoreticular broncho-occlusive lesion, which develops around dying or dead parasites in the lumina of bronchioles. The epithelium in contact with the parasite often showed a bizarre hyperplasia containing multinucleated and hyperplastic cells. However, much of the normal cellular organization was also apparent in the epithelial layer. The lamina propria was usually thickened and infiltrated with eosinophils, but there was also a multiplication of reticulum cells and a swelling of endothelial cells. Ulceration of the epithelium led to an outgrowth of fine granulomatous tissue from the lamina propria which invaded the eosinophilic exudate surrounding the parasite. The broncho-mediastinal lymph nodes showed oedema of the hilar area and infiltration of eosinophils into it. The cortices of the nodes showed increased activity of the germinal follicles and an increase in the number of immature plasma cells in the medullary cords. The medulla showed hypertrophy and hyperplasia of the sinus cells. In a few cases disintegrating larvae were seen surrounded by a foreign body reaction.

After 14 days areas of alveolar collapse were associated with plugging of associated bronchioles with disintegrating eosinophils. In the bronchiolar nodes the germinal centres were very obvious.

At 21 days some lobules showed central greyish nodes about 2 mm diam. which contained greenish plugs. These nodules developed from the broncho-occlusive lesions. The central dead larva was surrounded by a focus which sometimes contained epithelial cells, but which always contained a multiplication of reticulum cells, haemocytoblasts and immature plasma cells. The lesion had the appearance of a developing antibody-producing site.

After 35 days there was no evidence of bronchiolar plugging or alveolar collapse. A few broncho-occlusive lesions were observed macroscopically. Microscopically these showed further development of the lesion which basically consisted of a central dead nematode which stained in eosin and was surrounded by tissue similar to that found in lymph nodes. Germinal centres were present and these and other surrounding lymphocytes and plasma cells obscured the normal bronchiolar structure almost completely.

In another experiment Jarrett and Sharp (1963) utilized the double-vaccination procedure which has been so successful in the field and then challenged the calves each with 10000 larvae. The calves were then killed at varying intervals in order to determine the course of this infection. After 3 days the lungs were essentially normal apart from the presence of some broncho-occlusive lesions. After 7 days the challenging larvae had reached the bronchioles and epithelial hyperplasia was apparent. Broncho-occlusive lesions were present and near these there was a heavy eosinophilic infiltration into the septa. A similar infiltration was seen in the hilar and trabecular areas of the broncho-mediastinal lymph nodes.

After 14 days nodules denoting broncho-occlusive lesions were present over the surface of both diaphragmatic lobes. The histological findings denoted a midway stage in the development of lymphoreticular broncho-occlusive lesions. These lesions consisted of dead worms, giant cells and mesenchymal cells, and in some remains of a hyperplastic bronchiolar epithelium. External to this was a zone rich in eosinophils, proliferating endothelial cells, macrophages, immature plasma cells, pyroninophilic haemocytoblasts and reticulum cells. All these were surrounded by lymph and plasma cells showing germinal centre formation. The broncho-mediastinal lymph nodes showed eosinophilic infiltration.

After 21 days the broncho-occlusive lesion had progressed so that it appeared as lymph node tissue, the germinal centres being well developed. Thus, it was shown that lymphoreticular nodes developed in the lungs of immune calves. These foci have the morphological characteristics of antibody-producing sites, but at the present moment there is no proof that they do actually manufacture protective antibodies.

Michel *et al.* (1965) carried out an experiment in calves in which the histo-pathological changes in the lungs and other organs were examined with special reference to differences between immunized and susceptible animals after challenge with *Dictyocaulus viviparus*. They examined animals made immune by vaccination with irradiated larvae as well as other animals made immune by normal larvae and, having challenged these, compared them with sus-ceptible animals. The bronchi and trachea usually contained an abundant cellular exudate with many eosinophil leucocytes. This exudate appeared to develop in the presence of established adult lungworms.

Pulmonary nodules which were seen macroscopically were found to be parasitic granulomata or areas of focal oedema. Such foci were common in the immune animals, but were only seen occasionally in the susceptible calves. Several types of granuloma were recognized. A typical granuloma consisted of central eosinophilic cell debris composed predominantly of degenerating eosinophil leucocytes near which nematode material could be distinguished. The intermediate zone was composed of epithelioid and giant cells with an outer zone of lymphocytes, plasma cells and eosinophils. Similar granulomas originating within bronchioles where anaplasia of the epithelium provided the intermediate zone were seen and these corresponded to the broncho-occlusive lesion described by Jarrett and Sharp (1963). Michel *et al.* (1965) agree that the presence of such granulomas might be associated with an allergic or immune response. These workers also found small focal lesions which con-sisted of central accumulations of eosinophils surrounded by stroma contain-ing round cells.

Severe eosinophil infiltration of the connective tissue particularly of the subpleural zone and interlobular septa was seen in immune calves even two years after their initial treatments, and this was paralleled by increased peri-pheral eosinophil counts. Some eosinophil infiltration was also seen in primary lungworm infection. Septal oedema was also more prominent in immunized animals, but interstitial emphysema was more pronounced in susceptible calves.

Arterial changes were more common in immunized animals even after two years. The typical histological change consisted of muscular hypertrophy of the tunica media of small pulmonary arteries, often with vacuolation. There was also a dense eosinophilic leucocyte invasion of the intima of hypertrophied pulmonary arteries, together with intimal proliferation and disruption of the internal elastic laminae. Eosinophils could be seen migrating through the walls to a perivascular situation. The reaction was similar to that described by Mackenzie (1960) in cat lungworm infection. It is not known whether the change represents a localized physico-mechanical reaction or an allergic response at the site of antigen-antibody formation. Michel *et al.* (1965) also noted a dense infiltration by eosinophils in the intestinal wall, mesenteric lymph nodes, liver and heart which was obviously not dependent on the presence of lungworms or larvae in the affected sites. This eosinophilia was more pronounced in immunized than in susceptible cattle.

Results on the distribution of the lesions seen in experimental cases of *D. viviparus* infection in the calf have been obtained by Peacock, Poynter and Menear (unpublished observations) and are shown in Table I, in which the frequency of a given change is related to the phase of the disease. Each calf was infected on one occasion at a level of 60–80 larvae/lb body weight. Table II shows the times at which calves died.

TABLE I

Distribution of lesions in 107 cases of bovine parasitic bronchitis

	Eosinophilia	Pulmonary oedema	Hyaline membranes	Alveolar epithelialization	Macrophages	Larval fragments	Tattering of bronchiolar epithelium	Emphysema	Bronchiectasis	Pulmonary fibrosis
	% of calves with given lesions									
No. of calves dying during pre-patent phase of disease: 12	50	41	8	0	50	8	8	25	0	25
No. of calves examined during patency: 62	33	52	3	9	71	55	32	33	9	50
No. of post-patent calves examined: 33	39	45	3	15	64	30	39	27	24	76

TABLE II

The mortality pattern in calves infected with D. viviparus

No. of calves	No. dying before patency	Nos. dying in weeks after commencement of patency								Survivors
		1	2	3	4	5	6	7	8+	
281	42	16	22	16	28	19	17	18	27	76

B. *Dictyocaulus filaria*

The reactions of the lungs of sheep to infection with *Dictyocaulus filaria* are essentially similar to those of cattle to *D. viviparus*. Michel (1954) observed that pulmonary oedema could be caused by immature lungworms.

Sofrenovic *et al.* (1961) studied the pathology of *Dictyocaulus filaria* infection in 112 lambs which were reared parasite free and were treated in various ways with irradiated and non-irradiated larvae. The infected susceptible lambs showed pneumonic lungs with areas of atelectasis. Histologically there was a marked proliferation of alveolar and bronchiolar epithelium. Septal proliferation also occurred. Proliferation of the alveoli gave an adenomatous appearance and emphysema was apparent particularly near adult parasites. In vaccinated immune animals only isolated focal changes were noted. Small parasitic nodules which the authors called eosinophilic foci were present and it is obvious that these lesions were similar to the granulomatous lesion noted by other authors with other parasites.

c. *Dictyocaulus arnfieldi*

Katiyar (1964) made a histological study of the reactions to *D. arnfieldi*. He found the nematode in two out of twenty-eight donkeys, but not in any of thirteen ponies, and revealed epithelial hyperplasia of the bronchiolar epithelium with a heavy infiltration of lymphocytes and polymorphonuclear leucocytes in the peribronchial region. Perhaps surprisingly, eosinophils were rare.

d. *Protostrongylus rufescens*

This species produces lesions similar to those seen with *D. filaria*, but they are quantitatively less, are lobular in size and are located chiefly at the periphery of the diaphragmatic lobes.

e. *Muellerius capillaris*

The lesions resulting from infection with *M. capillaris* range in size from less than 1 mm to several cm diam. Rose (1958) infected sheep with larvae recovered from the common grey field slug *Agriolimax* spp. and the lesions obtained were all less than 5 mm diam. There were, however, marked differences in structure depending upon the extent of calcification. Rose (1959) noted that most nodules were superficial. The smallest of the non-calcified lesions were about a pin-point in size and contained fourth-stage larvae. The larger non-calcified lesions contained nematodes ranging from fourth-stage larvae to fully grown adults. Jubb and Kennedy (1963) have summarized the tissue changes. The larvae can disrupt groups of alveoli and slight emphysema may also occur. Although there may be little cellular reaction to a primary infection, subsequent infections may produce an eosinophilic infiltration. The adults in the alveolar tissue provoke a granulomatous reaction. There is little response to the eggs and larvae in the alveolar spaces, but mild fibrous thickening of the alveolar septa with lymphocytic infiltration is seen in the septa and around blood vessels and bronchioles. The cellular reaction is more marked in older animals, and this may be due to a developing resistance. Here there are marked foci of eosinophils around the larvae, macrophages and giant cells crowd the alveolar spaces and the alveolar walls become thickened by fibrous tissue. Larvae in the small bronchioles are enclosed in plugs of mucus and cellular debris and the bronchiolar epithelium is hyperplastic and the muscularis thickened. Once larvae leave the nodules the cellular reaction subsides, but thickening of the alveolar septa persists. Intense reactions are developed to adult worms with eosinophils, a zone of epithelioid and giant cells and a peripheral zone of fibroblastic tissue. Later calcification may occur.

Other pulmonary lesions in sheep suffering from strongyloidiasis were noted by Ceretto (1957)—metaplastic changes in the alveolar and bronchial epithelia which were secondary to interstitial chronic pneumonitis. Fibroadenoma were reported in regions of the lung where there had been interstitial inflammation. In examining about 100 cases three were found to have papillary adenoma in the branches of bronchioles. The relationship of the adenomatous changes to the parasitic infection is possibly purely fortuitous, since such changes are not regularly reported.

F. *Metastrongylus* SPP.

Mackenzie (1958a) in studying natural lungworm infections in pigs made some observations on the lung lesions. The lesions found in pigs with mild infections were usually confined to the posterior extremities of the diaphragmatic lobe of the lung, where well-defined lobular areas of pulmonary vesicular emphysema were associated with adult lungworms which were blocking related bronchi. Small pulmonary nodules were associated with the postpatent phase of the disease. Microscopic examination revealed a foreign body type cellular reaction, including multinucleate giant cells. There was also a hypertrophy of the bronchiolar smooth muscle similar to that reported in sheep and goats suffering from lungworm (Pei-Lin Li, 1946), and an eosinophilic leucocyte infiltration. Lymphoid nodules were common and there was also a mucoid metaplasia of the bronchiolar epithelium. Mackenzie (1958a) also found that the pig lungworm was able to produce occasional lesions of anterior pneumonia which resembled macroscopically a virus pneumonia. A similar macroscopic picture is seen in *D. viviparus* infection in calves when eggs and larvae become reaspirated into the anterior lobes.

Mackenzie (1958b) then went on to study the lesions in experimentally infected pigs which were known to be free from virus pneumonias. All the animals he infected developed pulmonary oedema and in some cases marginal consolidation was also seen. Using doses of 200–8000 *Metastrongylus elongatus* larvae, he obtained a clear correlation between the extent of the lesions and the size of the infecting dose. The emphysematous areas were paler than the rest of the lung and spongelike in texture. They were directly attributable to the presence of lungworms in the small bronchi and bronchioles of the region, and consequently they occurred in a lobular pattern, so that the emphysematous portions could easily be distinguished from the adjacent nonexpanding lung. The caudal extremities of the diaphragmatic lobes were primarily and consistently affected. With infective doses of 1000 and above lesions were disseminated in all lobes, but the diaphragmatic lobes were still the most severely affected.

Lungworms were present in the bronchi and bronchioles and the parasites were surrounded by a mucous exudate which contained a few eosinophils, neutrophils and mononuclear cells. In the larger bronchi, embryonated metastrongyle eggs were seen. The lungworms in the bronchi provoked a marked increase in the number of goblet cells, but this change did not extend to the bronchioles. Some hyperplasia of the bronchiolar epithelium was also seen and in other regions atrophy of the bronchiolar epithelium had occurred adjacent to adult lungworms. Infiltration of the epithelium with eosinophils, lymphocytes and plasma cells was seen together with a marked cellular infiltration of the lamina propria. Lymphoid hyperplasia around the bronchioles was present and hypertrophy of the smooth muscle of the bronchioles was also apparent. The connective tissue surrounding the bronchi showed an infiltration with histiocytes and non-granular leucocytes with some local lymphoid hyperplasia.

Pulmonary vesicular emphysema occurred, but did not extend into the interlobular or subpleural tissue. Irregular cellular infiltration of the alveolar walls and perivascular connective tissues with eosinophils and round cells was seen. Affected areas also contained small eosinophilic nodules. These consisted of a central mass of eosinophils and leucocytes surrounded by degenerating parasitic larvae with an outer zone of endothelioid-type cells. The surrounding lung tissue was infiltrated with lymphocytes and plasma cells.

Actual consolidation of the lungs was due to the proliferative reactions already mentioned and to the alveolar response to reaspirated lungworm eggs. Interstitial lymphoid hyperplasia was seen with cellular infiltration of the alveolar walls. Septal cell proliferation was apparent and gave the appearance of epithelialization of the alveoli. The alveolar exudate was composed of oedema fluid with eosinophils, polymorphous nucleate cells, together with lymphocytes, plasma cells and macrophages, whilst, as might be expected, giant cells were also present.

Having studied the pathology of the natural infection and given an account of the lesions present in experimentally infected cases after 35 days, Mackenzie (1959) went on to describe the progressive pathology of experimental infections. Twenty-two young pigs were infected with single large doses (2000–4000) of larvae and they were killed at intervals 1–80 days after infection. Four main types of reaction were recognized that could contribute to the production of pulmonary consolidation—eosinophil and leucocyte infiltration, mononuclear and giant cell reaction, coalescing eosinophilic nodules and peribronchial lymphoid hyperplasia. The first macroscopic changes were seen in the lungs 12 days after infection, and these consisted of small irregular pale red areas of consolidation accompanying early vesicular emphysema. Definite emphysema was present by the 21st day. Mackenzie again found that although at the levels of infection he used all lobes of the lung were involved, nevertheless the posterior extremities of the diaphragmatic lobes were the areas most severely affected. Distinct consolidation was present by 35 days, when areas of the lung appeared pink or plum red. At 40–60 days small grey subpleural nodules up to 2 mm in size were present. These were seen in lobules already affected by emphysema. When cut these nodules were found to have yellow or greenish centres, these being surrounded by a narrow zone of grey tissue. Mackenzie went on to describe the histological appearance of the lesions associated with different parts of the life cycle. During the early part (days 1–9) of the pre-patent stage of the disease lesions were only found in the lungs and bronchiolar lymph nodes. Changes in the lung were associated with the migration of lungworm larvae through the lung parenchyma. At this stage there was an increase in the cellularity in the alveolar walls, occasional alveolar mononucleate cell exudate and some intra-alveolar haemorrhage. Macrophages and occasional multinucleate giant cells were seen in the alveoli. There was no eosinophilic response at this time. During the later pre-patent stage (days 10–25) immature lungworms were found in the smallest bronchioles as well as in the lung parenchyma. At this time there was a pronounced eosinophilic reaction in the lung, so that marked infiltration of the bronchiolar mucosa occurred and many eosinophils migrated through this to form a cellular exudate around the immature lungworms in the lumen. There was also an increase in the cellularity of the alveolar walls due to the presence of mesenchymal cells and small mononuclear cells as well as multiplication of alveolar lining cells. After 2–3 weeks there was a dense eosinophil infiltration of the bronchiolar mucosa which sometimes extended to the interalveolar walls as well as to the connective tissue of the lung. Hypertrophy of the bronchiolar smooth muscle was seen after 18 days of infection at which time emphysema became more pronounced.

Ten days after infection the bronchiolar lymph nodes were enlarged with hyperplasia of lymphoid tissue and infiltration with eosinophils. During the early patent part of the disease (days 25–40) the eosinophilic reaction was less severe, but was still apparent in the connective tissue and in the septa and subpleural tissue. At this time a round cell infiltration of the alveolar walls occurred and the alveoli contained fluid, macrophages, eosinophils, lymphocytes and some granulocytes and free giant cells. Vesicular emphysema was very pronounced and at about 35 days a mucoid metaplasia of the bronchiolar epithelium commenced.

In the late patent stage (day 60 onwards) lymphoid hyperplasia, smooth muscle hypertrophy, mucoid metaplasia of the bronchiolar epithelium, chronic vesicular emphysema, chronic bronchitis and persistent cellular infiltration all became more pronounced. Some infiltrates of eosinophils were still seen and granuloma occurred. At 80 days the main changes were emphysema and lymphoid hyperplasia. The lymphoid follicles were observed to be particularly active and were of the type seen in long-standing natural infections.

The earliest consolidation was associated with the dense eosinophilic reaction that occurred during the immature lungworm phase, and Mackenzie believed its onset coincided with the commencement of feeding and excretion by the parasites. Pneumonia in the patent phase of the disease was often caused by the aspiration of lungworm eggs into the alveoli. The small eosinophilic granulomas were formed around degenerating lungworm eggs or larvae.

Ewing and Todd (1961), in a study of metastrongylosis in the field, also found that the diaphragmatic lobe of the lung appeared to be the preferred location. There was no tendency for any given species or sex to live in any specific area. The main lesions were emphysema and chronic inflammation.

An example of how microscopic examination may aid the elucidation of a nematode life cycle was provided by Kersten and Becht (1960), who studied by histological examination the migratory route of *Metastrongylus* larvae in experimentally infected guinea-pigs. They sectioned material at times varying from 12 h to 14 days after infection. The tissue migrations were distinguished by the tracks of polymorphonuclear leucocytes which were found together with nodules of larvae, larval sheaths, histiocytes and foreign-body giant cells. By these means they found that the larvae penetrated the intestine and migrated via the mesenteries, lymphatic vessels and glands, heart and pulmonary vessels to the lungs.

G. *Filaroides* SPP.

A good account of the lesions produced by *Filaroides osleri* was provided by Urquhart *et al.* (1954). The typical lesions seen, protruding submucosal nodules, were common near the bifurcation of the trachea, of variable size, the larger nodes being elongated in the long axis of the trachea, and greyish white in colour. The underlying worms may be visible through the intact mucosa. Nematodes live in tissue spaces in the walls of the trachea and bronchi on either side of the cartilages, as well as in the peribronchial tissue and lymphatics. Little reaction occurs as a result of living worms, but there is a thin capsule and some infiltration of the lamina propria by plasma cells and lymphocytes. Dead worms stimulate a foreign-body reaction with a neutrophilia and some giant cells. Immature worms are sometimes found in the lymphatics and occasionally in the alveoli, but there is little reaction to them in these sites. Olson and Bracken (1959) also gave an account of the lesions observed in a dog infected with *F. osleri*. Twenty-one hyperaemic granulomatous nodules were present on the mucosal surface of the trachea at the level of its bifurcation. Many were pedunculated and numerous nematodes protruded from their surfaces. The nodules partially occluded many of the lesser bronchial openings and that of the left apical bronchus was completely occluded. The nodules consisted of granulomatous lesions characterized by a loose network of supportive collagenous fibres containing numerous mononuclear macrophages and plasma cells with a lesser number of lymphocytes. No eosinophils were seen. Ogilvie *et al.* (1962) have demonstrated that the parasitic granulomas produced by *F. osleri* may be recognized by a distally lighted bronchoscope and the histological examination of tissue specimens removed with forceps.

Filaroides milksi described by Whitlock (1956) is a parasite of the dog and the lesions produced by it were recorded by Jubb (1960). The parasite causes a thickening of pulmonary pleura and a loss of elasticity of the lungs, which become very dense and contain firm grey airless masses with large white internal foci. Emphysema is present between the solid portions of lung.

Mature viviparous parasites are present in the bronchioles and also in the parenchymal tissue, and microfilariae may be seen in the terminal bronchioles as well as in the parenchyma. The main tissue reaction to the worms is granulomatous and may be a response to the presence of the microfilariae. When only mature worms are present in the bronchioles the reaction is minimal and consists of a copious secretion of mucus associated with hyperplastic peribronchiolar glands and numerous metaplastic goblet cells in the bronchiolar epithelium. If microfilariae are present in the bronchioles the local reaction is inflammatory and granulomatous, the larvae being surrounded by eosinophils, zones of epithelioid and giant cells and an outer zone of plasma cells. These granulomatous reactions may lead to bronchiolar obliteration and to an infiltration of the alveolar septa by large mononuclear cells and giant cells. In the lung parenchyma there is little reaction to the mature parasites, but again there is a gradual reaction to microfilariae.

The larvae of *F. milksi* may also be present in granulomas in the brain, liver, pancreas, ovary, gastric mucosa, intestinal mucosa and thyroid. Jubb (1960) found that the microfilariae are localized in the kidney shortly before death, larvae occurring in the lumen of tubules in areas of microscopic haemorrhage.

H. *Aelurostrongylus abstrusus*

A. abstrusus is a nematode parasite of the cat. Mackenzie (1960) observed that in kittens it causes an extensive patchy consolidation with certain resemblances to pulmonary tuberculosis. Young adult nematodes were found in the parenchyma, but neither in the bronchi nor in the pulmonary arteries. There was an absence of bronchiolar muscular hypertrophy such as is seen in metastrongyle infections in pigs. The pulmonary lesions were characteristic firm yellowish nodules 2–10 mm diam. which represent nests of eggs and larvae. These nodules were scattered throughout the parenchyma, mainly in the peripheral part of the lung. The alveolar septa are disrupted by eggs and larvae surrounded by mononuclear and giant cells. Alveolar epithelialization was seen in older lesions with some septal thickening. Mackenzie (1960) noted severe muscular hypertrophy with hyperplasia of the media and intimal proliferation in the pulmonary arteries which he suggested might denote a more intimate relationship between the muscular system and lungworms.

Hamilton (1963) found that in fatal cases the pleural cavity was filled with a thick milky fluid rich in larvae, eggs and cellular elements. Small foci of lymphocytes, eosinophils and macrophages were seen around nematode material. Changes in the bronchial and bronchiolar epithelium were minimal, but hypertrophy of the arterial and arteriolar smooth muscle was common. Masses of developing eggs and larvae were seen with neutrophils, eosinophils, lymphocytes, plasma cells, macrophages and numerous giant cells. Central necrosis was observed and calcification had occurred in a single case. Invasion of the bronchiolar mucosa with eosinophils, lymphocytes and plasma cells was a feature and occasional areas of ulceration were noted. Hyperplasia of the bronchial and bronchiolar mucosa with a multiplication of mucous cells occurred and hypertrophy of the smooth muscle, especially of the terminal bronchioles and alveolar ducts, was observed. Changes in the pulmonary arterial and arteriolar walls similar to those reported by Mackenzie (1960) occurred, and in some cases the muscular and endothelial changes were severe enough to obliterate the lumen. Vacuolation of the subendothelial space was seen and the muscle was often invaded by eosinophils.

In Mackenzie's cases peribronchial lymphoid hyperplasia was not seen, but Hamilton did find this to be present. Such a lesion may, of course, have several causes and it is difficult to ascribe any significance to this difference. Mackenzie remarked on the absence of bronchiolar muscular hypertrophy, but Hamilton regularly noted this feature. It is likely that this hypertrophy is initiated by the gradual obstruction of the bronchioles by eggs, larvae and exudate.

Hypertrophy and hyperplasia of the smooth muscle of the pulmonary arteries seems to be a constant feature in *A. abstrusus* infection in cats. Kell *et al.* (1956) thought that these arterial changes were a chronic response to long-standing vasomotor stimulation from sympathetic centres. It seems just as likely that the muscular changes are related to lungworm infestation. The parasite may directly irritate the vessels or the changes may be concerned with some product of the parasite or may reflect some aspect of the pulmonary pathology.

Seneviratna (1958a, b) found 60% of the cats he examined in Ceylon to be infected with *Anafilaroides rostratus*. The main symptoms were coughing, eosinophilia and nasal discharge. The parasite lives in the walls of the bronchi and bronchioles, causing chronic bronchitis and peribronchitis with marked hyperplasia of the bronchial mucosa. Sinous thickenings of the bronchial walls occurs. The dead adults provoke an intense infiltration of neutrophils with possible calcification and fibrosis of the bronchial wall. The changes then are not as marked as in the case of *Aelurostrongylus abstrusus*.

I. OTHER NEMATODES

Angiostrongylus vasorum which normally resides in the pulmonary arteries of the dog and fox owes most of its pathogenicity to its eggs, which may become impacted in arterioles to produce an obliterating vasculitis. The occlusions may be so severe that large portions of lung become consolidated.

Takeuch (1960) has studied the primary changes in the lungs of puppies infested with *Strongyloides stercoralis* and also carried out X-ray studies of thirty-five human cases. Using filariform larvae, he found petechiae and fresh haemorrhagic nodules of various sizes. Alveolar haemorrhages and cellular infiltration around the small bronchi and blood vessels were marked. The inflammatory changes in the lung gradually increased and serous fluid containing lymphocytes and histiocytes was seen in the alveoli. Bronchitis and bronchopneumonia were seen, but no parasitic nodules were found.

An account of the pathological changes produced in the lungs of horses and rabbits by *Protostrongylus* spp. was given by Babos (1962). *P. tauricus* produced nodules similar to those found in protostrongylosis in sheep, but in *P. pulmonalis* infection diffuse lesions were noted. The third-stage larvae were associated with an alveolar exudate and lymphocytic infiltration. When the larvae reached the upper respiratory tract peribronchitis and atelectasis were seen. The chronic lesions associated with the patent phase of the infection included desquamation and metaplasia of the bronchial epithelium with perivascular inflammation and necrosis of an allergic nature.

Kennedy (1954) infected calves with 10000 eggs of *A. lumbricoides*. One calf developed a mild dry cough, two other calves showed no signs of disease after an initial infection with 3000 eggs each, but after subsequent infections they developed signs which were interpreted as indicative of sensitivity.

Allen (1962) reported cases of acute atypical pneumonia in a group of cross-bred yearling cattle which had been brought from a poor summer pasture and housed in pig pens heavily contaminated with eggs of *Ascaris lumbricoides*; fifteen out of seventeen were affected and one died. At post-mortem examination the trachea and bronchi contained froth and the lungs showed numerous minute petechial haemorrhages. Bronchiectasis and atelectasis were present and the lung also showed congestion and slight oedema. Histopathological examination showed diffuse interstitial pneumonia with focal haemorrhage and diffuse oedema. A few larvae were detectable in the bronchi and in the atelectic areas surrounding the bronchiectasis. The lungs were examined for parasites and characteristic fourth-stage *A. lumbricoides* larvae recovered.

The pathology of lungworm infections have several obvious similarities. The development of eosinophilia is more pronounced in animals having previous experience of the parasites and in these the development of the lympho-broncho-occlusive lesion has been reported. These lesions seem to be related to the immune state of the host and suggest that some local resistance mechanism is in operation.

In *Muellerius* infections the cellular response is most pronounced in the older animal. *Filaroides osleri* produces its chief lesions in the large air passages where granulomatous reactions develop, but there is little reaction to immature worms in the lymphatics or alveoli. The lung reactions to *Filaroides milksi* are related to microfilariae and there is little response to mature parasites.

IV. Nematodes and Blood Vessels

Probably the most notorious nematode to occur in the blood vascular system is *Strongylus vulgaris* of the horse, which is particularly pathogenic because it migrates through the arterial system.

Ruysch (1665) found innumerable small worms in the cranial mesenteric artery of a horse. Since then many workers have made observations on the relationships between *S. vulgaris* and the horse, discussing various aspects of the pathology and life cycle, but as yet no general agreement has been reached on the migratory route of the parasite in its host.

The presence of *S. vulgaris* in the arteries is associated with endarteritis and thrombosis. Cronin and Leader (1952) found lesions of parasitic arteritis as far forward as the bulbus aortae and aortic sinuses and further cases were recorded by Farrelly (1954). In spite of the high incidence of parasitic endarteritis in horses some authors had been inclined to regard the presence of nematodes in arteries as aberrant, but Farrelly (1954) thought that these lesions indicated a route back to the caecum which the nematodes normally took. Poynter (1960) supported Farrelly and produced evidence from forty-three post-mortem examinations which explained certain facets of the pathogenesis of parasitic endarteritis. It was shown that lesions were produced in the arteries by the direct irritation of the nematode on the endothelium. Mural deposits were formed and these were eventually incorporated into the intima, which thereby became thickened by fibrinous deposits (Fig. 5A, B).

Pout (1964) found parasitic granulomata in the colon, lymph nodes, liver and arteries of horses and suggested a possible pathogenesis of such lesions. Macrophages and eosinophils were found around the cuticles of dead larvae, and a mass of collagenous fibres with eosinophilic granular material and dead nuclei was present in the central position. Fibroblasts were seen on the peri-

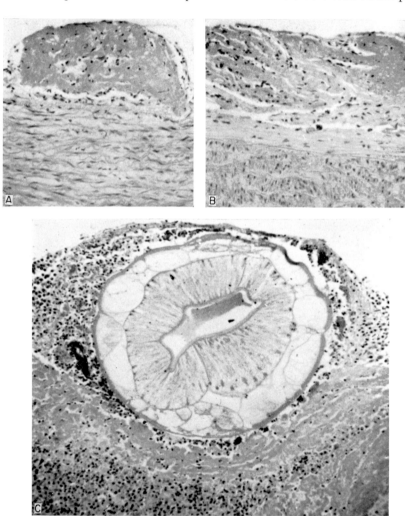

FIG. 5. A and B, Fibrinous deposits becoming incorporated into the intima. C, Parasite (*Strongylus vulgaris*) becoming incorporated into the intima by reactive endothelium.

phery. Many eosinophils were streaming in from the surrounding connective tissue to disgorge their granules at the edge of the lesions where mast cells and plasma cells were present. Later, eosinophils, mast cells and fibroblasts were absent from the periphery and were replaced by endothelioid cells and foreign-body giant cells. The end result was the formation of a soft cicatrix.

Skalinskii (1957) made some observations on the pathology of experimental and spontaneous *Strongylus vulgaris* infestations in horses. The arterial vessels showed primary and secondary thrombogenesis with the development of endo-, meso- and peri-arteritis and aneurism. He associated *S. vulgaris* with the development of parasitic nodules in the liver. Changes in the nerve cells and in the mesenchyma of nodules of the intramural ganglia of the thick part of the intestine and solar plexus were noted on the 1st day of infection. The most serious changes were, of course, seen in the arteries.

Jaskoski and Colglazier (1956) reported the presence of *Strongylus asini* in the caecum of a zebra and in a liver cyst. Post-mortem examination revealed extensive liver damage caused by parasitic cysts. The cysts were located singly or in groups and the liver was black and congested. Several coiled worms were present beneath the capsule of the liver and the parenchyma. Death was due to peritonitis believed to be initiated by the worms. The cyst material showed much fibrous connective tissue with areas of extensive leucocytic invasion.

Wetzel and Kersten (1956) described the liver phase in the migration of *Strongylus edentatus*. Infections with this parasite were associated with the formation of nodules in the liver, and the larvae produced burrows.

Chodnik (1958) found that many cattle in Ghana had aortic infections with *Onchocerca armillata* and gave detailed information on the resultant histo-pathological changes in the aorta. There were various lesions—extensive corrugations, thickened walls, occasional aneurisms, cellular invasion and calcification—which indicated a chronic type of tissue reaction to the parasite. The nature and sequence of the microscopical changes was followed. Small tissue haemorrhages occurred following injury and in early infections poly-morphs surrounded the parasite. These cells were progressively replaced by round cells with plasma cells and eosinophils gradually came to outnumber all the other cells. Foreign-body giant cells were seen, but not in abundance. As eosinophils became abundant fibrous changes were seen in the adjacent tissues. Little fibrosis was seen in the media, but it was pronounced in the intima and adventitia, where encapsulation occurred. Death of the parasite was followed by increased inflammation. Subsequently the degenerating parasite either became the centre of leucocytic invasion undergoing phagocytic absorption, followed by granulation and fibrous cicatrization, or it became the centre of calcification.

Microscopic examination of parasite tunnels showed many with no trace of a parasite. There is obviously extensive wandering in the tissues of the aortic wall. At intervals along the tunnels, large numbers of microfilariae were present in the surrounding tissues, in response to which an eosinophilia was seen. The tunnels occasionally opened into the aortic lumen.

Patnaik (1952) examined 167 aortae from adult cattle in India and found 165 to be affected with *Onchocerca armillata*. Examinations of five calves under 6 months of age proved negative. Most nodules on the outer wall of the aorta were degenerate or calcified, but those situated on the inner surface permitted the passage of microfilariae. Bulls showing epileptiform fits had high microfilariae counts and some became blind or developed periodic ophthalmia.

Nematodes of the genus *Elaephora* also occur in the arteries of mammals,

E. poeli in cattle, *E. schneideri* in sheep and deer and *E. bohmi* in horses. *E. poeli* lives in the thoracic aorta, where the females are attached to the intima by their heads around which fibrous nodules develop and in which the males are found. Fibrous thickenings of the vessel wall occur. *E. bohmi* in horses produces similar lesions. The adults of *E. schneideri* do not produce lesions in blood vessels, but the microfilariae produce dermatitis in sheep.

A most comprehensive account of the reactions associated with canine dirofilariasis was provided by Winter (1959). Characteristic lesions were found in the lungs, lymph nodes, spleen and liver. The parasites were found in the right side of the heart and they often extended into the pulmonary artery. Chronic fibrosis of the atrioventricular valves was common, but similar lesions were often found in uninfected dogs and their exact relationship to the parasite is not known. The lungs were often observed to have an unusual rust brown discoloration. Circumscribed, consolidated, irregular grey nodules of a few centimetres in diameter were found, particularly in the dorsal parts of the lungs. These nodules were associated with parasites and thrombi in the branches of the pulmonary artery. The lymph nodes of the thoracic cavity constantly showed brown discoloration of the medulla, and this discoloration was sometimes seen in lymph nodes and the superficial cervical, axillary, mandibular and iliac nodes.

When the disease progressed so far that circulatory disturbances occurred, liver congestion was seen. The amount of congestion varied from moderate enlargement to gross enlargement with distended lymph vessels. Gross liver enlargement was always accompanied by ascites and anasarca of the ventral part of the body. In advanced cases the spleen was firm and slightly enlarged and the kidneys showed brown discoloration, particularly in the cortex. The microscopic changes in the lungs showed an inflammatory infiltration, haemosiderosis and fibrosis.

In the inflammation the most prominent cells were macrophages. Around thrombosed arteries, numerous non-pigmented macrophages were seen as well as neutrophils, plasma cells and a few eosinophils. In these regions the walls of the blood vessels were eroded and infiltrated with inflammatory cells, whilst the lumen contained thrombi and sections of parasites. The bronchi showed an increased amount of mucus with a few inflammatory cells, the majority of which were macrophages. In chronic cases the interalveolar tissue was fibrotic. In the lymph nodes characteristic changes were seen in the sinuses and medullary cords. There were numerous erythrocytes in the sinuses, some of which were free and some of which were phagocytozed by macrophages. Some of the macrophages contained haemosiderin and deposits of this pigment were also seen in the reticular cells. The spleen contained much haemosiderin. In chronic cases, the liver congestion varied from a moderate dilatation of the central vein and surrounding sinusoids with occurrence of fat vacuoles in centrilobular liver cells, to an extensive dilatation of the blood vessels causing pressure atrophy of the parenchyma. Numerous dilated lymph vessels could be seen in the liver capsule. One out of twelve dogs showed a significant infiltration of the epithelial cells of the convoluted tubules with granules of haemosiderin.

The increased destruction of erythrocytes leads to an increased accumulation of haemosiderin. This pigment was present in the lungs and their regional lymph nodes, but lesser amounts were seen in the liver, spleen and other lymph nodes. This distribution indicated that the site of erythrocyte destruction is somewhere in the right side of the heart, pulmonary artery or the lungs. Pulmonary haemosiderosis may be produced by chronic venous congestion during the course of heart failure. No indications were found that the parasite produces a toxin which could cause the destruction of blood. The haemosiderosis probably resulted from the iron-containing waste products of the adult's digestion, and also inflammation of the lungs. The agent causing the inflammation was not toxic enough to stimulate a significant vascular reaction and exudation. The predominance of macrophages indicates a chronic process.

The greyish consolidated nodules in the lung were always associated with dead adult worms embedded in thrombi in the pulmonary artery. The occasional eosinophil indicated that there was little, if any, of the allergic reaction normally associated with helminths. No lesions of atherosclerosis were observed.

Later in the course of the disease fibrosis and moderate emphysema occur. Before Winter published his paper it was assumed that the mechanical interference of the adult parasites was responsible for the circulatory disturbances. This, however, offered no explanation for the poor clinical response in the treatment of chronic cases. The main obstacles to the circulation are, it seems, probably produced by the pulmonary fibrosis and moderate emphysema.

Lichtenberg et al. (1962) studied the hepatic lesions in dogs with dirofilariasis. Their material was based on twelve dogs with a clinical syndrome of sudden weakness, bilirubinurea, haemoglobinurea and death, with adult worms (*Dirofilaria immitis*) occupying the vena cava. In addition to the usual lesions of the heart and lungs, severe hepatic lesions were found. Most of the animals showed endarteritis with fresh thrombi and clots in the lung vessels. The frequency of dead worms and of granulomatous lesions around them was difficult to evaluate, but such lesions were distinctly less frequent than those associated with living worms.

Cavernomatous transformation of hepatic venules with associated thrombosis and phlebosclerosis was found. A large number of dilated vessels had replaced the centrilobular vein. In the kidneys, haemosiderosis of the convoluted tubules was seen with casts in the medullary and juxtamedullary tubules. The cavernomatous transformation was thought to represent a variation of cardiac cirrhosis peculiar to dirofilariasis and related to the presence of worms in the posterior vena cava and its factors. The acute terminal clinical syndrome of the dogs was correlated with centrilobular necrosis and bile stasis due to simultaneous cardiac and hepatic failure.

Adcock (1961) carried out a histological study on the lungs of fifty dogs with heart worms and found marked alteration of the pulmonary arterial tree. His results indicated that whilst embolic dead adult Dirofilariae occasionally lead to thrombosis and granuloma, the living adults often caused pulmonary endarteritis and obstructive fibrosis, which often takes the form of specific lesions described as rugose and villous endarterial fibrosis. These were believed to be of diagnostic significance. The high incidence of obstructive pulmonary arterial lesions observed led Adcock to conclude that they played an important part in the development of heart failure in the disease.

V. Nematodes and the Central Nervous System

A. CEREBROSPINAL NEMATODOSIS

Innes and Saunders (1962) have provided a comprehensive review of the effects of helminth parasites on the central nervous system (CNS).

There are no fundamental differences in the pathological aspects of any "neural nematodosis" and no essential points of pathological difference exist between the lesions illustrated by Innes and Shoho (1952), Innes *et al.* (1952), Innes and Pillai (1955) and Kennedy *et al.* (1952) in sheep and in those reported in equine wobblers by Jones *et al.* (1954). Sprent (1955) noted that there were considerable variations in the changes attributable to nematodes in the CNS and he classified these changes as either haemorrhagic, degenerative or proliferative.

Haemorrhagic changes occur when nematodes arrive in the brain through the arterial circulation. Yamaguchi (1925) observed superficial haemorrhagic foci in experimental ascariasis of rodents. Hassin and Diamond (1926) and Most and Abeles (1937) observed perivascular haemorrhage in the brain in cerebral trichinosis. Capdebielle and Hussenet (1911) noted that *Angiostrongylus vasorum* lacerates blood vessels in the CNS, and Burg *et al.* (1953) reported that *Protostrongyloides* spp. could cause similar lesions.

Degenerative changes are conspicuous in neurofilariasis (Innes *et al.*, 1952; Ishii *et al.*, 1953). Kennedy *et al.* (1952) have observed swelling of axis cylinders and zones of demyelination.

The amount of damage is proportional to the size of the parasite. Small larvae such as *Toxocara canis* can wander in the brain without causing any appreciable symptoms. Larger larvae such as *Ascaris columnaris* and the filarial nematodes do sufficient damage during their migration to cause definite derangement of the nervous system. Von Brand and Cullinan (1943) observed that the larvae of *Eustrongylides ignotus* migrating into the spinal cord of rats caused destruction of entire nerve tracts.

Proliferative changes may be diffuse or focal. The diffuse infiltrations include the perivascular infiltrations described by Dacorso (1944) and Kennedy *et al.* (1952) in neurofilariasis, by Hassin and Diamond (1926) in cerebral trichinosis, and Beautyman and Woolf (1951) in cerebral ascariasis, and the meningeal infiltrations described in neurofilariasis by Innes *et al.* (1952) and Ishii *et al.* (1953). The focal infiltrations usually consist of granulomatous cellular clusters in the vicinity of the parasite. In some instances the cellular reaction consists mostly of glial proliferation, as in trichinosis (Hassin and Diamond, 1926) and neurofilariasis (Kennedy *et al.*, 1952). In other instances the cells are mostly of mesenchymal origin, as described in another case of trichinosis by Most and Abeles (1937) and in cerebral ascariasis by Beautyman and Woolf (1951). The larvae found in the mole's brain by Bunzl (1904) were densely encapsulated.

In contrast, certain nematode infections of the CNS show no evidence of cellular reaction near the parasite, e.g. in experimental ascariasis of rodents (Hoeppli, 1923; Yamaguchi, 1925) and in the case described by Fenstermacher (1934). It is probable that degenerative and cellular changes in the vicinity of the parasite only appear if the parasite has become quiescent before fixation. If the parasite is moving at the moment of fixation it may lie in apparently normal tissue, while extensive damage may be found elsewhere in the CNS.

In some instances the nematodes are found in the meningeal spaces. In this location they may cause no effect on the CNS, as in the infection described by Cahall (1889), or they may produce severe nervous symptoms. These may result either by compression on the spinal cord, as may occur with *Stephanurus dentatus* (Price, 1928), or by distension and thrombosis of the blood vessels of the spinal cord as in infections with *Gurltia paralysans* (Wolffhugel, 1934), or by destruction of the meninges as described by Schwangart (1940), or by meningeal haemorrhage as described by Burg *et al.* (1953) in infection with *Protostrongyloides cervi*.

Sprent (1955) carried out experimental infections in mice with larvae of various *Ascaris* spp. When the larvae reached the brain they produced characteristic haemorrhages on the surface of the cerebral hemispheres. It was concluded that larvae reached the brain via the arterial blood-stream and left the arteries at those points where the diameter approximated to that of the larvae, i.e. mostly on the surface of the brain, and that the larvae penetrated into the brain from the subarachnoid and choroidal tissues. The larvae of *T. canis* occurred in the brains of mice in relatively greater numbers than larvae of other species, but they rarely caused nervous symptoms. The larvae of *A. columnaris* frequently caused nervous symptoms in mice due to traumatic damage related to their large size. The brains of mice showed very slight changes upon infection with *T. canis* larvae. The larvae moved actively through the tissues, leaving little or no cellular reaction but haemorrhagic tracts. The larvae of *A. columnaris* when in the extended state were usually found in normal tissue, but when coiled they were often associated with a necrotic focus infiltrated with leucocytes. The clinical signs are related to the actual part of the CNS which is invaded by the worm and to the lesions it produces.

In India a disease of horses known as *Kumree* or *ah-drung* by the natives had been known since the early colonial days. The name is derived from the Hindustani word meaning a weak back. Early workers (Percivall, 1828) noted a relationship between this disease and "ocular filariasis". Emoto (1927) in Japan provided the first report of "lumbar paralysis" in goats. Due to the efforts of the Japanese workers (Ishii *et al.*, 1953; Itagaki *et al.*, 1946; Tanaka *et al.*, 1945; Kimura and Niimi, 1940; Yamagiwa and Shoho, 1944) and those of Innes *et al.* (Innes, 1951; Innes and Pillai, 1955; Innes and Shoho, 1952, 1953; Innes *et al.*, 1952), it is now known that these diseases are caused by the migrations of nematodes of the genus *Setaria* to the CNS.

Innes and Saunders (1962) have summarized the pathological findings in cerebrospinal nematodosis, noting that in an intensive systematic search immense numbers of sections may have to be examined in order to find a suspected lesion, although if haemorrhage occurs the search is simplified. In many cases only one lesion may be found, but in others there are two or three and in a few cases more. Foci occur anywhere in the CNS. In Japan it was noted that the spinal cord and thalamus seemed to be common sites of larval damage, but foci were also seen in many other regions. The random distribution of lesions correlates with the reported variety of clinical signs; as might be anticipated, the lower the lesion is in the CNS, the less serious is the effect produced. In all species lesions tend to be of the same size, so that the symptoms in larger animals are not likely to be so marked as those in small ones. Tanaka *et al.* (1945), for instance, found lesions in the cerebral cortices of nine horses that had displayed no symptoms of infection.

Except for malacic lesions the nervous system is normal. An important feature is the restricted, but irregular, boundaries of the focal traumatic malacia. Several lesions have an obvious tracking inwards from the pia mater. Cellular infiltrations in the meninges are constant but variable. Lymphocytes and polymorphs are present and the eosinophil content is variable, but such cells may be common. These infiltrations may involve the epidural, subdural and leptomeningeal tissues as well as the spinal nerve roots. Such infiltrations are patchy and may extend away from areas adjacent to the malacic foci, where minute haemorrhages may occur.

Ishii *et al.* (1953) found that the subcutaneous injection of *Setaria digitata* produced eosinophilic infiltrations in the sciatic nerves and spinal nerve roots, such lesions being suggestive of a direct migration through tissue to the spinal cord.

A fully developed lesion is one of acute softening, in which all structures disappear. The end result is microcavitation. The softened areas may contain many gitter cells and these may also be present in the perivascular cuffs and sleeves which are formed by lymphocytes and eosinophils around the lesions.

In and near to malacic foci the axis cylinders become irregularly shaped and homogeneous globose bodies appear which stain faintly with cytoplasmic stains and are negative for lipids or myelin. Such altered cylinders stain deeply by metallic impregnation. Many of the globose bodies may be two to three times the diameter of a normal axis cylinder and some are much larger. Longitudinal sections of the axis cylinders may show all stages of change from delicate to gross beading and complete fragmentation.

As might be expected from its origin, a malacic focus may be small in girth but tortuous and long. It may involve the white matter or the grey matter or both. Tracts may start in the subpial zone and extend into the white or grey matter. Tracts leading from the pia mater in and out of the nervous tissue were seen many times by Kimura and Niimi (1940), Yamagiwa and Shoho (1944) and by Innes and his colleagues.

In cerebrospinal nematodosis there is little general vascular dilatation and no thrombosis. The vessels around the softened areas may be more obvious due to an increase of reticulin fibres in their walls. At the edges of the liquefied zones there is an astrocytic proliferation and fibrillary gliosis which becomes more pronounced as the lesions become chronic.

In some of the malacic lesions of sheep and goats, cross or oblique sections of immature nematodes have been found. The nematode origin of the disease was established by the Japanese and the work described by Ishii *et al.* (1953).

At present it is established that the disease is caused by species of the genus *Setaria*. The migratory path of the parasite is still in some doubt, but Innes and Shoho (1953) and Shoho (1955) thought that a direct tissue migration might be involved. Shoho and Nair (1960) experimentally produced the disease in goats by the inoculation of the infective larvae of *S. digitata*. Four out of five goats showed nervous disturbances and the post-mortem examination of three of these revealed lesions in the CNS typical of those associated with wandering nematodes. In one goat a cuticular ring was found in a tumour-like growth under the dura mater.

The pathology of the disease was identified in goats in Ceylon by Innes (1951) and Innes *et al.* (1952), but the causal worms were unidentified.

The nature of the lesion was shown by Innes and Shoho (1953) to be basically a mechanical trauma caused by the worm. Paralysis and essentially the same lesion apart from the eosinophilia can be induced by puncture of the lumbar cord of a sheep by a hypodermic needle. Innes and Saunders (1962) suggested that granulomatous lesions in the CNS might develop only when a larva stops migrating and dies.

Kennedy *et al.* (1952) described a neurological disease of sheep in New Hampshire and New York, U.S.A. Lesions typical of cerebrospinal setariosis were found and three worms were found in sections of the brains and cords of two animals. Whitlock (1959) finally identified the worm as *Elaphostrongylus tenuis*. A similar parasite *E. odocrilea* occurs in the meninges of deer in North America and Europe. In most cases there are no associated lesions, but sometimes accompanying haemorrhage has been noted. Hobmaier and Hobmaier (1934) found the worms in veins beneath the spines of the deer, but the only instance in which they are known to cause severe damage to the brain and cord is when they find their way into sheep (Whitlock, 1959).

Roneus and Nordkvist (1962) pointed out that the reindeer which lived in the forests and highland areas of Sweden commonly suffer from a disease characterized clinically by ataxia, paresis and convulsions. The aetiology of this disease has for a long time been unknown, but in December 1960 the authors carried out a post-mortem examination on a reindeer which had exhibited typical clinical signs. Meningomyelitis in the lumbar region and an eosinophilic granuloma in one sciatic nerve were observed. The abundance of eosinophils in the inflammatory exudate aroused the suspicion of a parasitic background to the lesion. Consequently, twenty further reindeer were examined, particular attention being paid to the brain and spinal cord. In practically all the animals which showed signs of locomotory disturbances, nematodes were found in the CNS. The nematodes were recognized as *Elaphostrongylus rangiferi*. The parasite was also found in the skeletal musculature of five of seven animals examined and in the middle ear of one animal. Larvae of the same species were present in various tissues of some animals and eggs often in large clumps were found in the CNS and the musculature as well as in the hypophysis of one animal.

The presence of the nematodes was associated with a lymphohistiocytic and eosinophilic meningitis, particularly at the level of the cauda equina, the junction between cervical and thoracic regions of the spinal cord, and over the brain. In some animals an inflammatory exudate was also present in the superficial layers of the brain. Granulomas were also found in the meninges about the cauda equina in many animals. No definite signs of mechanical damage were observed in the brain and spinal cord that were attributed to the nematodes. The meningitis was often associated with degenerative changes in the spinal nerve roots. Inflammatory and degenerative changes were observed in the proximal portions of the sciatic nerves.

The presence of *Elaphostrongylus* in the CNS was considered to be the cause of the lesions and the locomotory disability observed.

Experimental work on a neurologic disease of the wild moose (*Alces alces americana*) in north-eastern North America has recently been reported by Anderson (1964). He infected two calves with *Pneumostrongylus tenuis* obtained from the white-tailed deer (*Odocoileus virginianus borealis*). Two to three weeks after infection both the moose became lethargic. Weakness and ataxia became progressively more pronounced and terminated in paraplegia. At the post-mortem examinations on the 40th and 60th days, immature fifth-stage nematodes were recovered from the CNS. They were found in the saline in which the CNS of the first calf was placed and in the subdural spaces of the cranium and vertebral column of the second moose. Histological examination showed parasites and extensive traumatic damage in the central canal and dorsal horns of the cord of both calves. Focal malacia with microcavitation was seen in all regions of the cord. The ventral fissure, dorsal sulcus and leptomeninges showed infiltrations with lymphocytes, plasma cells and eosinophils. Perivascular cuffing with lymphocytes, petechial haemorrhages, neuron degeneration and loss, together with swelling and disappearance of axis cylinders and myelin sheaths, were seen.

Oguni *et al.* (1959) were interested in the diagnosis of cerebrospinal nematodiasis, and they concluded that the increase in the number of cells and the appearance of acidophils in the cerebrospinal fluid might be employed for this purpose.

Done (1957), in England, described two instances of malacic lesions in the spinal cords of two pigs with a nature and tracking like those of nematodosis.

There are differences in the tissue reactions produced by immature worms and those produced by microfilariae. Van Bogaert *et al.* (1955), in a review of filariasis due to *Loa loa*, described a case in which was present a subacute or chronic encephalitis with diffuse inflammation of the adventitia and vascular apparatus, producing a nodular reaction and subsequent granuloma which tended to be necrotic. Not all microfilariae do, however, produce pathological changes in the nervous system. In Africa, *Acanthocheilonema gracile* occurs as a threadlike adult in the connective tissue of man and apes. The human infection is usually asymptomatic. Innes and Saunders (1962) studied several cases in squirrel monkeys which showed no clinical signs, but in which the brain in all parts was literally teeming with microfilariae. These were present inside blood vessels, in neural substance and in the subarachnoid space. There was no surrounding reaction in the brain substance, but in parts of the cerebral hemisphere there was a mild and focal meningitis.

One of the most significant papers published on the infection of the CNS by nematodes was that of Mackerras and Sandars (1955), who worked with *Angiostrongylus cantonensis*. The adults of this parasite live in the pulmonary arteries of rats. Mackerras and Sandars (1955) showed that the larvae normally migrate to the CNS, which they reach within 17 h. The larvae aggregate in the frontal lobes of the cerebral hemispheres and wander through the grey matter without producing any haemorrhage or obvious reaction. After 7 days the larvae have moulted and inflammation occurs around some dead larvae and cast sheaths. There seems to be no tissue response to living larvae. About 11–13 days after infection another ecdysis occurs and the young adults migrate to the dorsal surface of the cerebrum. The meninges react by a dilatation of vessels and a leucocytic infiltration. They eventually heal with scar formation. The young adults remain in the surface of the cerebrum until about the end of 1 month from infection, when they return to the general circulation via the jugular veins and so reach the heart and pulmonary arteries. In heavy infections young adults may reach the ventral surface of the cerebrum and ventricles.

In experimentally infected mice the inflammatory response is much more severe than in the rat brain and may be accompanied by severe nervous symptoms with coma or death. In guinea-pigs only a few larvae reach the brain and these elicit a marked inflammatory response. Mackerras and Sanders (1955) stated that "although mice are closely related to rats, it appears that *A. cantonensis* cannot come to maturity in them. In fact, the two organisms are ill adapted to each other, as the worm may kill the mouse by its wanderings in the brain and the mouse in turn certainly destroys the worm." This important work of Mackerras and Sanders described a nematode life cycle which normally utilizes the CNS. The normal life cycle was not associated with clinical illness and there were no permanent lesions, in fact lesions only occurred in heavy experimental infections.

Alicata (1965) has reviewed extensively the association of *Angiostrongylus* and eosinophilic meningitis in man and animals.

In Chile there is a commonly occurring paralysis of domestic cats which Wolffhugel (1934) has ascribed to *Gurltia paralysans*, a metastrongylid nematode. Mackerras and Sandars (1955) suggested that the parasite normally inhabited the lungs of one of the native felines of Chile, and that in domestic cats it failed to complete its life cycle although able to reach sexual maturity within the veins of the spinal cord.

Stephanurus dentatus is normally an inhabitant of the kidney of pigs, but it has been found in the CNS. In two cases posterior paresis due to adult worms has been recorded (Price, 1928; Tromba et al., 1957). Raffensperger (1931) examined a heavily infected carcass in which three worms were present in the spinal canal. There were no clinical symptoms associated with these worms and no lesions were recorded.

In general, then, it may be stated that in the CNS a malacic lesion must be the immediate reaction to a nematode and a granulomatous reaction is the residual more chronic effect in which the parasite is usually dead. The marked reactions in the CNS are usually attributed to nematodes in an unusual host.

VI. VISCERAL LARVA MIGRANS

In 1947, Perlingiero and Gyorgy described a new clinical syndrome of children characterized by fever, hepatomegaly, leucocytosis with marked eosinophilia and hyperglobulinaemia. Two years later Zuelzer and Apt (1949) described their pathological findings and clinical observations in eight similar cases. In 1950 Mercer *et al.* found an ascarid larva in a liver lesion and Behrer (1951) recorded a similar finding. It was at first thought that the larvae were those of the human ascarid, but Beaver *et al.* (1952) described three cases and in one of these a larva was found and identified as *Toxocara canis.* They named the syndrome "visceral larva migrans" and were able to produce it experimentally in human beings. A fatal case was recorded by Brill *et al.* (1953), who found granulomas in the lungs, heart, liver and kidneys and demonstrated the presence of *Toxocara.* Other cases have been described by Milburn and Ernst (1953) and by Gault and Webb (1957). Karpinski *et al.* (1956) recorded a further two cases and demonstrated *Toxocara* larvae in the livers of each of them. They proposed to name the syndrome "larval granulomatosis", which accords with pathological terminology. Dent *et al.* (1956) described the post-mortem findings in a case which died from homologous serum jaundice. There were characteristic lesions, some of which contained parasites, and these were widely scattered in numerous organs, including the brain. In this connexion it is relevant to note that Wilder (1950) detected larval parasites in human eyes and that Nichols (1956) showed these to be *Toxocara canis* larvae. Ashton (1960) writing from London has described four cases of retinal granuloma due to *T. canis.* Beautyman and Woolf (1951) found an encapsulated ascarid in the thalamus of a child who died of poliomyelitis and *T. canis* was also found in a child's brain by Moore (1962). Smith and Beaver (1953) showed that the larvae could remain viable in the human host for one year or more. Dickson and Woodcock, writing from Bolton in 1959, recorded a further case of a child with visceral larva migrans. Typical lesions were found in the liver at biopsy; this organ was enlarged and studded with firm greyish nodules a few millimetres in diameter. Histological examination showed these to be inflammatory foci separated by normal liver tissue. In some fields, the liver cells were entirely replaced by eosinophils. Amorphous debris, probably of verminous origin, was also seen. Discrete granulomas were present, consisting of epithelioid cells and foreign-body giant cells with a surrounding zone of lymphocytes and plasma cells. The case is interesting because it included a history of convulsions.

Obscure cerebral symptoms and convulsions have been reported before and it was suggested by Zuelzer and Apt (1949) that an encephalopathy due to vascular sensitization was part of the syndrome. Sprent (1955), writing on the invasion of the CNS by nematodes, expressed the opinion on the basis of much experimental work that "the occurrence of the larvae of *T. canis* in the brain might be of considerable medical importance". He admitted that in his experiments with small animals the pathological significance of *T. canis* larvae appeared to be slight, but he did not discount the possibility that the larvae may instigate allergic reactions or carry micro-organisms into the CNS.

Beaver *et al.* (1952) suggested that the syndrome of visceral larva migrans develops in patients with an allergic diathesis. This may enhance the response to infection, the inflammatory reaction being more severe than with the homologous ascarid, so that the signs and symptoms of the disease are more marked. Behrer (1951) suggested that the cause of the eosinophilia is the keratin which the larva sheds when it moults in passing through the stages of its life cycle. Friedmann and Hervada (1960) described a case of visceral larva migrans with severe myocardial involvement, followed by complete recovery. They thought it likely that direct invasion of the myocardium by *T. canis* had occurred. Two cases of visceral larva migrans were recorded by Molina Pasquel (1961) in Mexico. Cases of visceral larva migrans are also recognized in Liverpool; Keidan (personal communication) states "We have seen five cases in which the diagnosis of visceral larva migrans was strongly suspected because of pulmonary infiltration, enlarged liver, eosinophilia and raised serum γ-globulin. Liver biopsy in one case showed typical granulomata. All the children appeared to make an uneventful recovery." This fortunately does seem to be the general rule, but there obviously are exceptions and enough is known to show that the condition can be serious.

In nearly all cases there is a history of pica and evidence of the contamination of the soil by the faeces of animals likely to be harbouring *T. canis* or *T. cati*. The majority of cases are seen in the "toddler" age group and pica is uncommon in children over the age of 3 years. Pulmonary symptoms may develop first and are often of short duration. Hepatomegaly is a constant finding and usually iron-deficiency anaemia is seen. Peripheral eosinophilia is present at some time in all cases, but may not appear until 2–3 months after the respiratory symptoms. The serum γ-globulin is raised and is suggestive of a marked antibody response. Heiner and Kevy (1956) found agar diffusion precipitation reactions between patients' serum and an antigen prepared from *Toxocara* larvae. Sprent (1958) used adult *T. canis* antigen in skin tests with promising results. Jung and Pacheco (1958) showed that the intradermal test had limitations with regard to its use in the diagnosis of the condition and published (1960) the results of haemagglutination tests which might provide useful evidence for the diagnosis of the condition.

Olson (1960) evaluated the larval precipitate test for use in the diagnosis of experimental and clinical *T. canis* infections. His results from an experimental rabbit system showed that the detection of *Toxocara* antibody was possible, but that it was complicated by a cross-reaction with anti-*Ascaris lumbricoides* sera. A similar detection was noted with sera from suspected clinical cases of *Toxocara* infection in children.

Typical lesions produced in a rabbit by three exposures to 5000 embryonated *T. canis* eggs are shown in Figs. 6A–E and 7A, B.

Visceral larva migrans associated with diabetes insipidus and with an eosinophilia was reported in a dog by Richards and Sloper (1964). A severe granulomatous inflammation of the hypothalamus and adjacent neurohypophysis proved to be due to a nematode larva which was probably *T. canis* or *Uncinaria stenocephala*. Neither of these parasites were hitherto recognized as a cause of encephalitis in the dog. Macroscopically the pituitary gland was

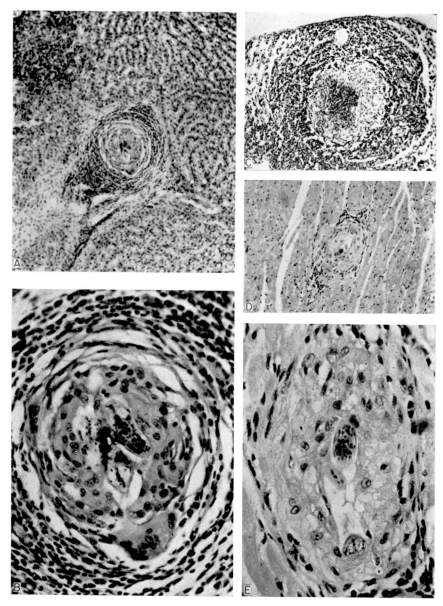

FIG. 6. A and B, *Toxocara canis* in the liver of the rabbit, showing (A) granulomatas, and (B) granuloma and a larva surrounded by fibroblastic reaction. C, *T. canis* in the lung of a rabbit. Eosinophilic granuloma seen after three exposures; there is a central zone of eosinophilic debris, an area of fibroblasts surrounded by an area of small round cells and an outer layer of eosinophils. D and E, *T. canis* in the myocardium of a rabbit, showing (D) a typical myocardial lesion, and (E) larva surrounded by fibroblastic reaction and slight inflammation.

abnormally small and histologically there was no posterior pituitary tissue. The principal signs of disease in the dog were those of diabetes insipidus. The case is interesting in that the severe reaction was directed against a nematode in the CNS of its natural host, whereas, as has already been mentioned, marked reactions are more commonly seen in cases of nematodes in the CNS of unusual hosts.

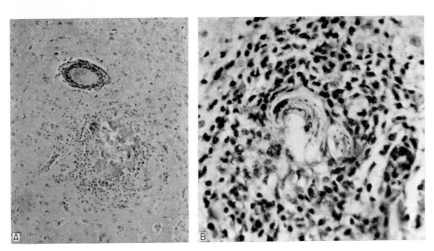

FIG. 7. *Toxocara canis* in the brain of a rabbit. A, Area of traumatic malacia with an associated inflammatory response. Note "cuffing" of adjacent blood vessel. B, Response seen after three exposures.

Perhaps some of the most tragic aspects of visceral larva migrans are seen when the larvae reach the eyes of young children. Ashton (1960) carried out histological examination of the retinal tumours of four cases, each of which consisted of a solitary granuloma resulting from *Toxocara* infection. Previously Wilder (1950) examined eyes of forty-six patients originally diagnosed pathologically as cases of pseudoglioma, Coats's disease or endophthalmitis. In most of these cases the patients were children and in many cases the eyes were enucleated for suspected retinoblastoma. In serial sections from twenty-four of these cases Wilder found evidence of nematode larvae and in the remaining twenty-two she considered the reaction characteristic of nematode endophthalmitis. Nichols (1956) identified the larval fragments in four of these cases as *T. canis*. Irvine and Irvine (1959) also reported a case of endophthalmitis in a young child which was due to infestation with *T. canis* and was originally diagnosed as a retinoblastoma. Ashton (1960) pointed out that histological diagnosis could only be made with certainty when the larvae had been demonstrated. The possibility of a nematode origin was suggested by unexplained granulomatous reactions in the eyes of young persons, by the eosinophilic infiltration or by the eosinophilic abscesses, by the presence of foreign-body giant cells or hyaline capsular material of the appropriate size, and by fibrinoid necrosis in the immediate vicinity of the larva.

Bourke and Yeates (1961) in Australia also reported a case of nematode endophthalmitis in a 5-year-old boy. Blindness was due to a cyclitic membrane and detachment of the retina. Four years earlier the child had suffered from recurrent fever, anaemia and enlargement of the liver. At that time, although the ocular fundi were normal, the clinical findings suggested infection with *T. canis*. A laparotomy was performed and the liver found to be studded with minute granulomatous lesions.

Chaudhuri and Saha (1959) were interested in reports of human cases of asthma with eosinophilia, tropical eosinophilia or eosinophil lung and the possibility that these might be due to invasion by nematode larvae, for which man is not a natural host. They therefore infected guinea-pigs with the embryonated eggs of *T. canis* and showed that the animals developed a peripheral eosinophilia. Histological sections of guinea-pig lungs showed peribronchiolar accumulations of eosinophils with eosinophilic exudates in the bronchioles and alveoli, together with a diffuse interalveolar eosinophilic infiltration. The livers showed numerous granulomatous areas, often with remnants of larvae in the centre and eosinophils in profusion at the periphery. They also demonstrated a peripheral eosinophilia in a human volunteer who received 100 embryonated eggs.

Webster (1958) published an account of the pathology associated with *T. canis* in the dog. She found that migrations of the parasite were able to induce extensive tissue damage. Seventy-two hours after infection liver sections showed three larvae in the parenchyma with an infiltration of leucocytes. During the next 48 h the number of leucocytes continued to increase, the predominant cells being neutrophils, monocytes and eosinophils. There was a tendency for these cells to accumulate, forming nodules, and occasionally a larva could be seen in their midst. The tissue became necrotic, haemorrhages were common and there was a marked fatty degeneration of liver cells. The first vestiges of capsules were seen on about the 10th day, when the larvae became surrounded by thin fibrous capsules. At the time of capsule formation there was a withdrawal of some of the leucocytes from the area. About 3 weeks after infection the liver tissue began to regenerate and the foci of liver-cell degeneration were repaired by fibrous tissue proliferation.

There was also an infiltration of leucocytes into the lungs with a high percentage of eosinophils. These cells tended to aggregate and form dense nodules. In light infections there was a lobular pneumonia and in heavy infections the pneumonia became severe with an exudate of red blood cells, epithelial cells, mucus and larvae in the bronchioles and alveoli.

Botti (1957) also carried out an investigation of the behaviour of *T. canis* in its natural canine host. Of particular interest to the author was the nature of the miliary nodules found in the kidneys. The lesions were mostly subcapsular in position. They showed fibroblastic activity with an infiltration of histiocytes and plasmocytes with tendencies to necrosis and calcification. Three basic types of lesion were distinguished. The first type showed well-preserved *T. canis* larvae, whilst the second showed a thick encapsulation of the necrotic zone. The third was almost exclusively composed of connective tissue. The lesions were obviously resolving.

Intraocular larva migrans was reported in dogs by Rubin and Saunders (1965). They described four cases and found granulomas resembling those seen in other organs. Larvae of the genus *Toxocara* were incriminated. Barron and Saunders (1966) found granulomas around *Toxocara* sp. larvae in a wide variety of canine tissues: kidney, liver, lung, myocardium, skeletal muscle, thyroid, pancreas, pituitary, lymph node, intestine, retina, brain and cauda equina. The larvae were presumed to be *T. canis*. The lesions resembled those seen in human beings, but no clinical signs were observed. Barron and Saunders (1966) pointed out that as the lesions occur in the host that also harbours the adult worm the previously accepted definition of visceral larva migrans is too narrow, and they proposed that the term be applied to any visceral lesions produced by migrating helminth larvae.

Experimental work on visceral larva migrans was carried out by Roneus (1963) utilizing *T. cati* in pigs and by Done *et al.* (1960) utilizing *T. canis* in the same host.

Roneus (1963) was interested in a liver lesion in swine which is usually called hepatitis interstitialis chronica parasitaria multiplex, white spots or parasitic scarring. These changes appear as macroscopic grey white spots with ill-defined borders. *Cysticercus tenuicolus* was incriminated as a cause of this liver damage, but latterly it has generally been considered that the lesions are due to the larval migrations of *Ascaris suum*.

However, it is known that pigs may have an abundance of *A. suum* in the intestine, although their livers may be practically free from parasitic damage. Other pigs may have numerous parasitic scars in the liver and completely lack the parasite in the intestine. Roneus (1963), stimulated by work on visceral larva migrans, experimented to see whether or not he could produce the lesions of white spot with *T. cati* larvae. He therefore infected pigs with *T. cati* eggs in numbers varying from 20000 to 100000 and killed them 3 days, 10 days and 63 days after infection. After 3 days a large number of small haemorrhages and grey white spots on the surface and in the body of the liver were observed macroscopically. *T. cati* larvae were demonstrated histologically in the intralobular liver tissue. Liver-cell degeneration occurred in the centre of the haemorrhages and glycogen was absent in the surrounding liver cells. The grey white spots were composed mainly of histiocytes and eosinophil leucocytes. By the 10th day the numbers of *T. cati* larvae seen were smaller. The haemorrhages and the degenerate liver cells were resorbed. The grey white spots had increased in area and now consisted exclusively of interlobular infiltrations of eosinophil leucocytes. There was no increase in the amount of connective tissue at this stage. On day 63 no larvae were found and only isolated grey white spots remained. At this stage these consisted of new formations of interlobular connective tissue with a moderate number of eosinophil leucocytes. Roneus (1963) then showed that the invasion of swine by *T. cati* produced parasitic liver lesions similar to those seen in the field. *T. cati* may be one of the causes of white spot in swine.

As a result of seeing a case of myelomalacia in a pig, Done *et al.* (1960) became interested in spinal nematodiasis. They decided to carry out some experiments and utilized *T. canis*, since this parasite was known to undergo a somatic migration and was also a species to which pigs might be exposed naturally. *Toxascaris leonina* was used in a limited fashion for comparable experiments.

In the pig *T. canis* larvae migrated by the somatic route and were distributed throughout the body. Their presence in the brain and spinal cord was associated with nervous signs which were apparently provoked by the host reaction to static larvae rather than by damage resulting from active migration.

Toxascaris leonina migrated transperitoneally and caused little tissue damage. A pig given 60000 eggs showed no clinical abnormalities. Lesions in the form of small semi-opaque nodules were numerous, but were confined to the gastro-splenic omentum and subserosa of the colon and caecum. Five similar lesions were present under the capsule of the liver. These nodules contained living *T. leonina* larvae. Sections of the large intestine showed granulomatous lesions in the submucosa and muscle layers and larvae were seen in these lesions. Tracts of eosinophils and round cells from the peritoneal surface through the muscle layers indicated a migration from the abdominal cavity towards the lumen of the large intestine. Multinuclear giant cells were present. No larvae were found in any other organs nor were any histological changes detected.

Using *T. canis* doses of 10000–1250000 embryonated eggs, these writers found that there were no significant differences either in the distribution of the larvae or in the nature of the lesions produced. However, only at the higher dosage levels were the techniques used sufficiently sensitive to reveal the full extent of systemic invasion.

In a pig given 250000 embryonated *Toxocara canis* eggs, clinical signs were seen on the 32nd day, when it was noted that the pig was inclined to stumble when made to turn or back. By the 39th day there was a severe posterior paresis with frequent collapse of the hind-quarters. Ataxia and paresis gradually increased and eventually the pig was unable to stand without swaying and falling. As well as showing nervous symptoms all the infected pigs showed a check in growth. Two days after infection larvae were found in the submucosa and in the crypts of the ileum. They provoked a reaction by round cells, eosinophils and a thin layer of fibroblasts. This reaction gradually diminished and no abnormalities were seen at 32 days.

The gross liver lesions consisted of white nodules present over the entire surface. By 16 days these lesions had become distinctly nodular and in places were confluent. The lesions reached a maximum size by 49 days, after which they regressed to firm white nodules connected by fibrous tracts.

Microscopically at day 2 there was local hepatic tissue destruction with haemorrhage and leucocyte infiltration. This was followed by oedema and the production of fibroblasts. The oedema gradually subsided as the fibrous tissue matured. By 4 days, round cells, foreign-body-type giant cells and eosinophils were present. The eosinophils were particularly common along the edges of oedematous zones. Typical granuloma were present by the end of the 1st week. These consisted of a mixture of eosinophils, lymphoid and epithelial cells round a central necrotic core which sometimes contained a larva. At the end of the experiment, in addition to the resolved intralobular granulomata, there was a considerable accumulation of fibrous tissue in portal tracts which were variably infiltrated with eosinophils.

Larvae were in the lungs by day 4 and after 8 days there were numerous haemorrhages in all lobes. At 16 days oedema of the septa was evident. The haemorrhages eventually disappeared, but the thickening of the septa was present 2 months after infection. Up to 4 days after infection there were few histological changes in the lung, but after 8 days the septa and pleura were thickened by oedema and the alveolar walls were swollen. There were some fairly extensive haemorrhagic areas in the lung tissue with necrotic foci and accumulations of round cells and eosinophils. Early granuloma formation was also seen at this time. At 16 days the reaction was similar, but at this time an uneven thickening in the media of the zone of the arterioles was seen. At 32 days giant cells were numerous and these were usually associated with nodular lesions. By 49 days healing was apparent and fibrous tissue was replacing the oedema. By 64 days all the larvae that were left were encapsulated.

Microscopic cardiac lesions were seen at 8 days. These consisted of small foci of myocardial degeneration with loose infiltration of round cells within the fibres. Not many eosinophils were seen. Some lesions were situated close to or within the endocardium. By 16 days the reaction was granulomatous in type. By 64 days the lesions were smaller in size and all were encapsulated.

In only one pig were significant macroscopic changes seen in the CNS, and this animal was clinically severely affected. The gross lesions in this pig consisted of swelling and yellowish discoloration in some of the posterior folia of the cerebellar vermis. Larvae were present in the brain by 8 days, but they provoked no lesions at this time apart from a slight focal eosinophil infiltration and a small amount of haemosiderin deposition. By 16 days there was some vascular cuffing with eosinophils and lymphocytes and the first signs were seen of a granulomatous reaction. By 28 days the granulomatous reactions were severe and widespread and there was evidence of a considerable disruption of nervous tissue, particularly in the neighbourhood of granulomata. There was necrosis of neurones, axonal swelling and distortion and fragmentation of myelin sheaths. Although all parts of the brain were affected, it was in the cerebellum that the greatest damage was found.

In the spinal cord the picture was similar in that the tissue response appeared at the same time. Eosinophil infiltration and granuloma formation were less pronounced, although multinucleate giant cells were common. In the cord the lesions were restricted to the white matter, but in the brain they occurred in both the grey and white matter. A characteristic feature of the experimental disease was the production in the cord of irregularly distributed areas of myelin degeneration. These lesions were essentially similar to those seen in cerebrospinal nematodiasis of sheep and goats (Innes et al., 1952). Fat laden macrophages were, however, rare. By 64 days granulomatous lesions were present in the kidney and it was noted that there was a relative absence of eosinophils. Other lesions characteristic of visceral larva migrans were found in gastro-splenic lymph nodes, pancreas, adrenal, tongue, diaphragm and voluntary muscle.

In the pig it seems that the lungs offer little resistance to the onward passage of *T. canis* larvae, which is in contrast to the situation seen with *Ascaris lumbricoides*. Although the pig may act as a transport host for *T. canis*, the relatively early death of most of the larvae in the tissues minimizes its importance in this respect. The lesions seen in the liver were similar to those of white spot, a condition usually attributable to *Ascaris suum*.

The marked local eosinophilia and granuloma formation which were observed, even in the early stages of infection, do not appear to bear out the contention of Sprent and English (1958) that such lesions are indicative of repeated infections. Unlike the situation described in mice by Sprent (1955) and in filariasis in goats and sheep by Innes *et al.* (1952), clinical nervous signs in the pig were associated with the development of local tissue reactions around dead or static worms and not so much with the trauma caused by actively migrating *T. canis* larvae. The histological picture in the pig's brain closely resembles that seen in *T. canis* infection in man (Dent *et al.*, 1956).

In the pig, eosinophil infiltration of the brain in proximity to static or encapsulated larvae was spectacular. However, in the spinal cord the eosinophilic infiltration was less marked and the lesions resembled those described in setariasis in sheep and goats (Innes *et al.*, 1952) and kumri of horses (Innes and Pillai, 1955).

Sweatman *et al.* (1962) in New Zealand infected sheep with a variety of parasites in an effort to elucidate the pathogenesis of focal fibrotic liver lesions which are again known colloquially as "white spot". They utilized protozoa, cestodes and the nematodes *Toxocara canis*, *T. cati*, *Toxascaris leonina* and *Ascaris lumbricoides*. Lesions caused by *T. canis* larvae were found in three lambs $6\frac{1}{2}$–7 months following infection. Small white scars were present on the surface of the livers and additional scars were found in the parenchyma. Microscopically these lesions proved to be granulomas containing eosinophils, lymphocytes, macrophages, fibrocytes and epithelioid cells around a central necrotic core which sometimes contained a larva. Many similar lesions occurred beneath the pleura of the lung and others were scattered throughout the lung parenchyma. Similar focal lesions were also found in the myocardium and lesions containing viable larvae were observed in the kidneys, muscles and brain. When lambs were infected with *T. cati*, no liver damage or larvae were found, although the feeding of the same eggs to mice showed them to be viable. Infections with *T. leonina* produced a very mild infection in one lamb, whilst infection with *A. lumbricoides* produced no lesions. The authors stated that the close association of dogs and sheep in New Zealand would seem ideal for *T. canis* infections, but they believed the feeding habits of sheep would make a massive infection, by direct ingestion of dog faeces, unlikely. The authors believe that the insignificant amount of liver damage produced by *T. leonina* was probably related to its transperitoneal route of migration. It is important to keep the position in perspective and point out that the main result of the work by Sweatman *et al.* was to show that parasitic liver damage in New Zealand sheep was almost entirely attributable to *Taenia hydatigina* or *Echinococcus granulosus* and not to nematodes.

Schaeffler (1960) also infected sheep with *Toxocara canis*. No clinical signs were produced. The lesions seen consisted of haemorrhages and infiltration with mononuclear cells, neutrophils and especially eosinophils. Focal necrosis occurred in the intestinal lymph nodes, liver and lungs, but few cellular changes were observed around actively migrating larvae in the brain and other organs.

Galvin (1964) carried out experimental infections with *T. canis* in chickens and pigeons and produced lesions of visceral larva migrans. It was further found that both these birds harboured living infective-stage larvae for at least 142 days after inoculation. Gross tissue changes were only seen in the liver. In the pigeon small foci of leucocytic infiltration were seen 6 days after inoculation. The basic lesion resulting from larval migration consisted of a central zone of necrosis surrounded by an inflammatory zone of variable intensity. The necrosis always involved the hepatic epithelium and in some instances the reticulo-endothelial cells were also involved. The inflammatory reaction consisted of varying degrees of hyperplasia of the reticulo-endothelial cells and infiltration of heterophils and a lesser number of eosinophils, monocytes and lymphocytes. Following on this stage, giant cell formation became apparent. Ninety-one days after infection the first granulomatous lesions were seen. These lesions were composed of a central zone of necrosis and foreign-body giant cells surrounded by a zone of reticular tissue containing a few leucocytes. The outermost layer was composed of fibrous connective tissue forming a capsule in which a large number of heterophils and some eosinophils were present.

In the chicken, the early liver lesions were generally less severe than in the pigeon. However, the granulomatous lesions differed in several respects. The connective tissue layer was partially or completely surrounded by lymphoid nodules and there seemed to be a lesser number of heterophils, eosinophils and giant cells.

Babero (1959) studied experimental infections with *Ascaris laevis* in species of rodents and other mammals. He found that the liver showed heavy leucocytic infiltrations with atrophy and necrosis of many hepatic cells. Larvae were often found in necrotic areas. Pneumonic changes were noted in the lungs and the slight kidney lesions were attributed to a toxin.

Munnick (1958) used a histochemical approach to study the changes in the livers of mice infected with *Ascaris lumbricoides*. In the foci initiated by the migrating larvae the content of glycogen and RNA was totally reduced and that of fat considerably reduced. Glycoprotein increased with the age of the foci and this was related to the proliferation of connective tissue. Alkaline phosphatase occurred only in small amounts in occasional foci.

Experimental granulomas were produced by Arean (1958), who inoculated *Ascaris lumbricoides* eggs into the livers and portal veins of rabbits. The inflammatory reaction produced was proportional in severity to the number of eggs which were present at a given site. Two hours after injection the eggs were surrounded by eosinophils and 14 h later monocytes, giant cells and fibroblasts were present. At the end of 1 week pseudotubercle formation was seen. Healing occurred by hyalinization and fibrosis. Further studies (Arean et al., 1962) on heat-killed eggs showed that the injection of these into subcutaneous tissue, skeletal muscle and the peritoneal cavity of rats as well as the liver of rabbits produced an identical inflammatory response to that seen with live eggs. It seems then that the metabolic products of live embryos play little or no role in the production of the inflammatory reaction. The chemical removal of the "chitinous" layer of the egg resulted in a less marked eosinophilic response. Evidence was provided of an immunological process being involved, because a more intense inflammatory response was seen in rabbits with previous experience of the material and in these animals the resorption of eggs and the healing of lesions were more rapid. Lesions were produced by whole eggs, lipid-free eggs and by lipids extracted from the eggs, suggesting that the tissue response is chiefly an unspecific response to foreign material.

Arean and Crandall (1962) also immunized rabbits with lyophilized larvae and injected second-stage larvae intravenously. The larvae were immobilized in the septal capillaries of the lung, where they rapidly degenerated. In control rabbits the larvae migrated to the interstitial tissue and alveolar spaces of the lung, where extensive haemorrhages were caused. The inflammatory response following challenge was characterized by accumulations of neutrophils and eosinophils and was more rapid in the immunized rabbits than the non-immunized. Granulomata containing epithelioid cells and multinucleate giant cells subsequently formed in immunized rabbits and more slowly in non-immunized rabbits. In the immunized animals an intensely acidophilic material which might represent an antigen-antibody complex was associated with the cuticle of degenerating larvae in the granulomata. Granulomata were resorbed by 20 days in immunized rabbits, but were still present at 30 days in non-immunized rabbits.

Chowdury (1960) placed living *Ascaris lumbricoides* eggs into the eyes of rabbits and guinea-pigs. Two weeks after inoculation into the vitreous body no eggs could be detected in the posterior chamber, but there was a marked eosinophilic response in the vitreous humour as well as an eosinophilic choroiditis. Eggs were seen in the peri-ocular tissue, where they were surrounded by an intense eosinophilic granulomatous reaction.

Work of considerable interest on the formation of parasitic granuloma was performed in Massachusetts, where experiments on granuloma formation in the laboratory mouse were carried out by Lichtenberg and Mekbel (1962). They believed that the granulomatous process was an attempt by the host to sequester antigens of low diffusability or their breakdown products and to localize them at their site of deposition, the response being basically the walling-off of an antigen-containing space.

For their experiments they utilized *Ascaris suis* eggs, which were injected intravenously so as to produce discrete granulomas. They showed that for the first 8 days the cellular reaction occurring in the adult mouse was more pronounced than in the newborn, but that by the 16th day there was no difference in the size of the granulomas.

In the adult mouse, from the 1st day there was a severe cellular infiltration with neutrophils, eosinophils and large mononuclear cells around vessels containing eggs. From the 2nd day alveolitis featured prominently, as was shown by an intra-alveolar accumulation of macrophages and leucocytes in the areas surrounding the forming granuloma. Large mononuclear cells and occasional foreign-body giant cells were also present. In foci with severe cellular reactions some disintegration of the eggs was seen. From day 8 perivascular infiltration with round cells and eosinophils occurred. By the 32nd day there was thickening, hyalinization and narrowing of small arteries and arterioles. By this time many of the granulomata were large and some showed evidence of healing.

However, in the newborn mouse there was little or no reaction during the first 8 days. Any cellular infiltrate present was composed mainly of neutrophils, some large mononuclear cells and a few eosinophils. In a few cases endothelial swelling and proliferation were evident, with occasional giant cell formation. Up until the 8th day there was little or no alveolitis. From the 16th day there was a progressive cellular infiltration around the eggs and the lesions came to resemble those seen in adult mice. There is then a diminished reactivity in the young mouse, but 8 days after birth the reaction gradually becomes comparable to that seen in the adult animal. The reasons for the delay in granulomatous response in the newborn remain speculative.

Further work by Mekbel and Lichtenberg (1962) compared the reaction in the unsensitized host with that which occurred in mice previously exposed to intraperitoneal injections of *Ascaris suis* eggs. Attempts were made to detect either enhancement and acceleration of the granuloma formation in the adult, or inhibition of the reaction in the newborn. It was found that mice sensitized at birth and those sensitized at 2 weeks of age reacted more promptly and more intensely than unsensitized mice. After the two initial days the reaction continued to increase in mice which were sensitized at birth, whilst it levelled off in a group which were sensitized when they were 2 weeks old. By the 32nd day the differences became less significant, but the group sensitized at birth still maintained the highest level of cellular reactivity.

The group sensitized at birth showed marked early cellular infiltrations around the eggs. There was an abundance of eosinophils, neutrophils and large mononuclear cells and by the 4th day multinuclear giant cells were present. Vascular involvement was earlier and more severe than in unsensitized mice. There was a diffuse infiltration of the walls of arteries and arterioles, with cuffing of venules by eosinophils and mononuclear cells. There was also an accumulation of large mononuclear cells in the alveoli surrounding the granulomata. By the 32nd day these lesions were still marked and there was also evidence of calcification in the granulomata. Thickening, hyalinization and narrowing of the lumen occurred in many small arteries and arterioles.

In the group sensitized at 2 weeks of age the lesions were milder than in the group sensitized at birth, and by 32 days many of them showed healing. However, the lesions were more marked than those seen in unsensitized mice. Thus the exposure of newborn mice to *Ascaris* eggs does not induce a state of tolerance; indeed, the opposite effect is demonstrated, namely sensitization. The sensitization effect demonstrated suggested that the formation of an ascaridial granuloma possibly had some immunological control and was not merely a straightforward foreign body-like reaction.

As a result of this work the following trend becomes apparent. The least reaction to challenge with *Ascaris* eggs occurs in the unsensitized newborn, followed in turn by the unsensitized 4-week-old and then the adult. All sensitized animals react more rapidly and strongly than unsensitized ones, but sensitization at 2 weeks of age appears to be less effective than at birth.

In Japan, work of a similar nature has been described. Nahamura (1959), working with extracts of pig *Ascaris* eggs and sensitized rabbits, found that on sensitization a remarkable parenchymal degeneration of the liver cells was produced which was probably an associated toxic effect. The rabbits were infected with viable eggs which were injected into the portal vein. Mononuclear cell nodules occurred in the sensitized group and some histiocytes were also seen. Surprisingly, these nodules were chiefly seen in the connective tissue, whereas they would have been expected around larvae or eggs in the sinusoids. The unsensitized rabbits when challenged showed slight infiltrations of "pseudo-eosinophilic" leucocytes, but no mononuclear cell nodes. Further work by Nahamura (1960a, b) led him to state that the histological changes in the liver associated with granulomata due to *Ascaris* eggs were similar to those seen in a generalized Schwartzman reaction. In sensitized rabbits which were injected with embryonated eggs, mononuclear cell nodes were clearly seen, but no fibrosis had developed by 10 days. These nodes became smaller after 1 month and fibrosis was present at 2 months. In non-sensitized rabbits, granulomata were seen 10 days after injection and fibrosis was present.

The eosinophil leucocyte has recently been the subject of a monograph by Archer (1963). He quoted work carried out by Archer and Poynter (1957), who examined a group of ponies deliberately subjected to heavy nematode infections. Sections from the thymus, suprarenals and bronchi were normal, but all the other tissues showed varying degrees of eosinophilic infiltration. In the lung a few eosinophils were found, but these were always in the capillaries and no tendency to penetrate the alveolar walls was evident. The liver showed local areas of eosinophilia and small round cells. These lesions varied in size from 100 μ to 1 mm diam. and either surrounded a central lobular vein or a fibrin scar. The central portions of the lesions consisted mainly of small round cells, the eosinophils being mainly peripheral. Some regions showed a marked disturbance of the lobular pattern and in these there was a diffuse eosinophilia and marked fibrosis.

The spleen contained zones of eosinophilia similar to those observed in the liver, but differing in the absence of small round cells. In kidneys showing parasites the larvae were surrounded by a zone of small round cells which sometimes included plasma cells. In many but not all cases there was a marked infiltration of kidney tissue with eosinophils at the periphery of the lesions. Lymph nodes from the mandibular or bronchial regions were normal, but nodes draining the bowel had many eosinophils just beneath the capsule. Some eosinophils were present in the trabeculae, but none were seen in the gland pulp. The alimentary canal showed eosinophilic infiltration. There was some eosinophilia of the oesophagus, stomach and duodenum, but in the colon and caecum there was a regular and heavy infiltration of eosinophils in the submucosa and to a lesser extent in the lamina propria. Control animals which were regularly treated had less tissue eosinophilia. In the parasitized ponies, the number of eosinophils per high power field was about 30–50, whereas in the treated ponies it was 1–10.

Archer (1963) concluded that larval migration in tissue produces a reaction, but the immediate response does not consist of eosinophilia. The tissue infiltration consists in the main of small round cells with some plasma cells and only at a later stage are eosinophils found. Frequently, the areas of eosinophilia are around the presumed sites of old tracks left by larvae in the tissue. On occasions, larvae may be encountered in sections of tissue and in these cases it is possible to see that the leading end of the larva is free of tissue reaction. A little behind the head an area of small round cells begins and spreads wider and wider into the tissues as the larva passes. Eosinophils may be seen outside this area of reaction towards the tail of the larva. The area of round cell infiltration thus becomes thinner, accompanied by a coating of eosinophils until at the end only eosinophils are left.

It is Archer's (1963) opinion that the eosinophil leucocyte is attracted by and concerned with the histamine liberated as a result of tissue damage.

Recent work by Fernex (1963) supports Archer's conclusions. Fernex showed that repeated stimulation of the mast cells of male white rats by compound 48/80, polymyxin B and helminth toxins could provoke mitosis, which led eventually to an increase in the numbers of such cells in connective tissue. Such a finding might account for the hyperplasia of the mast cell system seen in filariasis and schistosomiasis. Exhausted mast cells delay the formation of healthy scar tissue. It is known that mast cells synthesize and store histamine. Indeed, histamine is thought to be the only known truly eosinotactic substance. Other substances which appear to attract eosinophils probably work by a mastocytotoxin effect in that they can liberate histamine from the mast cell. Fernex (1963) concludes, then, that eosinophils neutralize an excess of histamine produced by mast cells after injury.

Hiraki and Inove (1959a, b) have carried out tissue cultures from the sternal marrows of normal persons and those suffering from hookworm or bronchial asthma. In the latter groups there was an increase in the number of eosinophils. They added emulsions from fresh hookworms to marrow cultures and concluded that an allergic reaction to proteins or metabolic products of the worms played an important role in the causation of eosinophilia.

VII. NEMATODES AND OTHER SITES

There are three species of the genus *Habronema*, parasitic in the horse, of which *H. megastoma* is of the greatest pathogenic significance. The parasite normally lives in the fundic glands of the stomach, where it becomes surrounded by an eosinophilic granulomatous reaction. Such lesions are large and bulge into the gastric lumen, but are covered with epithelium except for regions where small fistulous openings occur. The parasite is spread by flies of the genera *Musca* or *Stomoxys* and, if deposited into cutaneous wounds, an intense local reaction results which becomes granulomatous and densely infiltrated with eosinophils. Reid (1965) has recently published his observations on habronemiasis and *Corynebacterium*. He believes that *Habronema* larvae may themselves be infected with *Corynebacterium pseudotuberculosis* and that the "chest" abscesses in Californian horses are indeed caused by this bacterium in association with the parasite.

Knapp *et al.* (1961) reported cases of *Thelazia californiensis* in dogs and cats. The parasite produced pustular conjunctivitis with eye discharge and corneal opacities. In horses (E. J. Roberts and D. Poynter, unpublished observations) *T. lacrimalis* may produce a granulomatous thickening of the third eyelid which macroscopically might be mistaken for a carcinoma. Schebitz (1960) reported a case of ulcerous conjunctivitis in the horse caused by *T. lacrimalis.* A typical parasitic granuloma was present, but the ulcerations were believed to be due to secondary bacterial invaders which included *B. pseudotuberculosis ovis, Corynebacterium equi* and *B. proteus.*

The association, if any, between the microfilariae of *Onchocerca cervicalis* and equine periodic ophthalmia awaits clarification. A very full account of the fundus lesions seen in this disease was given by Roberts (1962). He examined 456 horses and found twenty-three with circumpapillary choroiditis. Fifteen eyes were enucleated and subjected to histological examination. Ten lesions were characterized by a moderate to severe inflammation of the uvea, classed as focal choroiditis or chorioretinitis. In five eyes there was no real evidence of inflammation; four of the affected eyes contained microfilariae of *O. cervicalis* in the conjunctiva and these were surrounded by a marked lymphocytic or eosinophilic infiltration.

An anonymous annotation in the *Lancet* (1958, *i*, 1165–1166) concerns work on the specific aetiology of the ocular lesions in onchocerciasis, with particular reference to the fundus lesion which may be a form of dominantly inherited generalized choroidal sclerosis. Should this view be substantiated, then any association with *Onchocerca* is possibly fortuitous.

Choyce (1959) quoted three instances to show that heavy infections with *O. volvulus* in a given area were not necessarily accompanied by an increase in the incidence of blindness.

Rodger (1959) described the changes seen following the death of microfilariae in the eye. Little reaction seemed to be evoked by the living parasite, but once it died eosinophils, lymphocytes and fibroblasts appeared. New capillaries grew towards the area, but at no time were giant cells seen. After dissolution a diffuse basophil reaction was seen in the area of inflammatory cells which Rodger attributed to a diffusing toxin.

In a later paper Rodger (1962) stated that he did not regard the skin changes as an allergic manifestation, but that they were due to poisoning of the tissue by the dead microfilariae. These caused a swelling of the endothelium of arterioles with resulting anoxia and loss of elastic tissue. Two types of posterior ocular lesions were described, one inflammatory and the other degenerative.

Skin lesions associated with onchocerciasis in animals were recorded by Thomas (1958). Lesions of the external genitalia were seen in geldings infected with microfilariae of *Onchocerca* spp. which resembled those of elephantoid scrotum seen in human beings infected with *O. volvulus.* The lesions in the skin of infected horses were comparable to the erysipelatoid lesions seen in human beings.

Duke (1960) made pathological observations on the spleens of monkeys infected with *Loa*, having particular regard to the changes associated with the destruction of microfilariae. Granulomatous nodules developed in the red pulp and caused distension of the capsule. The nodules were composed of a spherical honeycomb of reticulin fibres and macrophages. Blood could move through this network and many eosinophils were present. Multinuclear giant cells were seen containing disintegrating microfilariae. These lesions were resolvable.

D'Abrera (1958a) reported four cases of tropical eosinophilia in Ceylon from areas hyperendemic for *Wuchereria bancrofti*. D'Abrera (1958b) believed the syndrome to be an allergic condition which may be initiated by several parasites of which helminths are the most common and that it differs from Loeffler's syndrome only in degree.

Webb *et al.* (1960) provided a comprehensive account and discussion of "tropical eosinophilia". Microfilariae were found in the lungs, liver and lymph nodes and the pathological changes in these tissues were described. Ten cases were described, eight being children under 12 years of age. The lungs were soft and spongy, but nodules were palpable and easily seen on the cut surface, where they appeared white, of irregular distribution and of 3–5 mm diam. Microscopically there was a marked infiltration of the alveolar walls by eosinophils and areas where twenty to thirty alveoli were distended with eosinophils. In the centre of some of these nodules, alveolar walls were destroyed with the formation of an eosinophilic abscess, in the centre of which portions of microfilariae could be found. The livers also showed nodules, the structure of which was essentially similar to those seen in the lungs. They varied from lakes of eosinophils to fully developed granulomata with giant cells and epithelioid cells. Some cases showed enlargement of the lymph nodes with the medullary cords and sinuses containing large numbers of eosinophils in which microfilariae were sometimes found. The authors teased microfilariae out of the lymph nodes and identified them as *Wuchereria bancrofti*. They believed that tropical eosinophilia is usually due to infection with some form of filaria and that the diagnosis should be reserved for this type of infection.

Spencer (1962) in Uganda associated filariasis bancrofti with sinovitis and arthritis, especially of the knee and wrist.

Stemmermann (1961) discussed sixteen cases of eosinophilic granuloma of the appendix of patients in Hawaii. The excised appendices showed small, oval, tuberculoid granulomas in the lamina propria, submucosa, muscularis externa or serosal connective tissue. Some showed a central zone of necrosis and all a wide peripheral zone of tissue eosinophilia. The lesions were attributed to *Strongyloides stercoralis*.

Tremlett (1964) made observations on the skin of a black rhinoceros infected with *Stephanofilaria dinniki*. The lesions were characterized by erosions, ulcerations and crust formations. The centre of a lesion showed areas of necrosis with almost complete obliteration of the epidermal layers and replacement by inspissated exudate and debris. Underlying the necrotic areas, there was considerable increase in granulation and fibrous tissue. Perivascular accumulations of mononuclear cells, mainly of the macrophage type, were present. In the middle layers of the dermis the apocrine sweat glands were flattened and in the deep layers of the dermis foci of mononuclear and eosinophilic cells were associated with the small blood vessels. At the periphery of the lesions there was an eosinophilic exudate containing inflammatory cells and cellular debris. The epidermis showed proliferation with hyperplasia of the Malphigian layer. The irregularly branched retepegs penetrated deeply into the dermis. Numerous mitotic figures were seen in the germinal layer. Adult helminths were present in spaces lined with flattened epithelial cells. Between the retepegs the superficial layers of collagen contained fibroblastic tissue. Oedema was seen in some areas and a diffuse mononuclear reaction was present. Occasionally foreign-body type giant cells were present.

Eubanks and Pick (1963) recently described a case of *Dioctophyma renale* infection in a dog. At post-mortem examination two parasites were found in the right kidney and another was observed localized between the liver lobes. The dog had severe peritonitis. The infected right kidney had a thickened capsule and an irregularly pitted renal cortex. The uninfected left kidney showed hypertrophy. The histological findings were similar to those recorded by Grahame and Mark (1948). The normal structure of the right kidney was obscured by the thick capsule containing abundant fibrous tissue and glomerular tubular casts. Deposits of focal erosion of the epithelium of the renal pelvis were seen. There was marked fibrosis of the renal pelvis and numerous embryonated eggs and inflammatory cells. Foci of interstitial nephritis were present in the left kidney, but these were probably not directly related to the infection.

VIII. Nematodes and Cancer

Although definitive evidence is often lacking, nematodes have long been considered responsible for various types of tumours. Klopsch (1866) pointed out the possible aetiological role of *Trichinella spiralis* in the production of tumours, a relationship which Hoeppli (1933) regarded as fortuitous. Haaland (1911) suggested a relationship between the skin infections of mice with *Muspiela borreli* and mammary carcinoma, but Brumpt (1930) could find no real evidence of this. Previously, Brumpt (1922) had suggested that the presence of *Physaloptera* spp. in the stomach of *Macacus cynomolyus* might be related to carcinoma, and a similar conclusion was reached by Yokogawa (1921) in respect of the shrew (*Sorex*).

As its name suggests, *Spiroptera neoplastica* (*Gongylonema neoplasticum*) was once believed to have carcinogenic properties. The first suggestion of this was when Fibiger (1913) described carcinomatous lesions in the stomachs of infected rats. The adult worms live in the stratified epithelial mucosa of the tongue, oesophagus and stomach. If the stomach is heavily infected, a huge multiple papillary epithelial overgrowth occurs, and Fibiger believed that such overgrowths gradually became malignant and infiltrated the wall of the stomach, producing metastases in the lymph glands and lungs. Some rats also developed carcinoma of the tongue. However, Bullock and Rhodenburg (1918) were able to induce a carcinoma-like papillary overgrowth of the rat stomach by simple mechanical injury. They also observed a squamous metaplasia in the bronchial epithelium of rats affected with chronic bronchial pneumonia and showed the resemblance to the pulmonary metastases Fibiger found in his rats. Other workers also failed to obtain genuine tumours by use of the parasite and Passey *et al.* (1951) showed that the epithelial overgrowth was partly the result of a vitamin deficiency. This work was recently substantiated by Pellegrini (1957), who described the macroscopic and microscopic appearance of oesophageal epitheliomas in a case of *Gongylonema scutatum*. He concluded that under predisposing conditions such as hypovitaminosis, a heavy infection produced changes in the oesophageal mucous membrane with blastoma-like lesions.

Popova (1962) infected six 3-month-old lambs each with 300–350 larvae of *Gongylonema pulchrum*. Destructive and dystrophic lesions, hyperaemia, oedema and inflammation of the mucosa were seen 10 days after infection and these changes culminated in chronic glosso-pharyngeal oesophagitis. Nodules of the oesophageal mucosa were reported by Latini and Asdrubali (1964) in a 10-year-old *Capreolus capreolus*, which also contained many worms of the species *G. pulchrum*.

Recently, *Spirocerca lupi* was incriminated as an inciting cause of malignant lesions in the oesophagus of the dog. Seibold *et al.* (1955) were the first to associate this parasite with neoplasia, and the whole topic has recently been well reviewed by Bailey (1963). The original report mentioned ten cases of oesophageal carcinoma associated with *Spirocerca* infection. Ribelin and Bailey (1958) added eight additional cases and since that time a further twenty cases have been studied. Only four or possibly five other reports of the association of *Spirocerca* and oesophageal sarcoma have been made.

Jarrett and Urquhart (1956) studied two cases, one from Palestine and one from Jamaica, and Hansen *et al.* (1957) reported three malignant neoplasias in fifty-nine *Spirocerca*-infected dogs in Egypt. In Louisiana, Thrasher (1961) found three cases of oesophageal sarcoma associated with lesions suggesting *Spirocerca* infection. Later Thrasher *et al.* (1963) found *S. lupi* to be intimately associated with osteogenic sarcoma of the oesophagus in two foxhounds and a pointer. Babero *et al.* (1965) examined 193 dogs in Iraq and found *S. lupi* to have an overall incidence of 66%; twenty dogs had aortic nodules, twenty-eight had nodules in the oesophagus and aorta and eighty had oesophageal nodules only. The oesophageal lesions were granulomatous and simulated sarcomatous growths in two cases.

The main changes associated with *Spirocerca* infection in the dog are the development of aortic aneurisms, a deformitive ossifying spondylitis of the posterior thoracic vertebrae and reactive granulomatous reactions which develop around the parasite. The larval migration in the oesophagus leads to haemorrhage, necrosis, tissue eosinophilia and inflammation. The migration of larvae through the elastic fibres of the thoracic aorta produces a weakening of the vessel wall which leads to the formation of a dilatation of the vessel, i.e. an aneurism. When aneurisms rupture sudden death may supervene. The pathogenesis of the spondylitis is unknown, but it may be connected with an irritation of periostial tissue by migrating larvae. The reactive granulomatous lesions vary in shape and size according to the number of worms present and the pressure of the surrounding tissue. Most adult worms are found in the oesophagus and here pedunculated granulomas may protrude in the lumen of the oesophagus or multiple granulomata may grow out distally from the wall. Typical granulomatous responses also occur if worms remain in the wall of the stomach or aorta or migrate into the lung.

The granulomatous lesions have been described by several writers (Ribelin and Bailey, 1958; Hansen et al., 1957; Ponomarenko, 1935; Hsu, 1948; Chandrasekharon et al., 1958; Hu and Hoeppli, 1937; Barron, 1950). The primary lesion consists of highly vascular loose connective tissue which is oedematous. Many fibrin clots may be present. There are a limited number of mononuclear inflammatory cells around, but eosinophils are uncommon. Neutrophils are also seen and possibly appear when bacteria are present. There may be localized areas of necrosis, and thick pus is usually found in the cavernous tracts around the worm. These early granulomatous lesions often contain young fibroblasts with large oval or irregularly elongated nuclei having distinct membranes, small or inconspicuous nucleoli and dark, delicate chromatin. Mitotic figures can often be distinguished and collagenous fibres may be present. Ribelin and Bailey (1958) considered the very immature appearance of the fibroblasts suggestive of a pre-neoplastic state. Hansen et al. (1957) were impressed by the vast numbers of young active fibroblasts present, but they concluded that the majority of the granulomatas were well encapsulated "locally malignant fibro-carcinomas". As the lesion becomes older the mononuclear cells and vascular changes decrease and fibroblasts predominate. There may also be a marked increase of collagen, so that a very fibrous granulomatous lesion results. Ribelin and Bailey (1958) and Bailey (1963) have shown a good association between Spirocerca and sarcoma. Bailey (1963) reported metastases in twenty out of thirty-seven cases; in nine-teen cases the lung was affected and metastases also occurred in the lymph nodes, liver, heart, pleura and kidney. He also reported that hypertrophic pulmonary osteoarthropathy has a common oesophageal sarcoma, and that hounds are affected more frequently than other breeds of dog. This is accounted for on the basis of the unrestricted association of this type of dog with intermediate and transport hosts of the parasite.

At present the incidence of sarcomas associated with Spirocerca lupi is highest in south-east U.S.A. In Madras, Chandrasekharon et al. (1958) reported 23% of 910 dogs infected with Spirocerca, but found no evidence of tumour formation in relation to the worms, and V. S. Ershov (personal communication, quoted by Bailey, 1963) could find no known cases of neoplasia associated with Spirocerca in Russia.

Ressang and Hong (1963) studied the occurrence of S. lupi in dogs in Indonesia and its relationship to neoplasm formation. The incidence was relatively high, ranging from 37 to 50% according to the locality examined. Microscopic examination of the nodules revealed acute inflammation, granulomatous proliferation of tissue and bone formation due to metaplasia of connective tissue. Fibro-osteoma was diagnosed in two cases, but no malignant tumours were seen.

It is strange that the association between sarcomas and Spirocerca infection has not received wider confirmation. Bailey (1963) gave several explanations for this apparent difference in neoplasm prevalence, which include physiological differences in parasite populations, more frequent occurrence of an oncogenic agent in the parasite population in some areas than others, or differences in cancer predisposition in the dog populations.

Bailey *et al.* (1963) found third-stage nematode larvae in dung beetles (Scarabaeidae), and after feeding these larvae to a dog recovered worms from the wall of the aorta, which showed lesions characteristic of *Spirocerca lupi* infection.

It is notable that although canine animals act as the normal definitive hosts of *Spirocerca* spp. the genus has also been recorded in man (Biocca, 1959), goats (Neveu-Lemaire, 1936), donkeys (Pande *et al.*, 1961) and a bull (Du Plessis and Verster, 1964). A nodule was found in the abdominal aorta of the bull, and histopathological examination of sections revealed several haemorrhagic tracts, involving the entire wall of the vessel. The tracts were filled with blood, necrotic infiltrative cells and debris and were surrounded by a zone of round cell leucocytes on the adventitial side. There was an extensive proliferation of the intima, so that it bulged into the lumen of the vessel and early calcification was evident in the media.

Narzarova (1964) recently described work on the migration of *S. lupi* in the body of the dog. Infecting dogs with larvae obtained from dung beetles, he found that the larvae were present around the branches of the gastric artery within 48 h. On the 4th day they entered the arteries and during the next 3 weeks moved towards the thoracic aorta. Within $2\frac{1}{2}$–3 months the fifth-stage forms developed within the aorta and migrated by the 102nd day to the oesophagus, where characteristic fistulated swellings containing the adult worms developed.

As the life cycle can be completed in the laboratory, we can now look forward to experimental studies on the pathogenesis of the cellular changes and the possible causal relationship of the parasite to malignancy.

IX. Nematodes and Viral Diseases

It is now established that nematodes may exacerbate viral infections, at least where the CNS and lungs are concerned. Shope (1943) showed how the pathogenesis of swine influenza was connected with the earthworm, lungworm, a virus and *Haemophilus suis*. Beautyman and Wolff (1951) found an *Ascaris* larva in the thalamus of a child who also had acute poliomyelitis of the brain stem, and speculated on the possibility of a complex virus–helminth relationship. They pointed out that there were no neurological signs referable to the larval lesion but only to the poliomyelitis, and wondered about the possibility that larval migration might be connected with a focal or generalized epilepsy. Castro (1950) also suggested that helminth vectors might be concerned in the pathogenesis of poliomyelitis. Syverton *et al.* (1947) noted in guinea-pigs an association between *Trichinella spiralis* and lymphocytic choriomeningitis, whilst Innes (1951) suggested a possible adjuvant relation between *Setaria digitata* and Japanese B encephalitis in animals. Jarrett *et al.* (1953) observed that "cuffing pneumonia" of cattle may combine with *Dictyocaulus viviparus* infection to produce a serious syndrome.

Underdahl and Kelley (1957) carried out some work on the relationship between virus pneumonia in pigs and the migration of pig *Ascaris* larvae. It was once held that much of the pneumonia seen in pigs was directly attributable to *Ascaris* migration, but in 1954 Betts showed that massive numbers of migrating larvae in virus pneumonia-free pigs were incapable of producing lobar pneumonia. Underdahl and Kelley (1957) worked with pigs which were obtained by hysterectomy and kept in individual isolation units throughout the experiment. They infected pigs with a known pneumonia-producing virus, with *Ascaris* alone and with *Ascaris* and the virus. Pigs inoculated with the virus during the migration of the larvae of *Ascaris* through the lungs showed lung consolidation ten times as extensive as in pigs which received virus alone. No consolidation was present in the lungs of pigs given *Ascaris* alone. Underdahl (1958) infected young piglets with viral influenza at the time when larval migration was known to be occurring. Severe pneumonia developed and 56% of the piglets died as opposed to 40% of the control animals infected with the virus alone.

Nayak *et al.* (1963) found that the previous exposure of "germ-free" piglets to *Metastrongylus* infection enhanced a subsequent infection with influenza virus when this was given 7 days later. In piglets infected with lungworms and virus the lungs were larger and the consolidated areas were more extensive than in piglets infected with either organism alone.

Mackenzie (1963) carried out some observations on lungworm infection and virus pneumonia relationships in pigs. He infected weaner pigs with *Metastrongylus elongatus*, virus pneumonia alone, or with virus pneumonia superimposed on lungworm infection of 2 weeks' duration. In pigs infected with both agents the disease was very severe and more extensive than that produced by either agent alone. Further pigs infected with lungworms and placed in contact with virus pneumonia-infected animals developed more extensive lesions than did any in contact with controls. The pigs inoculated with virus pneumonia alone showed consolidation of the anterior lobes and anterior-ventral aspect of the diaphragmatic lobes of the lungs. Histological changes were typical of an uncomplicated proliferative pneumonia with peribronchiolar lymphoreticular hyperplasia.

The animals infected with lungworm larvae alone showed uncomplicated lungworm pneumonia. Small lobules of consolidation occurred, especially along the ventral margins of the anterior lobes. Vesicular emphysema was present in the posterior borders of the diaphragmatic lobes. In pigs given both infections the lesions were more severe than with either agent alone. The virus pneumonia lesions were not confined to the anterior lobes, but were found in addition throughout the caudal parts of the diaphragmatic lobes. Nearly all the remaining lung tissue was emphysematous in contrast to the limited emphysema found with uncomplicated lungworm or virus pneumonia infections. The histological changes in combined infections ranged from those associated with uncomplicated lungworm infection to those occurring in simple virus pneumonia. The mixture of lesions attributable to the two infective agents include lymphoid hyperplasia, eosinophilic infiltration with sections of parasites and occasionally giant cells. There was also bronchiolar epithelial proliferation with small adenomatous foci, bronchiole ingrowths and disruptive changes with occlusion of the lumen and structural disintegration of bronchiolar wall.

Mochizuki et al. (1954) found that when given to mice the embryonated eggs of T. canis might cause a fatal haemorrhage in a few days. They worked with a strain of Japanese B encephalitis virus which after twenty years of laboratory passage caused a clinically non-neurotropic silent infection when injected subcutaneously. However, in mice which previously received the embryonated eggs of T. canis and then the virus a neurotropic effect was seen and the mice died from encephalitis in 3–4 days. It is possible that the larvae, in destroying the blood–brain barrier, allow the virus to provoke encephalitis. Mochizuki (1959) later found that the first larvae reached the brain and produced haemorrhage 2½ days after infection. In those mice inoculated subcutaneously with the virus 2–4 days after infection with T. canis the typical encephalitis lesions masked the nematode lesions.

It is interesting to note that Peterson et al. (1961) found that extracts and suspensions of swine lungworms contained receptor-like substances capable of adsorbing influenza virus.

X. CONCLUSION

An attempt has been made to review some of the more recent work conducted on the reactions of the mammalian animal to its nematode parasites.

The associations between the parasite and host are of various kinds. In some, presumably those where the two organisms have been in association for long periods of time, there is little reaction, but in others the reactions are acute and are associated with disease. Foreign body and irritant responses are common, whilst eosinophils are of such regular occurrence that their presence in the tissues of a domestic animal leads to a suspicion of parasitism. Hyperplastic reactions occur and metaplasia is reported, but true neoplasia seems rare. Generally speaking, susceptible animals do not react like immune ones in which the responses are enhanced and lymphocytic and plasma cell proliferation may occur.

The concept of a strict host specificity has undergone revision in that it is now known that although some nematodes may not reach adulthood in an unusual host they do nevertheless gain entrance to the tissues, where the reaction to them may be so pronounced that disease results. This is especially true in visceral larva migrans.

This review does not pretend to be exhaustive and is no doubt influenced by the author's own particular interests. It is, however, hoped that it does show something of the significance of the reactions which occur and perhaps helps to illustrate the changing environment in which a nematode may have to live.

ACKNOWLEDGEMENTS

I wish to thank Mrs D. Lawrance and Mrs S. A. M. Selway for the considerable help given to me in preparing and checking the manuscript. I am indebted to Professor W. H. Jarrett and Mr J. Armour for Figs. 2A–D.

References

Adcock, J. L. (1961). *Am. J. vet. Res.* **22**, 655–662.

Alicata, J. (1965). *In* "Advances in Parasitology" (B. Dawes, ed.), Vol. 3, pp. 223–248. Academic Press, London and New York.

Allen, G. W. (1962). *Can. J. comp. Med.* **26**, 241–243.

Anderson, N., Armour, J., Jarrett, W. F. H., Jennings, F. W., Ritchie, J. S. D., and Urquhart, G. M. (1965). *Vet. Rec.* **77**, 1196–1204.

Anderson, R. C. (1964). *Pathologia Veterinaria, Basle* **1** (4), 289–322.

Archer, R. K. (1963). "The Eosinophil Leucocytes." Blackwell, Oxford.

Archer, R. K., and Poynter, D. (1957). *J. comp. Path. Ther.* **67**, 196–207.

Arean, U. M. (1958). *Archs Path.* **66**, 427–438.

Arean, U. M., and Crandall, C. (1962). *Am. J. trop. Med. Hyg.* **11** (3), 364–379.

Arean, U. M., Crandall, C. A., Castells, J., and Herron, C. (1962). *Am. J. trop. Med. Hyg.* **11**, 731–738.

Armour, J., Jarrett, W. F. H., and Jennings, F. W. (1966). *Am. J. vet. Res.* **27**, 1267–1278.

Ashton, N. (1960). *Br. J. Ophthal.* **44**, 129–148.

Ashworth, C. T., and Chears, W. C. (1962). *Fedn Proc. Fedn Am. Socs exp. Biol.* **21**, 880–890.

Babero, B. B. (1959). *Trans. Am. microsc. Soc.* **78**, 330–335.

Babero, B. B., Fawzi, A. H., and Aldabugh, M. A. (1965). *Br. vet. J.* **121**, 183–190.

Babos, S. (1962). *Magy. Allatorv. Lap.* **17**, 168–173.

Bailey, W. S. (1963). *Ann. N.Y. Acad. Sci.* **108** (3), 890–923.

Bailey, W. S., Cabrera, D. J., and Diamond, D. L. (1963). *J. Parasit.* **49**, 458–488.

Barron, C. N. (1950). Thesis. A. & M. College, Texas.

Barron, C. N., and Saunders, L. Z. (1966). *Path. vet.* (In press.)

Beautyman, W., and Wolff, A. L. (1951). *J. Path. Bact.* **63**, 635–648.

Beaver, P. C., Snyder, C. H., Carrera, G. M., Dent, J. H., and Lafferty, J. W. (1952). *Pediatrics* **9**, 7.

Behrer, M. R. (1951). *J. Pediat.* **38**, 635.

Betts, A. O. (1954). *Vet. Rec.* **66**, 749–751.

Biocca, E. (1959). *Parassitologia* **1**, 137–142.

Bogaert, L. van, Dubois, A., Janssen, P. G., Radermecker, J., Tverdy, G., and Wanson, M. (1955). *J. Neurol. Neurosurg. Psychiat.* **18**, 103–119.

Bogdanovich, V. V. (1958). *Medskaya Parazit.* **27**, 571–572.

Botti, L. (1957). *Atti Soc. ital. Sci. vet.* **11**, 737–740.

Bourke, G. M., and Yeates, F. M. (1961). *Med. J. Aust.* **2** (1), 12–14.

Brand, T. von, and Cullinan, R. P. (1943). *Proc. helminth. Soc. Wash.* **10**, 29–33.

Brill, R., Churg, J., and Beaver, P. C. (1953). *Am. J. clin. Path.* **23**, 1208.

Brumpt, E. (1922). "Precis de Parasitologie." Masson, Paris.

Brumpt, E. (1930). *Annls Parasit. hum. comp.* **8**, 309–343.

Bullock, F. D., and Rhodenburg, G. L. (1918). *J. Cancer Res.* **3**, 227.

Bunzl, V. (1904). *Arb. neurol. Inst. wien. Univ.* **11**, 156–170.

Burg, W. B., Baudet, E. A. R. F., and Verwey, J. H. P. (1953). *Proc. XVth int. Vet. Congr. Stockholm.* **1**, 414–416.

Cahall, W. C. (1889). *J. nerv. ment. Dis.* **16**, 361–365.

Capdebielle and Hussenet (1911). *Revue vét., Toulouse* **36**, 144–147.

Castro, J. G. (1950). *Revta ibér. Parasit.* **10**, 379–385.

Ceretto, F. (1957). *Atti Soc. ital. Sci. vet.* **11**, 763–766.

Chandrasekharon, K. P., Sastry, G. A., and Menon, M. N. (1958). *Br. vet. J.* **114**, 388–395.

Chaudhuri, R. N., and Saha, T. K. (1959). *Lancet i*, 493–494.
Chodnik, K. S. (1958). *Ann. trop. Med. Parasit.* **52**, 145–148.
Chowdury, A. B. (1960). *Am. J. Path.* **36**, 725–733.
Choyce, D. P. (1959). *Trans. R. Soc. trop. Med. Hyg.* **53**, 119–120.
Cronin, M. T. I., and Leader, G. H. (1952). *Vet. Rec.* **64**, 8.
D'Abrera, U. St E. (1958a). *Med. J. Malaya* **12**, 559–562.
D'Abrera, U. St E. (1958b). *Ceylon med. J.* **4**, 195–210.
Dacorso, F. P. (1944). *Bolm Soc. bras. Med. vet.* **13**, 211–217.
Dent, J. H., Nichols, R. L., Beaver, P. C., Carrera, G. M., and Staggers, R. J. (1956). *Am. J. Path.* **32**, 77.
Dickson, W., and Woodcock, R. C. (1959). *Archs Dis. Childh.* **34**, 63–67.
Done, J. (1957). *Vet. Rec.* **69**, 1341–1353.
Done, J. T., Richardson, M. D., and Gibson, T. E. (1960). *Res. vet. Sci.* **1**, 133–151.
Doran, D. J. (1955). *Am. J. vet. Res.* **16**, 401–409.
Duke, B. O. L. (1960). *Ann. trop. Med. Parasit.* **54**, 141–146.
Du Plessis, J. L., and Verster, A. (1964). *Jl S. Afr. vet. med. Ass.* **35** (4), 609–611.
Emoto, O. (1927). *Schweizer Arch. Tierheilk.* **69**, 297–321.
Eubanks, J. W., and Pick, J. R. (1963). *J. Am. vet. med. Ass.* **143**, 164–169.
Ewing, S. A., and Todd, A. C. (1961). *Am. J. vet. Res.* **22**, 606–609.
Farrelly, B. T. (1954). *Vet. Rec.* **66**, 53.
Fenstermacher, R. (1934). *Bull. Minn. agric. Exp. Stn*, No. 308.
Fernex, M. (1963). *Annls Soc. belge Méd. trop.* **43**, 325–341.
Fibiger, J. (1913). *Z. Krebsforsch.* **13**, 217–280.
Friedmann, S., and Hervada, A. R. (1960). *J. Pediat.* **56**, 91–96.
Galvin, T. J. (1964). *J. Parasit.* **50**, 124–127.
Gardiner, M. R., and Fraser, D. (1960). *Aust. vet. J.* **36**, 405–407.
Gault, E. W., and Webb, J. K. G. (1957). *Lancet ii*, 471.
Gibbs, H. C. (1958). *Can. J. comp. Med. vet. Sci.* **22**, 382–385.
Goldgraber, M. B., and Lewert, R. M. (1965). *J. Parasit.* **51**, 169–174.
Grahame, G. L., and Mark, J. H. (1948). *J. Parasit.* **35**, 15.
Haaland, M. (1911). Scientific report of the Imperial Cancer Research Fund No. 4.
Halliday, G. J., Mulligan, W., and Dalton, R. G. (1966). *Nature, Lond.* (In press.)
Hamilton, J. M. (1963). *Vet. Rec.* **75** (16), 417–422.
Hansen, H. J., Hindawy, M. R., and Moustafa, M. S. E. (1957). *Egyptian vet. med. J.* **4**, 149–164.
Hassin, G. B., and Diamond, I. B. (1926). *Archs Neurol. Psychiat.* **15**, 34–47.
Heiner, D. C., and Kevy, S. V. (1956). *New Engl. J. Med.* **254**, 629.
Hiraki, K., and Inove, M. (1959a). *Acta Med. Okoyama* **13**, 57–64.
Hiraki, K., and Inove, M. (1959b). *Acta Med. Okoyama* **13**, 65–70.
Hobmaier, A., and Hobmaier, M. (1934). *Proc. Soc. exp. Biol. Med.* **31**, 509–514.
Hoeppli, R. J. C. (1923). *Virchow's Arch. path. Anat. Physiol.* **244**, 159–182.
Hoeppli, R. J. C. (1933). *Chin. med. J.* **47**, 1075–1111.
Hsu, K. C. (1948). *Chin. med. J.* **66**, 366–370.
Hu, C. H., and Hoeppli, R. J. C. (1937). *Chin. med. J.* **51**, 489–495.
Innes, J. R. M. (1951). *Vet. Med.* **46**, 192–193.
Innes, J. R. M., and Pillai, C. P. (1955). *Br. Vet. J.* **111**, 223–235.
Innes, J. R. M., and Saunders, L. Z. (1962). "Comparative Neuropathology." Academic Press, New York and London.
Innes, J. R. M., and Shoho, C. (1952). *Br. med. J.* **2**, 366–368.
Innes, J. R. M., and Shoho, C. (1953). *Archs Neurol. Psychiat.* **70**, 325–349.
Innes, J. R. M., Shoho, C., and Pillai, C. P. (1952). *Br. vet. J.* **108**, 71–88.
Irvine, W. C., and Irvine, A. R. (1959). *Am. J. Ophthal.* **47**, 185.

Ishii, S., Yajima, A., Sugawa, Y., Ishiwara, T., Ogata, T., and Hashiguchi, Y. (1953). *Br. vet. J.* **109**, 160–167.

Itagaki, S., Taniguchi, M., and Kawata, M. (1946). *J. Jap. vet. med. Ass.* **3**, 79.

Jarrett, W. F. H., and Sharp, N. C. C. (1963). *J. Parasit.* **49** (2), 177–189.

Jarrett, W. F. H., and Urquhart, G. M. (1956). *Trans. R. Soc. trop. Med. Hyg.* **50**, 306.

Jarrett, W. F. H., McIntyre, W. I. M., and Urquhart, G. M. (1953). *Vet. Rec.* **65**, 163–165.

Jaskoski, B. J., and Colglazier, M. L. (1956). *J. Am. vet. med. Ass.* **129**, 513–514.

Jones, T. C., Doll, E. R., and Brown, R. G. (1954). *Proc. Am. vet. med. Ass.* **91**, 139–149.

Jubb, K. V. (1960). *Cornell Vet.* **50**, 319–325.

Jubb, K. V. F., and Kennedy, P. C. (1963). "Pathology of Domestic Animals." Academic Press, New York and London.

Jung, R. C., and Pacheco, G. (1958). *Am. J. trop. Med. Hyg.* **7**, 256.

Jung, R. C., and Pacheco, G. (1960). *Am. J. trop. Med. Hyg.* **9** (2), 185–191.

Karpinski, F. E., Evert-Snarez, E. A., and Sawitz, W. G. (1956). *Am. J. Dis. Childh.* **92**, 34.

Kates, K. C., and Turner, J. H. (1960). *Am. J. vet. Res.* **21**, 254–261.

Katiyar, J. C. (1964). *Indian vet. J.* **41**, 24–25.

Kell, J. F., Hennigar, G. R., and Hoff, E. C. (1956). *A.M.A. Archs Path.* **61**, 239.

Kennedy, P. C. (1954). *Cornell Vet.* **44**, 531–565.

Kennedy, P. C., Whitlock, J. H., and Roberts, S. J. (1952). *Cornell Vet.* **42**, 118–124.

Kersten, W., and Becht, H. (1960). *Dt. tierärztl. Wschr.* **67**, 173–177.

Kimura, T., and Niimi, D. (1940). *Trans. Soc. Path. Jap.* **30**, 539–544.

Klopsch, E. (1866). *Virchow's Arch. path. Anat. Physiol.* **35**, 609–610.

Knapp, S. E., Bailey, R. B., and Bailey, D. E. (1961). *J. Am. vet. med. Ass.* **138**, 537–538.

Larsh, J. E., Race, G. J., and Xarinsky, A. (1962). *Am. J. trop. Med. Hyg.* **11**, 633–640.

Latini, A., and Asdrubali, C. (1964). *Veterinaria ital.* **15**, 367–373.

Leland, S. E. (1963). *J. Parasit.* **49**, 617–622.

Leland, S. E., Drudge, J. H., Wyant, Z. N., Elam, G. W., and Hutzler, L. B. (1959). *Am. J. vet. Res.* **20**, 787–794.

Leland, S. E., Drudge, J. H., Wyant, Z. N., and Elam, G. W. (1960). *Am. J. vet. Res.* **21**, 449–457.

Leland, S. E., Drudge, J. H., Wyant, Z. N., and Elam, G. W. (1961). *Am. J. vet. Res.* **22**, 128–138.

Lichtenberg, F. von, and Mekbel, S. (1962). *J. infect. Dis.* **110**, 246–252.

Lichtenberg, F. von, Jackson, R. F., and Otto, G. F. (1962). *J. Am. vet. Med. Ass.* **141**, 121–128.

Liu, S. K. (1965a). *Expl Parasit.* **16**, 123–135.

Liu, S. K. (1965b). *Expl Parasit.* **17**, 136–147.

Mackenzie, A. (1958a). *Vet. Rec.* **70** (42), 843–846.

Mackenzie, A. (1958b). *Vet. Rec.* **70** (45), 903–906.

Mackenzie, A. (1959). *Vet. Rec.* **71** (11), 209–214.

Mackenzie, A. (1960). *Res. vet. Sci.* **1**, 255–259.

Mackenzie, A. (1963). *Vet. Rec.* **75**, 114–116.

Mackerras, M. J., and Sandars, D. F. (1955). *Aust. J. Zool.* **3**, 1–21.

Mekbel, S., and Lichtenburg, F. V. (1962). *J. infect. Dis.* **110**, 246–252.

Mercer, R. D., Lund, H. Z., Bloomfield, R. A., and Caldwell, F. E. (1950). *Am. J. Dis. Childh.* **80**, 46.

Michel, J. F. (1954). *Vet. Rec.* **66** (32), 460.

Michel, J. F., Mackenzie, A., Bracewell, C. D., Cornwell, R. L., Elliot, J., Herbert, N. C., Holman, H. H., and Sinclair, I. J. B. (1965). *Res. vet. Sci.* **6**, 344–395.

Milburn, R. D., Jr., and Ernst, K. F. (1953). *Pediatrics* **11**, 358.

Mochizuki, H. (1959). *Bull. Univ. Osaka Prefect.* Series B, **9**, 93–105.

Mochizuki, H., Tomimura, T., and Oka, T. (1954). *J. infect. Dis.* **95**, 260–262.

Molina Pasquel, C. (1961). *Salud públ. Méx.* **3**, 251–255.

Moore, M. T. (1962). *J. Neuropath. exp. Neurol.* **21**, 201–218.

Most, H., and Abeles, M. M. (1937). *Archs Neurol. Psychiat.* **37**, 589–616.

Müller, B. (1953). *Arch. exp. VetMed.* **7**, 153–175.

Mulligan, W., Dalton, R. G., and Anderson, N. (1963). *Vet. Rec.* **75**, 1104.

Munnick, H. (1958). *Naturwissenshaften* **45**, 552–555.

Nahamura, F. (1959). *Jap. J. Parasit.* **8** (6), 972–991.

Nahamura, F. (1960a). *Jap. J. Parasit.* **9** (1), 88–98.

Nahamura, F. (1960b). *Jap. J. Parasit.* **9** (1), 99–116.

Narzarova, N. S. (1964). *Trudy gel. mint Lab.* **14**, 131–135.

Nayak, D. P., Kelley, G. W., and Underdahl, N. R. (1963). Paper 1366, Nebraska Agricultural Experimental Station.

Neveu-Lemaire, M. (1936). "Traite d'helminthologie medicale et veterinaire," pp. 1217–1224. Vigot Frères, Paris.

Nichols, R. L. (1956). *J. Parasit.* **42**, 349.

Ogilvie, F. B., Folse, D. S., Koger, R. B., and Steele, C. H. (1962). *J. Am. vet. med. Ass.* **140**, 574–575.

Oguni, H., Kimata, H., Hosoya, H., and Miyamoto, Y. (1959). *Proc. int. vet. Congr. Madrid* **2**, 585–586.

Olson, L. J. (1960). *Tex. Rep. Biol. Med.* **18** (3), 473–479.

Olson, O. W., and Bracken, F. K. (1959). *J. Am. vet. med. Ass.* **134** (7), 330–334.

Oshio, Y. (1956). *Bull. nat. Inst. agric. Sci. Chiba, Japan*, Series G, **12**, 181–186.

Oshio, Y., and Furata, I. (1955). *Bull. nat. Inst. agric. Sci. Chiba, Japan*, Series G, **11**, 57–66.

Padykula, H. A. (1962). *Fedn Proc. Fedn Am. Socs. exp. Biol.* **21**, 873–879.

Pande, B. P., Rai, P., and Bhatia, B. B. (1961). *J. Parasit.* **47**, 951–952.

Passey, R. D., Dmochowski, L., Astbury, W. T., Reed, E., and Johnson, P. (1951). *Acta Un int. Cancr.* **7**, 299–303.

Patnaik, B. (1952). *J. Helminth.* **36**, 313–326.

Pellegrini, D. (1957). *Annali Fac. Med. vet. Univ. Pisa* **10**, 58–68.

Percivall, W. C. (1828). *Veterinarian, Lond.* **1**, 75–77.

Pei-Lin, Li (1946). *J. Path. Bact.* **58**, 373.

Perlingiero, J. G., and Gyorgy, P. (1947). *Am. J. Dis. Childh.* **73**, 34.

Peterson, W., Davenport, F. M., and Francis, T. (1961). *J. exp. Med.* **114**, 1023–1033.

Ponomarenko, F. M. (1935). *Z. InfektKrankh. parasit. Krankh. Hyg. Haustiere* **48**, 219–229.

Popova, Z. G. (1962). *Nauchnie Trudi. Ukr. Inst. Exp. Vet.* **28**, 119–123.

Porter, D. A. (1935). *J. Parasit.* **21**, 226–228.

Pout, D. (1964). *Vet. Rec.* **76**, 1325–1329.

Poynter, D. (1958). Ph.D. Thesis, London University.

Poynter, D. (1960). *Res. vet. Sci.* **1**, 205–217.

Poynter, D. (1963). *In* "Advances in Parasitology" (B. Dawes, ed.), Vol. 1, pp. 179–209. Academic Press, London and New York.

Price, E. W. (1928). *J. Parasit.* **14**, 59–60.

Raffensperger, H. B. (1931). *J. Parasit.* **18**, 44.

Rai, P. (1960). *Indian J. vet. Sci.* **31**, 141–148.

Reid, C. H. (1965). *Vet. Med.* **60**, 233–242.

Ressang, A. A., and Hong, L. Y. (1963). *Commun. vet. Bogor*, **7**, 9–17.

Ribelin, W. E., and Bailey, W. S. (1958). *Cancer* **11**, 1242–1246.

Richards, M. A., and Sloper, J. C. (1964). *Vet. Rec.* **76** (16), 449–451.

Ritchie, J. S. D., Anderson, N., Armour, J., Jarrett, W. F. H., Jennings, F. W., and Urquhart, G. M. (1966). *Am. J. vet. Res.* (In press.)

Roberts, S. R. (1962). *J. Am. vet. med. Ass.* **141**, 229–239.

Rodger, F. C. (1959). *Trans. R. Soc. trop. Med. Hyg.* **53**, 400–403.

Rodger, F. C. (1962). *Bull. Wld Hlth Org.* **24**, 429–448.

Roneus, O. (1963). *Acta vet. scand.* **4**, 170–196.

Roneus, O., and Nordkvist, M. (1962). *Acta vet. scand.* **3**, 201–225.

Rose, J. H. (1958). *J. comp. Path.* **68**, 359–362.

Rose, J. H. (1959). *J. comp. Path.* **69** (4), 414–422.

Ross, J. G. (1963). *Vet. Rec.* **75**, 129–132.

Ross, J. G., and Dow, C. (1965a). *Br. vet. J.* **121**, 18–27.

Ross, J. G., and Dow, C. (1965b). *Br. vet. J.* **121**, 228–233.

Rubin, L. F., and Saunders, L. Z. (1965). *Path. vet.* **2**, 600–608.

Ruysch, F. (1665). "Dilucidatio valvularum in vasis lymphaticis et lacteis. Accesserunti quaedam observationes anatomicae rariores." H. Gael, The Hague.

Schaeffler, W. F. (1960). *J. Parasit.* **46** (2), 17.

Schebitz, H. (1960). *Dt. tierärztl. Wschr.* **67**, 564–567.

Schwangart, F. (1940). *Berl. Munch. tierärtzl. Wschr.* (6), 9 Feb., pp. 61–66.

Seibold, H. R., Bailey, W. S., Hoerlein, B. F., Jordan, E. M., and Schwabe, C. W. (1955). *Am. J. vet. Res.* **16**, 5–14.

Seneviratna, P. (1958a). *J. comp. Path.* **68** (3), 352–358.

Seneviratna, P. (1958b). *Ceylon vet. J.* **6** (3/4), 36–38.

Sheehy, T. W., Meroney, W. H., Cox, R. S., and Soler, J. E. (1962). *Gastroenterology* **42**, 148–156.

Shoho, C. (1955). *Revta ibér. Parasit.* Special volume, pp. 927–951.

Shoho, C., and Nair, U. K. (1960). *Ceylon vet. J.* **8**, 2–12.

Shope, R. E. (1943). *J. exp. Med.* **77**, 127–138.

Skalinskii, E. I. (1957). *Trud. nauchn. Kontrol. Inst. vet. Preparatov.* **7**, 318–327.

Smith, M. H. D., and Beaver, P. C. (1953). *Pediatrics* **12**, 491–497.

Sofrenovic, D., Jovanovic, M., Sokolic, A., Nevenic, V., Cuperlovic, K., and Movsesijan, M. (1961). *Rad. primljen.* **8**, VII, 1–15.

Spencer, J. (1962). *J. trop. Med. Hyg.* **65**, 256–259.

Sprent, J. F. A. (1955). *Parasitology* **45**, 31–55.

Sprent, J. F. A. (1958). *Parasitology* **48**, 184–209.

Sprent, J. F. A., and English, P. B. (1958). *Aust. vet. J.* **34**, 161–171.

Stemmermann, G. N. (1961). *Am. J. clin. Path.* **36**, 524–531.

Stewart, D. F. (1953). *Aust. J. agric. Res.* **4**, 100–117.

Sweatman, G. K., Henshall, T. C., and Manktelow, B. W. (1962). *N. Z. vet. J.* **10** (5), 99–107.

Symons, L. E. A. (1957). *Aust. J. biol. Sci.* **10**, 374–383.

Symons, L. E. A., and Fairbairn, D. (1963). *Expl Parasit.* **13**, 284–304.

Syverton, J. T., McCoy, O. R., and Koomen, J. (1947). *J. exp. Med.* **85**, 759–769.

Takeuch, I. S. (1960). *Med. J. Kagoshima Univ.* **13**, 240–260.

Taliaferro, W. H., and Sarles, M. P. (1939). *J. infect. Dis.* **64**, 157–192.

Tanaka, T., Suu, S., Shoho, C., and Yamagiwa, S. (1945). *Jap. J. vet. Sci.* **7**, 117–130.

Thomas, A. D. (1958). *Trans. R. Soc. trop. Med. Hyg.* **52**, 298.

Thrasher, J. P. (1961). *J. Am. vet. med. Ass.* **138**, 27–30.

Thrasher, J. P., Ichinose, H., and Pitab, H. C. (1963). *Am. J. vet. Res.* **24**, 808–818.
Tomita, S. (1941). *Taiwan igakkai zasshi* **40**, 427–443.
Tremlett, J. G. (1964). *J. Helminth.* **38**, 171–174.
Tromba, F. G., and Douvres, F. W. (1958). *Am. J. Vet. Res.* **19**, 918–920.
Tromba, F. G., Sippel, W. L., and Mitchell, F. E. (1957). *N. Am. Vet.* **38**, 134–135.
Turner, J. H. (1959). *Am. J. vet. Res.* **20**, 102–110.
Turner, J. H., Shalkop, W. T., and Wilson, G. I. (1960). *Am. J. vet. Res.* **21**, 536–546.
Underdahl, N. R. (1958). *J. Am. vet. med. Ass.* **133** (7), 380–383.
Underdahl, N. R., and Kelley, G. W. (1957). *J. Am. vet. med. Ass.* **130** (4), 173–176.
Urquhart, J. M., Jarrett, W. F. H., and O'Sullivan, J. G. (1954). *Vet. Rec.* **66**, 143–144.
Webb, J. K. G., Job, C. K., and Gault, E. W. (1960). *Lancet*, **1**, 835–842.
Webster, G. A. (1958). *Can. J. comp. Med.* **22** (8).
Wetzel, R., and Kersten, W. (1956). *Wien. tierärztl. Mschr.* **11**, 664–673.
Whitlock, J. H. (1956). *Wien. tieräztl. Mschr.* **43**, 731.
Whitlock, J. H. (1959). *Cornell Vet.* **49**, 3–27.
Whur, P. (1966). *J. comp. Path.* **76**, 57–65.
Wilder, H. C. (1950). *Trans. J. Am. Acad. Ophthal.* **55**, 99.
Winter, H. (1959). *Am. J. vet. Res.* **20**, 366–371.
Wolffhugel, K. (1934). *Z. InfektKrankh. parasit. Krankh. Hyg. Haustiere* **46**, 28–48.
Yamagiwa, S., and Shoho, C. (1944). *Jap. J. Vet. Sci.* **6**, 413–422.
Yamaguchi, S. (1925). *Arch. Schiffs-u. Tropenhyg.* **29**, 589–604.
Yokogawa, S. (1921). *Proc. 12th Gen. meeting Jap. Path. Soc.*
Zuelzer, W. W., and Apt, L. (1949). *Am. J. Dis. Childh.* **78**, 153.

Author Index

Numbers in italics refer to pages in the References at the end of each article.

A

Abadie, S. H., 98, *105*
Abbott, R. H., 62, *101*
Abdou, A. H., 151, 152, 168, *178*
Abeles, M. M., 350, *381*
Adam, K. M. G., 36, *41*
Adcock, J. L., 349, *378*
Al-Dabagh, M. A., 24, *41*
Aldabugh, M. A., 373, *378*
Alicata, J., 355, *378*
Allen, G. W., 344, *378*
Allen, R. D., 33, *41*
Alvarado, R., 189, *250*
Amaral, A. D. F., 29, 30, *41*
Anderson, H. H., 24, *41*
Anderson, N., 328, *378*, *381*, *382*
Anderson, R. C., 256, *318*, 354, *378*
Andrews, M. N., 88, *101*
Ansfield, J., 34, 35, *49*
Antony, O., 98, *105*
Anya, A. O., 214, 225, 230, 231, 232, 233, 234, *250*
Apitz, R., 232, *251*
Apt, L., 356, *383*
Archer, R. K., 368, 369, *378*
Arean, U. M., 365, 366, *378*
Arai, K., 94, *105*
Armour, J., 328, 330, *378*, *382*
Arvy, L., 199, *250*
Ariyoshi, C., 82, 98, *101*
Asada, J., 78, 88, 94, *101*
Asdrubali, C., 373, *380*
Ashton, N., 356, 359, *378*
Ashworth, C. T., 323, *378*
Astbury, W. T., 373, *381*
Atchley, F. O., 36, *41*
Auernheimer, A. H., 36, *41*

B

Babero, B. B., 365, 373, *378*
Babos, S., 344, *378*

Baelz, E., 53, *101*
Baer, J. C., 150, 157, 159, *181*
Baer, J. G., 213, 239, *250*
Bailey, D. E., 370, *380*
Bailey, R. B., 370, *380*
Bailey, W. S., 373, 374, 375, *378*, *382*
Baker, E. E., 36, *47*
Balamuth, W., 30, 36, *41*, *50*
Ball, G. H., 5, 25, *42*, *45*
Barker, D. C., 8, *42*
Barretto, M. P., 5, 6, 7, *42*
Barron, C. N., 361, 374, *378*
Barrow, J. H., Jr., 26, 27, 32, *42*
Bartgis, I. L., 13, 30, *43*, *48*
Basnuevo, J. G., 99, *101*
Baudet, E. A. R. F., 350, 351, *378*
Baujean, R., 81, *104*
Beautyman, W., 350, 356, 375, *378*
Beaver, P. C., 356, 357, 364, *378*, *379*, *382*
Becht, H., 341, *380*
Beckett, E. B., 229, 230, *250*
Beesley, W. N., 273, *318*
Behrer, M. R., 356, 357, *378*
Beklemishev, V. N., 165, *178*
Bell, S. D., 270, *317*
Beneden, E., van, 139, 143, 146, *178*
Ben-Efraim, S., 36, 37, *51*
Berberian, D. A., 170, *178*
Berntzen, A. K., 169, 170, 177, 178, *178*
Berntzen, K., 139, 170, 171, *186*
Berthier, L., 199, *250*
Bertram, D. S., 257, 264, 268, 271, 272, 273, 276, 277, 278, 281, 286, 288, 289, 290, 293, 299, 300, 301, 302, 308, 310, 312, *317*, *318*
Betts, A. O., 376, *378*
Bhatia, B. B., 375, *381*
Biagi, F. F., 35, *42*
Biocca, E., 375, *378*
Bird, A. F., 217, 220, 221, 222, 224, 230, 231, 232, 233, 234, 237, *250*, *251*

Subject Index

H

Habronema megastoma, horse infection, 369

Haemagglutination test, and *Entamoeba*, 39

Haematoloechus medioplexus, cuticle, function, 201
structure, 192–4, 196

Haemonchus,
cuticle, chemical composition, 231
contortus,
cuticle,
chemical composition, 231, 232
structure, 230
gastrointestinal reaction, 327

Haemophilus suis, swine influenza, 375

Heterodera,
cuticle, structure, 215, 219
glycines, cuticle,
chemical composition, 232
structure, 219
rostochiensis, cuticle,
chemical composition, 232
structure, 219–20

Hetol, and clonorchiasis, 100

Hexachloroparaxylol, and clonorchiasis, 100

Hexamermis, cuticle, structure, 219

Himasthla quissetensis, cercaria, ultrastructure, 197

Holostephanus lühei, cuticle, structure, 195–7

Hookworm disease, 322, 323–4

Hoplolaimus tylenchiformis (=*H. coronatus*), cuticle, chemical composition, 232

Hydatigera taeniaeformis,
cuticle, chemical composition, 208, 209, 210
hatching, 170

Hymenolepididae, penetration glands, 162

Hymenolepis,
embryonic envelope, 138
excretory glands, 162
oncospheral membrane, 151
spermatogenesis, 115–6
citelli,
cuticle, chemical composition, 210
hatching, 170

diminuta,
cuticle,
chemical composition, 208, 209, 210–1
function, 210
structure, 203, 204, 205–6
embryonic envelope, 138, 139, 147 150
hatching, 170, 171
hook development, 152, 154
muscle development, 161, 162
oncosphere, 160
penetration glands, 155, 162, 165
spermatogenesis, 111, 116, 117
vitelline cells and capsule formation, 124
microstoma, cuticle, chemical composition, 209, 210
nana,
cuticle,
chemical composition, 208, 209, 210
structure, 203, 204
embryonic envelope, 137, 138, 150
hatching, 170
oocytes, 118
spermatogenesis, 111, 112

I

Immobilization test, and *Entamoeba*, 35–6

Immune response, in cotton rat filariasis, 282–6

Immune stimulus, in cotton rat filariasis, 280–2

Indirect haemagglutination test, and *Entamoeba*, 39

Infula macrophallus, 150

K

Khawia iowensis, embryonic envelope, 166

Kumree, 351

L

Leptorhynchoides thecatus, cuticle, chemical composition, 248